# Stories About Us

**Geri Dasgupta**
Centennial College

·

**Jennifer Jiang-hai Mei**
Centennial College

THOMSON

—✳—™

NELSON

Australia   Canada   Mexico   Singapore   Spain   United Kingdom   United States

**THOMSON**

**NELSON** ™

Stories About Us

by Geri Dasgupta and Jennifer Jiang-hai Mei

**Associate Vice-President and Editorial Director:**
Evelyn Veitch

**Executive Editor:**
Anne Williams

**Marketing Manager:**
Lisa Rahn

**Senior Developmental Editor:**
Mike Thompson

**Permissions Coordinator:**
Patricia Buckley

**Production Editor:**
Wendy Yano

**Copy Editor/Proofreader:**
Gilda Mekler

**Production Coordinator:**
Ferial Suleman

**Creative Director:**
Angela Cluer

**Interior Design:**
Tammy Gay

**Cover Design:**
Angela Cluer

**Cover Image:**
"InPlace-Aven" by Snaige Sileika
Open Studio

**Compositor:**
Doris Chan/Carol Magee

**Printer:**
Webcom

**Library and Archives Canada Cataloguing in Publication**

Main entry under title:

Stories about us / edited by Geri Dasgupta and Jennifer Jiang-hai Mei.

Includes index.
ISBN 0-17-641456-8

1. Short stories. 2. College readers. 3. Short story.
I. Dasgupta, Geri, 1949–
II. Mei, Jennifer Jiang-hai

PE1121.S82 2004    808.3'1
C2004-902610-0

# Preface

*'Tis the good reader that makes the good book.*
RALPH WALDO EMERSON

Thanks to modern technology our world seems to be getting smaller while the scope of our knowledge about it is paradoxically becoming wider. *Stories About Us* appears as a result and a reflection of this paradox that confronts each of us, especially in North America. Designed as a textbook for general education and for literature courses at colleges and universities, *Stories About Us* collects short stories written by authors from all corners of the globe. As editors of the book, we have endeavoured to transcend geographical, cultural, ethnic, and linguistic boundaries to reveal what Samuel Johnson calls "the common humanity" that connects us all—teachers, students, and readers of every kind. This is an anthology of stories about *us* that strives to be enriching, enlightening, and entertaining. Above all, it is intended to be mind-opening.

The book consists of two parts, "Elements of the Short Story" and "More Short Stories."

Part One begins with a brief introduction to the short story as a unique literary genre. It then branches into six units to explain how major elements (plot, character, narrative point of view, setting, literary devices, and theme) work together to make a story interesting and worth reading. Each unit begins with an essay on the element under consideration to prepare students for analytical reading and for classroom discussion. Following the essay are three short stories that exemplify different aspects of that particular element and concepts discussed earlier in the unit. Every story is preceded by headnotes, which contain information about the author's life and work in general, and the story to follow in particular. Any cultural references requiring explanation are also glossed in the headnotes.

At the end of every story, two sets of questions are provided to facilitate understanding and to stimulate classroom discussion. Questions under Following the Story are concerned with comprehension and analysis of the story, whereas those under Responding to the Story expand on the issues presented in the story to develop students' critical thinking skills. These questions are intentionally detailed and comprehensive so that teachers may select, modify, or redesign them. To recapitulate and reinforce the pedagogic content, we have also included Guidelines at the end of each unit.

Part Two, "More Stories," contains 26 selections of varied types and lengths by writers of different cultural, linguistic, and ethnic backgrounds, prefaced by a brief biographical note about the author. Each story has been chosen to enlarge and enrich the students' reading experience. Teachers may assign them as further readings in general or, according to their specific curricula, use them for oral presentations, seminars, or research projects. As a handy reference tool, a glossary of literary terms is provided at the end of the book.

Part One is arranged according to the major elements in a short story; Part Two is arranged in alphabetical order by author. To allow teachers greater flexibility, we have added two alternative tables of contents: The Thematic Table of Contents facilitates an approach by subject matter, while the Geographical Table of Contents anticipates an interest in reading the stories in their cultural contexts. With the format we have carefully adopted, we hope that the classroom teacher will find sufficient variety and flexibility to make stimulating and ingenious choices. To suit specific teaching/learning needs, units in Part One can be rearranged freely; the subheadings in the introductory essays also make it easier to regroup the concepts covered in the book. Furthermore, cross-references to stories offer yet greater flexibility.

We have aimed to collect a wide range of stories by writers from around the world while maintaining a clear focus on Canadian authors to cater to our intended audience—college and university students in Canada and the United States.

Each story in this anthology has its own merits; together the collection forms a multi-coloured and multi-faceted tapestry exhibiting *our* life and *our* experience as human beings. As claimed in its inclusive and intimate title, *Stories About Us* encompasses representative pieces by representative writers of both the West and the East. It is one of the few college anthologies, if not the only one, that includes translated works, especially by writers in the eastern hemisphere.

Our decision to include stories in translation was made with a clear understanding of the ongoing dispute over the quality or purity of translated literary works. Our position is that if we have gladly read Dante, Cervantes, Balzac, and Tolstoy in translation, why should we close the door on such world-class writers as Yasunari Kawabata, Liu Xinwu, Naguib Mahfouz, and Rabindranath Tagore? It cannot be that translations of their works are less *pure* than of those written in Italian, French, Spanish, and Russian. Rather, the argument against inclusion of non-Western writers in English anthologies points to a disappointing and damaging narrow-mindedness. If we want to be open to the world, we must simply trust translators.

We sincerely hope that *Stories About Us* will shorten "the distance we must travel to discover that our most private perceptions are, in fact, universally felt" as Carol Shields asserts in "The Case for Curling up with a Book." Foreign and irrelevant as it may seem at first, reading stories about people who live half a world away will contribute to—to borrow another cogent phrase from Shields' essay—"enlarging our sense of self, our multiplying possibilities and expanded experience."

## Instructor's Manual

This book is accompanied by an instructor's manual, which provides a wealth of additional exercises, activities, and other resources for instructors teaching this course in various settings. Material is also included that focuses on the needs of the second language learner. Contact your Nelson sales representative to receive a copy.

## Acknowledgments

This book belongs to our students. They have read with us in creating it, and we are grateful for all their responses. We also owe thanks to the team at Nelson: to Anne Williams, the mother of invention; to Patricia Buckley, a persistent tracker; to production editor Wendy Yano; to our careful copy editor Gilda Mekler; and especially to Mike Thompson for his encouragement, patience, and guidance. We want to thank Jean Vale for her meticulous editing and proofreading. Of course, our heartfelt gratitude belongs to our families— to Kieran for sharing a love of stories; to John for his perseverance in laborious scanning and researching, and to Yang Yang for being her exuberant and exhilarating self. Thank you all.

The authors and publisher wish to thank the following reviewers for their comments and suggestions during the development of this book: Cynthia Beech, Georgian College; Devon Boucher, University College of the Cariboo; David Bouvier, Capilano College; Sue Ann Cairns, Kwantlen University College; Nicholas Collins, Capilano College; Mary Gossage, Dawson College; Christine Hoppenrath, University of British Columbia; Graham J. Murphy, Seneca College; and Megan Otton, Langara College.

# Table of Contents

# Thematic Table of Contents

## Love and Marriage

## Nature, Ecology, and Environment

## Parent-Child Relationship

## Personal Relationships

## Social, Religious, and Political Contexts

## Story, Art and Creativity

## War

# Geographic Table of Contents

## NORTH AND SOUTH AMERICA

1. ALGERIA
2. EGYPT
3. GHANA
4. NIGERIA
5. SUDAN
6. ENGLAND
7. FRANCE
8. GERMANY
9. IRELAND
10. ITALY
11. RUSSIA
12. PEOPLE'S REPUBLIC OF CHINA
13. INDIA
14. JAPAN
15. SOUTH KOREA
16. NEPAL
17. PAKISTAN
18. PHILIPPINES
19. SINGAPORE
20. SRI LANKA

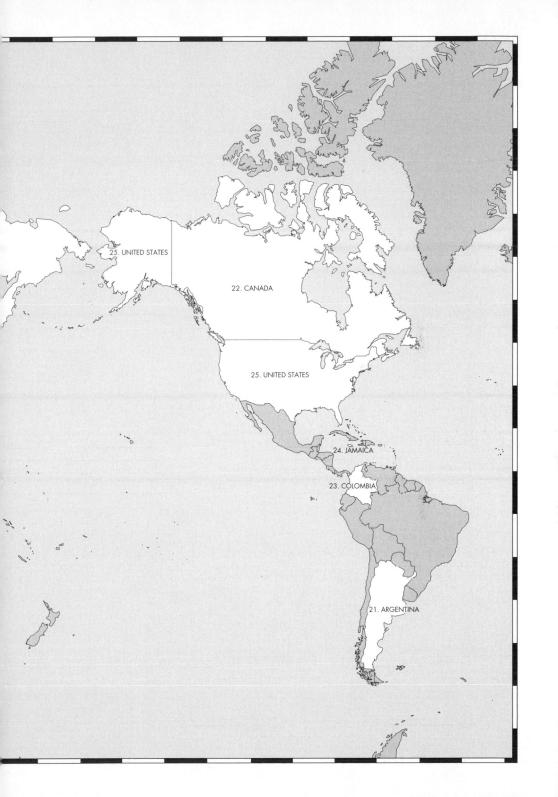

25. UNITED STATES

22. CANADA

25. UNITED STATES

24. JAMAICA

23. COLOMBIA

21. ARGENTINA

# Part  1

## Elements of the Short Story

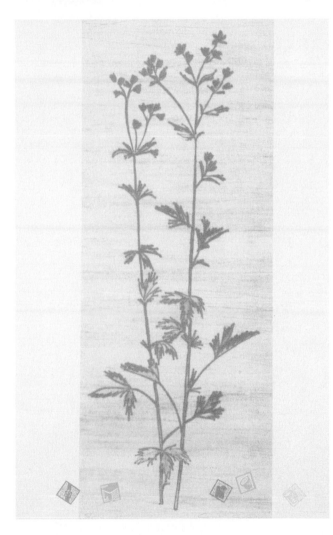

# Introduction to the Short Story

*A story is a way to say something that can't be said any other way, and it takes every word in the story to say what the meaning is. You tell a story because a statement would be inadequate. When anybody asks what a story is about, the only proper thing is to tell him to read the story.*

FLANNERY O'CONNOR

## What Is a Short Story?

The **short story** is a distinct literary **genre** that is usually defined as a relatively brief fictional **narrative** in prose, containing between 500 and 15 000 words in length. Belonging to the family of **prose fiction**, the short story has recognizable ancestors in the long oral tradition of **myth**, **legend**, **parable**, **fairy tale**, **fable**, **tale**, and **folklore**. Also, the short story finds close cousins in the **novel** and **novella**, two other major genres of prose fiction, which also gradually evolved into their present written form. As its name suggests to us, length seems to be the most prominent of all the differences that set the short story apart from the novel and novella.

Edgar Allan Poe (1809–1849), regarded by many as the originator of the short story, presents in his review of Nathaniel Hawthorne's *Twice-Told Tales* (1842) a definition of both the key word "story" and its adjective "short." Instead of limiting its size to a fixed number of words, Poe defines a short story by the time required to read it. He states that "the short prose narrative" requires "from a half-hour to one or two hours in perusal." However, as you will see in this anthology, short stories may vary greatly in length. For example, "Acute Triangle" by Frederic Raphael of England (page 426), and "The Cage" by Neil Bissoondath of Canada (page 154), together display the long and the short of the short story.

As to the special features of the short story, Poe points out that a short story should produce the "totality" of a "unique or single *effect*." It requires "a skilful literary artist" to conceive "with deliberate care," so as to affect "the soul of the reader." Using Poe's definition, we may say that a short story can be concerned with any brief yet special experience in life, such as a scene, an encounter with a character or a group of characters, or simply a fantasy. The story can take any shape, and its events can be arranged by the author in any order. Nevertheless, we can normally recognize the beginning, middle, and end of a short story. Its unity has to be achieved not only through format and plot, but also through a "unique or single effect" projected through **theme**, **character**, **tone**, and **style**.

No matter how natural and formless a short story may sometimes seem, it must, as the American novelist Henry James (1843–1916) insists, "be an idea....It should be a little gem of bright, quick, vivid form." In spite of these enlightening comments, the short story has displayed so much vitality and flexibility that we cannot possibly reduce its special features to a few hard and fast rules. For example, if we read "Traplines" by Canadian First Nations writer Thomas King (page 202), "The Half-Closed Eyes of the Buddha and the Slowly Setting Sun" by Shankar Lamichhane of Nepal (page 125), and "Something to Talk about on the Way to the Funeral" by Ama Ata Aidoo (page 239), we will find out how stories about similar subjects—human dialogue, or lack of it—can differ in form and content.

## Why the Short Story?

Understandably the short story is a popular literary form among writers, readers, and English teachers around the world. On the one hand, its relatively brief form allows what the English novelist Virginia Woolf (1882–1941) calls the common reader to read without "weariness or interruption." On the other hand, its pithiness, versatility, and flexibility in both form and content have made it an ideal choice for different literature courses. In many ways the short story makes it possible to do a lot within a limited period of time. As Nadine Gordimer (1923–), a South African short story writer who won the Nobel Prize for Literature in 1991, poignantly points out in her *Selected Stories* (1975), "Each of us has a thousand lives and a novel gives a character only one. *For the sake of the form.*"

The short story not only exposes the students to a wide range of thought-provoking human experience through what the Russian writer Anton Chekhov (1860–1904) calls "slices of life," but it also reveals unique skills and crafts-manship. To quote from the accomplished American short story writer Flannery O'Connor (1925–1964), "The short story requires more drastic proce-dures than the novel because more has to be accomplished in less space. The details have to carry more immediate weight." As many have recognized, of all forms of prose narrative, the short story has the closest relation to poetry, especially the lyric, because of the "fierce pleasure," to borrow a useful phrase from the American writer Raymond Carver (1938–88), which the short story writer consciously evokes.

## How Does the Short Story Work?

Like other forms of prose narrative, a number of contributing factors account for a short story's unique artistic appeal and literary value. Therefore, to appre-ciate and interpret a short story analytically, a reader needs to go beyond the immediate instinctive process, which often leads to sweeping statements, such as "I like this story because it's fun" or "I don't like this story because it's so boring." In contrast, analytical reading requires knowledge and perception of the essential elements of a good, interesting story. The reader has to realize that, besides the "story" or the plot, an interesting or "fun" story also depends on such appealing elements as **characterization, narrator, narrative point of view** and tone, theme, **conflict, setting,** and use of a variety of literary devices ranging from **simile** to **symbolism.** Only when we become sensitive to and familiar with these elements can we acquire an insight into how a story appeals, or fails to appeal, to the reader.

Altogether 46 stories by fine short story writers of different eras and coun-tries are collected in this book for you to read, analyze and enjoy. We hope that, through in-depth analysis and discussion of these stories, either led by the teacher or on your own, you will start to see things that you would otherwise miss, and obtain a clearer idea of what a short story is and how at the same time it is "pleasing and instructive," to use a quotation from Samuel Johnson (1709–1784). Nevertheless, when picking the story apart, always remember that the purpose of analyzing *parts* of a story is to aid your understanding and appreciation of the artistry of the *whole*

# Unit 1

## Plot: Action and Development

*That's about all that can be said about plots, which anyway are just one thing after another, a what and a what and a what. Now try How and Why.*

MARGARET ATWOOD

Whether or not we are avid readers, one of the ways we understand ourselves and the world around us is through the stories we share with one another. Story telling is a vital part of our daily lives. We tell each other what we have done, what we feel, what we hope to achieve, what we want for those we love, what failures we have experienced, and so on. As we tell about our lives, we are telling our own stories. Our stories express our reality, our hopes, our fears, our possibilities. In one sense, then, we are all familiar with storytelling and with its purpose. It organizes and enriches our existence, enables us to share our experiences and helps us understand our lives. Most stories are intended to explain or increase our understanding of the world in which we live.

A short story is a carefully designed narrative. Its author shapes the story to help us experience life around us in a different way, providing us with reflection and pleasure. We can understand and enjoy short stories better if we know more about how they are composed and told. One aspect of critical analysis is to see the relationship of the parts to the whole. In literary analysis or criticism, those parts are called the **elements of fiction**.

## Plot Sequence

The first element of the short story we will consider is **plot**. Quite simply, a plot is the arrangement of the events in a story: the *what* that happens in the story, the action of the story.

The action of a story has a beginning, a middle, and an end. The story encourages the reader to wonder *what* will happen next, especially when the plot is told in **chronological sequence**; that is when one event is presented after the other as it happens in time (see "The Jade Pendant" by Catherine Lim on page 13). Sometimes an author moves away from chronological sequence and begins the story with its conclusion; then the preceding action is told in a **flashback** or a series of flashbacks. In this case the reader may already know the outcome, but is curious to discover *why* and *how* it has come about (see "A Handful of Dates" by Tayeb Salih on page 20). Sometimes a story can also begin *in medias res*—a Latin phrase meaning in the middle of things. In this case, the author can tell the story forwards or backwards (see "All Is Burning" by Jean Arasanayagam on page 98). No matter how the author chooses to develop the action, the events are arranged in a causal manner, and the details are selected and related carefully so that the story's conclusion is believable and effective.

The short story is essentially a written form. However, even in early precursors such as fables and folk tales, which were originally told orally, we can see just how vital plot sequence is. The fascination of *what happens next* is what has made these **tales** last for thousands of years.

The following fable helps us see the ancestry and development of the short story. A **fable** is a brief story that explicitly illustrates a moral or teaches a lesson, and most frequently its characters are animals. A fable is deliberately simple in order to deliver its lesson clearly, but it is often humorously narrated.

# Zhuang Shu-liang in the Moonlight (Retold)

Xun Zi (China) c.300 B.C.E.–c.230 B.C.E.

## About the Author

*The author's original name was Xun Kuang (also spelled Hsun K'uang), but he is commonly referred to as Xun Zi (also spelled Hsun-tze), Zi being an honorary suffix meaning "master," attached to the names of many philosophers in China. He was the first great Confucian philosopher to express his ideas not only by means of the sayings and conversations recorded by his disciples, but also in his own well-organized essays. Xun Zi also made important contributions to psychology, education, logic and many other subjects. He was responsible for organizing and developing the philosophical system of ancient Confucianism.*

O nce in a small town south of Xia-Shou, there lived a man named Zhuang Shu-liang. One night as he was walking home in bright moonlight, he glanced down and saw his shadow. He mistook his shadow for a crouching ghost. Whirling around, he glimpsed his own hair and mistook that for a demon standing behind him. Terrified, he began to run. When he reached home, he collapsed and died.

Moral of the fable: Suspicion is the father of ghosts.

(c. 250 B.C.E.)

In this fable, the events are presented in a chronological sequence:

Man sees shadow—believes it is a ghost

Man sees hair—believes it is a demon

Man runs home and dies

In the events listed above, we can see a **causal relationship** between one event and another. This is also the basis for the plot of more complicated stories: one event is the cause of, or provides a reason for, the next.

Why does the man think he has seen a ghost?

Why does the man think he has glimpsed a demon?

Why does the man collapse and die?

These are the sorts of questions that interest the short story writer, who designs a plot or arranges the events in the story in order to enable the reader to see relationships between them. In other words, plot not only presents *"what"* happens, but should also imply *"how and why"* the sequence of the action is constructed. Very often the enjoyment of reading a story lies in our ability to discern *"how and why"* as well as to apprehend *"what."*

## Plot Development

Whichever plot design the author chooses, the short story usually focuses on conflict or struggle. The **conflict** can be a clash between individuals, ideas, beliefs, deeds, or cultures. The struggle can be personal, psychological, social, moral, environmental, or supernatural. What sort of conflict can we find in the fable we have just read? The clash is between what the man sees and what he thinks he has seen, so this clash seems to be psychological. Regardless of its beginning, a plot develops in a typical manner through a series of stages. Usually the conflict is established in an introduction, or **exposition**.

The exposition provides us with the information we need in order to follow and understand the events that occur later. In this fable, the exposition locates the action near Xia-Shou and introduces Zhuang Shu-liang. It also informs us about the moonlight, which is the cause of the conflict Zhuang Shu-liang experiences. The moonlight also produces the next stage in the plot: a **complication**—the beginning of the **rising action**. The moonlight makes Zhuang Shu-liang see familiar things as strange, so the action develops from this complication.

From the complication, a plot rises towards a **climax** through one or more **crises**. When Zhuang Shu-liang mistakes his shadow for a ghost, tension is created. Things get worse for Zhuang Shu-liang as he believes that not only is a ghost in front of him, but a demon is behind him. The climax of the story, the moment of greatest tension or importance, occurs when he turns and runs.

The last stage of a plot is the **resolution**, which concludes the action by tidying up any loose ends through the **falling action**. A resolution is sometimes called a **dénouement**—a French word meaning "to untie the knot." In this fable, Zhuang Shu-liang is so afraid that he runs home, where he dies of fright. The resolution of a short story can be happy or sad; it can also be deliberately indefinite or open-ended, leaving the reader wondering just what will happen next to the character or characters. In terms of the plot, the ending of this fable is definitely clear. We know exactly what happens to Zhuang Shu-liang, and we are also told what we should learn from his story; in typical fable fashion, this is pointed out in the moral at the end.

Nevertheless, it is important to remember that the **plot structure** we have just introduced represents only the basic pattern of the development of a story. As you will see in the many stories collected in this book, this pattern varies and mutates to suit the authors' intentions. Sometimes a writer such as Jean Arasanayagam ("All Is Burning") uses flashbacks and flash-forwards freely to portray the character's subtle emotional responses to reality. At other times, either the story ends in an ambiguous or puzzling manner, as in "The Immaculate Conception Photography Gallery" (page 280) and "Zaabalawi" (page 359), or the story just does not follow the pattern very closely in terms of rising action, falling action and so on, as in "Tuesday Siesta" (page 370). To know the general development of a conventional story, therefore, is to acquire an insight into the plot structure. Then enjoyment arises from our realization of *how* an author follows, deviates from, or runs counter to the prescribed pattern. Even greater enjoyment will occur when we finally figure out *why*.

# The Old Man and His Grandson

Jacob Grimm (1785–1863) and Wilhelm Grimm (1786–1859) (Germany)

## About the Authors

*Born to the leading family in the administrative seat of Steinau, Germany, Jacob and Wilhelm Grimm produced in their lifetime many important works on language, philosophy, law, mythology, and **folklore**. To most readers in the world, however, they are remembered as the Brothers Grimm. Determined to preserve traditional stories, the brothers collected and published two volumes of **fairy tales** between 1812 and 1815. Published under the title of* Children's and Household Tales, *their fairy tales were translated into English and published in 1823 under the title* German Popular Stories. *In the two centuries following its first publication, this collection of "popular stories" has been translated into most of the world's languages and includes some of the best known fairy tales ever produced in human history.*

## About the Story

*The elements of plot can be seen at work in a longer story when we read "The Old Man and His Grandson." This **folk tale** had been part of the oral tradition for hundreds of years when the two brothers collected and rewrote it for publication. In spite of its brevity, this folk-tale depends upon a plot in which the "how and why" are more challenging to the reader. Unlike a fable, a folk-tale does not contain an explicit moral; however, this particular story suggests the golden rule: treat others as you would want them to treat you.*

*The elements of plot have been identified in the margins for you.*

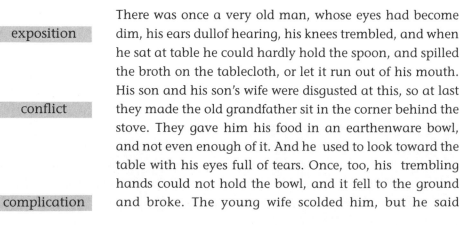

exposition

conflict

complication

There was once a very old man, whose eyes had become dim, his ears dullof hearing, his knees trembled, and when he sat at table he could hardly hold the spoon, and spilled the broth on the tablecloth, or let it run out of his mouth. His son and his son's wife were disgusted at this, so at last they made the old grandfather sit in the corner behind the stove. They gave him his food in an earthenware bowl, and not even enough of it. And he used to look toward the table with his eyes full of tears. Once, too, his trembling hands could not hold the bowl, and it fell to the ground and broke. The young wife scolded him, but he said

crisis 1

nothing and only sighed. Then they bought him a wooden bowl for a few pennies out of which he had to eat.

They were once sitting thus when the little grandson of four years old began to gather some bits of wood together on the ground.

"What are you doing there?" asked the father.

"I'm making a little trough," answered the child, "for

crisis 2

father and mother to eat out of when I am big."

The man and his wife looked at each other for a while

climax

and presently began to cry. Then they took the old grandfather to the table and henceforth always let him eat with them and likewise said nothing if he did spill a little of anything.

(1823)

# Following the Story

1. What type of plot sequence does this folk-tale follow?
2. List the plot sequence in point form.
3. What information are we given in the exposition? List the facts.
4. What sort of conflict do we see in this story? Who or what is clashing?
5. Based on the exposition and the conflict that arises from it, what details can we gather about this family and its circumstances: are they rich or poor; do they live in a town or the countryside? How can we tell?
6. Explain any similarities you find in the two crises.
7. How does the climax relate to the rest of the story?
8. In what ways does the resolution or dénouement reflect the exposition?
9. Is the resolution believable? Why or why not?
10. Does the conclusion seem complete, or does some uncertainty remain?

# Responding to the Story

1. What has the child learned from observing his parents' treatment of the grandfather?
2. This simple story suggests complex motivations. Why do the parents start crying and how believable is their response?
3. A short story is not just a plot. According to Edgar Allan Poe, it presents a "unique or single effect." What could the effect of this story be?
4. What experience of family life does this story provide?

5. Folk tales often transcend, or go beyond, their specific time and culture. Does this story do that?

# Foreshadowing and Suspense

These are two important techniques that authors employ to engage and sustain a reader's attention. In the story of "The Old Man and His Grandson," the Brothers Grimm introduce details that arouse sympathy for this old man. Then they subtly add to the details of his mistreatment, culminating in the fact that he is not even given enough to eat. Although this is a simple folk-tale, the element of **suspense** is employed to lead the interested and sympathetic reader to read on and find out: What will become of the old man? The next step in the story involves a new character, the young grandson, and what he does at the same time serves as foreshadowing for the later events and sustains the suspense necessary for the reading: "What is he doing?" "How will he treat his parents when he grows up?" The boy's innocent answer brings the tale to a happy dénouement, much to the reader's satisfaction.

**Foreshadowing** involves hints of what will happen later in the story. The suggestion can be made by a situation, event, character, or thing. The foreshadowing may seem significant when it happens, or may seem trivial; we, the readers, only grasp the full significance of the foreshadowing when we come to the actual occurrence at which it has hinted. Foreshadowing builds unity and coherence in the plot and involves us in the plot development. We reflect on how appropriate an event or character's response is because foreshadowing provided by the author encourages us to form reasonable expectations and emotional involvement. We wonder sometimes with hope and sometimes with fear: What does this mean? What will happen next? In this unit, "The Jade Pendant," "A Handful of Dates," and "The Stolen Party" all use the technique of foreshadowing. Look for it as you read each story, and be aware of your own emotional response as you read along.

Foreshadowing is frequently used to create suspense about what's next, how and why, whetting the reader's appetite to read on to the conclusion. However, suspense can be generated without the use of foreshadowing. For example, "The Jade Pendant" creates an air of suspense from the very beginning by telling the fantastic history of the pendant itself. Then when the pendant is finally displayed, two fervent and unsophisticated responses to it are deliberately recorded: those of Ron and Ah Soh's daughter. What will happen to this pendant, which seems to have such power over the imagination of people? That is the question author Catherine Lim intends to form in the reader's mind

at the beginning of the story, and that is also the question that she v
leave unanswered until the very end.

## Irony

"The Jade Pendant" also exemplifies how irony is conducive to an ir
plot. Irony is but one of the literary devices and techniques at the writer's disposal to maintain the reader's interest in the story. By definition, "irony" is a
broad term referring to the recognition of a reality different from the masking
appearance (see Unit 5, page 142, for an expanded definition). "Being" versus
"seeming" is exactly what Lim's story is about. From its very beginning the
author carefully prepares the reader for the ending by making frequent references to Mrs. Khoo's desperate concern for "keeping up appearances."

Unlike the fable, however, the short story cannot be reduced to an abstract
moral or lesson, such as "appearances are deceptive," "money is the root of all
evil," or "love makes the world go round." Rather, the short story provides a
perspective on, a comment about, or a shared experience of our lives. The short
story writer wants to engage our senses, emotions, and imaginations by
offering us a chance to share, and only perhaps benefit from, the life of
another person or other people. In his book *Aspects of the Novel*, E. M. Forster
points out that to grasp plot we need three faculties: our curiosity, our intelligence, and our memory. Let us apply these faculties to the three stories in this
unit, "The Jade Pendant," "A Handful of Dates," and "The Stolen Party."

# The Jade Pendant

Catherine Lim (Singapore) 1942–

### About the Author

*Born in Kedah, Malaysia, in 1942, Catherine Lim immigrated to Singapore in 1970
and is now a Singaporean citizen. She received a B.A. (Honours) in English at the
University of Malaysia and earned an M.A. and Ph.D. in Linguistics at the National
University of Singapore. She has worked as a teacher and in other areas of education
in Singapore. Her first collection of short stories,* Little Ironies: Stories of Singapore
*(which contains "The Jade Pendant"), was published in 1978. In the following*

*decades, she has published several collections of short stories as well as some novels and poems. She is now acclaimed by some critics as "the best writer in Singapore."*

*Lim's literary works are mostly concerned with clashes between generations and cultures, the varied attitudes and lifestyles adopted by people of different social classes and the paradoxical contrast between society's material affluence and its moral poverty. Although her style is generally simple, direct, and understandable, a full appreciation of her subtle irony always requires careful reading and in-depth analysis.*

## About the Story

*"The Jade Pendant" has a plot that is developed in chronological sequence; it is straightforward and linear. As the title suggests, this story focuses on the jade pendant whose history and value are presented in detail. Jade is a hard green stone that can be carved into sculptures and ornaments or set as jewellery. It is especially prized in various Chinese cultures for its lucent beauty and for its reputed healing properties.*

*The story examines family relationships and questions social standing that is defined by wealth. Mrs. Khoo's efforts to "keep up appearances" serve to foreshadow the surprising yet believable dénouement of this story, and throw an ironic light on the relationship between her and Ah Soh, "a relative who was no better than a servant." In her details and surprise ending, Lim implicitly criticizes a society in which money is the only measure, surprising the reader with the contrast between reality and appearance.*

The Jade Pendant had gathered round it a number of myths, some of which were quite absurd, such as the one that it was worth half-a-million dollars, but the reality was astonishing enough to raise gasps of admiration and envy. The jewel, as big as the palm of a child's hand, consisted
5 of a thick circular piece of intricately carved jade of the most brilliant and lucid green, surrounded by innumerable diamonds arranged in floral designs. It was to be worn on a chain round the neck, but the sheer weight of the jewel, not to mention the extreme folly of risking loss or theft, had caused it to be little disturbed in its place in the bank vaults. Mrs. Khoo
10 had worn it only twice—once at a banquet given by a sultan—the jewel had been specially flown, under strict security, to the royal town where it made a stir, even at a function that glittered with fabulous jewels—and again, at the wedding of her nephew. Since then, it had lain safely in the bank vaults, for the myriad weddings and other functions that Mrs. Khoo
15 had subsequently attended were considered too insignificant to justify the presence of this jewel, the like of which nobody had ever seen. But its

absence on the broad perfumed bosom of Mrs. Khoo was as likely to provoke comments as its presence: "Ah, you're not wearing the Jade Pendant! That's a disappointment to me, for I had hoped to see it. I've
20  heard so much about it."

To make up for the loss of pleasure that would have been afforded by the sight of the Jade Pendant, Mrs. Khoo would talk about its history—how it had come down to her from her mother who had got it from her own mother, and if its origin was traced far enough, it could be ascertained that
25  the first possessor was a concubine of a Vietnamese emperor of the seventeenth century. Its continuing connections with royalty must be something predestined, for, confided Mrs. Khoo, her mother had once told her that the wife of a sultan who had seen it had wanted to buy it, no matter how great the cost; she had actually sent emissaries to begin the task of negotiation
30  and purchase. It was an extremely difficult thing to do, but the persistent royal lady was at last turned down.

The engrossing question had been: whom would Mrs. Khoo leave the jewel to when she died—her daughter-in-law or her daughter? Mrs. Khoo had actually long settled the matter in favour of her daughter. There was
35  nothing she would not do for Lian Kim, her favourite child. Moreover, she would not wait for her death to hand over the jewel—when Lian Kim got married, the gift would be made. The bride would wear the Jade Pendant at the wedding dinner, for every one of the guests to see.

When Lian Kim was home for the holidays with her fiancé, she had
40  insisted on her mother taking the jewel out of the bank for him to see. He was an Art student whom she had met in London, and the wonder on his face and the long whistle of admiration and incredulity as he looked at the Jade Pendant that Lian Kim had laughingly placed on his artist's begrimed sweater, was a small but definite step toward the mollification
45  of his future mother-in-law whose chagrin, when her daughter wrote to her of being engaged to a foreigner, was great indeed. How vexing, she had thought to herself and later said to her husband, although she would not have dared to say the same to her daughter. How vexing to have a daughter married to a foreigner, and a poor one at that. But there was
50  nothing to be done, once the young people of today made up their minds. Her vexation was increased that day by a very humiliating incident. She had just shown the Jade Pendant to Lian Kim and Ron and was getting ready to put it back in its case of red velvet, when she heard Ah Soh sweeping outside the room. Upon impulse, she called Ah Soh into the
55  room to view the jewel, thinking afterwards, in the generosity of her heart, that even a humble widowed relative who made cakes and puddings for

sale in the streets, could be given the pleasure of looking at the jewel. Ah Soh was all gratitude. She left her broom outside, tiptoed in with a great show of respect and awe, and raised her hands in shrill wonderment even
60 before the box was opened to reveal its treasure. She exclaimed, she praised, she was breathless with the effort of pleasing a rich relative who allowed her and her daughter to live in a room at the back of the great house, to eat the food left on the great table, to benefit by the sale of old clothes, beer-bottles and newspapers.

65 Unfortunately, Ah Soh's daughter, a simple-minded girl of Lian Kim's age, had ambled in then, looking for her mother and on seeing the jewel, had crowed with childish delight, and actually snatched it up and pranced round the room, shrilly parading it on her chest. The terror of her mother who had quickly glanced up to see the look of violent disgust and dis-
70 pleasure on the face of Mrs. Khoo, was itself terrifying to behold. She shrieked at the girl, snatched the jewel back, laid it reverently back in its case and began scolding the erring daughter as vehemently as she could. The insulted pride of the lady whose countenance had taken on a look of extreme hauteur, was to be mollified by no less than a severe thrashing of
75 the offender, which Ah Soh immediately executed, secret anger against her rich relative lending great strength to her thin scrawny arms. The girl who looked no more than a child though she was over twenty, whimpered, and would have been thrashed sick had not Mrs. Khoo intervened by saying stiffly. "That will do, Ah Soh. Do you want to kill the child?" "Better for her
80 to be killed than to insult you in this way!" sobbed Ah Soh.

Mrs. Khoo, who found the incident too disgusting to be mentioned to her husband or daughter, soon forgot it. She spent the three weeks of her daughter's vacation home, in pleasing the young couple as much as she could. She got the servants to cook all kinds of delicacies, and Ah Soh, anx-
85 ious to pacify her further, helped as much as she could, endlessly. Whenever she could spare the time from her mah-jong, Mrs. Khoo entertained them, not sparing any expense. Mr. Khoo who doted on his youngest daughter was even willing to take time off from his gambling and his race-horses to take the couple round and introduce them proudly to his wide circle of
90 friends. Lian Kim and Ron were to be married by the end of the year. "A sad occasion for the mother, ha! ha! do you know why?" Mr. Khoo would laugh heartily, his round florid face wreathed in smiles. "Because the Jade Pendant will be made over from mother to daughter. Ah, these women! They and their jewels. But I tell you, that trinket's worth at least—" he
95 would then whisper conspiratorially into the ears of his friend, revelling in the look of amazement on the face of the listener.

It would never have occurred to any of their friends to ask Mr. or Mrs. Khoo about whether they were thinking of selling the Jade Pendant—it would have been an insult too great to be borne. Yet the possibility had occurred to Mrs. Khoo, and the realisation, after some time, that it *would* have to be sold brought a spasm of terror to the lady as she paced about in her room, thinking what a sad state of affairs the family was in financially. The money and the property that had come down to them from their parents and grandparents—almost all dissipated! Mr. Khoo and his gambling and his horses and entertaining, the expensive education of her two sons and her daughter abroad—they were forever writing home for more money.

The immediate worry was the expense of Lian Kim's wedding. It could not, must not, be on a scale less than that of the wedding of her elder brother two years ago, or the wedding of a cousin, for that would be a severe loss of family face. Mrs. Khoo made a quick calculation of the cost of the wedding dress and trousseau, specially ordered from a French house of fashion, the furnishings for the new flat in London to be rented by the couple after their marriage, the wedding dinner for at least five hundred people in the Imperial Hotel—where was she to get the money from? She uttered little cries of agitation and wrung her hands in vexation, as she walked about in her room. She had on one occasion represented the difficulties to her husband, but he had only laughed, pinched her cheek and said, "Now, now, you are always worrying. We are O.K., O.K. and you go and get whatever you like, old girl." She had not dared to speak of her difficulties to Lian Kim—she could not bear to spoil the happiness of her beloved child.

Once she was tempted to approach Ah Soh to borrow some money—she had heard whispers of the immense sum of money that Ah Soh had slowly accumulated over forty years, money she had saved from her sale of cakes and puddings, and from extreme frugality. Ah Soh made her own cigarettes by rolling the tobacco salvaged from thrown-away cigarette ends, in little square pieces of paper, and her simple-minded daughter wore only the cast-off clothes of Lian Kim and other relatives. But she had quickly rejected the idea. What, degrade herself by seeking help from a relative who was no better than a servant? Mrs. Khoo's inherent dislike of Ah Soh was increased by her suspicion that behind all that effusive humility and deference was a shrewdness and alertness that saw everything that was going on, and she even fancied that the little frightened-looking eyes in the thin pallid face sometimes laughed at her. After Lian Kim's wedding I shall no longer tolerate her in the house, thought Mrs. Khoo resentfully. She and that imbecile daughter she dotes on so much can pack up and leave.

The thought of the wedding which should have given so much pleasure to her fond mother's heart distressed her, for again and again she wondered where the money was to come from. Their two houses were already
140 mortgaged; the shares would fetch but little. No matter how hard she tried to avoid it, the conclusion she inevitably reached was: the Jade Pendant had to go. The impact of so awesome a decision caused Mrs. Khoo to have a violent headache. The only consolation she could find in so dismal a situation was the thought that nobody need know that the Jade Pendant had
145 been sold, as she could always give some explanation or other for its not being worn at the wedding, whereas if the wedding celebration were to be scaled down, how dreadful a loss of face that would be!

She then went into urgent and secret family consultation in which her husband finally assented to the sale, stressing that they should get as good
150 a price for such a jewel as they possibly could. It was not so easy to win her daughter round—Lian Kim fretted excessively about the loss of something she had been promised, and it was only after a great deal of sulking that she could consent to the sale. The prospect of a modest wedding celebration was even more appalling than that of having to do without the Jade
155 Pendant, and of the numerous excuses thought up to account for its absence, she at last settled on this one: that the huge old-fashioned jewel would not go nicely with her Dior gown.

The secrecy with which the sale of the Jade Pendant was to be effected became a matter of first importance. Following the very discreet inquiries
160 about potential buyers, an offer came and with conditions that could not but please Mrs. Khoo—the interested party was a very wealthy lady who made her home in another country, she wanted absolute secrecy in the entire proceeding, she would send round a third person to collect the item. Her offer moreover was generous. Insist on cash, said Mr. Khoo. You never
165 know about these so-called rich foreigners. Cash it was, and the Jade Pendant left its place in the bank vaults forever.

With the matter settled, Mrs. Khoo was happy again, and bustled about in the wedding preparations. My daughter has decided not to wear the Jade Pendant, she told her friends. Oh, these young people nowadays, they
170 do not appreciate the beautiful things left them by their ancestors, and they are so intolerant of our old ways! Mrs. Khoo, caught up happily in the whirl of invitations and other preparations, did not, however, forget to tell Ah Soh, but in a kindly voice, "There will be so many guests all dressed grandly and with their jewels, that it is better for you to dress well too. I
175 hope you have bought new clothes for the occasion?" Ah Soh humbly and gratefully assured her that she had.

The wedding dinner and celebration was on a scale as to merit talk for at least the next three days. At least one Minister and three Members of Parliament, together with numerous business tycoons, were present. Mrs.
180 Khoo moved briskly among the guests, and even in the flutters of maternal anxiety and happiness, had the time to hope that that simple-minded daughter of Ah Soh would not do anything to mar the splendour of the occasion. She had wanted, tactfully, to tell Ah Soh not to bring her along, but had decided to be generous and charitable for such an occasion as
185 this—the wedding of her youngest and favourite daughter.

Her gaze swept briefly over the heads in that large resplendent, chandeliered room, and rested on a spot in the far corner, where she could easily pick out Ah Soh, decently dressed for once, sitting with her daughter and some relatives. Mrs. Khoo wondered why the eyes not only of those at
190 that table, but of those from the neighbouring tables were fixed on the imbecile child—people were positively staring at her, and not only staring, but whispering loudly, urgently among themselves. The whispering and the staring spread outwards in widening ripples of mounting excitement and tension. Mrs. Khoo made her way towards this focus of tremulous
195 attention, and she too stared—not at the idiot child-like face but at the jewel that rested awkwardly on the flat, child-like chest. The Jade Pendant! The idiot girl crowed with pleasure, and her mother who sat very near to her, holding her hand affectionately, was nodding to the faces crowding in upon them, the frightened look gone forever from her eyes.
200 Oh, where is Mr. Khoo! Please do something! shrieked Mrs. Khoo, moving about distractedly, wringing her hands. Oh, what shall we do? How shall we bear it? Lian Kim, she mustn't know, it will kill her to know! And I will kill her for having done this to me! How could she do such a thing to me!

(1978)

## Following the Story

1. The plot sequence of this story is chronological; list in point form what happens.
2. The first three paragraphs provide the exposition and most of the details are about the pendant and Mrs. Khoo's attitude towards it. Based on this information, what do you expect to happen in the story?
3. Who or what is in conflict?
4. Trace the rising action, the series of crises, that leads to the climax.

5. Two crises are introduced in paragraphs 4 and 5. In what ways are they similar?
6. What instances of foreshadowing can you find in this story?
7. Decide how the climax, the secret sale of the jade pendant, relates to the rest of the story.
8. Trace the falling action that follows the secret sale of the pendant.
9. How does Catherine Lim create the surprise at the end of the story?
10. Decide how the dénouement reflects the exposition.

## Responding to the Story

1. In what different ways does Lim convey the value of the jade pendant in the exposition?
2. Using details in the story for support, how would you describe Mrs. Khoo?
3. Using details in the story for support, how would you describe Ah Soh?
4. Throughout the story Mrs. Khoo and Ah Soh are implicitly compared. In what ways are they alike and how are they different?
5. Why do you think Ah Soh's daughter is never named?
6. Both Mrs. Khoo's daughter and Ah Soh's daughter touch the pendant. What effect does Lim create by recording the two events and their aftermath in sequence?
7. In paragraphs 6 and 7, how are the Khoos' financial problems presented?
8. What examples are provided to show that one of the things this story focuses on is 'keeping up appearances'?
9. How does Lim present social status and class differences in this story?
10. The story ends with Mrs. Khoo exclaiming, "How could she do such a thing to me!" Who is the "she" to whom Mrs. Khoo refers and why does Lim choose to end the story with these words?

# A Handful of Dates

Tayeb Salih (Sudan) 1929–

*(translated from Arabic by Denys Johnson-Davies)*

## About the Author

*Born in a northern province of Sudan, Tayeb Salih studied first at the University of Khartoum and then gained an advanced university degree in London, England. He* worked for the British Broadcasting Corporation as Head of Drama in the Arabic Service. Over the years, he has worked for UNESCO in Paris and as UNESCO's representative in Qatar. On his return to Sudan, he became director of Sudanese National Radio and then took the position of Director-General of Information in Qatar in the Arabian Gulf. He now lives in Qatar.

Since the publication of his first novel, Season of Migration to the North *(1969)*, *and his 1968 collection of short stories,* The Wedding of Zein *(which contains "A Handful of Dates"), Salih has earned the reputation of being one of the best writers in modern Arabic literature. With a deep knowledge of life and literature in both the East and the West, he centres his literary works on people and their complex relationships, general themes of reality and illusion, and cultural conflicts between East and West. Tayeb Salih strongly believes that a harmony of existence is possible for individuals in a society of values and ethics. His works have been translated into several languages.*

## About the Story

*"A Handful of Dates" develops its plot by the use of a flashback. In this case the flashback is a man's memory of a childhood event. As a result of this event, the little boy sees his grandfather differently. Because the details are recounted from the child's point of view, the reader has to figure out the true nature of the relationship between the grandfather and Masood. This story takes place in a farming community in a northern province of Sudan where the main cash crop of the region is dates and the inhabitants are Muslim.*

## Terms Appearing in the Story

**Sheikh** a religious teacher

**times for prayers** Muslims pray five times a day, either in the mosque, or on a prayer mat

**ablutions** ceremonial washing of the face, hands, and feet before prayer

**feddan** a measurement of land, approximately one acre

**three wives** traditional Muslim law allows a man to have up to four wives simultaneously

*galabia* a straight, full-length garment

I must have been very young at the time. While I don't remember exactly how old I was, I do remember that when people saw me with my grandfather they would pat me on the head and give my cheek a pinch—things they didn't do to my grandfather. The strange thing was
5 that I never used to go out with my father, rather it was my grandfather

who would take me with him whenever he went, except for the mornings when I would go to the mosque to learn the Koran. The mosque, the river and the fields—these were the landmarks in our life. While most of the children of my age grumbled at having to go to the mosque to learn the Koran, I used to love it. The reason was, no doubt, that I was quick at learning by heart and the Sheikh° always asked me to stand up and recite the *Chapter of the Merciful* whenever we had visitors, who would pat me on my head and cheek just as people did when they saw me with my grandfather.

Yes, I used to love the mosque, and I loved the river too. Directly we finished our Koran reading in the morning I would throw down my wooden slate and dart off, quick as a genie, to my mother, hurriedly swallow down my breakfast, and run off for a plunge in the river. When tired of swimming about I would sit on the bank and gaze at the strip of water that wound away eastwards and hid behind a thick wood of acacia trees. I loved to give rein to my imagination and picture to myself a tribe of giants living behind that wood, a people tall and thin with white beards and sharp noses, like my grandfather. Before my grandfather ever replied to my many questions he would rub the tip of his nose with his forefinger; as for his beard, it was soft and luxuriant and as white as cotton-wool—never in my life have I seen anything of a purer whiteness or greater beauty. My grandfather must also have been extremely tall, for I never saw anyone in the whole area address him without having to look up at him, nor did I see him enter a house without having to bend so low that I was put in mind of the way the river wound round behind the wood of acacia trees. I loved him and would imagine myself, when I grew to be a man, tall and slender like him, walking along with great strides.

I believe I was his favourite grandchild: no wonder, for my cousins were a stupid bunch and I—so they say—was an intelligent child. I used to know when my grandfather wanted me to laugh, when to be silent; also I would remember the times for his prayers° and would bring him his prayer-rug and fill the ewer for his ablutions° without his having to ask me. When he had nothing else to do he enjoyed listening to me reciting to him from the Koran in a lilting voice, and I could tell from his face that he was moved.

One day I asked him about our neighbour Masood. I said to my grandfather: "I fancy you don't like our neighbour Masood?"

To which he answered, having rubbed the tip of his nose: "He's an indolent man and I don't like such people."

I said to him: "What's an indolent man?"

My grandfather lowered his head for a moment, then looking across at the wide expanse of field, he said: "Do you see it stretching out from the edge of the desert up to the Nile bank? A hundred feddans.° Do you see all those date palms? And those trees—*sant*, acacia, and *sayal*? All this fell
50 into Masood's lap, was inherited by him from his father."

Taking advantage of the silence that had descended upon my grandfather, I turned my gaze from him to the vast area defined by his words. "I don't care," I told myself, "who owns those date palms, those trees or this black, cracked earth—all I know is that it's the arena for my dreams and
55 my playground."

My grandfather then continued: "Yes, my boy, forty years ago all this belonged to Masood—two-thirds of it is now mine."

This was news to me, for I had imagined that the land had belonged to my grandfather ever since God's Creation. "I didn't own a single feddan
60 when I first set foot in this village. Masood was then the owner of all these riches. The position has changed now, though, and I think that before Allah calls me to Him I shall have bought the remaining third as well."

I do not know why it was I felt fear at my grandfather's words—and pity for our neighbour Masood. How I wished my grandfather wouldn't do
65 what he'd said! I remembered Masood's singing, his beautiful voice and powerful laugh that resembled the gurgling of water. My grandfather never used to laugh. I asked my grandfather why Masood had sold his land.

"Women," and from the way my grandfather pronounced the word I
70 felt that "women" was something terrible. "Masood, my boy, was a much-married man. Each time he married he sold me a feddan or two." I made the quick calculation that Masood must have married some ninety women. Then I remembered his three wives°, his shabby appearance, his lame donkey and its dilapidated saddle, his *galabia*° with the torn sleeves.
75 I had all but rid my mind of the thoughts that jostled in it when I saw the man approaching us, and my grandfather and I exchanged glances.

"We'll be harvesting the dates today," said Masood. "Don't you want to be there?"

I felt, though, that he did not really want my grandfather to attend. My
80 grandfather, however, jumped to his feet and I saw that his eyes sparkled momentarily with an intense brightness. He pulled me by the hand and we went off to the harvesting of Masood's dates.

Someone brought my grandfather a stool covered with an ox-hide—while I remained standing. There was a vast number of people there, but
85 though I knew them all, I found myself for some reason watching Masood:

aloof from that great gathering of people he stood as though it were no concern of his, despite the fact that the date palms to be harvested were his own. Sometimes his attention would be caught by the sound of a huge clump of dates crashing down from on high. Once he shouted up at the boy perched on the very summit of the date palm who had begun hacking at a clump with his long, sharp sickle: "Be careful you don't cut the heart of the palm."

No one paid any attention to what he said and the boy seated at the very summit of the date palm continued, quickly and energetically, to work away at the branch with his sickle till the clump of dates began to drop like something descending from the heavens.

I, however, had begun to think about Masood's phrase "the heart of the palm." I pictured the palm tree as something with feeling, something possessed of a heart that throbbed. I remembered Masood's remark to me when he had once seen me playing about with the branch of a young palm tree: "Palm trees, my boy, like humans, experience joy and suffering." And I had felt an inward and unreasoned embarrassment.

When I again looked at the expanse of ground stretching before me, I saw my young companions swarming like ants around the trunks of the palm trees, gathering up dates and eating most of them. The dates were collected into high mounds. I saw people coming along and weighing them into measuring bins and pouring them into sacks, of which I counted thirty. The crowd of people broke up, except for Hussein the merchant, Mousa the owner of the field next to ours on the east, and two men I'd never seen before.

I heard a low whistling sound and saw that my grandfather had fallen asleep. Then I noticed that Masood had not changed his stance, except that he had placed a stalk in his mouth and was munching at it like someone surfeited with food who doesn't know what to do with the mouthful he still has.

Suddenly my grandfather woke up, jumped to his feet and walked towards the sacks of dates. He was followed by Hussein the merchant, Mousa the owner of the field next to ours, and the two strangers. I glanced at Masood and saw that he was making his way towards us with extreme slowness, like a man who wants to retreat but whose feet insist on going forward. They formed a circle round the sacks of dates and began examining them, some taking a date or two to eat. My grandfather gave me a fistful, which I began munching. I saw Masood filling the palms of both hands with dates and bringing them up close to his nose, then returning them.

Then I saw them dividing up the sacks between them. Hussein the merchant took ten; each of the strangers took five. Mousa the owner of the field next to ours on the eastern side took five, and my grandfather took five. Understanding nothing, I looked at Masood and saw that his eyes were
130 darting about to left and right like two mice that have lost their way home.

"You're still fifty pounds in debt to me," said my grandfather to Masood. "We'll talk about it later."

Hussein called his assistants and they brought along donkeys, the two strangers produced camels, and the sacks of dates were loaded on to them.
135 One of the donkeys let out a braying which set the camels frothing at the mouth and complaining noisily. I felt myself drawing close to Masood, felt my hand stretch out towards him as though I wanted to touch the hem of his garment. I heard him make a noise in his throat like the rasping of a lamb being slaughtered. For some unknown reason, I experienced a sharp
140 sensation of pain in my chest.

I ran off into the distance. Hearing my grandfather call after me, I hesitated a little, then continued on my way. I felt at that moment that I hated him. Quickening my pace, it was as though I carried within me a secret I wanted to rid myself of. I reached the river bank near the bend it made
145 behind the wood of acacia trees. Then, without knowing why, I put my finger into my throat and spewed up the dates I'd eaten.

(1968)

# Following the Story

1. The plot sequence of this story is told as a flashback. How does Tayeb Salih establish the flashback?
2. The first three paragraphs provide the exposition. What facts do we learn about the child and his daily life?
3. The boy's relationship with his grandfather is the focus of this story. Based on the details in the exposition, how could that relationship best be described?
4. The conflict in this story is introduced in the conversation between the boy and his grandfather before Masood arrives. Who or what is in conflict?
5. As the dates are harvested, the boy watches Masood. What sorts of details does he notice or recall about Masood?
6. How do the details about Masood develop the rising action in this story?
7. The grandfather is seated on a leather stool during the harvesting of the dates, and he even falls asleep. How do these facts add to the plot?

8. After the harvest, Masood munches on a stalk "like someone surfeited with food." Explain how this foreshadows the rest of the story and how it is ironic.
9. Decide how the climax (that Masood keeps none of his harvest and is still in debt to the grandfather) relates to the rest of the story.
10. Decide how the dénouement, the boy's realization that at that moment he hates his grandfather, reflects the exposition.

## Responding to the Story

1. Using details from the story, how would you describe the boy?
2. Using details from the story, how would you describe the grandfather?
3. Using details from the story, how would you describe Masood?
4. What is the effect of Salih letting the reader figure out the relationship between the grandfather and Masood rather than stating it directly?
5. How does the boy show his distrust for his grandfather?
6. What examples does Salih use to show the boy's growing empathy for Masood?
7. What is the effect of the others eating the dates, while Masood only smells them?
8. What is the "secret" the boy wants be rid of in the dénouement?
9. Why does the boy need to throw up at the end of this story?
10. What is the significance of the "handful of dates" referred to in the title of this story?

# The Stolen Party
## Liliana Heker (Argentina) 1943–

*(translated from Spanish by Alberto Manguel)*

## About the Author

*Born in Buenos Aires, capital of Argentina, in 1943, Liliana Heker began to write at a young age. Her first book,* Those That Saw the Bramble, *was published in 1966, marking the beginning of her reputation as one of the most noteworthy contemporary Argentine writers. Heker's contribution to the Argentine literary arena also includes her long-time editorship of two influential literary magazines:* El Escarabajo de Oro *and* El Ornitorrinco, *which have greatly enriched the country's ideological and cultural* life in the past 30 years. Her most recent novel, The Aim of History, *was published in 1996.*

*Liliana Heker's works have been translated into English and many other languages. "The Stolen Party" was first published in Spanish in 1982. Written in the tradition of social* **realism***, psychological realism, and* **magic realism***, Heker's stories are primarily concerned with social and moral issues, throwing light on profound truths about personal struggle in the face of poverty, social injustice, and other distressful situations in life.*

## About the Story

*"The Stolen Party" was published in Spanish in 1982. It was translated into English and anthologized by Alberto Manguel in* Other Fires: Short Fiction by Latin American Women *in 1985, and has been translated and collected in several literary anthologies. "The Stolen Party" begins with Rosaura going "straight to the kitchen to see if the monkey was there," and then develops its plot through a flashback. Although Rosaura is not telling the story herself, much of the action is seen from her point of view. One way that Liliana Heker is able to achieve this perspective is by presenting a lot of the events through direct speech. Rosaura either takes part in the dialogue or listens to it.*

*This story is set in a hierarchical, class-based society, which Rosaura, as a child, doesn't fully understand. Heker plays with Rosaura's innocence and her mother's cynicism to examine the values of this society. Rosaura simply doesn't know her place; this is something the girl with the bow tries to point out. Just what is the state of the "infinitely delicate balance" of social standing at the end of this story?*

A s soon as she arrived she went straight to the kitchen to see if the monkey was there. It was: what a relief! She wouldn't have liked to admit that her mother had been right. *Monkeys at a birthday?* her mother had sneered. *Get away with you, believing any nonsense you're told!* She was
5 cross, but not because of the monkey, the girl thought; it's just because of the party.

"I don't like you going," she told her. "It's a rich people's party."

"Rich people go to Heaven too," said the girl, who studied religion at school.

10 "Get away with Heaven," said the mother. "The problem with you, young lady, is that you like to fart higher than your ass."

The girl didn't approve of the way her mother spoke. She was barely nine and one of the best in her class.

"I'm going because I am invited," she said. "and I've been invited
15 because Luciana is my friend. So there."

"Ah yes, your friend," her mother grumbled. She paused. "Listen,
Rosaura," she said at last. "That one's not your friend. You know what you
are to them? The maid's daughter, that's what."

Rosaura blinked hard: she wasn't going to cry. Then she yelled: "Shut
20 up! You know nothing about being friends!"

Every afternoon she used to go to Luciana's house and they would
both finish their homework while Rosaura's mother did the cleaning.
They had their tea in the kitchen and they told each other secrets.
Rosaura loved everything in the big house, and she also loved the people
25 who lived there.

"I'm going because it will be the most lovely party in the whole world,
Luciana told me it would. There will be a magician, and he will bring a
monkey and everything."

The mother swung around to take a good look at her child, and
30 pompously put her hands on her hips.

"Monkeys at a birthday?" she said. "Get away with you, believing any
nonsense you're told!"

Rosaura was deeply offended. She thought it unfair of her mother to
accuse other people of being liars simply because they were rich. Rosaura
35 too wanted to be rich, of course. If one day she managed to live in a beautiful palace, would her mother stop loving her? She felt very sad. She
wanted to go to that party more than anything else in the world.

"I'll die if I don't go," she whispered, almost without moving her lips.

And she wasn't sure whether she had been heard, but on the morning
40 of the party she discovered that her mother had starched her Christmas
dress. And in the afternoon, after washing her hair, her mother rinsed it in
apple vinegar so that it would be all nice and shiny. Before going out,
Rosaura admired herself in the mirror, with her white dress and glossy
hair, and thought she looked terribly pretty.

45 Señora Ines also seemed to notice. As soon as she saw her, she said:
"How lovely you look today, Rosaura."

Rosaura gave her starched skirt a slight toss with her hands and
walked into the party with a firm step. She said hello to Luciana and
asked about the monkey. Luciana put on a secretive look and whispered
50 into Rosaura's ear: "He's in the kitchen. But don't tell anyone, because it's
a surprise."

Rosaura wanted to make sure. Carefully she entered the kitchen and
there she saw it: deep in thought, inside its cage. It looked so funny that

the girl stood there for a while, watching it, and later, every so often, she
55 would slip out of the party unseen and go and admire it. Rosaura was the
only one allowed into the kitchen. Señora Ines had said: "You yes, but not
the others, they're much too boisterous, they might break something."
Rosaura had never broken anything. She even managed the jug of
orange juice, carrying it from the kitchen into the dining room. She held
60 it carefully and didn't spill a single drop. And Señora Ines had said: "Are
you sure you can manage a jug as big as that?" Of course she could
manage. She wasn't a butterfingers, like the others. Like that blonde girl
with the bow in her hair. As soon as she saw Rosaura, the girl with the
bow had said:

65     "And you? Who are you?"

"I'm a friend of Luciana," said Rosaura.

"No," said the girl with the bow, "you are not a friend of Luciana
because I'm her cousin and I know all her friends. And I don't know you."

"So what," said Rosaura. "I come here every afternoon with my mother
70 and we do our homework together."

"You and your mother do your homework together?" asked the girl,
laughing.

"I and Luciana do our homework together," said Rosaura, very seriously.
The girl with the bow shrugged her shoulders.

75     "That's not being friends," she said. "Do you go to school together?"

"No."

"So where do you know her from?" said the girl, getting impatient.

Rosaura remembered her mother's words perfectly. She took a deep
breath.

80     "I'm the daughter of the employee," she said.

Her mother had said very clearly: "If someone asks, you say you're the
daughter of the employee; that's all." She also told her to add: "And proud
of it." But Rosaura thought that never in her life would she dare say something of the sort.

85     "What employee?" said the girl with the bow. "Employee in a shop?"

"No," said Rosaura angrily. "My mother doesn't sell anything in any
shop, so there."

"So how come she's an employee?" said the girl with the bow.

Just then Señora Ines arrived saying *shh shh*, and asked Rosaura if she
90 wouldn't mind helping serve out the hotdogs, as she knew the house so
much better than the others.

"See?" said Rosaura to the girl with the bow, and when no one was
looking she kicked her in the shin.

Apart from the girl with the bow, all the others were delightful. The one
95 she liked best was Luciana, with her golden birthday crown; and then the
boys. Rosaura won the sack race, and nobody managed to catch her when
they played tag. When they split into two teams to play charades, all the
boys wanted her for their side. Rosaura felt she had never been so happy
in all her life.

100 But the best was still to come. The best came after Luciana blew out the
candles. First the cake. Señora Ines had asked her to help pass the cake
around, and Rosaura had enjoyed the task immensely, because everyone
called out to her, shouting "Me, me!" Rosaura remembered a story in
which there was a queen who had the power of life or death over her sub-
105 jects. She had always loved that, having the power of life or death. To
Luciana and the boys she gave the largest pieces, and to the girl with the
bow she gave a slice so thin one could see through it.

After the cake came the magician, tall and bony, with a fine red cape.
A true magician: he could untie handkerchiefs by blowing on them and
110 make a chain with links that had no openings. He could guess what cards
were pulled out from a pack, and the monkey was his assistant. He called
the monkey "partner." "Let's see here, partner," he would say, "turn over a
card." And, "Don't run away, partner: time to work now."

The final trick was wonderful. One of the children had to hold the
115 monkey in his arms and the magician said he would make him disappear.

"What, the boy?" they all shouted.

"No, the monkey!" shouted back the magician.

Rosaura thought that this was truly the most amusing party in the
whole world.

120 The magician asked a small fat boy to come and help, but the small fat
boy got frightened almost at once and dropped the monkey on the floor.
The magician picked him up carefully, whispered something in his ear,
and the monkey nodded almost as if he understood.

"You mustn't be so unmanly, my friend," the magician said to the fat boy.
125 "What's unmanly?" said the fat boy.

The magician turned around as if to look for spies.

"A sissy," said the magician. "Go sit down."

Then he stared at all the faces, one by one. Rosaura felt her heart
tremble.

130 "You with the Spanish eyes," said the magician. And everyone saw that
he was pointing at her.

She wasn't afraid. Neither holding the monkey, nor when the magician
made him vanish; not even when, at the end, the magician flung his red

cape over Rosaura's head and uttered a few magic words...and the monkey
135 reappeared, chattering happily, in her arms. The children clapped furiously. And before Rosaura returned to her seat, the magician said:

"Thank you very much, my little countess."

She was so pleased with the compliment that a while later, when her
mother came to fetch her, that was the first thing she told her.

140 "I helped the magician and he said to me, 'Thank you very much, my
little countess."

It was strange because up to then Rosaura had thought that she was
angry with her mother. All along Rosaura had imagined that she would
say to her: "See that the monkey wasn't a lie?" But instead she was so
145 thrilled that she told her mother all about the wonderful magician.

Her mother tapped her on the head and said: "So now we're a
countess!"

But one could see that she was beaming.

And now they both stood in the entrance, because a moment ago
150 Señora Ines, smiling, had said: "Please wait here a second."

Her mother suddenly seemed worried.

"What is it?" she asked Rosaura.

"What is what?" said Rosaura. "It's nothing; she just wants to get presents for those who are leaving, see?"

155 She pointed at the fat boy and at a girl with pigtails who were also
waiting there, next to their mothers. And she explained about the presents. She knew, because she had been watching those who left before her.
When one of the girls was about to leave, Señora Ines would give her a
bracelet. When a boy left, Señora Ines gave him a yo-yo. Rosaura preferred
160 the yo-yo because it sparkled, but she didn't mention that to her mother.
Her mother might have said: "So why don't you ask for one, you block-
head?" That's what her mother was like. Rosaura didn't feel like
explaining that she'd be horribly ashamed to be the odd one out. Instead
she said:

165 "I was the best-behaved at the party."

And she said no more because Señora Ines came out into the hall with
two bags, one pink and one blue.

First she went up to the fat boy, gave him a yo-yo out of the blue bag,
and the fat boy left with his mother. Then she went up to the girl and gave
170 her a bracelet out of the pink bag, and the girl with the pigtails left as well.

Finally she came up to Rosaura and her mother. She had a big smile on
her face and Rosaura liked that. Señora Ines looked down at her, then looked
up at her mother, and then said something that made Rosaura proud:

"What a marvelous daughter you have, Herminia."

175     For an instant, Rosaura thought that she'd give her two presents: the bracelet and the yo-yo. Señora Ines bent down as if about to look for something. Rosaura also leaned forward, stretching out her arm. But she never completed the movement.

Señora Ines didn't look in the pink bag. Nor did she look in the blue
180 bag. Instead she rummaged in her purse. In her hand appeared two bills.

"You really and truly earned this," she said handing them over. "Thank you for all your help, my pet."

Rosaura felt her arms stiffen, stick close to her body, and then she noticed her mother's hand on her shoulder. Instinctively she pressed her-
185 self against her mother's body. That was all. Except her eyes. Rosaura's eyes had a cold, clear look that fixed itself on Señora Ines's face.

Señora Ines, motionless, stood there with her hand outstretched. As if she didn't dare draw it back. As if the slightest change might shatter an infinitely delicate balance.

(1982)

## Following the Story

1. What facts do you learn from the exposition of "The Stolen Party," presented in the conversation between Rosaura and her mother at the beginning of the story?
2. What conflicts are introduced in the exposition?
3. What expectations of the plot do you have based on reading the exposition? Can you identify any foreshadowing?
4. How does the conversation between Rosaura and "the girl with the bow" add a complication to the rising action?
5. List the things that Rosaura does to help Señora Ines at the birthday party.
6. After the party, Rosaura's mother is delighted her daughter had a good time, so why was it that she "suddenly seemed worried" (line 151)?
7. How does line 55, "Rosaura was the only one allowed into the kitchen," foreshadow the dénouement of this story?
8. Explain what is meant by "Señora Ines looked down at her" (line 172).
9. The climax of the story occurs when Señora Ines hands Rosaura the money. Explain what she means when she says to Rosaura, "You really and truly earned this" (line 181).
10. Is the dénouement a natural consequence of the events in the plot?

# Responding to the Story

1. Rosaura's mother tells her she doesn't like Rosaura going to a rich people's party. Is she right to be worried about Rosaura going to this party?
2. How do the ideas about friendship held by Rosaura and the girl with the bow differ?
3. What sort of friendship exists between Rosaura and Luciana?
4. In what ways does Rosaura show she is self-confident?
5. How do Liliana Heker's descriptions of Rosaura's responses to events throughout the story build suspense?
6. Based on the details in the story, how would you describe Rosaura?
7. In what ways can you compare the monkey in this story with Rosaura?
8. How does the ending of this story reflect the statement in the beginning that Rosaura "wouldn't have liked to admit her mother had been right"? Is this an ironic statement?
9. What is meant by the "infinitely delicate balance" in the final line and how does it relate to the story?
10. How is this party stolen, and from whom is it stolen?

# Unit Review

When analyzing plot, be sure to follow these guidelines:

- Identify the type of plot sequence.
- List in point form what happens.
- List the information given in the exposition and the facts given about the characters.
- Examine who or what is in conflict and why.
- Identify the crisis or crises.
- Trace the rising action.
- Decide how the climax relates to the rest of the story.
- Trace the falling action.
- Identify any foreshadowing, suspense, or irony.
- Decide how the resolution or dénouement reflects the exposition.

# Unit 2

## Character and Characterization

*What is character but the determination of incident?*
*What is incident but the illustration of character?*

HENRY JAMES

Incidents in life are turned into plot in stories, and people or objects we know directly or indirectly in reality provide the basis for characters in **fiction**. As we read stories, we cannot help loving, hating, sympathizing with, or reacting against people or objects that exist in the fictional world of the stories. One of the greatest challenges for a short story writer is to make the characters realistic and credible, in order to achieve what the English poet Samuel Taylor Coleridge (1772–1834) calls "suspension of disbelief." Although all characters in the short story are fictional (an invention of the mind) or fictitious (not real), we suspend our disbelief and accept them as real because, in a sense, we recognize them as people in our life.

## Types of Character

A **character** could be anything the writer chooses to tell a story about. Although by character we most often refer to a person, occasionally it could be an animal or an object such as the wind or a mere stick lying on the street. A short story could be about one character, as in "Prairie Widow" (page 39), or two characters, as in "Look Out" (page 50), or a group of characters, as in "The Farewell Party" (page 58).

Characters can be divided into different types according to their features and functions in stories. In most stories there are **major** characters and **minor** characters. The chief character is known as the **protagonist** (from Greek drama, meaning the first or chief player in a play) or the **hero/heroine**. The protagonist sometimes has to fight, or at least oppose, the **antagonist** (opponent, rival). An antagonist need not be an actual person;; a protagonist can struggle with emotions, social expectations, or nature itself. In the three short stories we will study in this unit, the protagonists are Gum-may Yee ("Prairie Widow"), the nameless young woman "she" ("Look Out"), and Bina and Raman ("The Farewell Party"). However, in none of these stories do we encounter a distinctive antagonist in human shape.

Minor characters are those who often form the background for the major characters' action and reaction. For example, Gum-may's husband Gordon, sons David and John, Gordon's cousin, and two waitresses Kay and Mabel in "Prairie Widow" are such minor characters, as are the nameless young linesman "he" and the young woman's brother and sister-in-law in "Look Out." Sometimes, as in "The Farewell Party," minor characters are portrayed as stereotypes or **stock characters** (from early English drama, referring to characters who show one single outstanding trait). These characters are there mostly to serve the theme, the central idea the story develops and explores (see Unit 6). Characters like Mrs. Ray, the self-important yet empty-headed Commissioner's wife, and the snobbish and noisy "company wives" are typical stock characters. Miss Dutta, the ever-present and thick-skinned busybody of the town, and the three pairs of robotic neighbours who appear near the end of the story are portrayed simply as **caricatures**. These characters not only call for the reader's amusement, but also serve to add depth to the portrayal of the protagonists by providing an implicit comparison.

Characters can also be classified as **dynamic** or **static**. Dynamic characters develop or change as a result of action, interaction, and reaction in the story. In contrast, static characters change little regardless of what happens in a story. In that sense, we may confidently call Gum-may in "Prairie Widow" a dynamic character because in the short space of time covered by the story we see her change significantly. On the other hand, the young woman in "Look Out" and Bina and Raman in "The Farewell Party," are dynamic only to those who recognize the subtle emotional changes and psychological development depicted in the story.

Literary characters may also be characterized as **round** or **flat**, terms introduced by English novelist E. M. Forster (1879–1970) in his book *Aspects of the Novel* (1927). As the terms suggest, round characters are three-dimensional, well-developed, and frequently unpredictable, whereas flat characters are two-dimensional, underdeveloped, and often stereotypical.

Using Forster's terms, we could easily identify Gum-May, "she," and Bina and Raman as round characters in their respective stories. We are informed not only of what they say and do, but also of what they think and how they feel. The rest of the cast is flat or two-dimensional. Usually major characters are round and dynamic, and minor characters are flat and static. Yet, as with everything else, there are exceptions. Classifications of characters are meant to make it easier rather than harder for us to understand and analyze those who live in the stories. In the short story, as in life, nothing is clear-cut or definitive.

# Characterization

**Characterization** refers to the methods the short story writer uses to create and portray characters. There are three principal methods of characterization in fiction. While one method may predominate in a story, an author often uses a mixture of all three means to present and reveal the characters.

In the first method, the author *explicitly presents characters through direct exposition*, which is often referred to as **telling**. Explicit presentation is most frequently conducted by the narrator (see Unit 3), who normally begins the narration by *telling* and keeps on *telling* about the characters throughout the story.

Here are some typical examples taken from our sample stories.

As far as she was concerned, the mourning period was over. She had wept as any widow would, but more from fear and fury than from grief. (From the beginning of "Prairie Widow," page 40)

Harassed, perspiring, his feet burning, Raman was nevertheless pleased to be so obviously employed and be saved the strain of having to converse with his motley assembly of guests: he had no more gift for society than his wife had. (From lines 179–182 of "The Farewell Party," page 64)

And suddenly she wanted to cry. But not here, where he could see her. Inside in her own little room. Where no one could see her. She would just put her head down and cry. And not because she was sad. And not because she was happy.... (From the end of "Look Out," page 57)

The second method is an *implicit presentation of characters in action*, also known as **showing**. This method is used primarily through **dialogue** or action of characters in a story with little or no explicit comment made by the author or the narrator. The purpose is to let the reader see, hear, and deduce the characters' personality or traits independently. The stories chosen for examination in this unit provide abundant examples of presentation of characters in action.

The occasional exchange of words between Bina and some of her guests in "The Farewell Party," for instance, is frequently more revealing of the hostess's awkward manners and antisocial personality at her own party than the narrator's lengthy *telling*. Also, in their different ways, the brief dialogues (in reminiscences) between Gum-may and her husband in "Prairie Widow" and the ongoing conversation between the nameless young woman and her potential admirer in "Look Out" *show* us more vividly how the two women have to be submissive to the men who dominate their lives.

The third method requires the **in-depth presentation** from within a character, which is almost like **mind reading**, so that the reader can experience the character's inner self and see things directly through the character's eyes in order to have a better understanding. Again, the stories in this unit are filled with such insightful moments. For example, at an early moment of the encounter between the young woman and the young man in "Look Out," we are given a chance to read the protagonist's mind: "The man was a fool. She would snub him. She would wait for him to say something to her, and she would take pains to snub him" (line 63). This peep into the character's thoughts not only provides us with the key to understanding her ambivalent attitude toward the linesman, but also sets the stage for the subtle changes that occur to her in the course of action. Similarly, Anita Desai succeeds in describing Bina and Raman from within, as does Paul Yee with Gum-may. In so doing, they make their characters psychologically truthful and credible to the reader.

We see then that skillful writers frequently use a combination of all three methods to make characters *breathe* and *live* in their stories. They *tell*, they *show*, and they try to *read the characters' minds*. As a result, we are able to understand the characters' **motivations** as well as their actions and reactions to external events. When a character's action can be justified by inner feelings and psychological traits, we say it is *in character*; otherwise, it is *out of character*. Naturally a story loses its credibility and appeal when its characters speak or act out of character.

The short story writer's job is like that of a sculptor in that they both choose to be confined in time and space. One of the most difficult tasks for them to perform is to lock in their character(s)/subject(s) at a crucial point of time and portray them as they act and react to "the moment." Paul Yee, Roger Mais, and Anita Desai are all masters in catching that *crucial moment* in their characters' respective lives—beginning of widowhood for Gum-may in "Prairie Widow," the first conversation with a young man in the city for the young woman in "Look Out" and a social occasion, a farewell party, for an antisocial couple in "The Farewell Party." Within the limited time and space, characters, both major and minor, dynamic and static, round and flat, play their assigned roles, developing the plot of their respective stories while demonstrating their unique characteristics.

Now let us read these three stories, typical "slices of life," as Chekhov would call them, and have a close look at the characters whom we now have the opportunity to meet.

---

# Prairie Widow
Paul Yee (Canada) 1956–

## About the Author
*Born in Spalding, Saskatchewan, Paul Yee is a Chinese-Canadian of the third gener-ation who grew up in Vancouver and earned his B.A. and M.A. in history at the University of British Columbia. He has worked as an archivist and policy analyst for the government of Ontario. He became known as a writer of children's literature when his first book of stories,* Teach Me to Fly, Skyfighter! *was published in 1983. His major works include* The Curses of Third Uncle *(1986),* Saltwater City *(1989),* Tales from Gold Mountain *(1990), and* Struggle and Hope *(1996). Yee's literary works have won many awards, including the Governor General's Award in 1996.*

*Having had a typical Chinese-Canadian childhood, Yee is determined to "carve a place in the North American imagination for the many generations of Chinese who have settled here as Canadians and Americans, and help them stake their claim to be known as pioneers, too."*

## About the Story
*"Prairie Widow" is set in Wilding, a fictitious town in Western Canada, in the late 1950s. The story presents a memorable portrait of a Chinese-Canadian woman, Gum-may Yee, as well as a realistic picture of her social surroundings. In this story, characterization is most noteworthy. Different facets of the character of Gum-may are*

*portrayed through her thoughts, her action, and occasionally through her words in reminiscences. Past, present, and future are all skillfully mingled together by allowing the reader to share some reflective moments with Gum-may while she is browsing through some family photos after her husband's death.*

## Terms Appearing in the Story

**Mencius** (371–288 B.C.E.)(also spelled Mengzi or Meng-tse) a great philosopher and scholar of the Confucian School of Thought in ancient China. As recorded in Chinese folklore, his widowed mother is synonymous with maternal devotion.

**Gum San** "the gold mountains" in Toisanese, referring to North America, where many Chinese at the time believed money could be easily made

**The immigration laws** the *Chinese Immigration Act* enacted by the Government of Canada in 1923. Better known as the "Chinese Exclusion Act," it barred Chinese from entering Canada until it was repealed almost a quarter-century later in1947. It was the only racially and nationally specific exclusion in Canadian law.

A s far as she was concerned, the mourning period was over. She had wept as any widow would, but more from fear and fury than from grief. Four days had passed since the funeral, and the café remained sealed to the townspeople and travellers who frequented it. Only the rattle of an
5 occasional car or truck and the steady hum of the refrigerator slipped through the soft slitted grey of the afternoon. Gum-may Yee sat at one of the dining tables, sifting through the tin can holding all their important documents. Only the photographs made sense to her, for she could read little Chinese and even less English.
10 She had discovered Gordon's cousin leafing through the box just before his departure. 'Leave it!' she had shouted, her voice rising loud and shrill as her face suddenly glared ferocious. 'That box, it's not yours! His things, I don't want you touching them!'

His intrusion had shaken loose her grim silences. At first, the raging
15 anger had conquered the fear. Her mind cursed the worm of a husband who had deserted her in a strange country with children but without means. Once again she felt betrayed, now to face the uncertainty and townspeople of Wilding alone. The Yees were the sole Chinese family there, forty miles over the horizon and down the highway from the next prairie bus stop.
20 Gum-may knew only a few words of English. Could she run the café herself? How was she to raise her two sons? She had already decided to stay.

'Stay?' the cousin had asked incredulously. 'How? You can't speak, can't write! You're a woman, do you know that?'

She had shaken her head stubbornly. 'Here, it's better.'

25 'Come out, with the children, to Vancouver,' he had pleaded. 'Come out after the month is full. We have Chinese stores, Chinese schools, theatres, everything you want. Come out!'

Gum-may had shrugged and looked away. She did not know why she had instinctively decided to stay. She had not thought out reasons and pro-
30 cedures. She only knew that she could not leave the café even though she had never felt at home in Wilding. The townspeople had watched Gordon with distant, guarded eyes for twenty years, suspicious that a wifeless young Oriental might somehow sully the farming settlement. Nor had they changed after Gum-may's arrival in 1950. After business hours, the
35 Yees were left to themselves and their box-like home sank silently into the deep prairie night. Gum-may had learned to wrap the isolation around her like a blanket, sealing in the warmth of a solitary beating heart.

In the days after the funeral, Gum-may had moved about dazedly, cooking for the children with hands that acted of their own accord. Her
40 mind wandered far and near. At moments, all things seemed workable: her sons would start school once again, the two waitresses Kay and Mabel would return, and she would resume baking, cooking, and washing. But at other times, her mind lost its calm. What if the supplies did not come? Suppose there was a fire? Whom would she turn to in case of sudden ill-
45 ness? She detested the idiotic smiling and nodding she used to turn away the banter of customers. Over and over she wondered why she had decided to stay.

She slept soundly and dreamlessly through all the nights as if exhausted from a long journey. This morning, she had awakened late and then stum-
50 bled groggily into the kitchen. The boys had already eaten and slipped outside. She saw the empty bowls, the bread bag lying open, and the milk bottle standing uncapped, and was stricken with panic.

'Are you fit to be a mother?' Self disgust had slashed at her. 'Look at you, sleeping like a pig. No brains at all! Are you crazy?' She pictured her-
55 self wandering the street, hair dishevelled, and crooning shrill lullabies to herself. The smirking townsfolk walked wide arcs around her. Then she saw a ring of dancing chanting children encircling her sons.

'Crazy lady, *deen-pob*,' they screamed, 'Your mother's a crazy lady!' To possess sons and then lose her mind was an unbearable idea. In terror,
60 Gum-may had darted to the wash basin and splashed cold water onto her face.

For the rest of the morning, she had worked herself furiously. She pulled on a baggy sweater and went out to water and hoe her neglected vegetables. This was her fifth garden in as many years, and the earth continued
65 to send up beans and potatoes despite Gordon's dire predictions. Of course, Gum-may nursed the soil thoroughly with the outhouse offerings once the winter relaxed.

The uneven rows of green formed her only lines of reference over the vast terrain. In China, a river streamed by one side of the village, moun-
70 tains rolled in the distant north, and castle-like watchtowers had guarded the opposite horizons. Here, she felt adrift in a swaying, unyielding ocean, and she clung to her hoe and shovel as if they were life-preservers.

'Widows are work-mules,' she muttered at the weeds, and she was no exception. The famous Third Lady of an earlier dynasty, when widowed,
75 had laboured late into the night at her weaving. Then she immortalized herself with a scissor slash across the loom to admonish her delinquent son. In front of the devastated threads, she hissed, 'An unschooled man is like an unfinished bolt of cloth—unsaleable, irreparable, and wasted!' Wisdom and drama, it seemed, were incumbent for widowhood, and Gum-
80 may prayed that she could afford both.

Returning to the kitchen, she had started to wash the accumulated piles of dishes. Dull grey sheets of galvanized tin framed the once-white sink. She checked if the lard pail underneath required emptying before cranking the water pump. Beside it stood the sturdy gas stove, the mainstay of their
85 livelihood. This kitchen would be her loom, Gum-may thought, to transform her efforts into food for her sons. It was a pity that she did not possess the pretty face or shapely figure that less dutiful widows exploited. Small eyes on a face too broad glared back when she glanced in the mirror. The rigours of bearing children and enduring Canadian winters had thick-
90 ened her body.

Gum-may pumped a steady flow of water to rinse the soap away. Perhaps, she thought, she should follow the cousin's advice and move. Her lips tightened as the familiar questions reasserted themselves in her mind. She did not want to move. But had not the widowed mother of the sage
95 Mencius° moved three times before satisfying herself? The wise matron had finally settled by the schoolmaster's house where her son could observe studious habits. Mencius had almost become a butcher when the slaughterhouse was located next door.

Of course, Gum-may reminded herself, she would situate her family
100 wherever the advantages for her sons lay. Yet the thought of moving left her cold. Vancouver seemed ten thousand miles away, across oceans and

mountains that would claim her life if she ventured away. She dreaded the boarding of trains, the changing of scenery, and the meeting of new faces—and she was not sure why. She had always considered herself quite
105 fearless and brave.

Next, Gum-may had filled the wash bucket to go out to scrub the café floor. On her knees, she pushed the bristle brush with renewed energy, hoping that weariness would displace the unease. In earlier days, she had imagined herself a gentry-woman, presiding over private and public quar-
110 ters. The two bedrooms ran side by side to the length of the café, connected only at the kitchen. It had been wondrously sinful to lie in bed and listen to the unsuspecting customers eat and chat on the other side of the thin wall.

But the work soon destroyed her imagination. She rose at six to knead bread and doughnuts for the first busload of customers. Day after day, the
115 diners ordered from the same unchanging menu. The plates and glasses were washed and reused every two hours. She and Gordon ate the left-overs, whatever could not be served next day. This was Gum San,° the mountains of gold that men in China dreamt about? There were neither mountains in the prairie nor gold in the café kitchen. Gum-may learned
120 to let her mind hum the old tunes carried by opera troupes across the Toisan countryside.

As the floor dried, Gum-may had gone into the bedroom and started to empty Gordon's clothes from the drawers. It was then that she had come across the tin box with the papers and photographs. She carried it into the
125 dining room and opened it curiously. Not much had accumulated: a few letters, some heavy folded documents, their passports. She had never seen the box's contents before.

'Why am I looking through this?' she wondered. 'Me, a woman without schooling.' Even if Gordon had left instructions for her future life, she
130 would have been unable to decipher them. She recognized rows of num-bers, but nothing made sense. Every sheet was meaningless until she came to the snapshots at the bottom.

The first photograph brought a fleeting smile to her face. Five Chinese couples stared solemnly out at her. The café's menu board hung behind
135 them, chalk marks grinning off the soda pop company's blackboard. Gum-may cradled her first-born son in the centre. The gathering had marked the full-month celebration of David's birth. She put names to the faces: the men were addressed as 'uncles' and the women as 'elder sisters' or 'sisters-in-law' to establish a simple intimacy quickly among strangers.
140    It had been the first time that guests had come to the café since Gum-may's arrival in Wilding. Gordon's friends had journeyed from several

neighbouring towns, bearing gifts of oranges and red packets of good-luck money. They too were small businessmen, operating laundries and cafés in their own visions of Gum San. The men might meet by chance in Regina 145 or Saskatoon, but contact was otherwise scarce. Yet they greeted one another affectionately as brothers, bound by unspoken aspirations and desperations shaped by a common destiny.

Like Gum-may, the wives had come to Canada only after the immigration laws° were changed. After the introductions of the day, the women had 150 eyed each other's newly curled hair and long full dresses with momentary suspicion. But in the kitchen away from the men, they had giggled, touched one another, and talked without restraint. They traded names of home villages and details of travelling to their new homes. They fretted over the Communists in China and laughed at the raised toilets of Canada, won-155 dering how the bowels could possibly move when perched two feet above the ground. Their voices filled the room along with the steam from numerous bowls and pots of tea and tangy ginger-vinegar broth.

For them, every aspect of life here proved a new discovery and they had withdrawn from public sight in their awkwardness. Only when they shared 160 the hurt could they laugh at themselves and look at the world around them. Only then did Canada become real. There were drunks and cheats who never paid their bills, and farmers' wives who refused even to nod at them in passing. Their own husbands gambled and drank, to be sure, and there were whispered tales of less able men gone mad and 'kept' women 165 still waiting. But all things taken, the women celebrated their arrival in Gum San. The men welcomed the helping hand and moved eagerly to water the family tree. Gum-may had basked in the rhythms of village dialects but she had told none of her secrets.

Even then she had feared that Gordon's drinking was excessive. He 170 would pull out the whiskey once the blind was drawn and the front door latched for the night. 'I'm all tired out,' he announced curtly, 'The tendons are all tight.' During the months of pregnancy, it seemed to Gum-may that her husband was greying and shrinking before her very eyes. After a long swallow from the bottle, he sat motionless, eyes clenched shut on his pale 175 and haggard face. Was it liquor that had eased his years alone in this land? Gum-may could not help but wonder who and how many he had slept with. Could he be trying to forget or remember someone?

She had hovered silent and apprehensive, a nervous hand over her growing belly. An unfathomable gulf hung between them. It had been too 180 late after her arrival to test for new intimacies. For the first weeks he had smiled constantly at her, as if to reassure and to encourage her. They had

both aged, but separately, in different worlds. She knew nothing about the man who pulled her body into his on the sagging bed. And for either to cast about coyly for new sensations or fresh information seemed unbe-
185 coming for their age and a cruel mockery of their situation.

After she had mastered the locations and processes of her new home, silence filled their relationship and drove them apart. Gordon disappeared at night, and came back very late with his clothes reeking of tobacco and more alcohol. Soon she realized that the townsmen had set up a gambling
190 table behind the barber shop. Gum-may consoled herself with the child, but found herself wishing that she had been more attentive when they had first met in their younger and more playful days.

'More playful?' Gum-may jolted back to the present and sneered. What a waste of time to daydream. Youth was a bird spreading its wings; once
195 aloft, it never returned. The next photo she picked up showed a younger, prettier version of her with hair braided into sturdy pigtails. She stood erect behind her seated parents, careful not to stir a wrinkle into her new blouse. She had never visited the photographer's shop in the county seat before. Little did she suspect that the print would be employed by her father to
200 solicit a useful son-in-law.

Gum-may hardly knew her father and trusted him less. She was out in the paddy fields by the time he arose and already asleep when he returned at nights. He was nicknamed Big-gun Ming for his frequent volleys of opin-ions and plans. But the money-minded advice went to everyone else while
205 he lived off the remittances received from a brother in America. The family fields he rented out, reserving only a small plot for his wife and daughter to tend to.

The announcement of marriage had demolished the sixteen-year-old Gum-may. She expected that her body would ultimately be surrendered to
210 a husband. But already? It seemed that it was only yesterday that she had discovered the supple strength of her body. She was tall and bold, carrying laden baskets to trade at the country marketplace. The pride of filial accomplishment filled her when she slipped the coins into her mother's hand, tendering them as proof of her devotion and ability. She had dared
215 to think the shame of a son-less family could be redeemed by hard work.

Her father had presided loudly at the wedding banquet, toasting all the guests with a ready glass. Gum-may kept her eyes lowered, but on one upward glance, she had caught her father staring at her. The setting sun glinted off his sweaty jowls and his eyes narrowed to squint at her.
220 'You better do well,' came the silent command. Gordon's family had sev-eral men working in Gum San. Gum-may was her parents' only child. No

one would fault her if she kept ties to her own family. As for her new husband, he behaved like other returnees from abroad: cocky and confident in talk and movement. He had looked at her and seemed relieved that she
225 resembled the photograph and had not concealed moles, buck teeth or the like from him.

Gum-may had not wanted to lie with Gordon. He had smiled at her with knowing eyes. His pale stocky body smelled sharply sweet when he moved up to her on the bed. Gum-may retreated and looked away. But
230 Gordon knew what to do, he knew what he wanted. She kept her eyes and hands tightly clenched as he eased her legs apart and slid between them. The pain swirled with her fear. Two months later, he departed. Gordon was afraid they might change the immigration laws in his absence and block his re-entry.

235 Gum-may had not shed tears for him in the two decades that followed. The years of war and hunger swept her thoughts into survival, away from wishful sentimentality. Her own mother died during the invasion, and Gum-may felt her body harden and her gums loosen. There was no aching or dreaming for this distant stranger who had moved painfully inside her.
240 No special quirks to his speech or movements called him to her. She mused that even the scrawny water buffalo was a more intimate companion. When Gum-may did weep, it was for those definitions that Gordon's absence denied her—wife to his needs, mother of his sons, partner to his labour. Gordon's mother had not been overly cruel, taking Gum-may's
245 barrenness as a reassuring sign of her chastity.

Gum-may's hands trembled over the photos. 'Why bring these memories back?' she demanded. 'Forget them! Cast them aside, they're useless. Everything is different now.' She tried to think of the future. The café was a routine she had lived for six years. The customers would return if she
250 acted quickly. She could re-open the doors if Mabel watched the cash register in the front. She could be trusted with the money for she too was a widow. Mabel had sat silently by her side that first night before the relatives had arrived. They both wept: Mabel's tears slid down her round cheeks while Gum-may's wails clawed the air. The boys were huddled in a
255 corner with lost looks on their frightened faces.

The boys' faces leapt up at her from more snapshots. David's eyes resembled hers, small and set close to the nose. John's over-sized ears were a sign of future longevity. In a rare gesture of affection, Gordon had trimmed their hair the night before seeing the photographer. It had been
260 Gum-may's suggestion to send family portraits to their relatives in China. There, she had reasoned, she and the boys might finally receive a measure

of appreciation. Her sons testified to her virtue: she had violated no taboos and had produced hardy insurance to guarantee the lineage's future fortunes. In the village, Gum-may's high status would have been confirmed.

265    But out here, her sons drew no special attention. The town was a closed circle: she spoke to no one and no one came to visit. The boys became dusty treasures that depreciated daily. They played with the twins from across the street, stealing candy and soda pop from the café to trade for wild flowers and limp rodents plucked from the rolling fields. The boys
270 came home with burrs and grass tangled in their hair and gaping holes in their pants. Gum-may looked and sighed.

Gordon glared at them with dulled eyes. He did not speak or play with them. If they angered him, his eyes flashed at Gum-may, and she would scold and discipline them. She had once hoped that the boys might restore
275 some youth in their father or even entice him to stay home. Maybe he would teach them to count and write in Chinese. But Gordon played the cold hard father of Confucian virtue and the boys only became another topic of argument.

'What do I do, that makes you so angry?' she had ventured recently.
280    Gordon had snapped back, 'I'm not angry! Who says I'm angry?'

She had bit her lip. 'Then why don't you look at the children? Don't you know how to be a father?'

Gordon's eyes had blazed. 'I'm tired, that's what! Don't I do enough? There's rice to eat, the children have clothes. You have money to send
285 home. What more do you want?'

All fighting over money, gambling, and alcohol ended with this standard challenge, 'Are you not satisfied, woman?'

She had been forced to concede that she was indeed not in want, for their joint labours in the café met all their needs well enough. But the
290 futility of these confrontations had slowly given her strength, for they revealed the weaknesses of her husband. She saw that Gordon's despair of life could find no release anywhere.

During the day, Gordon appeared in the kitchen only when fat Mister Martinsen and his friends congregated at the café for their weekly coffee
295 sessions. They hunched around one table for the afternoon, nudging and chortling and welcoming every additional body with a hearty chorus of hullo's. Gordon left them a pot of coffee and a pie and then went behind his counter. Soon he came into the back, searching for odd jobs to do. Gum-may had observed his downcast eyes, but it was some time before she
300 realized that it would take more than a wife and sons to fill the void inside him roused by the camaraderie and confidences of menfolk.

She had watched her husband wipe the grill and strain the soup over and over with deliberate care. This man of hers was like her father, eager to play the word games that men devised for business and merriment. But
305 Gordon was treated like a servant in his own proprietorship and a mute among his peers: The farmers and truck-drivers would never accept him as their equal, yet Gordon had made a commitment to a life in this country.

Gordon had wanted the strangest things in life—things denied him because he was Chinese, because he was a newcomer. Why did he yearn
310 for the impossible? Gum-may wondered. He should have tasted China's starvation and the panic of refugees pursued by soldiers, guns, and bandits. Had life in Canada become too soft, too easy? If he had huddled under the droning airplanes swooping low with bombs, he might have valued life more. If he had touched the clammy darknesses she once bat-
315 tled before awakening, he might have clasped his sons to him.

The door slammed and Gum-may looked up as the boys rushed in. Her hands moved to cover the photographs as if they were delicate shards of a broken bowl being pieced together.

'They want to know if we are moving to Vancouver,' David blurted in a
320 child's clear Toisanese. Gum-may looked at the bright eyes focused on her and answered slowly, 'No, we're staying.'

'Hurrah!' The boys shouted with joy and rushed out. Gum-may stacked the photographs carefully and replaced them in the tin box. She would go through the rest later. Now it was time to prepare dinner.

325 Yes, they were staying, Gum-may repeated as she turned on the kitchen light. An unusual sense of peace filled her now. Surely she had learned and suffered enough to survive whatever twists heaven might throw at her. Surely her life was not meant to be a continual trek through the doors of strangers to fall under their baneful staring. She felt at once weary and
330 energized: too tired to pack her bags for another move, but more than ready to show everyone her determination to succeed. The pieces of life she had gathered along the road to Gum San made best sense here, within the four walls of this café. She had finally arrived at a place she understood.

(1990)

## Following the Story

1. What facts are given about Gum-may Yee, the protagonist, in the first paragraph?

2. List the minor characters. What relationship does each one have with Gum-may?
3. Is Gum-may Yee a round and dynamic character? Why or why not?
4. Is Gordon Yee a flat and static character? Why or why not?
5. How are the events in the story arranged? Draw a chart to show the order of events, past and present, as they are presented in the story.
6. Where are the moments of flashback? What do they tell us about the prairie widow Gum-may?
7. How long was Gum-may married to Gordon? How long has she been in Canada?
8. What does the café mean to Gum-may? Why does she feel that way?
9. What are the possible reasons for Gum-may's decision to remain in Wilding and run the cafe?
10. What methods does the author use for characterization: telling, showing, in-depth presentation, or a combination of all? Support your argument with specific examples in the story.

## Responding to the Story

1. If you were to use five adjectives to describe Gum-may as a young woman back in her hometown in Toisan, China, what would be your choice of words?
2. Is Gordon Yee a good husband and father? Why or why not?
3. Is Gum-may a good wife and mother? Why or why not?
4. Why does Gum-may suffer "more from fear and fury than from grief" at the beginning? How does the author explain it?
5. How would you describe the attitude of residents in Wilding, the small town where the story is set, toward the Yees?
6. What have you learned about the life of Chinese immigrants in Canada in the 1950s?
7. How do you respond to the dénouement of the story? How does it relate to the last sentence of the third paragraph: "She had already decided to stay"?
8. Do you think Gum-may has made the right decision? What would you do if you were in Gum-may's situation?
9. How do you feel about the fact that Paul Yee presents the incidents out of chronological order? Is it appropriate for the story? Why or why not?
10. What do you think is the "unique or single effect" of this short story?

# Look Out

Roger Mais (Jamaica) 1905–1955

## About the Author

*Born in Kingston, Jamaica, into a respectable middle-class family, Roger Mais first attracted public attention as a journalist who took part in the nationalist movement and was imprisoned in 1944 for an essay he wrote entitled "Now We Know," which attacked British colonialism. His major novels include* The Hills Were Joyful Together *(1953),* Brother Man *(1954), and* Black Lightning *(1955), which form a kind of trilogy. "Look Out" is collected in his book of short stories,* Listen, the Wind and Other Stories, *which was published in 1986, 31 years after he died of cancer at age 49.*

*Roger Mais, acclaimed by many as "the spokesman of emergent Jamaica," is known for his novels of social protest, which realistically examined the country's squalid urban conditions and exposed social ills in mid-twentieth-century Jamaica.*

## About the Story

*"Look Out" is a story that catches its protagonist, an unidentified young woman from the country, in her significant moment as she looks out from the front gate of her brother's confining house where she is staying as a "mother's help" for her pregnant and "half-crazy" sister-in-law. Through a skillfully staged dialogue between her and an unnamed young man (a stranger to her), the reader is shown how interestingly the two characters interact, unfold, and evolve. Telling and in-depth presentation, on the other hand, also form a crucial part of characterization in the story. What amazes the reader most, however, is Mais's talent in depicting his characters with such artistry that every detail seems to be artless.*

*One special aspect of the story lies in its language and **diction**. To reflect the linguistic features of the local dialect spoken by the characters, the author presents their speech and thoughts in an "as-is" manner. That is why there are a great number of Jamaican slang expressions and colloquialisms along with an abundance of sentence fragments. It is important to use your imagination when interpreting these expressions. For example,* short of them hog-tying her and dragging her here *presents a vivid picture in the reader's mind when read in the context while* What sort of fast one did he think he was pulling out from up his sleeve now? *simply means "What kind of new tricks is he playing here?"* Get fresh with *as a colloquial expression means "too bold with someone of the opposite sex."*

She was at the gate, resting her arm on the top rail, her chin on her arms, looking out. Out being just any place that wasn't in. The moon rode high in the sky above great banks of clouds. Last night the moon was in eclipse. It was like someone had pulled a red curtain down over the face
5 of the moon. But it was the moon all the same. Come clouds, come eclipse, it was all the same moon.

Somebody was calling to her from the house. That would be her sister-in-law. Her dear brother's wife. But she didn't pay no attention to her. She was a little cracked in the head. It was the moon. The moon made her
10 come out from inside herself where she was locked away; inside her head, behind a smile that was like the double-blank in the box of dominoes. The moon made her come out from behind that dead smile and talk her head off. And shout her head off. But nobody paid no attention to her at all. Her brother's half-crazy wife.

15 She heard the sound of boots. Someone was coming slowly up the road. She didn't bother to turn her head to look. Just someone coming up the road. No matter.

She said out loud. Just thinking: 'Couldn't be gone ten yet.'

He stopped as though she had spoken to him. He was wearing khaki
20 pants and a blue sports shirt. There was something about him that was lean and hard, and clean. Clean like he'd just come out of the tub. He stopped right under the street lamp that was before the gate and looked at his wrist-watch.

'Ten past,' he said.

25 She made a little sound with her tongue against her teeth.

But he was still there. Hesitating in his mind. Whether to stop and chat with her, or go on. She didn't give him any encouragement, or otherwise. She just kept on looking out, her chin resting upon her arms, her arms resting on the top of the gate.

30 'You waiting for someone,' he said. But he wasn't asking. He stood there still hesitating in his mind whether to stop and chat or to go on along his way.

Under the lamp-post there was a diamond-shaped sign that said 'Bus Stop'.

35 'The bus stops here,' he said. But he wasn't asking. He said it like he was reading the sign aloud, but to himself.

'It's going to rain,' he said. Lifting his face to the moon. 'Did you see the eclipse of the moon last night?' As you might say, 'read any good books lately?'

40 'Uh-huh,' she said.

Somebody was calling her from the house. Calling in a loud queer voice. He moved just one step. That took him one step nearer to the bus sign, so that he now stood on neutral ground. He might be waiting for the bus at the stop sign, or he might be talking to a girl at her gate, if the bus should 45 come along and he didn't want to take it.

'That's just my sister-in-law,' she said. 'I don't pay no mind to her.' Lifting a foot to the lowest rail of the gate, but without otherwise changing her position.

He lit a cigarette carelessly and looked up at the moon. He stood for a 50 while like that, not saying anything, just looking up.

The clouds were banked up high against the moon, so that she looked wild and stormy tonight, and as though filled with a great unrest.

But cho! It was only the moon. Always the moon. The rest was trimmings. They didn't mean anything.

55 The man said: 'It's going to rain.' Blowing out a cloud of smoke. To him the trimmings meant nothing.

She wanted to laugh.

'What you are? A weather prophet?'

'Them clouds,' he said. 'See them dark ones underneath like? They say 60 rain!'

'Ain't you smart,' she mocked.

'That's right,' he said, without his face changing.

The man was a fool. She would snub him. She would wait for him to say something to her, and she would take pains to snub him.

65 Besides it wasn't right she should be here chatting with him. At any moment her brother might ride up on his bicycle. He would scold her, inside. Though who could say she was in fact chatting with anyone? Wasn't her fault there was a bus stop just outside their gate. Wasn't she put it there.

70 She said: 'Weren't you going for a walk?'

He said without looking at her: 'I was.'

'I changed my mind now,' he said. 'I'm waiting for the bus.'

Her foot on the rail started of itself bouncing her knee up and down. Like she might have been hushing a baby to bye-bye. She was doing 75 that without thinking about it. But he saw it out of the corner of his eye. Without looking around. Saw her bare knee bouncing. It was a pretty knee—to pass up just like that. She might be waiting for someone, sure. But all the same where he was standing was public thoroughfare. He might be going some place, or not. Wasn't anybody's business. She 80 didn't have to answer back if she didn't want. He could say, it's going to rain, without talking to anyone. Just saying it looked like it was going to rain.

The three children had been put to bed long ago. Her brother's children. Couldn't be anything she could do that her sister-in-law kept calling, 85 calling at her. She just wouldn't pay any mind to her. Let her call. It was the moon. The moon was full tonight. Last night there had been an eclipse, and it looked just like someone had drawn a red blind down over the face of the moon. And bit by bit the blind had lifted. Until the last time she had looked at it, it was just like someone had broken a piece out of the 90 moon somewhere near the top.

A few people passed in the street. She heard them come and go without looking at them. Except when they passed her line of vision looking straight out before her, she didn't see them. Two three bicycles went by, but nothing to make her take her mind off what she was thinking about— 95 nothing.

She wasn't thinking about anything tonight. She wasn't waiting for anyone either. Leastways she didn't know anyone she *could* be waiting for. Except it was that she was waiting for her brother to come home? And why *should* she be waiting for her brother to come home? She was 100 just tired of staying indoors doing nothing. With a crazy woman for company. She was just leaning against the gate, looking out, doing nothing. Thinking about nothing. Sometimes it got so bad sitting indoors with only her sister-in-law for company, that she wanted to put her hands up to her head and scream!

105 But she wasn't going to do that. She wasn't going to let it get her that way. The loneliness. The emptiness of everything. Ever since she had left home and come to live with her brother in the city. Because his wife was that way again, bringing them into the world faster than she could look after them.

110 If she let it get her, someday she would be getting like her sister-in-law. All shut inside her head. Her face blank. Her eyes. That fixed dead smile. All like the double-blank in the box of dominoes. She hadn't known it was going to be like this in the city. Else she wouldn't have left home in the first place. Short of them hog-tying her and dragging her here. She hadn't 115 known her brother meant to lock her inside a house and not want her to see anyone from outside, and not want her to have any friends or go anywhere. *If* she had known!

Maybe he was just one of those fresh guys. The city, she was warned, was full of them. Or maybe he was a married man himself with a family of

120 three squalling children, and his wife that way again. But cho! That didn't bother her. She wasn't even giving him a thought. That way.

'Ever seen a man climb right up one of them electric-line poles?' he said, looking at her.

'No,' she said. Was he trying to be funny?

125 Ever seen a man climbing a pole! What was he coming with now. What did he take her for? A fool? What was his line? What was he getting at? Ever seen a man climbing a pole, indeed! What sort of fast one did he think he was pulling out from up his sleeve now? What was he getting around to? What was he coming with now?

130 Cho! It must be one of those jokes he was trying to tell her. Just one of those fresh guys. Trying to get fresh with her.

'What you talking about, a man climbing a pole?' she said.

'That's me,' he said. 'Linesman.'

'Linesman?' she said.

135 'Linesman. That's what they call us. Wire-monkeys. We look after the lines.'

So. That was it. He was telling her about himself.

'So what?' she said. Doing her stuff. Pretending she was indifferent.

'You ought to see me going up one of them poles,' he said.

140 'Why?' she said. Like what.

'With my steel spurs on,' he said.

Steel spurs! What next. What did he take her for, anyway?

'Steel spurs,' he said again. Looking at her.

At the sides of his boots, he said, for gripping the pole. How else could
145 you climb a pole, he said, if you come to think about it?

But she didn't say anything. Just kept on as she was, leaning against the gate looking out. Her bare knee kept on bouncing like all the time she didn't know she was doing it.

So he was a wire-monkey. He climbed poles! He did that for a living. She
150 could see him in her mind's eye climbing up that pole across the way hand over hand—like a monkey—without thinking about it. Wondering how soon her brother might be happening along.

He too was silent. Thinking his own thoughts.

Why didn't he say something? She was suddenly and unaccountably
155 annoyed with him. What did he think he was doing just standing there pulling at his cigarette in a self-satisfied way, like the world and everything in it belonged to him tonight, not saying anything? Just taking it in. Just letting things come to him, and taking it all in. He had a nerve!

She wanted to hear more about him. About this queer occupation of his,
160 anyway. Fancy doing *that* for a living! Or was he just taking her along?
Trying to get fresh with her?

'What you do when you climb the pole?' she said.

'Oh, things. Fix the lines. Put in new ones. Tend them in general.'

That made sense at least. The lines *would* need fixing. Somehow she had
165 never thought of it before. What a lot of queer occupations there must be
in the world. So many queer jobs to be done. Somebody had to do them. It
was the same all over the world. Her job for instance. Taking care of her
sister-in-law, her brother's children. That was one of them. Somebody had
to do it. That was why her brother didn't want her to have any friends.
170 Because he wanted her to do that job. He had a long head to his body; her
brother.

It was dangerous work too. He might easily get killed fooling with them
wires. They were charged with electricity. She knew that. She could see him,
without thinking about it, atop one of them poles, caught somehow in
175 amongst the wires, burning up.

'Isn't it dangerous?' she said.

'Not worth speaking of,' he said. 'That is, if you know what you're
doing. Them wires carry a powerful lot of volts. If I was to tell you how
much you wouldn't believe me. Some of them. Could kill you quicker than
180 thinking. If you don't mind your step.'

She said: 'I should *think* so!' And he looked at her quickly, and smiled.

So then: 'That don't seem to me much of a way for a man to make his
living,' she said.

He laughed at that. Just laughed. As though he was saying to himself,
185 well *she* didn't know anything. A girl like that!

The bus came up to the stop then. Somebody got off. Two people. A girl
first, and a man after her. They went on down the road. She saw them
without looking at them. The bus went on again.

'Weren't you waiting for the bus?' she said.
190 'Did I say I was?' he said. She made no answer.

'Maybe I changed my mind,' he said. Without looking at her.

'You live here,' he said. But he wasn't asking. He had a way of saying
things like that. Like he was just thinking out aloud.

She said nothing.
195 'Maybe you would care to go for a walk,' he said. Looking at her. 'Not
tonight,' he said, before she could say anything. 'Some other night.' And
left it like that.

'No! No!' she said quickly, shaking her head.

'Why?' he said.

200 'Don't ask me why. It can't be, that's why.'

He just laughed.

'Maybe you'll change your mind,' he said.

'No! No!' she said.

'All right,' he said, 'I was just saying. Anyone can change their mind.'

205 A bicycle came round the bend up the road. She knew, without knowing, that it was her brother coming home.

'You must go now,' she said, quickly. 'Please go now.'

He looked at her. His face started to laugh, but dropped it. It was as though he understood everything, without her saying it.

210 'Your husband, eh?'

'No, my brother. You must go now. Please!'

In those few words he understood everything. More than enough to go on. Things she hadn't meant to let out to him. Had let out without knowing!

215 *You must go now! Please*! That made it right with him. That told him something besides. That already there was something between them. Something tacit, and implicit. He wasn't slow in these things.

'Goodnight, then. Be seeing you,' he said, without looking at her.

With his hands in his pockets he sauntered off carelessly. A young man 220 taking the air.

'What you doing here? Who you waiting for?' her brother questioned suspiciously as he came up.

'Nothing. Nobody,' she answered.

'You should be inside,' he said. 'No sense to stand at the gate looking 225 out for nothing.'

The wind died down. Suddenly there was no wind at all. Not so much as would stir a leaf. A great drop of rain fell *plop* against her cheek. She put her hand up to her cheek and took it away wet.

'It's going to rain!' she said, looking at her hand, as though she had 230 made a wonderful discovery.

'Get inside,' he said, harshly. 'Get inside now. You have no business standing out here like that, for nothing.'

She moved slowly to do his bidding. As though it was his will not hers that moved the muscles in her body. That moved her legs along. But her 235 mind. That was not his. She looked up at the face of the moon. Last night it was in eclipse. Tonight it was restless and driven, with great black clouds driving across the face of it.

And suddenly she wanted to cry. But not here, where he could see her. Inside in her own little room. Where no one could see her. She would just 240 put her head down and cry. And not because she was sad. And not because she was happy. She only knew she wanted to put her head down and cry and cry her eyes out. And all for nothing.

(1986)

## Following the Story

1. Who is "she"? What is she doing at the beginning of the story?
2. Is the young woman a round and dynamic character? Why or why not?
3. Who is "he"? What details can you find about him in the story?
4. Is the young man a flat and static character? Why or why not?
5. The brother and sister-in-law are minor characters. How would you describe them?
6. What is the young woman's attitude toward her brother? Use details from the story to support your answer.
7. How does she feel about her sister-in-law? Use details from the story to support your answer.
8. How does the story develop after the exposition in the first few paragraphs? Is it in or out of chronological order?
9. How does "he" begin the conversation with the young woman, and what does "he" do to keep it going?
10. What methods does the author use for characterization: telling, showing, in-depth presentation, or a combination of all? Support your argument with specific examples.

## Responding to the Story

1. Why do you think none of the characters in the story have names?
2. Why does the young woman want to look out at the beginning of the story? Is this the first time she has done this, and how can you tell?
3. At what point of the story does the young woman begin to show real interest in the young man? Can you explain why her attitude changed at this moment?
4. The moon is mentioned repeatedly in the story. What do you think is the meaning of this repetition?
5. What can you make out of the dénouement of the story? Why does the young woman want to cry?

6. How do you feel about the dénouement? What do you think might happen to the young woman?
7. What would you do if you were in the young woman's situation?
8. Do you find the characters believable? Why or why not?
9. How would you describe the young woman? Use details from the story to support your response.
10. How does this short story differ from "Prairie Widow" in characterization?

# The Farewell Party

Anita Desai (India) 1937–

## About the Author

*Born in Mussoorie, India, the daughter of a Bengali father and a German mother, Anita Desai earned her B.A. in English literature at Delhi University. She came to the United States in 1987 and has taught writing at Smith College (1987–1988), Mount Holyoke College (1988–1993), and Massachusetts Institute of Technology (1993 to the present). She has been an award-winning writer of novels and short stories since the early 1960s, and has been shortlisted for Britain's prestigious Booker Prize three times. Her major works include* Cry, the Peacock *(1963),* Clear Light of Day *(1980),* Custody *(1984),* Baumgartner's Bombay *(1989) and* Fasting, Feasting *(1999). "The Farewell Party" was published in 1978 in a collection entitled* Games at Twilight and Other Stories.

*Anita Desai focuses her works on personal struggles in the face of the cultural and social changes that India has undergone since its independence from British rule. One of her major themes is the emotional tribulations of women in traditional Indian society. Her portrayal of contemporary Indian life is noted for its harmonious blend of social and psychological realism.*

## About the Story

*"The Farewell Party" demonstrates Anita Desai's sophisticated skills in characterization as well as her perceptive view of the social picture in post-Independence India. The farewell party held by the Ramans is in every sense a showcase, an "aquarium" as the author puts it symbolically, in which all types of characters inhabiting a middle-class community in an unidentified Indian town gather together to socialize and interact.*

Dynamic characters are made to experience new feelings in very subtle ways emotionally and psychologically, while static characters, stock characters including some caricatures, all play their assigned roles in an amusing and thought-provoking manner. Social realism and psychological realism are seamlessly combined, revealing to us a whole gallery of breathing men and women who call for our sympathy, our ridicule, and our dislike.

## Terms Appearing in the Story

**torenia** subtropical flowering plants

**Ajanta frescoes** the paintings on the walls of rock-caves at Ajanta, done by Buddhist monks around 700 C.E.

**Indus Valley seals** the seals from the early civilization that flourished in the Valley of the River Indus (now in central Pakistan) about 4000 years ago

**ayah** a nanny in middle-and upper-class modern Indian households

**Fanta** the brand name of a popular orange-flavoured pop

**Independence Eve** the evening of August 14 (India won its independence from British colonial rule on August 15, 1947.)

**kochias** subtropical flowering plants

**Dacca sari** an expensive silk sari, with distinctive colours and patterns, made in Dacca (now the capital of Bangladesh)

**Shantiniketan** a town in the state of West Bengal in India; the location of Vishwabharati, a distinguished university founded by the Bengali writer Rabindranath Tagore

**(Rabindranath) Tagore (1861–1941)** a Bengali poet, dramatist, fiction writer and lyricist, as well as a philosopher, painter and musician, who won the Nobel Prize for Literature in 1913. (See "The Cabuliwallah," pages 456–463.) He wrote the lyrics and composed the music for several hundred songs, which are popular in India.

B efore the party she had made a list, faintheartedly, and marked off the items as they were dealt with, inexorably—cigarettes, soft drinks, ice, kebabs and so on. But she had forgotten to provide lights. The party was to be held on the lawn: on these dry summer nights one could plan a lawn
5 party weeks in advance and be certain of fine weather, and she had thought happily of how the roses would be in bloom and of the stars and perhaps even fireflies, so decorative and discreet, all gracefully underlining her unsuspected talent as a hostess. But she had not realized that there would be no moon and therefore it would be very dark on the lawn. All the
10 lights on the veranda, in the portico and indoors were on, like so many

lanterns, richly copper and glowing, with extraordinary beauty as though aware that the house would soon be empty and these were the last few days of illumination and family life, but they did very little to light the lawn which was vast, a still lake of inky grass.

15     Wandering about with a glass in one hand and a plate of cheese biscuits in another, she gave a start now and then to see an acquaintance emerge from the darkness which had the gloss, the sheen, the coolness but not the weight of water, and present her with a face, vague and without outlines but eventually recognizable. 'Oh,' she cried several times that evening, 'I

20 didn't know you had arrived. I've been looking for you,' she would add with unaccustomed intimacy (was it because of the gin and lime, her second, or because such warmth could safely be held to lead to nothing now that they were leaving town?). The guest, also having had several drinks between beds of flowering balsam and torenias° before launching

25 out onto the lawn, responded with an equal vivacity. Sometimes she had her arm squeezed or a hand slid down the bareness of her back—which was athletic: she had once played tennis, rather well—and once someone said, 'I've been hiding in this corner, watching you,' while another went so far as to say, 'Is it true you are leaving us, Bina? How can you be so cruel?'

30 And if it were a woman guest, the words were that much more effusive. It was all heady, astonishing.

It was astonishing because Bina was a frigid and friendless woman. She was thirty-five. For fifteen years she had been bringing up her children and, in particular, nursing the eldest who was severely spastic. This had

35 involved her deeply in the workings of the local hospital and with its many departments and doctors, but her care for this child was so intense and so desperate that her relationship with them was purely professional. Outside this circle of family and hospital—ringed, as it were, with barbed wire and lit with one single floodlight—Bina had no life. The town had scarcely

40 come to know her for its life turned in the more jovial circles of mah-jong, bridge, coffee parties, club evenings and, occasionally, a charity show in aid of the Red Cross. For these Bina had a kind of sad contempt and certainly no time. A tall, pale woman, heavy-boned and sallow, she had a certain presence, a certain dignity, and people, having heard of the spastic

45 child, liked and admired her, but she had not thought she had friends. Yet tonight they were coming forth from the darkness in waves that quite overwhelmed.

Now here was Mrs Ray, the Commissioner's wife, chirping inside a nest of rustling embroidered organza. 'Why are you leaving us so soon, Mrs

50 Raman? You've only been here—two years, is it?'

'Five,' exclaimed Bina, widening her eyes, herself surprised at such a length of time. Although time dragged heavily in their household, agonizingly slow, and the five years had been so hard that sometimes, at night, she did not know how she had crawled through the day and if she would crawl through another, her back almost literally broken by the weight of the totally dependent child and of the three smaller ones who seemed perpetually to clamour for their share of attention, which they felt they never got. Yet now these five years had telescoped. They were over. The Raman family was moving and their time here was spent. There had been the hospital, the girls' school, the boys' school, picnics, monsoons, birthday parties and measles. Crushed together into a handful. She gazed down at her hands, tightened around glass and plate. 'Time has flown,' she murmured incredulously.

'Oh, I wish you were staying, Mrs Raman,' cried the Commissioner's wife and, as she squeezed Bina's arm, her fragrant talcum powder seemed to lift off her chalky shoulders and some of it settled on Bina who sneezed. 'It's been so nice to have a family like yours here. It's a small town, so little to do, at least one must have good friends...'

Bina blinked at such words of affection from a woman she had met twice, perhaps thrice before. Bina and her husband did not go in for society. The shock of their first child's birth had made them both fanatic parents. But she knew that not everyone considered this vital factor in their lives, and spoke of 'social duties' in a somehow reproving tone. The Commissioner's wife had been annoyed, she always felt, by her refusal to help out at the Red Cross fair. The hurt silence with which her refusal had been accepted had implied the importance of these 'social duties' of which Bina remained so stubbornly unaware.

However, this one evening, this last party, was certainly given over to their recognition and celebration. 'Oh, everyone, everyone is here,' rejoiced the Commissioner's wife, her eyes snapping from face to face in that crowded aquarium, and, at a higher pitch, cried 'Renu, why weren't you at the mah-jong party this morning?' and moved off into another powdery organza embrace that rose to meet her from the night like a moth and then was submerged again in the shadows of the lawn. Bina gave one of those smiles that easily frightened people found mocking, a shade too superior, somewhat scornful. Looking down into her glass of gin and lime, she moved on and in a minute found herself brought up short against the quite regal although overweight figure, in raw silk and homespun and the somewhat saturnine air of underpaid culture, of Bose, an employee of the local museum whom she had met once or twice at the art competitions and exhibitions to which she was fond of hauling her children, whether reluctant or enthusiastic, because 'it made a change,' she said.

'Mrs Raman,' he said in the fruity tones of the culture-bent Bengali, 'how we'll miss you at the next children's art competitions. You used to be
95 my chief inspiration—'

'Inspiration?' she laughed, incredulously, spilling some of her drink and proffering the plate of cheese biscuits from which he helped himself, half-bowing as though it were gold she offered, gems.

'Yes, yes, inspiration,' he went on, even more fruitily now that his
100 mouth was full. 'Think of me—alone, the hapless organizer—surrounded by mammas, by primary school teachers, by three, four, five hundred children. And the judges—they are always the most trouble, those judges. And then I look at you—so cool, controlling your children, handling them so wonderfully and with such superb results—my inspiration!'

105 She was flustered by this unaccustomed vision of herself and half-turned her face away from Bose the better to contemplate it, but could find no reflection of it in the ghostly white bush of the Queen of the Night, and listened to him murmur on about her unkindness in deserting him in this cultural backwater to that darkest of dooms—guardian of a provincial
110 museum—where he saw no one but school teachers herding children through his halls or, worse, Government officials who periodically and inexplicably stirred to create trouble for him and made their official presences felt amongst the copies of the Ajanta frescoes° (in which even the mouldy and peeled-off portions were carefully reproduced) and the cupboards of
115 Indus Valley seals.° Murmuring commiseration, she left him to a gloomy young professor of history who was languishing at another of the institutions of provincial backwaters that they so deplored and whose wife was always having a baby, and slipped away, still feeling an unease at Bose's unexpected vision of her which did not tally with the cruder reality, into the
120 less equivocal company provided by a ring of twittering 'company wives.'

These women she had always encountered in just such a ring as they formed now, the kind that garden babblers form under a hedge where they sit gabbling and whirring with social bitchiness, and she had always stood outside it, smiling stiffly, not wanting to join and refusing their effusively
125 nodded invitation. They were the wives of men who represented various mercantile companies in the town—Imperial Tobacco, Brooke Bond, Esso and so on—and although they might seem exactly alike to one who did not belong to this circle, inside it were subtle gradations of importance according to the particular company for which each one's husband worked
130 and of these only they themselves were initiates. Bina was, however

unwillingly, an initiate. Her husband worked for one of these companies but she had always stiffly refused to recognize these gradations, or consider them. They noted the rather set sulkiness of her silence when amongst them and privately labelled her queer, proud, boring and difficult. Also,
135 they felt she belonged to their circle whether she liked it or not.

Now she entered this circle with diffidence, wishing she had stayed with the more congenial Bose (why hadn't she? What was it in her that made her retreat from anything like a friendly approach?) and was taken aback to find their circle parting to admit her and hear their cries of welcome and
140 affection that did not, however, lose the stridency and harshness of garden babblers' voices.

'Bina, how do you like the idea of going back to Bombay?'

'Have you started packing, Bina? Poor you. Oh, are you having packers over from Delhi? Oh well then it's not so bad.'

145 Never had they been so vociferous in her company, so easy, so warm. They were women to whom the most awful thing that had ever happened was the screw of a golden ear ring disappearing down the bathroom sink or a mother-in-law's visit or an ayah° deserting just before the arrival of guests: what could they know of Bina's life, Bina's ordeal? She cast her
150 glance at the drinks they held—but they were mostly of orange squash. Only the Esso wife, who participated in amateur dramatics and ran a boutique and was rather taller and bolder than the rest, held a whisky and soda. So much affection generated by just orange squash? Impossible. Rather tentatively, she offered them the remains of the cheese biscuits,
155 found herself chirping replies, deploring the nuisance of having packing crates all over the house, talking of the flat they would move into in Bombay, and then, sweating unobtrusively with the strain, saw another recognizable fish swim towards her from the edge of the liquescent lawn, and swung away in relief, saying, 'Mrs D'Souza! How late you are, but I'm
160 so glad—' for she really was.

Mrs D'Souza was her daughter's teacher at the convent school and had clearly never been to a cocktail party before so that all Bina's compassion was aroused by those school-scuffed shoes and her tea-party best—quite apart from the simple truth that she found in her an honest individuality
165 that all those beautifully dressed and poised babblers lacked, being stamped all over by the plain rubber stamps of their husbands' companies—she hurried off to find Mrs D'Souza something suitable to drink. 'Sherry? Why yes, I think I'll be able to find you some,' she said, a bit flabbergasted at such an unexpected fancy of the pepper-haired schoolteacher,
170 'and I'll see if Tara's around—she'll want to see. you,' she added, vaguely

and fraudulently, wondering why she had asked Mrs D'Souza to a cocktail party, only to see, as she skirted the rose bed, the admirable Bose appear at her side and envelop her in this strange intimacy that marked the whole evening, and went off, light-hearted, towards the table where her husband
175 was trying, with the help of some hired waiters in soggy white uniforms with the name of the restaurant from which they were hired embroidered in red across their pockets, to cope with the flood of drinks this party atmosphere had called for and released.

Harassed, perspiring, his feet burning, Raman was nevertheless pleased
180 to be so obviously employed and be saved the strain of having to converse with his motley assembly of guests: he had no more gift for society than his wife had. Ice cubes were melting on the tablecloth in sopping puddles and he had trouble in keeping track of his bottles: they were, besides the newly bought dozens of beer bottles and Black Knight whisky, the remains
185 of their five years in this town that he now wished to bring to their end—bottles brought by friends from trips abroad, bottles bought cheap through 'contacts' in the army or air force, some gems, extravaganzas bought for anniversaries such as a nearly full bottle of Vat 69, a bottle with a bit of crème de menthe growing sticky at the bottom, some brown sherry with a
190 great deal of rusty sediment, a red Golconda wine from Hyderabad, and a bottle of Remy Martin that he was keeping guiltily to himself, pouring small quantities into a whisky glass at his elbow and gulping it down in between mixing some very weird cocktails for his guests. There was no one at the party he liked well enough to share it with. Oh, one of the doctors
195 perhaps, but where were they? Submerged in grass, in dark, in night and chatter, clatter of ice in glass, teeth on biscuit, teeth on teeth. Enamel and gold. Crumbs and dregs. All awash, all soaked in night. Watery sound of speech, liquid sound of drink. Water and ice and night. It occurred to him that everyone had forgotten him, the host, that it was a mistake to have
200 stationed himself amongst the waiters, that he ought to move out, mingle with the guests. But he felt himself drowned, helplessly and quite delightfully, in Remy Martin, in grass, in a border of purple torenias.

Then he was discovered by his son who galloped through the ranks of guests and waiters to fling himself at his father and ask if he could play
205 the new Beatles record, his friends had asked to hear it.

Raman considered, taking the opportunity to pour out and gulp down some more of the precious Remy Martin. 'All right,' he said, after a judicious minute or two, 'but keep it low, everyone won't want to hear it,' not adding that he himself didn't, for his taste in music ran to slow and melan-
210 choly, folk at its most frivolous. Still, he glanced into the lighted room

where his children and the children of neighbours and guests had collected, making themselves tipsy on Fanta° and Coca-Cola, the girls giggling in a multicoloured huddle and the boys swaggering around the record-player with a kind of lounging strut, holding bottles in their hands
215 with a sophisticated ease, exactly like experienced cocktail party guests, so that he smiled and wished he had a ticket, a passport that would make it possible to break into that party within a party. It was chillingly obvious to him that he hadn't one. He also saw that a good deal of their riotousness was due to the fact that they were raiding the snack trays that the
220 waiters carried through the room to the lawn, and that they were seeing to it that the trays emerged half-empty. He knew he ought to go in and see about it but he hadn't the heart, or the nerve. He couldn't join that party but he wouldn't wreck it either so he only caught hold of one of the waiters and suggested that the snack trays be carried out from the kitchen straight
225 onto the lawn, not by way of the drawing-room, and led him towards a group that seemed to be without snacks and saw too late that it was a group of the company executives that he loathed most. He half-groaned, then hiccuped at his mistake, but it was too late to alter course now. He told himself that he ought to see to it that the snacks were offered around
230 without snag or error.

Poor Raman was placed in one of the lower ranks of the companies' hierarchy. That is, he did not belong to a British concern, or even to an American-collaboration one, but merely to an Indian one. Oh, a long-established, prosperous and solid one but, still, only Indian. Those ciga-
235 rettes that he passed around were made by his own company. Somehow it struck a note of bad taste amongst these fastidious men who played golf, danced at the club on Independence Eve° and New Year's Eve, invited at least one foreign couple to every party and called their decorative wives 'darling' when in public. Poor Raman never had belonged. It was so
240 obvious to everyone, even to himself, as he passed around those awful cigarettes that sold so well in the market. It had been obvious since their first disastrous dinner party for this very ring of jocular gentlemen, five years ago. Nono had cried right through the party, Bina had spent the evening racing upstairs to see to the babies' baths and bed-time and then crawling
245 reluctantly down, the hired cook had got drunk and stolen two of the chickens so that there was not enough on the table, no one had relaxed for a minute or enjoyed a second—it had been too sad and harrowing even to make a good story or a funny anecdote. They had all let it sink by mutual consent and the invitations to play a round of golf on Saturday afternoon
250 or a rubber of bridge on Sunday morning had been issued and refused with

conspiratorial smoothness. Then there was that distressing hobby of Raman's: his impossibly long walks on which he picked up bits of wood and took them home to sandpaper and chisel and then call wood sculpture. What could one do with a chap who did that? He himself wasn't sure if he pursued such odd tastes because he was a social pariah or if he was one on account of this oddity. Not to speak of the spastic child. Now that didn't even bear thinking of, and so it was no wonder that Raman swayed towards them so hesitantly, as though he were wading through water instead of over clipped grass, and handed his cigarettes around with such an apologetic air.

But, after all, hesitation and apology proved unnecessary. One of them—was he Polson's Coffee or Brooke Bond Tea?—clasped Raman about the shoulders as proper men do on meeting, and hearty voices rose together, congratulating him on his promotion (it wasn't one, merely a transfer, and they knew it), envying him his move to the metropolis. They talked as if they had known each other for years, shared all kinds of public schoolboy fun. One—was he Voltas or Ciba?—talked of golf matches at Willingdon as though he had often played there with Raman, another spoke of *kebabs* eaten on the roadside after a party as though Raman had been one of the gang. Amazed and grateful as a schoolboy admitted to a closed society, Raman nodded and put in a few cautious words, put away his cigarettes, called a waiter to refill their glasses and broke away before the clock struck twelve and the golden carriage turned into a pumpkin, he himself into a mouse. He hated mice.

Walking backwards, he walked straight into the soft barrier of Miss Dutta's ample back wrapped and bound in rich Madras silk.

'Sorry, sorry, Miss Dutta, I'm clumsy as a bear,' he apologized, but here, too, there was no call for apology for Miss Dutta was obviously delighted at having been bumped into.

'My dear Mr Raman, what can you expect if you invite the whole town to your party?' she asked in that piercing voice that invariably made her companions drop theirs self-consciously. 'You and Bina have been so popular—what are we going to do without you?'

He stood pressing his glass with white-tipped fingers and tried to think what he and Bina had provided her with that she could possibly miss. In any case, Miss Dutta could always manage, and did manage, everything single-handedly. She was the town busy-body, secretary and chairman of more committees than he could count: they ranged from the Film Society to the Blood Bank, from the Red Cross to the Friends of the Museum, for Miss Dutta was nothing if not versatile. 'We hardly ever saw you at our

film shows of course,' her voice rang out, making him glance furtively over his shoulder to see if anyone were listening, 'but it was so nice knowing you were in town and that I could count on you. So few people here care, you know,' she went on, and affectionately bumped her comfortable
295 middle-aged body into his as someone squeezed by, making him remember that he had once heard her called a man-eater, and wonder which man she had eaten and even consider, for a moment, if there were not, after all, some charm in those powdered creases of her creamy arms, equalling if not surpassing that of his worn and harassed wife's bony
300 angles. Why did suffering make for angularity? he even asked himself with uncharacteristic unkindness. But when Miss Dutta laid an arm on top of his glass-holding one and raised herself on her toes to bray something into his ear, he loyally decided that he was too accustomed to sharp angles to change them for such unashamed luxuriance, and, contriving to remove
305 her arm by grasping her elbow—how one's fingers sank into the stuff!—he steered her towards his wife who was standing at the table and inefficiently pouring herself another gin and lime.

'This is my third,' she confessed hurriedly, 'and I can't tell you how gay it makes me feel. I giggle at everything everyone says.'
310 'Good,' he pronounced, feeling inside a warm expansion of relief at seeing her lose, for the moment, her tension and anxiety. 'Let's hear you giggle,' he said, sloshing some more gin into her glass.

'Look at those children,' she exclaimed, and they stood in a bed of balsam, irredeemably crushed, and looked into the lighted drawing room
315 where their daughter was at the moment the cynosure of all juvenile eyes, having thrown herself with abandon into a dance of monkey-like movements. 'What is it, Miss Dutta?' the awed mother enquired. 'You're more up in the latest fashions than I am—is it the twist, the rock or the jungle?' and all three watched, enthralled, till Tara began to totter and, losing her
320 simian grace, collapsed against some wildly shrieking girl friends.

A bit embarrassed by their daughter's reckless abandon, the parents discussed with Miss Dutta whose finger by her own admission, was placed squarely on the pulse of youth, the latest trends in juvenile culture on which Miss Dutta gave a neat sociological discourse (all the neater for
325 having been given earlier that day at the convocation of the Home Science College) and Raman wondered uneasily at this opening of floodgates in his own family—his wife grown giggly with gin, his daughter performing wildly to a Chubby Checkers record—how had it all come about? Was it the darkness all about them, dense as the heavy curtains
330 about a stage, that made them act, for an hour or so, on the tiny lighted

stage of brief intimacy with such a lack of inhibition? Was it the drink, so freely sloshing from end to end of the house and lawn on account of his determination to clear out his 'cellar' (actually one-half of the side-board and the top shelf of the wardrobe in his dressing-room) and his
335 muddling and mixing them, making up untried and experimental cock-tails and lavishly pouring out the whisky without a measure? But these were solid and everyday explanations and there was about this party something out of the ordinary and everyday—at least to the Ramans, normally so austere and unpopular. He knew the real reason too—it was
340 all because the party had been labelled a 'farewell party', everyone knew it was the last one, that the Ramans were leaving and they would not meet up again. There was about it exactly that kind of sentimental euphoria that is generated at a ship-board party, the one given on the last night before the end of the voyage. Everyone draws together with an
345 intimacy, a lack of inhibition not displayed or guessed at before, knowing this is the last time, tomorrow they will be dispersed, it will be over. They will not meet, be reminded of it or be required to repeat it.

As if to underline this new and Cinderella's ball-like atmosphere of friendliness and gaiety, three pairs of neighbours now swept in (and three
350 kochias° lay down and died under their feet, to the gardener's rage and sorrow): the couple who lived to the Ramans' left, the couple who lived to their right, and the couple from across the road, all crying, 'So sorry to be late, but you know what a long way we had to come,' making everyone laugh identically at the identical joke. Despite the disparity in their looks
355 and ages—one couple was very young, another middle-aged, the third grandparents—they were, in a sense, as alike as the company executives and their wives, for they too bore a label if a less alarming one: Neighbours, it said. Because they were neighbours, and although they had never been more than nodded to over the hedge, waved to in passing cars
360 or spoken to about anything other than their children, dogs, flowers and gardens, their talk had a vivid immediacy that went straight to the heart.

'Diamond's going to miss you so—he'll be heartbroken,' moaned the grandparents who lived alone in their spotless house with a black labrador who had made a habit of visiting the Ramans whenever he wanted young
365 company, a romp on the lawn or an illicit biscuit.

'I don't know what my son will do without Diamond,' reciprocated Bina with her new and sympathetic warmth. 'He'll force me to get a dog of his own, I know, and how will I ever keep one in a flat in Bombay?'

'When are you going to throw out those rascals?' demanded a father of
370 Raman, pointing at the juvenile revellers indoors. 'My boy has an exam

tomorrow, you know, but he said he couldn't be bothered about it—he had to go to the Ramans' farewell party.'

One mother confided in Bina, winning her heart forever, 'Now that you are leaving, I can talk to you about it at last: did you know my Vinod is
375 sweet on your Tara? Last night when I was putting him to bed, he said "Mama, when I grow up I will marry Tara. I will sit on a white horse and wear a turban and carry a sword in my belt and I will go and marry Tara." What shall we do about that, eh? Only a ten year difference in age, isn't there—or twelve?' and both women rocked with laughter.

380 The party had reached its crest, like a festive ship, loud and illuminated for that last party before the journey's end, perched on the dizzy top of the dark wave. It could do nothing now but descend and dissolve. As if by simultaneous and unanimous consent, the guests began to leave (in the wake of the Commissioner and his wife who left first, like royalty)
385 streaming towards the drive where cars stood bumper to bumper—more than had visited the Ramans' house in the previous five years put together. The light in the portico fell on Bina's pride and joy, a Chinese orange tree, lighting its miniature globes of fruit like golden lanterns. There was a babble, an uproar of leavetaking (the smaller children, already in
390 pyjamas, watched open-mouthed from a dark window upstairs). Esso and Caltex left together, arms about each other and smoking cigars, like figures in a comic act. Miss Dutta held firmly to Bose's arm as they dipped, bowed, swayed and tripped on their way out. Bina was clasped, kissed— ear rings grazed her cheek, talcum powder tickled her nose. Raman had
395 his back slapped till he thrummed and vibrated like a beaten gong.

It seemed as if Bina and Raman were to be left alone at last, left to pack up and leave—now the good-byes had been said, there was nothing else they could possibly do—but no, out popped the good doctors from the hospital who had held themselves back in the darkest corners and made
400 themselves inconspicuous throughout the party, and now, in the manner in which they clasped the host by the shoulders and the hostess by the hands, and said 'Ah *now* we have a chance to be with you at last, now we can begin *our* party,' revealed that although this was the first time they had come to the Ramans' house on any but professional visits, they were
405 not merely friends they were almost a part of that self-defensive family, the closest to them in sympathy. Raman and Bina both felt a warm, moist expansion of tenderness inside themselves, the tenderness they had till today restricted to the limits of their family, no farther, as though they feared it had not an unlimited capacity. Now its close horizons stepped
410 backwards, with some surprise.

And it was as the doctors said—the party now truly began. Cane chairs were dragged out of the veranda onto the lawn, placed in a ring next to the flowering Queen of the Night which shook out flounces and frills of white scent with every rustle of night breeze. Bina could give in now to her
415 two most urgent needs and dash indoors to smear her mosquito-bitten arms and feet with Citronella and fetch Nono to sit on her lap, to let Nono have a share, too, in the party. The good doctors and their wives leant forward and gave Nono the attention that made the parents' throats tighten with gratitude. Raman insisted on their each having a glass of Remy
420 Martin—they must finish it tonight, he said, and would not let the waiter clear away the ice or glasses yet. So they sat on the veranda steps, smoking and yawning.

Now it turned out that Dr Bannerji's wife, the lady in the Dacca sari° and the steel-rimmed spectacles, had studied in Shantiniketan,° and she
425 sang, at her husband's and his colleagues' urging, Tagore's° sweetest, saddest songs. When she sang, in heartbroken tones that seemed to come from some distance away, from the damp corners of the darkness where the fireflies flitted,

*'Father, the boat is carrying me away,*
430 *Father, it is carrying me away from home,'*

the eyes of her listeners, sitting tensely in that grassy, inky dark, glazed with tears that were compounded equally of drink, relief and regret.

(1978)

# Following the Story

1. Are Bina and Raman round and dynamic characters? Why or why not?
2. Does Bina enjoy the party? What about her husband Raman? How can you tell?
3. Who are the major characters and minor characters? Make a list of them according to the order they are introduced in the story.
4. Look at the list you created in answering Question 3 and name at least three flat and static characters and one stock character in the story.
5. Why doesn't Bina get along with people like Mrs. Ray and the "company wives"?
6. Why does Raman feel inferior when he is with the company executives?
7. Among all the guests, who are the real friends of the Ramans? How can we tell they are real friends?

8. What is the one thing that Bina forgets to provide for the party? What are the consequences of this omission?
9. Bina is a mother of four children and has to take care of a disabled child. What is the significance of these details in the story?
10. What methods does the author use for characterization: telling, showing, in-depth presentation, or a combination of all? Support your response with specific examples.

## Responding to the Story

1. Why do the Ramans bother to hold the party if they both feel so uncomfortable about it?
2. In what ways can you relate to Bina and Raman? Have you experienced a situation similar to theirs before?
3. What would you do if you were in the Ramans' situation?
4. Choose five adjectives to describe the party, and explain your choice.
5. The farewell party is held in darkness. What is the significance of darkness in the story?
6. There are frequent water references in the story: water, fish, aquarium, etc. Find them and consider the author's purpose in making such references.
7. What exactly happens at the end of the party? Are Bina and her husband happy or sad and how can you tell?
8. How do you respond to characters such as Mrs. Ray and Miss Dutta? Do you find them believable? Why or why not?
9. What have you learned about the upper-middle-class social life of India in the 1960s through reading the story?
10. How does this short story differ from "Prairie Widow" and "Look Out" in terms of characterization?

# Unit Review

When analyzing character and characterization, be sure to follow these guidelines:

- Make a list of all the characters in the story.
- Identify the major characters (e.g., protagonist and antagonist) and their relationship.
- Collect the information given about the major characters, including a) physical appearance, b) personality traits, c) social and educational background, d) past experience, and e) other noticeable characteristics.
- Identify the minor characters and figure out their respective roles and relationships with the other characters.
- Distinguish dynamic characters from static characters, stock characters, and caricatures (if any).
- Distinguish round characters from flat characters.
- Determine the method(s) used to portray the characters from these choices: a) *telling*—explicit presentation of characters through direct exposition; b) *showing*—implicit presentation of characters in action; c) *in-depth presentation* from within a character; or d) a combination of a), b), and c).
- Decide to what extent the characters are believable and the characterization effective.
- Consider your own response to the character(s).

# Unit 3

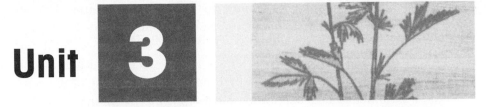

## Narration: Narrator and Narrative Point of View

*My task ... is by the power of the written word to make you
hear, to make you feel—it is above all to make you see.*

JOSEPH CONRAD

A short story is carefully designed and shaped by its **author** to provide us with
a new experience, fresh understanding, or increased appreciation of life. To
enable us to hear, feel, and see this experience, the author guides us through
the development of the plot and the presentation of the characters in a story.
Another important aspect of creating a story is **narration**, which refers to the
way in which the story is told. It is the next element of the short story we will
examine.

## The Narrator

The author creates a **narrator** to tell the story. We need to keep in mind that
the *author* is never the same person as the *narrator*; in fact, the narrator often
has a different personality from the author and may hold quite different opin-
ions. The narrator is the ***persona*** through whom the author chooses to speak;
*persona* was originally a Latin word meaning an actor's mask.

"Cages," the first short story in this unit, exemplifies the difference between
author and narrator. The author of this story is Guy Vanderhaeghe, a distinguished Canadian author, but the narrator of "Cages" is a 17-year-old boy

named Billy. Clearly, they are not the same person; Billy is Vanderhaeghe's creation, his *persona*. As a major character in the story, Billy is limited in his role of narrator by what he actually knows about characters or events around him. For example, he declares at one point "Maybe Pop *loves* me as much as he does Gene, but Gene is still his favourite kid" (line 14). In the course of the story, however, it becomes clear to us that Mr. Simpson is more demanding of Billy than of Gene simply because he can trust Billy and rely on him to do the right thing. Billy is limited and biased in his opinion about his father because of his youth and his personal feelings about the family relationships.

It becomes evident that the narrator's personality, knowledge, and feelings about the characters and events significantly influence our understanding of and response to the story. Some narrators, in fact, cannot be trusted completely because of their personal feelings or bias.

Why would an author choose an unreliable narrator to tell the story? The answer to this question involves a deeper understanding of story telling and story reading. A story recounted in a straightforward manner may not be as enjoyable as one that makes use of suspense, foreshadowing and irony. The use of a totally or partially unreliable narrator adds an extra "twist" to the plot, reminding us of the incongruity or irony in life (see Unit 5, page 142). The sense that we must be on guard against being taken in by the storyteller makes reading the story more interesting and challenging. The challenge we face when we discover a discrepancy between what we learn from the narrator and what we find out on our own can draw us into the story; our efforts to determine just what can be known or trusted can make us feel interested, involved, in the story as we begin to appreciate the author's ingenuity.

Again, taking Billy as our example, we can trust him to tell us *what* happens, but not always to explain *why* or *how*. Because of his limited view of the action, the characters and the dénouement, we have to read carefully *between the lines* to discern the real situations and motivations in this story. As a result, we realize, in spite of Billy's limitations and bias, the "cages" in Vanderhaeghe's story represent not only those social conditions that restrict possibility and freedom, but also the family obligations and personal bonds that tie us and that we choose to accept. At the same time, because of Billy the narrator, we are able to share the events as they are experienced by a sensitive 17-year-old young man in the summer of 1967. It is by using Billy as his *persona* that the author, Guy Vanderhaeghe, achieves the desired effect of his story and doubly entertains the reader. Without Billy as the narrator, "Cages" would be a totally different story.

# Narrative Voice and Tone

The **narrative voice** conveys the feelings of the narrator about the events of the story and the relationship of the narrator to the characters in the story. As E. M. Forster points out, "it is on the precise tone of voice we employ now that our subsequent conclusions will depend." The attitude of the narrator is expressed through the **tone** of the narrative voice. Narrative tone is often evident in word choice, sentence structure, and the juxtaposition of events in the story. The tone of the narrator can be distant or intimate, amused or bored, happy or sad, angry or calm, sincere or ironic, respectful or condescending, sympathetic or critical, and so on. We have "heard" a variety of narrative voices speaking in different tones in the short stories we have studied so far in Units 1 and 2. How different did they seem? How would you describe each of these narrative voices and tones?

For example, the narrative tone of "The Jade Pendant" appears detached from the events and the characters, but through the repetition of words, with a shift in emphasis or meaning, it subtly conveys its attitude and offers criticism. This is an ironic voice that sets the story in a mercenary atmosphere by frequent references to the cost of things. We soon learn that this is a family in which money measures the worth of everything. Possessions determine social status in Mrs. Khoo's world, and the narrative voice disapproves of her greed. Through the repetition of words, the narrator's attitude to the character becomes clear. For example, "Whenever she could spare time from her mah-jong, Mrs. Khoo entertained them, sparing no expense" (line 85). Now we know that Mrs. Khoo is too aware of the cost of everything.

The incident in which Ah Soh's daughter seizes the pendant, the turning point of this story, can be used to confirm the narrator's tone and attitude to Mrs. Khoo. As her daughter innocently parades with the pendant, the narrator reports Ah Soh sees "the look of violent disgust and displeasure on the face of Mrs. Khoo" (Lim, line 69), and she translates Mrs. Khoo's "violent disgust and displeasure" into action by thrashing her daughter. Then we hear another comment from the narrator: "Mrs. Khoo found the incident too disgusting to be mentioned" (Lim, line 81). At this point we are left wondering about the difference in the two feelings of "disgust" Mrs. Khoo experiences, the one erupting in violence and the other producing apathy.

The narrative voice and tone of "The Jade Pendant" remain detached because the narrator is not a participant in the story. The narrator of "The Jade Pendant" is simply the voice that tells the story; in effect, it is a "voice-over" that offers no direct or explicit comment. However, a non-participant narrative voice can present the events through the thoughts and feelings of a character, as in "Prairie Widow" or "Look Out." Sometimes the narrative voice belongs to a participant in the story, like the boy in "A Handful of Dates" or Billy in "Cages." These variations in voice and tone contribute to the **narrative point of view** of the short story.

# Narrative Point of View

Apart from developing a character, a *persona*, to tell the story, the author also determines the **point of view** through this creation of the narrator and narrative voice. Point of view is the angle or perspective from which we see the story unfold. Basically, we can classify narrative voices as **first person** (I or we), **third person** (she, he, and they), and very rarely **second person** (you). There are further variations in each of these points of view, but without exception, the author of a short story selects a particular angle of vision to achieve and support the purpose of the story.

## First-person Point of View

This point of view means that the story is told by a character in the story, someone who participates in the action in some way. An author who wants a subjective, personal, or intimate account is likely to select the first-person narrator, "I." A first-person narrator takes part in the action and has a relationship, sometimes very strong, with other characters in the story. The "I" character may be the protagonist, or a minor character in the story, but all the action of the plot, and the appearances and motivations of the characters, are seen through the eyes of the "I" narrator, or recorded as they are known by the narrator.

However, the first-person narrator can only know and see what is reasonable for one character in this position. This means the first-person point of view is always limited, subjective, and possibly unreliable. Although this type of narrator can be an objective and trustworthy person, most frequently there is bias because of personal likes and dislikes, or because of naiveté, inexperience, or self-deception, enabling the readers to realize the irony, the contrast between what they see and what the narrator reports (see Unit 5, page 142). The author develops the character of the narrator while making him or her tell the story, so the narrator's personality frequently determines the *what, how,* and *why* of the story being told.

The first-person narrator can be a full participant in the story, in which case the story is essentially about the narrator, as with Billy in "Cages"; however, the first-person narrator may simply be an observer of the action like the unnamed narrator of "Salvatore" (page 106). The first-person narrator often tells the story as a flashback or begins the narrative *in medias res*.

# Third-person Point of View

The choice of this narrative point of view ("she" or "he") provides the author with a different range of possibilities. The author can make this narrator **omniscient**, **limited omniscient**, or **objective**.

## Omniscient point of view

"Omniscient" means all-knowing. The use of the **omniscient narrator** gives an author great freedom not only to tell the story, but also to analyze it. This type of narrator is said to act like "a fly on the wall." Knowing everything about the characters, their actions, feelings, and thoughts, the omniscient narrator frequently intersperses the narration with commentary, guidance, or interpretation. The omniscient point of view is able to present a detailed and accurate account of all that happens. This narrative voice is reliable because, instead of being restricted to a single character's opinion, it can maintain a distance from the events and the characters, while commenting on them.

For example, in "The Jade Pendant," the omniscient narrator not only tells us what Mrs. Khoo is thinking and feeling, but also occasionally presents Ah Soh's thoughts and feelings, as we can see italicized in the following quotation from the story:

> The insulted pride of the lady whose countenance had taken on a look of extreme hauteur was to be mollified by no less than a severe thrashing of the offender, which Ah Soh immediately executed, *secret anger against her rich relative lending great strength to her scrawny arms.* (lines 73–76; emphasis added)

The omniscient narrative voice of "The Farewell Party" presents the experiences of both Bina and Raman. However, this narrative voice is not detached in the way that the one in "The Jade Pendant" is. Rather this narrative voice allows us to be with the main characters, Bina and Raman, throughout the party. As we follow them around the garden and the house, we see and hear what Bina and Raman see and hear. It is as if we are looking over the shoulder of these characters and seeing events from their point of view, because a "voice-over" adds comments about their responses from time to time.

For example, we are told "Raman and Bina both felt a warm, moist expansion of tenderness inside themselves, the tenderness they had till today restricted to the limits of their family" (Desai, line 406). At the same time, this narrator also includes the response of other party-goers to a shared experience as they listen to Dr. Bannerji's wife sing a Bengali song written by Rabindranath Tagore. The omniscient narrator informs us "the eyes of her listeners, sitting tensely in that grassy, inky dark, glazed with tears that were compounded equally of drink, relief and regret" (line 431).

## Limited omniscient point of view

This point of view sees the action from the perspective of one character. The narrator tells the story through the eyes of a single character, often the protagonist. The narrator is able to present everything this character does, sees, hears, thinks, feels, and says by telling the story through the actions and interactions of this character. In "All Is Burning," the second story in this unit, we find a limited omniscient point of view, as most incidents are depicted from the viewpoint of the protagonist, Alice.

The narrative voice sometimes moves into the mind of a character, creating what is known as **internal monologue**. This technique is effective in providing an intimate tone that is coloured by a character's emotional intensity while appearing detached from the action. Entering the mind of the character without warning tends to make the reader identify with and experience with the character. To continue using "All Is Burning" as our example, Jean Arasanayagam, the author, successfully uses internal monologue to record and display Alice's thoughts, responses, and reflections throughout the highly emotional narrative. To appreciate the full effect of these insightful moments, let us read this excerpt from "All Is Burning," and notice how the reader is moved into the mind of Alice:

> She stumbled, almost fell against one of the bodies. I'll have to be careful she thought. I mustn't jostle them even in death. Perhaps, some of them still have that last breath ... the soul that's reluctant to leave the body. No funeral orations for any of them. Individual burials are no longer practicable. It is within our minds that we carry the reminders of what each man was to each woman. Till each one is claimed, if they are claimed, they are anonymous. It's happening elsewhere too, perhaps at this very moment.... Soon there'll be no birds left in the village. Startled by gunshot they'll fly to another village. Who's going to start life here all over again....
> (Arasanayagam, lines 163–172)

The limited omniscient narrator creates a bond with one particular character but is normally more reliable than a first-person narrator because she or he is not as affected by the limitations of personality or knowledge as a first-person narrator. The *persona* of the limited omniscient narrator lets the author focus on one character while still maintaining the ability to comment. For example, in "Prairie Widow," the narrator frequently reveals to us what Gum-may is thinking and feeling as she deals with the death of her husband. To see how Gum-may's inner life is presented through her thoughts, let us look at the last paragraph of this story:

Yes, they were staying, Gum-may repeated as she turned on the kitchen light. An unusual sense of peace filled her now. Surely she had learned and suffered enough to survive whatever twists heaven might throw at her. Surely her life was not meant to be a continual trek through the doors of strangers to fall under their baneful staring. She felt at once weary and energized: too tired to pack her bags for another move, but more than ready to show everyone her determination to succeed. The pieces of life she had gathered along the road made best sense here, within the four walls of this café. She had finally arrived at a place she understood. (Yee, lines 325–333)

Likewise, in "The Stolen Party," Rosaura is the character through whose eyes the third-person narrator presents the story, as we see in this presentation of Rosaura's thoughts:

Rosaura was deeply offended. She thought it unfair of her mother to accuse other people of being liars just because they were rich.... She felt very sad. She wanted to go to that party more than anything else in the world. (Heker, lines 33–37)

## Objective point of view

This is sometimes also referred to as **dramatic point of view**: that is, presenting scenes as in a play or a movie. This point of view is like a video camera recording what can be seen or heard. The objective narrator cannot enter the minds of the characters and doesn't know what they are thinking and feeling unless they express their thoughts and feelings openly. The use of an objective point of view enables the narrator to be detached and just record what happens without any direct comment or interpretation.

We see the use of **objective point of view** in Basil Johnston's "Cowboys and Indians" (page 315) in which we learn nothing about the characters through their thoughts or feelings. Only speech, action, and observable reaction are presented by the narrator. However, in this case as in many other cases, the "objective" point of view is employed in such a way that the reader draws certain conclusions and is guided to an interpretation. Frequently the use of irony is one factor that encourages the reader to make this interpretation (see Unit 5, page 142).

To see how irony can be used to create a point of view, consider this statement from the opening of "Cowboys and Indians": "And of course viewers' tastes became more refined and discriminating, requiring of Hollywood and the studios more authenticity and less artificiality in their productions" (line 5). This statement seems to be objectively made, but the implied discrepancy between Hollywood's version of "Indian" lifestyle and the reality of the life lived by the Crows in this story offers an ironic and implicit comment on North American culture and history. That is why we need to be careful with the narrative point of view no matter how "objective" it appears to be.

The three stories in this unit are "Cages" by Guy Vanderhaeghe, "All Is Burning" by Jean Arasanayagam, and "Salvatore" by Somerset Maugham. Each has a distinct narrative voice through which the author tells the story.

---

# Cages
Guy Vanderhaeghe (Canada) 1951–

## About the Author

*Born in Esterhazy, Saskatchewan, Guy Vanderhaeghe graduated from the University of Saskatchewan with an Honours B.A. in 1972 and an M.A. in 1975. He then earned a B.Ed. at the University of Regina in 1978. He worked as an archivist, editor, and high school teacher before becoming a full-time writer in 1981. He won the Governor General's Award for fiction for his first book,* Man Descending *(a collection of short stories), in 1982. In 1996, his novel* The Englishman's Boy *earned him the same prestigious award for the second time. He now lives in Saskatoon, Canada.*

*When talking about the prevailing theme in his work, Guy Vanderhaeghe once com-mented: "I regard myself as a writer who celebrates endurance—particularly the endurance of the ordinary person whose life is a series of small victories fashioned from small resources and whose hard-won realism is the result of life lived without the buffers that privilege brings." With a special interest in depicting unheroic men and their uneventful lives, Vanderhaeghe has displayed in his short stories extraordinary insight and artistry as well as an unusual sensibility for the perfect fit of narrative voice.*

## About the Story

*Published in* Man Descending *(1982), Vanderhaeghe's first collection of short sto-ries, this story is set in a small mining town in northern Saskatchewan, Canada. The year is 1967, one hundred years after the confederation of Canada, a year in which there were many national birthday celebrations across the country. There are also many references to popular culture, especially TV. For example, Billy refers to* Bugs Bunny, *a popular cartoon show. He also mentions names of movie stars from his*

*father's generation, such as Gary Cooper, Mickey Rooney, and Cary Grant, and base-*
*ball players, such as Mickey Mantle and Maury Wills.*

*Billy, a 17-year-old young man, is the narrator of this story, and he struggles with*
*family and social expectations. Vanderhaeghe creates a powerful and sensitive por-*
*trait of the young protagonist by letting him tell his story in his own words. So the lan-*
*guage in which this story is told is full of the slang and swear words that would be*
*typical in 1967 and appropriate for someone like Billy. As an adolescent, Billy is in*
*the process of discovering and accepting who he is. Because this is a first-person nar-*
*rative, the reader shares Billy's experiences. As is usually the case with a first-person*
*narrator, Billy reveals more about himself than he actually knows or realizes.*

Here it is, 1967, the Big Birthday. Centennial Year they call it. The whole country is giving itself a pat on the back. Holy shit, boys, we made it.

I made it too for seventeen years, a spotless life, as they say, and for presents I get, in my senior year of high school, my graduating year for

5 chrissakes, a six-month suspended sentence for obstructing a police officer, and my very own personal social worker.

The thing is I don't *need* this social worker woman. She can't tell me anything I haven't already figured out for myself. Take last Wednesday, Miss Krawchuk, who looks like the old widow chicken on the Bugs Bunny

10 Show, the one who's hot to trot for Foghorn Leghorn, says to me: "You know, Billy, your father loves you just as much as he does Gene. He doesn't have a favourite."

Now I can get bullshit at the poolroom any time I want it—and without having to keep an appointment. Maybe Pop *loves* me as much as he does

15 Gene, but Gene is still his favourite kid. Everybody has a favourite kid. I knew that much already when I was only eight and Gene was nine. I fig-ured it out right after Gene almost blinded me.

Picture this. There the two of us were in the basement. It was Christmas holidays and the old man had kicked us downstairs to huck darts at this

20 board he'd give us for a present. Somehow, I must've had horseshoes up my ass, I'd beat Gene six games straight. And was he pissed off! He never loses to me at nothing ever. And me being in such a real unique situation, I was giving him the needle-rooney.

"What's that now?" I said. "Is that six or seven what I won?"

25 "Luck," Gene said, and he sounded like somebody was slowly strangling him. "Luck. Luck. Luck." He could hardly get it out.

And that's when I put the capper on it. I tossed a bull's-eye. "Read 'er and weep," I told him. That's what the old man says whenever he goes out at rummy. It's his needle-rooney. "Read 'er and weep."

30    That did it. The straw what broke the frigging camel's back. All I saw was his arm blur when he let fly at me. I didn't even have time to *think* about ducking. Bingo. Dead centre in the forehead, right in the middle of the old noggin he drills me with a dart. And there it stuck. Until it loosened a bit. Then it sagged down real slow between my eyes, hung for a second,
35    slid off of my nose, and dropped at my feet. I hollered bloody blue murder, you better believe it.

For once, Pop didn't show that little bastard any mercy. He took after him from room to room whaling him with this extension cord across the ass, the back of the legs, the shoulders. Really hard. Gene, naturally, was
40    screaming and blubbering and carrying on like it was a goddamn axe murder or something. He'd try to get under a bed, or behind a dresser or something, and get stuck halfway. Then old Gene would really catch it. He didn't know whether to plough forward, back up, shit, or go blind. And all the time the old man was lacing him left and right and saying in this sad,
45    tired voice: "You're the oldest. Don't you know no better? You could of took his eye out, you crazy little bugger."

But that was only justice. He wasn't all that mad at Gene. Me he was mad at. If that makes any sense. Although I have to admit he didn't lay a hand on me. But yell? Christ, can that man yell. Especially at me.
50    Somehow I'm the one that drives him squirrelly.

"Don't you *never*, *never* tease him again!" he bellowed and his neck started to swell. When the old man gets mad you can see it swell, honest. "You know he can't keep a hold of himself. One day you'll drive him so goddamn goofy with that yap of yours he'll do something terrible!
55    Something he'll regret for the rest of his life. And it'll all be your fault!" The old man had to stop there and slow down or a vein would've exploded in his brain, or his arsehole popped inside out, or something, "So smarten up," he said, a little quieter, finally, "or you'll be the death of me and all my loved ones."

60    So there you are. I never pretended the world was fair, and I never bitched because it wasn't. But I do resent the hell out of being forced to listen to some dried-up old broad who gets paid by the government to tell me it is. Fuck her. She never lived in the Simpson household with my old man waiting around for Gene to do that *terrible* thing. It spoils the atmos-
65    phere. Makes a person edgy, you know?

Of course, Gene has done a fair number of *bad things* while everybody was waiting around for him to do the one great big *terrible thing*; and he's done them in a fair number of places. That's because the old man is a miner, and for a while there he was always telling some foreman to go piss

70 up a rope. So we moved around a lot. That's why the Simpson household
has a real history. But Gene's is the best of all. In Elliot Lake he failed grade
three; in Bombertown he got picked up for shoplifting; in Flin Flon he
broke some snotty kid's nose and got sent home from school. And every
grade he goes higher, it gets a little worse. Last year, when we were both in
75 grade eleven, I'm sure the old man was positive Gene was finally going to
pull off the *terrible thing* he's been worrying about as long as I can
remember.

It's crazy. Lots of times when I think about it, I figure I don't get on with
the old man because I treat him nice. That I try too hard to make him like
80 me. I'm not the way Gene is, I respect Pop. He slogs it out, shift after shift,
on a shitty job he hates. Really hates. In fact, he told me once he would
have liked to have been a farmer. Which only goes to show you how crazy
going down that hole day after day makes you. Since we moved to
Saskatchewan I've seen lots of farmers, and if you ask me, being one
85 doesn't have much to recommend it.

But getting back to that business of being nice to Dad. Last year I started
waiting up for him to come home from the afternoon shift. The one that
runs from four p.m. in the afternoon until midnight. It wasn't half bad.
Most nights I'd fall asleep on the chesterfield with the TV playing after
90 Mom went to bed. Though lots of times I'd do my best to make it past the
national news to wait for Earl Cameron and his collection of screwballs.
Those guys kill me. They're always yapping off because somebody or
something rattled their chain. Most of those characters with all the
answers couldn't pour piss out of a rubber boot if they read the instructions
95 printed on the sole. They remind me of Gene; he's got all the answers too.
But still, quite a few of them are what you'd call witty. Which Gene is in
his own way too.

But most times, as I say, I'd doze off. Let me give you a sample evening.
About twelve-thirty the lights of his half-ton would come shooting into the
100 living-room, bouncing off the walls, scooting along the ceiling when he
wheeled into the driveway like a madman. It was the lights flashing in my
eyes that woke me up most nights, and if that didn't do it there was always
his grand entrance. When the old man comes into the house, from the
sound of it you'd think he never heard of door knobs. I swear sometimes
105 I'm sure he's taking a battering-ram to the back door. Then he thunks his
lunch bucket on the kitchen counter and bowls his hard hat into the
landing. This is because he always comes home from work mad. Never
once in his life has a shift ever gone right for that man. Never. They could
pack his pockets with diamonds and send him home two hours early and

110 he'd still bitch. So every night was pretty much the same. He had a mad
on. Like in my sample night.

He flicked on the living-room light and tramped over to his orange
recliner with the bottle of Boh. "If you want to ruin your eyes, do it on
school-books, not on watching TV in the goddamn dark. It's up to some-
115 body in this outfit to make something of themselves."

"I was sleeping."

"You ought to sleep in bed." *Keerash*! He weighs two hundred and forty-
four pounds and he never sits down in a chair. He falls into it. "Who's that?
Gary Cooper?" he asked. He figures any movie star on the late show taller
120 than Mickey Rooney is Cooper. He doesn't half believe you when you tell
him they aren't.

"Cary Grant."

"What?"

"Cary Grant. Not Gary Cooper. Cary Grant."

125 "Oh." There he sat in his recliner, big meaty shoulders sagging, belly
propped up on his belt buckle like a pregnant pup's. Eyes red and sore, hair
all mussed up, the top of his beer bottle peeking out of his fist like a little
brown nipple. He has cuts all over those hands of his, barked knuckles and
raspberries that never heal because the salt in the potash ore keeps them
130 open, eats right down to the bone sometimes.

"How'd it go tonight?"

"Usual shit. We had a breakdown." He paused. "Where's your brother?
In bed?"

"Out."

135 "Out? Out? *Out*? What kind of goddamn answer is that? Out where?"

I shrugged.

"Has he got his homework done?" That's the kind of question I get
asked. *Has your brother got his homework done*?

"How the hell would I know?"

140 "I don't know why you don't help him with his school-work," the old
man said, peeved as usual.

"You mean do it for him."

"Did I say that? Huh? I said help him. Didn't I say that?" he griped, getting his shit in a knot.

145 He thinks it's that easy. Just screw the top off old Gene and pour it in.
No problem. Like an oil change.

"He's got to be around to help," I said.

That reminded him. He jumped out of the chair and gawked up and
down the deserted street. "It's almost one o'clock. On a school night. I'll

150 kick his ass." He sat down and watched the screen for a while and sucked on his barley sandwich.

Finally, he made a stab at acting civilized. "So how's baseball going?"

"What?"

"Baseball. For chrissakes clean out your ears. How's it going?"

155 "I quit last year. Remember?"

"Oh yeah." He didn't say nothing at first. Then he said: "You shouldn't have. You wasn't a bad catcher."

"The worst. No bat and no arm—just a flipper. They stole me blind."

"But you had the head," said the old man. And the way he said it made
160 him sound like he was pissed at me for mean-mouthing myself. That surprised me. I felt kind of good about that. "You had the head," he repeated, shaking his own. "I never told you but Al came up to me at work and said you were smart back there behind the plate. He said he wished Gene had your head."

165 I can't say that surprised me. Gene is one of those cases of a million-dollar body carrying around a ten-cent head. He's a natural. Flop out his glove and, smack, the ball sticks. He's like Mickey Mantle. You know those stop-action photos where they caught Mickey with his eyes glommed onto the bat, watching the ball jump off the lumber? That's Gene. And he runs
170 like a Negro, steals bases like Maury Wills for chrissake.

But stupid and conceited? You wouldn't believe the half of it. Give him the sign to bunt to move a runner and he acts as if you're asking him to bare his ass in public. Not him. He's a big shot. He swings for the fence. Nothing less. And old Gene is always in the game, if you know what I
175 mean? I don't know what happens when he gets on base, maybe he starts thinking of the hair pie in the stands admiring him or something, but he always dozes off at the wheel. Once he even started to comb his hair at first base. Here it is, a 3 and 2 count with two men out, and my brother forgets to run on the pitch because he's combing his hair. I could have died. Really
180 I could have. The guy is such an embarrassment sometimes.

"He can have my head," I said to Pop. "If I get his girls."

That made the old man wince. He's sure that Gene is going to knock up one of those seat-covers he takes out and make him a premature grandpa.

"You pay attention to school. There's plenty of time later for girls." And
185 up he jumped again and stuck his nose against the window looking for Gene again. Mom has to wash the picture window once a week; he spots it all up with nose grease looking for Gene.

"I don't know why your mother lets him out of the house," he said. "Doesn't she have any control over that boy?"

190　That's what he does, blames everybody but himself. Oh hell, maybe nobody's to blame. Maybe Gene is just Gene, and there's nothing to be done about it.

"I don't know what she's supposed to do. You couldn't keep him in if you parked a tank in the driveway and strung barbed wire around the lot."

195　Of course that was the wrong thing to say. I usually say it.

"Go to bed!" he yelled at me. "You're no better than your brother. I don't see you in bed neither. What'd I do, raise alley cats or kids? Why can't you two keep hours like human beings!"

And then the door banged and we knew the happy wanderer was home. 200 Gene makes almost as much noise as the old man does when he comes in. It's beneath his dignity to sneak in like me.

Dad hoisted himself out of the chair and steamed off for the kitchen. He can move pretty quick for a big guy when he wants to. Me, I was in hot pursuit. I don't like to miss much.

205　Old Gene was hammered, and grinning from ass-hole to ear-lobes. The boy's got a great smile. Even when he grins at old ladies my mother's age you can tell they like it.

"Come here and blow in my face," said my father.

"Go on with you," said Gene. All of a sudden the smile was gone and 210 he was irritated. He pushed past Pop, took the milk out of the fridge and started to drink out of the container.

"Use a glass."

Gene burped. He's a slob.

"You stink of beer," said the old man. "Who buys beer for a kid your 215 age?"

"I ain't drunk," said Gene.

"Not much. Your eyes look like two piss-holes in the snow."

"Sure, sure," said Gene. He lounged, he swivelled over to me and lifted my Players out of my shirt pocket. "I'll pay you back tomorrow," he said, 220 taking out a smoke. I heard that one before.

"I don't want to lose my temper," said Dad, being patient with him as usual, "so don't push your luck, sunshine." The two of them eyeballed it, hard. Finally Gene backed down, looked away and fiddled with his matches. "I don't ride that son of a bitch of a cage up and down for my 225 health. I do it for you two," Dad said. "But I swear to God, Gene, if you blow this year of school there'll be a pair of new work boots for you on the back step, come July 1. Both of you know my rules. Go to school, work, or pack up. I'm not having bums put their feet under my table."

"I ain't scared of work," said Gene. "Anyways, school's a pain in the ass."

230 "Well, you climb in the cage at midnight with three hours of sleep and see if *that* ain't a pain in the ass. Out there nobody says, please do this, please do that. It ain't school out there, it's life."

"Ah, I wouldn't go to the mine. The mine sucks."

"Just what the hell do you think you'd do?"

235 "He'd open up shop as a brain surgeon," I said. Of course, Gene took a slap at me and grabbed at my shirt. He's a tough guy. He wasn't really mad, but he likes to prevent uppityness.

"You go to bed!" the old man hollered. "You ain't helping matters!"

So off I went. I could hear them wrangling away even after I closed my 240 door. You'd wonder how my mother does it, but she sleeps through it all. I think she's just so goddamn tired of the three of us she's gone permanently deaf to the sound of our voices. She just don't hear us any more.

The last thing I heard before I dropped off was Pop saying: "I've rode that cage all my life, and take it from me, there wasn't a day I didn't wish I'd 245 gone to school and could sit in an office in a clean white shirt." Sometimes he can't remember what he wants to be, a farmer or a pencil-pusher.

The cage. He's always going on about the cage. It's what the men at the mine call the elevator car they ride down the shaft. They call it that because it's all heavy reinforced-steel mesh. The old man has this cage on 250 the brain. Ever since we were little kids he's been threatening us with it. *Make something of yourself*, he'd warn us, *or you'll end up like your old man, a monkey in the cage!* Or: *What's this, Gene? Failed arithmetic? Just remember, dunces don't end up in the corner. Hell no, they end up in the cage! Look at me!* My old man really hates that cage and the mine. He figures it's the worst 255 thing you can threaten anybody with.

I was in the cage, once. A few years ago, when I was fourteen, the company decided they'd open the mine up for tours. It was likely the brainstorm of some public relations tit sitting in head office in Chicago. In my book it was kind of like taking people into the slaughterhouse to prove 260 you're kind to the cows. Anyway, Pop offered to take us on one of his days off. As usual, he was about four years behind schedule. When we were maybe eleven we might have been nuts about the idea, but just then it didn't thrill us too badly. Gene, who is about as subtle as a bag of hammers, said flat out he wasn't interested. I could see right away the old man 265 was hurt by that. It isn't often he plays the buddy to his boys, and he probably had the idea he could whiz us about the machines and stuff. Impress the hell out of us. So it was up to me to slobber and grin like some kind of half-wit over the idea, to perk him up, see? Everybody suffers when the old man gets into one of his moods.

270      Of course, like always when I get sucked into this good-turn business, I shaft myself. I'd sort of forgotten how much I don't like tight places and being closed in. When we were younger, Gene used to make me go berserk by holding me under the covers, or stuffing a pillow in my face, or locking me in the garage whenever he got the chance. The jerk.

275      To start with, they packed us in the cage with twelve other people, which didn't help matters any. Right away my chest got tight and I felt like I couldn't breathe. Then the old cables started groaning and grinding and this fine red dust like chili powder sprinkled down through the mesh and dusted our hard hats with the word GUEST stencilled on them. It was rust.

280 Kind of makes you think.

"Here we go," said Pop.

We went. It was like all of a sudden the floor fell away from under my boots. That cage just dropped in the shaft like a stone down a well. It rattled and creaked and banged. The bare light bulb in the roof started to

285 flicker, and all the faces around me started to dance and shake up and down in the dark. A wind twisted up my pant-legs and I could hear the cables squeak and squeal. It made me think of big fat fucking rats.

"She needs new brake shoes," said this guy beside me and he laughed. He couldn't fool me. He was scared shitless too, in his own way.

290      "It's not the fall that kills you," his neighbour replied. "It's the sudden stop." There's a couple of horses' patoots in every crowd.

We seemed to drop forever. Everybody got quieter and quieter. They even stopped shuffling and coughing. Down. Down. Down. Then the cage started to slow, I felt a pressure build in my knees and my crotch and my

295 ears. The wire box started to shiver and clatter and shake. *Bang!* We stopped. The cage bobbed a little up and down like a yo-yo on the end of a string. Not much though, just enough to make you queasy.

"Last stop, Hooterville!' said the guide, who thought he was funny, and threw back the door. Straight ahead I could see a low-roofed big open

300 space with tunnels running from it into the ore. Every once in a while I could see the light from a miner's helmet jump around in the blackness of one of those tunnels like a firefly flitting in the night.

First thing I thought was: *What if I get lost? What if I lose the group? There's miles and miles and miles of tunnel under here*. I caught a whiff of the air. It

305 didn't smell like air up top. It smelled used. You could taste the salt. *I'm suffocating*, I thought. *I can't breathe this shit*.

I hadn't much liked the cage but this was worse. When I was in the shaft I knew there was a patch of sky over my head with a few stars in it and clouds and stuff. But all of a sudden I realized how deep we were. How we

310 were sort of like worms crawling in the guts of some dead animal. Over us were billions, no, trillions, of tons of rock and dirt and mud pressing down. I could imagine it caving in and falling on me, crushing my chest, squeezing the air out slowly, dust fine as flour trickling into my eyes and nostrils, or mud plugging my mouth so I couldn't even scream. And then
315 just lying there in the dark, my legs and arms pinned so I couldn't even twitch them. For a long time maybe. Crazy, lunatic stuff was what I started to think right on the spot.

My old man gave me a nudge to get out. We were the last.

"No," I said quickly and hooked my fingers in the mesh.

320 "We get out here," said the old man. He hadn't caught on yet.

"No, I can't," I whispered. He must have read the look on my face then. I think he knew he couldn't have pried me off that mesh with a gooseneck and winch.

Fred, the cage operator, lifted his eyebrows at Pop. "What's up, Jack?"

325 "The kid's sick," said Pop. "We'll take her up. He don't feel right." My old man was awful embarrassed.

Fred said, "I wondered when it'd happen. Taking kids and women down the hole."

"Shut your own goddamn hole," said the old man. "He's got the flu. He
330 was up all last night."

Fred looked what you'd call sceptical.

"Last time I take you any place nice," the old man said under his breath.

The last day of school has always got to be some big deal. By nine o'clock
335 all the dipsticks are roaring their cars up and down main street with their goofy broads hanging out their windows yelling, and trying to impress on one another how drunk they are.

Dad sent me to look for Gene because he didn't come home for supper at six. I found him in the poolroom playing dollar-a-hand poker pool.

340 "Hey, little brother," he waved to me from across the smoky poolroom, "come on here and I'll let you hold my cards!" I went over. He grinned to the goofs he was playing with. "You watch out now, boys," he said, "my little brother always brings me luck. Not that I need it," he explained to me, winking.

345 Yeah, I always brought him luck. *I* kept track of the game. *I* figured out what order to take the balls down. *I* reminded him not to put somebody else out and to play the next guy safe instead of slamming off some cornball shot. When *I* did all that Gene won—because I brought him luck. Yeah.

Gene handed me his cards. "You wouldn't believe these two," he said to
350 me out of the corner of his mouth, "genuine plough jockeys. These boys
couldn't find their ass in the dark with both hands. I'm fifteen dollars to
the good."

I admit they didn't look too swift. The biggest one, who was *big*, was
wearing an out-of-town team jacket, a Massey-Ferguson cap, and shit-
355 kicker wellingtons. He was maybe twenty-one, but his skin hadn't cleared
up yet by no means. His pan looked like all-dressed pizza, heavy on the
cheese. His friend was a dinky little guy with his hair designed into a duck's
ass. The kind of guy who hates the Beatles. About two feet of a dirty comb
was sticking out of his ass pocket.

360 Gene broke the rack and the nine went down. His shot.

"Dad's looking for you. He wants to know if you passed," I said.

"You could've told him."

"Well, I didn't."

"Lemme see the cards." I showed him. He had a pair of treys, a six, a
365 seven, and a lady. Right away he stopped to pocket the three. I got a teacher
who always talks about thought processes. Gene doesn't have them.

"Look at the table," I said. "Six first and you can come around up her."
I pointed.

"No coaching," said Pizza Face. I could see this one was a poor loser.

370 Gene shifted his stance and potted the six.

"What now?" he asked.

"The queen, and don't forget to put pants on her." I paused. "Pop figured you were going to make it. He really did, Gene."

"So tough titty. I didn't. Who the hell cares? He had your suck card to
375 slobber over, didn't he?" He drilled the lady in the side pocket. No back-
spin. He'd hooked himself on the three. "Fuck."

"The old man is on graveyard shift. You better go home and face the
music before he goes to work. It'll be worse in the morning when he needs
sleep," I warned him.

380 "Screw him."

I could see Gene eyeballing the four. He didn't have any four in his
hand, so I called him over and showed him his cards. "You can't shoot the
four. It's not in your hand."

"Just watch me." He winked. "I've been doing it all night. It's all pitch
385 and no catch with these prizes." Gene strolled back to the table and coolly
stroked down the four. He had shape for the three which slid in the top
pocket like shit through a goose. He cashed in on the seven. "That's it,
boys," he said. "That's all she wrote."

I was real nervous. I tried to bury the hand in the deck but the guy with the runny face stopped me. He was getting tired of losing, I guess. Gene doesn't even cheat smart. You got to let them win once in a while.

"Gimme them cards," he said. He started counting the cards off against the balls, flipping down the boards on the felt. "Three." He nodded. "Six, seven, queen. I guess you got them all," he said slowly, with a look on his face like he was pissing ground glass.

That's when Duck Ass chirped up. "Hey, Marvin," he said, "that guy shot the four. He shot the four."

"Nah," said Gene.

Marvin studied on this for a second, walked over to the table and pulled the four ball out of the pocket. Just like little Jack Horner lifting the plum out of the pie. "Yeah," he said. "You shot the four."

"Jeez," said Gene, "I guess I did. Honest mistake. Look, here's a dollar for each of you." He took two bills out of his shirt pocket. "You got to pay for your mistakes is what I was always taught."

"I bet you he's been cheating all along," said Duck Ass.

"My brother don't cheat," I said.

"I want all my money back," said Marvin. Quite loud. Loud enough that some heads turned and a couple of tables stopped playing. There was what you would call a big peanut gallery, it being the beginning of vacation and the place full of junior high kids and stags.

"You can kiss my ass, bozo," said Gene. "Like my brother here said, I never cheated nobody in my life."

"You give us our money back," threatened Marvin, "or I'll pull your head off, you skinny little prick."

Guys were starting to drift towards us, curious. The manager, Fat Bert, was easing his guts out from behind the cash register.

"Give them their money, Gene," I said, "and let's get out of here."

"No."

Well, that was that. You can't change his mind. I took a look at old Marvin. As I said before, Marvin was *big*. But what was worse was that he had this real determined look people who aren't too bright get when they finally dib on to the fact they've been hosed and somebody has been laughing up his sleeve at them. They don't like it too hot, believe me.

"Step outside, shit-head," said Marvin.

"Fight," somebody said encouragingly. A real clump of ringsiders was starting to gather. "Fight." Bert came hustling up, bumping his way through the kids with his bay window. "Outside, you guys. I don't want nothing broke in here. Get out or I'll call the cops."

Believe me, was I tense. Real tense. I know Gene pretty well and I was
430 sure that he had looked at old Marvin's muscles trying to bust out everywhere. Any second I figured he was going to even the odds by pasting old
Marvin in the puss with his pool cue, or at least sucker-punching him.

But Gene is full of surprises. All of a sudden he turned peacemaker. He
laid down his pool cue (which I didn't figure was too wise) and said: "You
435 want to fight over this?" He held up the four ball. "Over this? An honest
mistake?"

"Sure I do," said Marvin. "You're fucking right I do, cheater."

"Cheater, cheater," said Duck Ass. I was looking him over real good
because I figured if something started in there I'd get him to tangle with.

440 Gene shrugged and even kind of sighed, like the hero does in the movies
when he has been forced into a corner and has to do something that is
against his better nature. He tossed up the four ball once, looked at it, and
then reached behind him and shoved it back into the pocket. "All right,"
he said, slouching a little and jamming his hands into his jacket pockets.
445 "Let's go, sport."

That started the stampede. "Fight! Fight!" The younger kids, the ones
thirteen and fourteen, were really excited; the mob kind of swept Marvin
and Gene out the door, across the street and into the OK Economy parking
lot where most beefs get settled. There's lots of dancing-room there. A nice
450 big ring.

Marvin settled in real quick. He tugged the brim of his Massey-Ferguson
special a couple of times, got his dukes up and started to hop around like
he'd stepped right out of the pages of *Ring* magazine. He looked pretty
stupid, especially when Gene just looked at him, and kept his hands
455 rammed in his jacket pockets. Marvin kind of clomped from foot to foot for
a bit and he said: "Get 'em up."

"You get first punch," said Gene.

"What?" said Marv. He was so surprised his yap fell open.

"If I hit you first," said Gene, "you'll charge me with assault. I know
460 your kind."

Marvin stopped clomping. I suspect it took too much co-ordination for
him to clomp and think at the same time. "Oh no," he said, "I ain't falling
for that. If I hit *you* first, you'll charge *me* with assault." No flies on Marvin.
"*You* get the first punch."

465 "Fight. Come on, fight," said some ass-hole, real disgusted with all the
talk and no action.

"Oh no," said Gene. "I ain't hitting *you* first."

Marvin brought his hands down. "Come on, come on, let fly."

"You're sure?" asked Gene.

470 "Give her your best shot," said Marvin. "You couldn't hurt a fly, you scrawny shit. Quit stalling. Get this show on the road."

Gene uncorked on him. It looked like a real pansy punch. His right arm whipped out of his jacket pocket, stiff at the elbow like a girl's when she slaps. It didn't look like it had nothing behind it, sort of like Gene had smacked
475 him kind of contemptuous in the mouth with the flat of his hand. That's how it looked. It *sounded* like he'd hit him in the mouth with a ball-peen hammer. Honest to God, you could hear the teeth crunch when they broke.

Big Marvin dropped on his knees like he'd been shot in the back of the neck. His hands flew up to his face and the blood just ran through his fin-
480 gers and into his cuffs. It looked blue under the parking-lot lights. There was an awful lot of it.

"Get up, you dick licker," said Gene.

Marvin pushed off his knees with a crazy kind of grunt that might have been a sob. I couldn't tell. He came up under Gene's arms, swept him off
485 his feet and dangled him in the air, crushing his ribs in a bear hug.

"*Waauugh!*" said Gene. I started looking around right smartly for something to hit the galoot with before he popped my brother like a pimple.

But then Gene lifted his fist high above Marvin's head and brought it down on his skull, hard as he could. It made a sound like he was banging
490 coconuts together. Marvin sagged a little at the knees and staggered. *Chunk! Chunk!* Gene hit him two more times and Marvin toppled over backwards. My brother landed on top of him and right away started pasting him left and right. Everybody was screaming encouragement. There was no invitation to the dick licker to get up this time. Gene was still
495 clobbering him when I saw the cherry popping on the cop car two blocks away. I dragged him off Marvin.

"Cops," I said, yanking at his sleeve. Gene was trying to get one last kick at Marvin. "Come on, fucker," he was yelling. "Fight now!"

"Jesus," I said, looking at Gene's jacket and shirt, "you stupid bugger,
500 you're all over blood." It was smeared all over him. Marvin tried to get up. He only made it to his hands and knees. There he stayed, drooling blood and saliva on the asphalt. The crowd started to edge away as the cop car bounced up over the curb and gave a long, low whine out of its siren.

I took off my windbreaker and gave it to Gene. He pulled off his jacket
505 and threw it down. "Get the fuck out of here," I said. "Beat it."

"I took the wheels off his little red wagon," said Gene. "It don't pull so good now." His hands were shaking and so was his voice. He hadn't had half enough yet. "I remember that other guy," he said. "Where's his friend?"

I gave him a shove. "Get going." Gene slid into the crowd that was slip-
510 ping quickly away. Then I remembered his hockey jacket. It was wet with
blood. It also had flashes with his name and number on it. It wouldn't take
no Sherlock Holmes cop to figure out who'd beat on Marvin. I picked it up
and hugged it to my belly. Right away I felt something hard in the pocket.
Hard and round. I started to walk away. I heard a car door slam. I knew
515 what was in that pocket. The controversial four ball old Gene had palmed
when he pretended to put it back. He likes to win.

I must have been walking too fast or with a guilty hunch to my shoulders, because I heard the cop call, "Hey you, the kid with the hair." Me, I'm
kind of a hippy for this place, I guess. Lots of people mention my hair.

520    I ran. I scooted round the corner of the supermarket and let that pool
ball fly as hard as I could, way down the alley. I never rifled a shot like that
in my life. If coach Al had seen me trigger that baby he'd have strapped
me into a belly pad himself. Of course, a jacket don't fly for shit. The bull
came storming around the corner just as I give it the heave-ho. I was kind
525 of caught with shit on my face, if you know what I mean?

Now a guy with half a brain could have talked his way out of that without
too much trouble. Even a cop understands how somebody would try to
help his brother. They don't hold it too much against you. And I couldn't
really protect Gene. That geek Marvin would have flapped his trap if I
530 hadn't. And it wasn't as if I hadn't done old Gene *some* good. After all, they
never found out about that pool ball. The judge would have pinned Gene's
ears back for him if he'd known he was going around thwacking people
with a hunk of shatter-proof plastic. So Gene came out smelling like a rose,
same suspended sentence as me, and a reputation for having hands of
535 stone.

But at a time like that you get the nuttiest ideas ever. I watched them
load Marvin in a squad car to drive him to the hospital while I sat in the
back seat of another. And I thought to myself: *I'll play along with this. Let
the old man come down to the cop shop over me for once. Me he takes for*
540 *granted. Let him worry about Billy for a change. It wouldn't hurt him.*

So I never said one word about not being the guy who bopped Marvin.
It was kind of fun in a crazy way, making like a hard case. At the station
I was real rude and lippy. Particularly to a sergeant who was a grade A
dink if I ever saw one. It was only when they took my shoelaces and belt
545 that I started to get nervous.

"Ain't you going to call my old man?" I asked.

The ass-hole sergeant gave me a real smile. "In the morning," he said. "All in good time."

"In the morning?" And then I said like a dope: "Where am I going to sleep?"

"Show young Mr. Simpson where he's going to sleep," said the sergeant. He smiled again. It looked like a ripple on a slop pail. The constable who he was ordering around like he was his own personal slave took me down into the basement of the station. Down there it smelled of stale piss and old puke. I kind of gagged. I got a weak stomach.

Boy, was I nervous. I saw where he was taking me. There were four cells. They weren't even made out of bars, just metal strips riveted into a cross hatch you couldn't stick your hand through. They were all empty.

"Your choice," said the corporal. He was real humorous too, like his boss.

"You don't have to put me in one of them, sir," I said. "I won't run away."

"That's what all the criminals say." He opened the door. "Entrezvous."

I was getting my old crazy feeling really bad. Really bad. I felt kind of dizzy. "I got this thing," I said, "about being locked up. It's torture."

"Get in."

"No—please," I said. "I'll sit upstairs. I won't bother anybody."

"You think you've got a choice? You don't have a choice. Move your ass."

I was getting ready to cry. I could feel it. I was going to bawl in front of a cop. "I didn't do it," I said. "I never beat him up. Swear to Jesus I didn't."

"I'm counting three," he said, "and then I'm applying the boots to your backside."

It all came out. Just like that. *"It was my fucking ass-hole brother, Gene!"* I screamed. The only thing I could think of was, if they put me in there I'll be off my head by morning. I really will. *"I didn't do nothing! I never do nothing! You can't put me in there for him!"*

They called my old man. I guess I gave a real convincing performance. Not that I'm proud of it. I actually got sick on the spot from nerves. I just couldn't hold it down.

Pop had to sign for me and promise to bring Gene down in the morning. It was about twelve-thirty when everything got cleared up. He'd missed his shift and his ride in the cage.

When we got in the car he didn't start it. We just sat there with the windows rolled down. It was a beautiful night and there were lots of stars

585 swimming in the sky. This town is small enough that street-lights and neon don't interfere with the stars. It's the only thing I like about this place. There's plenty of sky and lots of air to breathe.

"Your brother wasn't enough," he said. "You I trusted."

"I only tried to help him."

590 "You goddamn snitch." He needed somebody to take it out on, so he belted me. Right on the snout with the back of his hand. It started to bleed. I didn't try to stop it. I just let it drip on those goddamn furry seat-covers that he thinks are the cat's ass. "They were going to put me in this place, this cage, for him, for that useless shit!" I yelled. I'd started to cry. "No
595 more, Pop. He failed! He failed on top of it all! So is he going to work? You got the boots ready on the back step? Huh? Is he going down in the fucking cage?"

"Neither one of you is going down in the cage. Not him, not you," he said.

600 "Nah, I didn't think so," I said, finally wiping at my face with the back of my hand. "I didn't think so."

"I don't have to answer to you," he said. "You just can't get inside his head. You were always the smart one. I didn't have to worry about you. You always knew what to do. But Gene... " He pressed his forehead
605 against the steering-wheel, hard. "Billy, I see him doing all sorts of stuff. Stuff you can't imagine. I see it until it makes me sick." He looked at me. His face was yellow under the street-light, yellow like a lemon. "I try so hard with him. But he's got no sense. He just does things. He could have killed that other boy. He wouldn't even think of that, you know." All of
610 a sudden the old man's face got all crumpled and creased like paper when you ball it up. "What's going to happen to him?" he said, louder than he had to. "What's going to happen to Eugene?" It was sad. It really was.

I can never stay mad at my old man. Maybe because we're so much
615 alike, even though he can't see it for looking the other way. Our minds work alike. I'm a chip off the old block. Don't ever doubt it.

"Nothing."

"Billy," he said, "you mean it?"

I knew what he was thinking. "Yes," I said. "I'll do my best."

(1982)

# Following the Story

1. Billy is the narrator of this story, so what is the point of view?
2. What facts do we learn about Billy in the exposition?
3. Billy tells the story through a number of flashbacks. What is the effect of this technique?
4. Is Billy reliable as a narrator? Why or why not?
5. How is the conflict presented in this story?
6. How does Billy create suspense for "*the terrible thing*" Gene does at the climax of the story?
7. Just before the climax, Billy says of Gene, "Yeah, I always brought him luck" (line 345). Is this ironic, and how can you tell?
8. What is ironic about the comment of Billy's father, "Last time I take you anywhere nice" (line 332)?
9. Does Mr. Simpson love his two sons? How can you tell?
10. Billy ends by saying, "I'll do my best" (line 619). How successful do you think he will be?

# Responding to the Story

1. How does Billy feel about his brother, Gene? Support your answer with details from the story.
2. What sort of character is Gene? How would you describe his personality?
3. How does Billy feel about his father? Support your answer with details from the story.
4. What sort of character is Mr. Simpson? How would you describe his personality?
5. What sort of character is Billy? How would you describe his personality?
6. What does Billy mean when he says, "I'm a chip off the old block" (line 616)? Is he correct to think this?
7. What do you think about the way Billy narrates this story? Is the sort of language he uses appropriate? Why or why not?
8. Billy presents a number of experiences with cages. How do they relate to the title? What is the meaning of these cages in Billy's life?
9. How would this story be different if Mr. Simpson were the narrator, or if Gene were the narrator?
10. What does the author achieve by having a first-person narrator like Billy, rather than a third-person narrator, tell this story?

# All Is Burning

Jean Arasanayagam (Sri Lanka) 1934–

## About the Author

*Born into a Dutch Burgher (descendants of Dutch colonists) family in Sri Lanka in 1934, Jean Arasanayagam graduated from the University of Ceylon and the University of Strathclyde in Scotland. In addition to being a novelist, poet and short story writer, she has also taught English and writing at colleges and universities in Sri Lanka, England, and the United States.* Kindura, *her first collection of poems, was published in 1973, and* All Is Burning, *from which the following story is taken, was published in 1995. Married to a Tamil artist, Arasanayagam now lives in Kandy, Sri Lanka.*

*As an internationally renowned contemporary Sri Lankan writer, Arasanayagam has the advantage of experiencing first hand the traditions of English and European literature as well as of indigenous folk tales and Indian poetry and epics. Her works are primarily concerned with pursuit of the true meaning of life and personal identity in a cross-cultural and interracial context, depiction of the cultural and ethnic conflicts between the Sinhalese and the Tamils in Sri Lanka, women's identity, and other social issues concerning women. Imbued with the sensitivity and perceptivity of a poet, Arasanayagam's stories appeal to the reader's senses as well as to the mind.*

## About the Story

*"All Is Burning" takes place in Sri Lanka during a period of violent political conflict between the Tamils and the Sinhalese. The events in this story happen in a village that has been ransacked; only the women and children have been spared from death. The story takes place in an atmosphere of fear and anguish.*

*This story begins* in medias res—*in the middle of the events—and moves backwards and forwards in time. We only learn what has happened in this village gradually as Alice searches for Sena, the young man her daughter was going to marry. The Buddha's "Fire Sermon," which provides the opening quotation, preaches against violence, and it is a bitterly ironic comment on the story that follows. This irony continues throughout the story because Alice recalls the sermon during her search. Beside her at all times, she sees Yama, the Hindu god of death, whose presence adds a symbolic intensity to this story. The narrator often presents the action through internal monologue. Notice that there are sudden changes of verb tenses in this story. Why might that be?*

*Bhikkus, all is burning. And what is the all that is burning? Bhikkus, the eye is burning, visible forms are burning, visual consciousness is burning, visual impression is burning.... Burning with what? Burning with the fire of lust, with the fire of hate, with the fire of delusion; I say it is burning with birth, aging and death, with sorrows, with lamentations, with pains, with griefs, with despairs.*

—The Buddha's Fire Sermon

She blew out the flame of the bottle lamp, leaving the room in darkness. She took a towel off the line and wrapped it about her shoulders. Seela, her daughter, a young woman in her twenties, sat at the table with her head in her hands.

5     Night sounds filtered in through the clay walls of the hut. Not just the sounds of insects rasping against the leaves or of wakened birds, but also a vast sighing that rippled through the thick blue-black shadows that lay like welts on the earth.

    Seela lifted her head wearily. The weight of melancholy, of despair 10 pressed each image onto her consciousness. She had aged. Felt older than her mother. In the cavern of her being images of dead fish, silver bellies upturned, floated in an inky pool.

    "Mother," she whispered. "Mother, shall we go in search of Sena? He may still be alive if he has not been taken away. I'll come with you. You 15 can't go alone. They may still be there, who knows. We can guide each other. It's still not light, we have to search for the path. It may be an unfamiliar one."

    Alice was already at the door. She spoke under her breath. "No, you wait. Don't open the door to anyone. Remain in darkness. Don't light the 20 lamp."

    "Mother."

    "Yes?"

    "Don't go alone." Seela rose wearily and dragged her feet to the door.

    "No. It is my mission. A journey by myself will be safer. I'll come back 25 here. Don't move. Wait and keep that door barred. Just don't open to any knock."

    Alice stepped out, treading softly, warily on her bare feet. It would be easier that way. No sound of any footfall. She closed the door behind her very quietly. She peered into the darkness with yet its hint of light. Her 30 nerves felt on edge. Her instincts alert, she must let herself be guided, by odours—unusual odours of gunshot, of blood, borne by the slight, chill tremors of wind. There would be that human odour too, of fear, that rank smell of bodies through whose pores fear had breathed.

35 She still felt her flesh raw, hurt by the events of the night. That sense of peace which came with late evening and the dusk which settled over the river, the trees, the road and their little hamlet had been deceptive. The bathers had returned from the river, they did not linger very long these days. The water, silver shot with ripples of gold, soon turned dark and opaque, vanishing into the dense clumps of trees. The woodsmoke curled
40 up from the huts, spiralling into the sky, a pale wreathing grey.

She had been busy preparing the evening meal. The pot of rice was still on the fire, the fish and vegetables simmering in their pots. Seela, her daughter, was talking to Sena, the young man whom she was going to marry. Alice wanted this marriage for Seela. Her own man had deserted
45 her when she was pregnant, leaving her to bring up the child alone. She had been a servant in so many houses, cooking, minding children, washing piles of linen, dressing her child in the clothes outgrown by other people's children—her mistress's daughter's clothes and those of her friends' children. No more of that for Seela. She had been a bright, intelli-
50 gent child, had gone to school, passed examinations. She had a future before her. All that was through the efforts, undoubtedly, that Alice had made.

But it had come to their hamlet too—the *bhishanaya*, the trouble. Yes, it had reached them. There were rumours. The young men in the village,
55 were they too involved in all those happenings? The country was on fire. Everything was on fire. All was burning, burning. Yes, the fires were burning. Fires that burnt down the huts. These and hundreds of other vil-lages burning. The self burning. The unconscious, the visual impressions, burning. The fire of lust and hate, the fire of delusion. The Buddha's Fire
60 Sermon that the villagers heard in the temple—the monk repeated it on the last poya day when they went to hear him, to find some relief for their suffering minds.

"Burning," he said, "with birth, aging and death, with sorrows, with lamentations, with pains, with griefs, with despairs."

65 And what do we do? Alice thought to herself. Become dispassionate, detached? To reach that liberation must I first go out among the dead and their ruined houses? I cannot forget the sound of the vehicles on the road...

They had stopped at the entrance to the village. The darkness had moved like an open door to admit them. And they had entered. The vil-
70 lagers heard the sounds of their boots. The knocking at the doors. The commands.

"Open up."

There was nothing else to do.

Screams. Dying away. Growing fainter. Fainter. She had to go. But not
75 at once. Wait for sometime. Till they heard the sound of the vehicles
moving off. Then she would go out, in search of Sena, for Seela's sake. She
thought of herself. An ordinary woman. Very ordinary. Even the name
Alice did not matter to anyone. She knew that she had to do it. Even if
there were a vestige of life left she would confront those last moments. And
80 she would have to do it alone.

Seela too had been strong during those last moments. "Mother, our generation, my generation, we know the consequences. We are not afraid."

Now Alice was walking along pathways. They had to lead to the
deathspot. Through the grove of trees—wild guava, hard-shelled green
85 belly fruit and straggling palms. A cluster of thambili nestled among some
of the thicker fronds, a very pale orange. Her throat felt parched, as if
death were already clutching at it. Dry tongued, her belly cavernous and
hollow. Out of the trees, out of the grove, she emerged like a sleepwalker
into a space where the grass had been trampled and crushed.

90 Now it was over. The sound of gunshot still echoed in her ears. Yama
had visited every house in the village where there were males. They had
all been taken away. She had to summon all her strength for this mission.
The vision of Yama, the god of death, filled her mind.

I am an ordinary woman, she told herself. I have been a servant in
95 other people's homes for the greater part of my life. Always subservient,
obeying orders. Eating after everyone else had eaten. Sleeping on my mat
in a corner of a room, seeing that other people were comfortable. And now,
now that I had hopes for a different kind of life, now when I thought things
would change—but no, things *have* changed, though not for the better. Yet
100 I have to do this for my daughter, look at the faces of the dead and dying.
No, Seela couldn't do it. I'll do it for her. I am her mother. Who else has
she had all her life? Myself and her grandmother. Two women. There has
never been a man to give me strength. I have done things that I never
believed possible for a woman to do. No, it will never end for me. My
105 strength grows with each crisis. I've been well trained through the years.
There's no one else I can turn to. I'll do it by myself. I can't help it if my
mind keeps going back to all the events of the night. I'll relive this experience for ever.

The knocking on all those doors resounded in her ears. She had opened
110 the door. What else could she have done? They wanted Sena. As they did
all the males in the village. Behind them she saw that vision—Yama.

Yama, the god of death. He too was with them. On whose side was he? He was a constant guest on both fronts these days.

They pointed the guns at Sena. No, he couldn't escape. Nor could all the others. Weeping, shrieking echoed through the night, the night that Alice had thought would be so peaceful. She smelt burning rice. The brands crackled and the fire raced, shedding sparks as it blew up.

Yama, Yama. Was it only she who saw him? Eye for an eye, tooth for a tooth, the men kept saying as they pointed the gun at Sena, prodded him with the butt.

"Don't try to resist," said one of them. "And don't say you are innocent. You want to be martyrs. Then where are the victims? Someone has to be the victim. Who put up all those posters with their violent messages? Who carried off the weapons after the attacks on police stations and the army camps? To use for what purpose? To use against whom? The men of this village—we have proof. The last attack...there were deaths. Now get on, move on...The fires are spreading all over the country. Come on, hurry up."

Her daughter had fallen at the feet of the men. She had pleaded and wept. "Don't take him away. Don't. Don't." It had all fallen on deaf ears.

There had been so much shouting outside their walls. Commands. Tramp of boots. Sounds of running feet. They had heard the guns. The volley of shots. Went on ceaselessly. Would they ever stop firing?

It seemed a lifetime ago. Alice now smelt the odour of death. Rank. Foetid. Like rotting vegetation. They lay there, clumps of them, their bodies spreadeagled on the earth. Men. Bodies. A mirror of light flickered across her gaze with their distortions, black specks, rust coloured streaks—chiaroscuric images that almost stoned her eyeballs.

She knew she had to go among them. How else would she find Sena? He had to be there. He had to, unless...but could he have had a chance of escaping, in the dark? No, there must have been flashlights. The darkness violated by those coruscating beams. At least if she could find him...She was a woman who needed certainty. The certainty of truth. It had to be one way or the other. She had never deceived Seela. Nor had she deceived herself. At this moment she did not want the comfort of any human being. This would be her final test, her trial. And Sena, if he still had some life in him, even if he was barely breathing, perhaps he could gasp out a word, perhaps she could even drag him out of this welter of bodies.

She looked at them, almost dispassionately. They were finished. There was nothing more left for them. Their women would have to fend for themselves now. The women were strong enough. And they had their children. They couldn't give up at this stage.

She wiped her face with the edge of her towel. The towel was damp with morning dew. Her face chill and sharp like the edge of a keen blade.

Death walk. That's what this is, she thought. I'll have to turn them over.
155 I have to see the faces. How else can I recognize them? How can I recognize Sena? Men who had belonged to other women. I would never have touched them at any other time.

Her bare feet slid cautiously through the huddle of bodies. They felt so soft. Even the sinewy ones.

160    She bent over, turned up face after face. All she recognized were the empty faces of men. Men who were all akin, all brothers, husbands, fathers. All gone. To leave life in so unfinished, so haphazard a manner.

She stumbled, almost fell against one of the bodies. I'll have to be careful, she thought. I mustn't jostle them even in death. Perhaps, some of
165 them still have that last breath...the soul that's reluctant to leave the body. No funeral orations for any of them. Individual burials are no longer practicable. It is within our minds that we carry those reminders of what each man was to each woman. Till each one is claimed, if ever they are claimed, they are anonymous. It's happening elsewhere too, perhaps at this very
170 moment.... Soon there'll be no birds left in the village. Startled by gunshot, they'll fly away to another village. Who's going to start life here all over again....

Her movements now became mechanical. But she wove her way through, a searcher who could never give up the search.

175    Where would the pyres be lit? And where the secret graves? They would be silently carried away, secretly buried. Their names would be mentioned only in whispers. So this was the journey that Yama took daily? Difficult. But she had the strength.

She flicked at a fly with a towel. They were already there, the blue-bot-
180 tles. The smell of death, it was choking her. She felt suffocated but could not stop. She would go on till she found him.

Could this be Sena...? She peered into a face, called his name softly: "Sena, Sena, Sena." It could be Sena—a young body, but the face all smeared with blood. If she wiped the blood off she might recognize him.
185 She wiped his face gently with the end of her towel and gazed into the face.

No, this was not him. Resembled him...

She stroked his head, caressingly. A woman's gesture. Her towel was sodden. Her clothes felt damp.

He is still warm, she told herself. My towel is soaked with blood. My
190 clothes too—damp, stained. She felt dead, her limbs numbed. She stumbled against yet another body.

There must be so many...so many of them.... Forgive me, son, brother, father, husband, forgive me for touching your sleeping body with my foot, it is not that I mean to insult you...

195 No, not this one either. Where was he? And such a silence in the village. Where was everybody? Asleep? Awake? Afraid to come out? All the women, the children? Such a silence in the village.

Her head was full of images, strange thoughts.... All the blood must seep into the earth, as if the gods must be propitiated, as if we have had a long
200 drought. What new plants will grow here? Or will it remain a desert, haunted by ghosts and spirits? Shouldn't we leave it this way, to remember them? I must go down to the river, wash my clothes, bathe, watch the water change colour—like my dreams, the dreams that will visit me night after night.

205 When can I ever complete this journey? Yama told me—somewhere— that this is my first journey into the darkness of the underworld.... What's that sound...a groan? Not all are dead then.

She knelt down. Her back ached with so much bending. She felt the man's breath touch the palm of her hand like a slight vapour, a cobweb of
210 mist that faintly wreathed round her fingers.

"I won't leave you alone. I'll stay by you," she said, sitting beside him, wiping his face with the corner of her towel, pushing away the tangled strands of hair from his forehead. She supported his head in her arms.

"Mother," he uttered faintly. His life was ebbing away.
215 "Mother," he repeated. "Thirsty."

"Wait, I'll bring you a sip of water. I'll go back to my hut. Wait. Don't move."

No, there wasn't time to go back, to fetch water, to give him that drink. Life-giving water? No. It would soon be over. She felt the spasms of his
220 chest, the painful heaving of that wounded breast. She held him until he was still. Her hands were stained with blood. She wiped them slowly but the blood felt sticky, oozing into her skin, her flesh.

That was the end. All she could give him was the hope of that sip of water. And he had called her Mother. That was enough. She was a comfort
225 to him and that was more than all the others had on all the battlefields where they gasped out their lives.

Already, so many bodies and she hadn't found Sena yet.

What could a village do without all its men? We'll have to take their place now, we women, she thought. I'll go back to my daughter. Perhaps
230 there's still hope. They may have taken him away for questioning. Seela

will have to continue living, like all the other women. It won't be the end for us, not while we still have breath.

She rose wearily. She wanted to retch but her mouth was dry, her throat parched.

235 Two hundred and fifty of them. All the men in the village. Gone. Swept away in that great flood of death. But the women would bear more sons. Life had to, would go on.

(1995)

## Following the Story

1. What is the narrative point of view in this story? Support your answer with details from the story.
2. What facts does the narrator present us in the first few lines of this story before Alice steps out of the room?
3. The conflict in this story is literal, as the story actually deals with a war. Which words and images in the first section (to line 40) does the narrator use to convey the violence and destruction?
4. The narrator interrupts the account of what happened in the village from lines 74–109. What is the effect of this delay, and how does it add suspense to the rising action?
5. Sometimes the narrative voice directly presents Alice's mind. Does this use of internal monologue make the narrative voice inconsistent? Why or why not?
6. Alice's thoughts are given in the present tense, while the events are told in the past tense. Why do you think the narrator does this?
7. Find examples to show how the narrator presents Alice's respect for life.
8. Find examples to show how the narrator depicts Alice's respect for death.
9. Find a variety of examples to show the kind of mother Alice is.
10. The religious and supernatural elements in this story occur in Alice's internal monologues. Find examples of them. What do they suggest about Alice's character?

## Responding to the Story

1. Alice thinks she is "an ordinary woman." What facts are we given about Alice's life, and how well do they support this view? Do you think she is ordinary?

2. Is the fact that such terrible and extraordinary things happen to "an ordinary woman" ironic? Why or why not?
3. What sort of character is Alice? How would you describe her personality?
4. What sort of character is Seela? How would you describe her personality?
5. Alice thinks, "I can't help it if my mind keeps going back to all the events of the night." What do we learn about Alice from this statement? Is this pattern of remembering typical of people in general?
6. As Alice walks to the clearing to find Sena's body, she thinks, "So this was the journey that Yama took daily" (line 177)? What does Yama's presence in this story suggest to you?
7. What is the attitude of the narrator to the events in this story? Support your response with details.
8. Examine the frequent use of repetition in this story. What is the effect of such repetition?
9. The climax of the story occurs when Alice finds a young man who is barely alive. Why does the narrator describe his death in such detail?
10. The action in this story begins as "She blew out the flame..." and ends with an internal monologue. How do these narrative techniques affect the dénouement of "All Is Burning"?

---

# Salvatore

Somerset Maugham (England) 1874–1965

## About the Author

*Born in Paris, France, Somerset Maugham studied medicine and completed his internship, but never practised as a physician. Having determined at an early age to devote his life to literature, he established his fame as a dramatist with humorous plays like* Lady Frederick *(1907) before he became known for his novels and short stories. He wrote eight novels before his masterpiece,* Of Human Bondage, *was published in 1915. His many volumes of short stories also won him a worldwide reputation as an expert storyteller and master of fiction technique. He died in Nice, France in 1965.*

*His short stories are witty and ironic, and they mostly portray the conflicts of Europeans in foreign surroundings that provoke strong emotions. He demonstrates in his stories a profound understanding of human nature, yet his style is clear and simple. He travelled extensively in Europe, Asia, and other continents, and many of the exotic places he visited provide settings for his stories. Maugham is remembered as an accomplished short story writer whose skill in handling plot and building suspense rivals that of the French author Guy de Maupassant (1850–1893), one of the true masters of short story writing.*

## About the Story

*First published in 1936, "Salvatore" appeared in a collection of short stories by Somerset Maugham entitled* Cosmopolitans. *Although Somerset Maugham is English, his story takes place on a small Italian island, Ischia, off the south-west coast of Italy. From the island, Salvatore can see the volcano, Vesuvius, and the great city of Naples on the Italian mainland. Maugham presents not only realistic geographical details, but also historical background by setting this story during the reign of King Victor Emanuel III (1869–1947), in the period before World War II. Salvatore's way of life is typical of Italian fishermen at that time.*

*Maugham says he wanted his style to possess a "contrary plainness and simplicity." In "Salvatore" we can see that he has achieved this. From the narrator's opening address to the reader, through the few details of Salvatore's life to the narrator's final commentary, the vocabulary and syntax are plain and simple. What adorns this story is the profound notion that only in the ordinary do we discovery the extraordinary. This story reveals through its depiction of Salvatore's life the quintessential goodness in our world, and shows it is found when and where you would least expect it to be.*

I wonder if I can do it.

I knew Salvatore first when he was a boy of fifteen with a pleasant, ugly face, a laughing mouth and care-free eyes. He used to spend the morning lying about the beach with next to nothing on and his brown body was as
5  thin as a rail. He was full of grace. He was in and out of the sea all the time, swimming with the clumsy, effortless stroke common to the fisher boys. Scrambling up the jagged rocks on his hard feet, for except on Sundays he never wore shoes, he would throw himself into the deep water with a cry of delight. His father was a fisherman who owned his own little
10  vineyard and Salvatore acted as nursemaid to his two younger brothers. He shouted to them to come in shore when they ventured out too far and made them dress when it was time to climb the hot, vineclad hill for the frugal midday meal.

But boys in those Southern parts grow apace and in a little while he was
15  madly in love with a pretty girl who lived on the Grande Marina. She had eyes like forest pools and held herself like a daughter of the Caesars. They

were affianced, but they could not marry till Salvatore had done his military service, and when he left the island which he had never left in his life before, to become a sailor in the navy of King Victor Emmanuel, he wept
20 like a child. It was hard for one who had never been less free than the birds to be at the beck and call of others; it was harder still to live in a battleship with strangers instead of in a little white cottage among the vines; and when he was ashore, to walk in noisy, friendless cities with streets so crowded that he was frightened to cross them, when he had been used to
25 silent paths and the mountains and the sea. I suppose it had never struck him that Ischia, which he looked at every evening (it was like a fairy island in the sunset) to see what the weather would be like next day, or Vesuvius, pearly in the dawn, had anything to do with him at all; but when he ceased to have them before his eyes he realized in some dim
30 fashion that they were as much part of him as his hands and his feet. He was dreadfully homesick. But it was hardest of all to be parted from the girl he loved with all his passionate young heart. He wrote to her (in his childlike handwriting) long, ill-spelt letters in which he told her how constantly he thought of her and how much he longed to be back. He was sent here
35 and there, to Spezzia, to Venice, to Bari and finally to China. Here he fell ill of some mysterious ailment that kept him in hospital for months. He bore it with the mute and uncomprehending patience of a dog. When he learnt that it was a form of rheumatism that made him unfit for further service his heart exulted, for he could go home; and he did not bother, in
40 fact he scarcely listened, when the doctors told him that he would never again be quite well. What did he care when he was going back to the little island he loved so well and the girl who was waiting for him?

When he got into the rowing-boat that met the steamer from Naples and was rowed ashore he saw his father and mother standing on the jetty
45 and his two brothers, big boys now, and he waved to them. His eyes searched among the crowd that waited there, for the girl. He could not see her. There was a great deal of kissing when he jumped up the steps and they all, emotional creatures, cried a little as they exchanged their greetings. He asked where the girl was. His mother told him that she did not
50 know; they had not seen her for two or three weeks; so in the evening when the moon was shining over the placid sea and the lights of Naples twinkled in the distance he walked down to the Grande Marina to her house. She was sitting on the doorstep with her mother. He was a little shy because he had not seen her for so long. He asked her if she had not
55 received the letter that he had written to her to say that he was coming home. Yes, they had received a letter, and they had been told by another

of the island boys that he was ill. Yes, that was why he was back; was it not a piece of luck? Oh, but they had heard that he would never be quite well again. The doctors talked a lot of nonsense, but he knew very well that
60 now he was home again he would recover. They were silent for a little, and then the mother nudged the girl. She did not try to soften the blow. She told him straight out, with the blunt directness of her race, that she could not marry a man who would never be strong enough to work like a man. They had made up their minds, her mother and father and she, and her father
65 would never give his consent.

When Salvatore went home he found that they all knew. The girl's father had been to tell them what they had decided, but they had lacked the courage to tell him themselves. He wept on his mother's bosom. He was terribly unhappy, but he did not blame the girl. A fisherman's life is hard
70 and it needs strength and endurance. He knew very well that a girl could not afford to marry a man who might not be able to support her. His smile was very sad and his eyes had the look of a dog that has been beaten, but he did not complain, and he never said a hard word of the girl he had loved so well. Then, a few months later, when he had settled down to the
75 common round, working in his father's vineyard and fishing, his mother told him that there was a young woman in the village who was willing to marry him. Her name was Assunta.

'She's as ugly as the devil,' he said.

She was older than he, twenty-four or twenty-five, and she had been
80 engaged to a man who, while doing his military service, had been killed in Africa. She had a little money of her own and if Salvatore married her she could buy him a boat of his own and they could take a vineyard that by a happy chance happened at that moment to be without a tenant. His mother told him that Assunta had seen him at the *festa* and had fallen in
85 love with him. Salvatore smiled his sweet smile and said he would think about it. On the following Sunday, dressed in the stiff black clothes in which he looked so much less well than in the ragged shirt and trousers of every day, he went up to High Mass at the parish church and placed himself so that he could have a good look at the young woman. When he
90 came down again he told his mother that he was willing.

Well, they were married and they settled down in a tiny white-washed house in the middle of a handsome vineyard. Salvatore was now a great big husky fellow, tall and broad, but still with that ingenuous smile and those trusting, kindly eyes that he had had as a boy. He had the most
95 beautiful manners I have ever seen in my life. Assunta was a grim-visaged female, with decided features, and she looked old for her years. But she

had a good heart and she was no fool. I used to be amused by the little smile of devotion that she gave her husband when he was being very masculine and masterful; she never ceased to be touched by his gentle sweet-
100 ness. But she could not bear the girl who had thrown him over, and notwithstanding Salvatore's smiling expostulations she had nothing but harsh words for her. Presently children were born to them.

It was a hard enough life. All through the fishing season towards evening he set out in his boat with one of his brothers for the fishing grounds. It was
105 a long pull of six or seven miles, and he spent the night catching the profitable cuttlefish. Then there was the long row back again in order to sell the catch in time for it to go on the early boat to Naples. At other times he was working in his vineyard from dawn till the heat drove him to rest and then again, when it was a trifle cooler, till dusk. Often his rheumatism prevented
110 him from doing anything at all and then he would lie about the beach, smoking cigarettes, with a pleasant word for everyone notwithstanding the pain that racked his limbs. The foreigners who came down to bathe and saw him there said that these Italian fishermen were lazy devils.

Sometimes he used to bring his children down to give them a bath. They
115 were both boys and at this time the elder was three and the younger less than two. They sprawled about at the water's edge stark naked and Salvatore, standing on a rock would dip them in the water. The elder one bore it with stoicism, but the baby screamed lustily. Salvatore had enormous hands, like legs of mutton, coarse and hard from constant toil, but
120 when he bathed his children, holding them so tenderly, drying them with delicate care, upon my word they were like flowers. He would seat the naked baby on the palm of his hand and hold him up, laughing a little at his smallness, and his laugh was like the laughter of an angel. His eyes then were as candid as his child's.

125     I started by saying that I wondered if I could do it and now I must tell you what it is that I have tried to do. I wanted to see whether I could hold your attention for a few pages while I drew for you the portrait of a man, just an ordinary Italian fisherman who possessed nothing in the world except a quality which is the rarest, the most precious and the loveliest
130 that anyone can have. Heaven only knows why he should so strangely and unexpectedly have possessed it. All I know is that it shone in him with a radiance that, if it had not been so unconscious and so humble, would have been to the common run of men hardly bearable. And in case you have not guessed what the quality was, I will tell you. Goodness, just goodness.

(1936)

# Following the Story

1. What is the point of view in this story?
2. Does the point of view seem consistent? Why or why not?
3. Before you read the end of the story, how did you react to the opening line?
4. What do you learn about marriage customs in Italy at the beginning of the last century?
5. What do you learn about the traditional way of life on the island?
6. What facts does the narrator provide about Salvatore in the first two paragraphs after the opening line?
7. The narrator gives the details of Salvatore's rejection in indirect speech. What is the effect of this style?
8. The narrator compares Salvatore to a dog more than once. Find these comparisons, and explain why they do not present a negative image of Salvatore.
9. The narrator describes Salvatore's eyes several times. What do you gather from these descriptions? Why do you think the narrator includes them?
10. Why do you think the narrator includes two descriptions of Salvatore caring for children: his younger brothers and his two sons?

# Responding to the Story

1. What sort of character is the narrator? How would you describe the narrator's personality?
2. What sort of person is Salvatore? How would you describe his personality?
3. Only Salvatore and his wife, Assunta, are given names. None of the other characters are named. Does this anonymity seem appropriate? Why or why not?
4. In the first line and the closing paragraph, the narrator directly speaks to the reader. What is the effect of this technique?
5. The narrative voice seems reliable. It even creates an air of authority. How is this effect achieved?
6. Why does the narrator include the response of "the foreigners who came down to bathe" (line 112)? How is their attitude ironic?
7. In the final paragraph, the narrator tells us what he wanted to accomplish in his story. Does he succeed in attaining his stated aim? Why or why not?
8. Were you surprised that the narrator presented Salvatore as the epitome of goodness? Why or why not?
9. Can such an ordinary and simple human being as Salvatore actually be the true "hero"?
10. Could Salvatore have told his own story? Why or why not?

# Unit Review

When analyzing narration (narrator and narrative point of view) be sure to follow these guidelines:

- Identify the point of view—first or third person.

- For a first-person narrator, determine the role—participant or observer.

- Decide how reliable the first-person narrator is and identify inconsistencies or misrepresentations in the telling of the story.

- For a third-person narrator, determine the point of view—omniscient, limited omniscient, or objective.

- Decide if the point of view remains consistent, identify any shifts, and think about the effect they have on the story.

- Identify any irony created by the point of view, and think about its impact.

- Think about the persona of the narrative voice, and find details to support the conclusions you draw.

- Determine how the narrator thinks or feels about the characters in the story by analyzing the narrative tone(s).

- Decide how the choice of narrative voice and point of view helps the author accomplish his or her purpose.

- Think about the effect a change in point of view would have on the story.

# Unit 4

## Setting: Background and Contexts

*Nothing can happen nowhere. The locale of the happening always colours the happening, and often, to a degree, shapes it.*

ELIZABETH BOWEN

**Setting** refers not only to the location of the story, but also to the time and period in which it takes place. It provides the *where* and *when* of the story. Setting determines the range of possibilities in the short story: what can possibly happen, what is possible for the character(s) to do, feel and think, what is possible for the narrator to know and tell. Setting provides the background details necessary to establish interest and expectations about the events and the characters involved. Setting also makes the short story believable and understandable by providing the historical, political, and social contexts. The where and the when in the story, therefore, not only help the writer shape *what* happens but also influence *why* and *how* it happens.

The American novelist Henry James notes, "The place in which an event occurred...had a part to play; it needed to be made as definite as anything else." In order to determine what part the setting plays in a story, we need to consider how the setting is described, whether in great detail or as a simple statement. We need to remember that setting is not just the environment or atmosphere in which the story takes place, but also the context of the time period when the action occurs. Think of the classic beginning of fairy tales:

"Once upon a time, in a land faraway..." Here both time and space are indefinite, partly to reflect the oral tradition or the norm of these stories and partly to free the story from any temporal or spatial ties.

When the setting of a short story is vague, the author has usually kept it vague deliberately, and we need to note this decision. Similarly, in making the setting definite and specific, the author tends to draw a connection between a character and the environment, and we must pay attention to this too. As we read, we should notice whether the time and location are stated, implied, or not mentioned at all by the narrator. Setting frequently forms the "big picture" against which the story is placed, and it provides us with valuable information or sets the mood for the action to develop. To discuss setting, we divide it into different types; however, as the different kinds of setting often overlap, we tend to consider more than one of them when analyzing a story.

## Historical Setting

All stories, including **fantasies** or **science fiction**, take place in time, but some are quite specific about their time periods. For example, "Salvatore" by Somerset Maugham is set during the reign of Victor Emmanuel III of Italy. The intensity of Alice's experience in "All Is Burning" is more profound because it is set in the context of a real conflict, the violent civil war between the Tamils and Sinhalese in Sri Lanka during the last quarter of the twentieth century. Knowing something about the historical context of a story is sometimes vital to our understanding of its characters' actions and motivations. In the three stories in this unit, the historical context is crucial in helping us understand them.

"The Hockey Sweater" is set in Quebec in the late 1940s, against the background of English-French political rivalry. "The Half-Closed Eyes of the Buddha and the Slowly Setting Sun" is a contemporary story about tourism set in Nepal, which questions current relationships between developed countries in the West and developing nations in the East. Set in Italy, "War" takes place in 1918, near the end of World War I. While its setting reflects the tragic deaths of millions of young men in that conflict, it raises the moral issue of dying for one's country.

Cultural, social, political, and economic realties often underlie a short story. When we know something about the historical period in a story, we are better able to explain the attitudes, thoughts, and actions of its characters. For example, we are more sympathetic to Gum-may in "Prairie Widow" when we realize that she "had come to Canada only after the immigration laws were changed" (line 148). In fact, for 24 years, she was unable to join her husband because the Canadian immigration law at that time specifically forbade Chinese men to bring their wives. In Yee's story, as in many other stories, we can understand and accept events that would be unthinkable without some insight into the historical time period of the story.

## Cultural and Social Setting

Social norms and cultural traditions and conventions vary from country to country. When we consider **cultural setting**, we take into account where in the world the story takes place, and the cultural aspects related to the characters. We also consider how a particular geographical background limits or expands the cultural setting of the story. For example, marriage is a universal custom, but an account of a wedding celebration in Canada would be quite different from one that takes place in Nigeria or the Philippines. When you read "The Immaculate Conception Photography Gallery" (page 280) and "Marriage Is a Private Affair" (page 195), notice the details given about the various wedding ceremonies depicted. Although the marriage ceremony is not the main focus in either of these stories, we can still glean facts about the rites, practices, and expectations that reflect the culture in each story.

The following examples of cultural setting all involve marriage, and in each case the historical time period is identified. Now let us read them and consider the implications of culture.

From "Salvatore": The girl Salvatore loves will not marry him because he "would never be strong enough to work like a man...and her father would never give consent" (Maugham, lines 63–65). What does this tell us about Italian culture with regard to marriage in the early 1920s? How does this aspect of setting affect Salvatore?

From "A Handful of Dates": Masood has sold his inheritance to the narrator's grandfather in order to marry three wives. "Each time he married he sold me a feddan or two" (Salih, line 71). What does this tell us about Sudanese culture with regard to marriage in the 1940s? How does the young narrator of "A Handful of Dates" respond to what his grandfather tells him?

From "Prairie Widow": "The announcement of marriage had demolished the sixteen-year-old Gum-may. She had expected that her body would ultimately be surrendered to a husband. But already?" (Yee, lines 208–210) What does this tell us about Chinese culture with regard to marriage in the 1930s? How does Gum-may's life change with her marriage?

From "The Farewell Party": "Mama, when I grow up I will marry Tara. I will sit on a white horse and wear a turban and carry a sword in my belt and I will go and marry Tara" (Desai, lines 376–377). What does this tell us about Indian culture and the marriage ceremony in the 1960s? Why does this conversation amuse Bina?

**Social setting** can also be important in a story. What sort of society does the character live in? Is it urban or rural? How important is politics or economics in the society? Is the family part of this story? Is the story set in a social institution, such as a school, a business or a hospital? How does the character fit into this society? Is the character at ease with or in conflict with the social setting?

Think about Rosaura in "The Stolen Party." Her social status as the child of a servant in a wealthy household determines the dénouement. In "Cages," Billy describes his father's daily routine in great detail and with sympathetic respect. Would we have different expectations of Billy if his father were the mine owner rather than a miner?

Wealth or lack of it also determines the characters in "The Jade Pendant." Mrs. Khoo is desperate to maintain the appearance of her wealthy status, a social setting she was born into. At the same time, Ah Soh is quietly and diligently amassing a fortune, in order to change her status in the wealth-worshipping society. A reversal of social status connected to wealth is also presented in "A Handful of Dates."

In "Prairie Widow," Gum-may struggles to define her place in the prairie community in which she finds herself. She recognizes she is an outsider, for "[t]he town was a closed circle: she spoke to no one and no one came to visit" (Yee, line 265). It is her social setting that determines her loneliness. Yet Gum-may resolutely chooses to continue in this society and to make her home there, displaying her resilient personality. It is clear then that characters are shaped by their settings, but, at the same time, they can also make an impact on their surroundings.

# Physical Setting

**Physical setting** means the immediate environment of the story, whether it is indoors or outdoors. However, it frequently refers to more than just the actual location where the action occurs; it includes natural phenomena, such as the weather, the season, the sun and the moon, or the time of day. Occasionally the physical setting is stated to establish the background for the action or characters, but often it is simply sketched in or just implied.

For instance, in the folk tale, "The Old Man and His Grandson" by Jacob and Wilhelm Grimm (page 10), no particular place or time is given for the action. Nevertheless, we are provided with sufficient details to suggest a setting. We can assume the location is a kitchen, based on the fact that the grandfather is placed behind the stove to eat; we assume a farm rather than a town house because the grandson is familiar with feeding animals and can find wood to fashion into a trough.

The physical setting can also influence a character's behaviour. For example, Salvatore's relationship to his island, his place, both defines and shapes him. His story is set outdoors among the vineyards, but especially by the sea, as the narrator makes clear:

> I suppose it had never struck him that Ischia, which he looked at every evening (it was like a fairy island in the sunset) to see what the weather would be like next day, or Vesuvius, pearly in the dawn, had anything to do with him at all; but when he ceased to have them before his eyes he realised in some dim fashion that they were as much a part of him as his hands and his feet. He was dreadfully homesick. (Maugham, lines 25–31)

When Salvatore returns from the army, he is unable to work as hard in his natural environment, and this fact costs him the woman he loves. In fact, in this story the physical setting determines the protagonist's life. The setting is effectively used to suggest tension and heighten the conflict. We see Salvatore is no longer welcome in the home of the girl he loves after he returns as an invalid as a result of his army service. He is not invited into her house, but finds her "sitting on the doorstep" where she announces she can never marry him.

Setting can have a powerful effect on the story's **atmosphere** or **mood**, as well as on the development of the plot and a character's expectations. Gummay's setting in "Prairie Widow" is the café. After her husband's death, she reflects on her life in China and in Canada. In both settings, she is searching for herself and hoping to reach Gum San, the Golden Mountain. In the end, it is in the physical setting, the café, that she finds the meaning of her life as an independent and capable woman:

> The pieces of life she had gathered along the road to Gum San made best sense here, within the four walls of this café. She had finally arrived at a place she understood. (Yee, lines 331–333)

Clearly, the physical setting can be more than a background component; it can play a role of its own in the development of plot and characters. For example, in "A Handful of Dates," the actual physical setting of the story, the land, is transferred from Masood to the narrator's grandfather. The grandfather expresses scorn for Masood, who cannot even hold onto the land that "fell into his lap." Masood's failure in the grandfather's eyes lies in his inability to retain property, his inheritance.

Do you see it stretching out from the edge of the desert up to the Nile bank? A hundred feddans. Do you see all those date palms? And those trees — *sant*, acacia, and *sayal*? All this fell into Masood's lap, was inherited by him from his father. (Salih, lines 47–50)

The transfer of this land is the crux of this story, for it seems Masood is ruled by his emotions, by love—for women, for the dates and for this fertile land, but not by money. The grandfather, on the other hand, understands commerce and exploits the land that he possesses. These attitudes toward the physical environment influence the protagonist's behaviour and create one of his strongest childhood memories. They also suggest a crucial question: can we truly own that which we love?

## Emotional or Psychological Setting

In each of the examples above, we can see how the physical setting is used to imply and to intensify the conflict or even to influence a character's behaviour. The author can use setting to establish or reveal the personality of a character in a story. This means the setting is not simply physical, but can also be considered **emotional or psychological**. In "Cages," Billy's father hopes his son can escape going down the mines because he is intelligent and does well in school. In the end, though, because Billy feels commitment to his brother, he finds himself in a different cage from the one that carries the miners up and down the shaft each day. In fact, Billy finds himself confined in a series of actual cages (the mine elevator, the jail), each of which restricts and frustrates him, though he finally realizes his psychological "cage" is love and family obligation and this he enters willingly.

A garden party on a moonless night is the setting for "The Farewell Party." The actual darkness of the physical setting enables Bina and Raman to "hide" from their guests and to keep their true feelings unknown. However, Raman also psychologically places his party guests in this setting:

Submerged in grass, in dark, in night and chatter, clatter of ice in glass, teeth on biscuit, teeth on teeth. Enamel and gold. All awash, all soaked in night. (Desai, lines 195–197)

Only at the end, after most guests have left, do Bina and Raman relax as they sit in the light of the veranda with their friends:...the party now truly began. Cane chairs were dragged out of the veranda onto the lawn, placed in a ring next to the flowering Queen of the Night which shook out flounces and frills of white scent with every rustle of night breeze. (Desai, lines 411–414)

Obviously the light and the darkness are no longer simply part of the physical environment; here, they cast emotional and psychological shadows on the mood of the characters as well.

In "Look Out" there is much description of the moon, its eclipse, and its appearance in the sky. The moon has long been connected with emotionally turbulent moods (think of the word *lunatic*). The author even draws a direct connection between the moon and the sister-in-law's "half-crazy" behaviour by stating: "The moon made her come out from inside herself where she was locked away.... The moon made her come out from behind that dead smile and talk her head off" (lines 9–13).

Later in the story, the moon and the promise of rain reflect the psychological state of the protagonist and allow us to experience her mood:

> The wind died down. Suddenly there was no wind at all. Not so much as would stir up a leaf. A great drop of rain fell *plop* against her cheek. She put her hand up to her cheek and took it away wet.
>
> "It's going to rain!" she said, looking at her hand as though she had made a wonderful discovery. (Mais, lines 226–230)

Through his ingenious use of the physical setting, Roger Mais creates trust for the linesman who predicted the rain, and foreshadows the tears the young woman will shed in the safety of her own room that night. In this story, the physical setting is **symbolic** (see Unit 5), as it represents the emotional state of the protagonist.

In "All Is Burning," the location is a small village in Sri Lanka, but fear pervades the setting. Think of how the isolated village in the forest is so vulnerable when the troops arrive. In this story the night-time is also significant because the darkness intensifies the fear that Alice feels as she searches for the body of Sena. Jean Arasanayagam portrays with striking sensory details the landscape through which Alice searches, but all the **imagery** (see Unit 5) reflects the terrifying violence that has just occurred: "the thick blue-black shadows that lay like welts on the earth"; "chill tremors of the wind"; "reddened contusions that bruised the clouds." These are but a few examples of how this physical setting has been transformed into a place of fear and threat.

In this story we also see an ironic contrast between the lush and beautiful scenery in the background and the death and destruction in the foreground:

> They had to lead to the deathspot. Through the trees—wild guava, hard-shelled green belly fruit and straggling palms. A cluster of thambili nestled among some of the thicker fronds, a pale orange. (Arasanayagam, lines 83–86)

As all stories happen in space and time, setting is essential even if the author leaves it unidentified. In some stories the setting is vital for establishing plot and character, and in others, the setting is itself the subject. In a few stories, notably "The Half-Closed Eyes of the Buddha and the Slowly Setting Sun," the setting is not only the subject but is treated as a character in the story.

In each of the stories in this unit, the setting is a crucial component.

# The Hockey Sweater

Roch Carrier (Canada) 1937–

*(translated from French by Sheila Fischman)*

## About the Author

*Born in Quebec in 1937, Roch Carrier received a B.A. in French literature from L'Université de Montréal, where he also took an M.A. in 1961. He went to the University of Paris to prepare his doctoral dissertation from 1961 to 1964. He held teaching positions at College Militaire Royal de Saint-Jean, Quebec and at L'Université de Montréal before becoming secretary-general of the Théatre du Nouveau Monde in 1970. In 1975 he decided to leave the theatre and return to teaching and writing. Carrier first earned recognition with a trilogy of novels (La Guerre, Yes Sir!; Floralie, Where Are You?; and Is It the Sun, Philibert?), which were published from 1970 to 1972. Since then, he has become an award-winning author with nearly two dozen books to his credit. Carrier now lives in Montreal, Canada.*

*Considered one of the most important writers in Canada, Roch Carrier is also one of the most widely read Quebecois authors in North America and Europe. Although well known for his novels and plays, Carrier has also written many short stories for both children and adults. One dominant theme in his work is the misunderstandings between French-speaking and English-speaking Canadians. He describes himself as an author who writes to discover rather than to display what he knows and whose style and point of view do not come from literature but from the life of his native village of Sainte-Justine-de-Dorchester, Quebec.*

## About the Story

*"The Hockey Sweater" has been published many times, but it first appeared in print in a collection of short stories by Roch Carrier entitled* The Hockey Sweater and

Other Stories. *This story takes place in a small Quebec town in the late 1940s. It reflects the political and social tensions of its setting, and it includes a number of references to the Catholic Church, which at that time had as much power as the government in Quebec.*

*Roch Carrier provides many hockey facts that confirm the skating rink as the key setting in this story. The story focuses on Maurice "Rocket" Richard, one of Canada's greatest hockey players. As the story makes clear, Richard played for the Montreal Canadiens and wore number 9 on his sweater. Among the issues raised by this story are the role of "heroism" and the degree to which one can imaginatively "live in three places."*

*The story refers to Eaton's, once Canada's largest retail chain. The company headquarters were in Toronto, which made this company "English" in the eyes of those in the boy's town. Its catalogue was mailed to Canadian homes each year and people made purchases by mail.*

The winters of my childhood were long, long seasons. We lived in three places—the school, the church and the skating-rink—but our real life was on the skating-rink. Real battles were won on the skating-rink. Real strength appeared on the skating-rink. The real leaders showed themselves
5 on the skating-rink. School was a sort of punishment. Parents always want to punish children and school is their most natural way of punishing us. However, school was also a quiet place where we could prepare for the next hockey game, lay out our next strategies. As for church, we found there the tranquility of God: there we forgot school and dreamed about the next
10 hockey game. Through our daydreams it might happen that we would recite a prayer: we would ask God to help us play as well as Maurice Richard.

We all wore the same uniform as he, the red, white and blue uniform of the Montreal Canadiens, the best hockey team in the world; we all combed
15 our hair in the same style as Maurice Richard, and to keep it in place we used a sort of glue—a great deal of glue. We laced our skates like Maurice Richard, we taped our sticks like Maurice Richard. We cut all his pictures out of the papers. Truly, we knew everything about him.

On the ice, when the referee blew his whistle the two teams would rush
20 at the puck; we were five Maurice Richards taking it away from five other Maurice Richards; we were ten players, all of us wearing with the same blazing enthusiasm the uniform of the Montreal Canadiens. On our backs, we all wore the famous number 9.

One day, my Montreal Canadiens sweater had become too small; then
25 it got torn and had holes in it. My mother said: "If you wear that old

sweater people are going to think we're poor!" Then she did what she did whenever we needed new clothes. She started to leaf through the catalogue the Eaton company sent us in the mail every year. My mother was proud. She didn't want to buy our clothes at the general store; the only things that
30 were good enough for us were the latest styles from Eaton's catalogue. My mother didn't like the order forms included with the catalogue; they were written in English and she didn't understand a word of it. To order my hockey sweater, she did as she usually did; she took out her writing paper and wrote in her gentle schoolteacher's hand: "Cher Monsieur Eaton,
35 Would you be kind enough to send me a Canadiens' sweater for my son who is ten years old and a little too tall for his age and Docteur Robitaille thinks he's a little too thin? I'm sending you three dollars and please send me what's left if there's anything left. I hope your wrapping will be better than last time."
40   Monsieur Eaton was quick to answer my mother's letter. Two weeks later we received the sweater. That day I had one of the greatest disappointments of my life! I would even say that on that day I experienced a very great sorrow. Instead of the red, white and blue Montreal Canadiens sweater, Monsieur Eaton had sent us a blue and white sweater with a
45 maple leaf on the front—the sweater of the Toronto Maple Leafs. I'd always worn the red, white and blue Montreal Canadiens sweater; all my friends wore the red, white and blue sweater; never had anyone in my village ever worn the Toronto sweater, never had we even seen a Toronto Maple Leafs sweater. Besides, the Toronto team was regularly trounced by
50 the triumphant Canadiens. With tears in my eyes, I found the strength to say:
  "I'll never wear that uniform."
  "My boy, first you're going to try it on! If you make up your mind about things before you try, my boy, you won't go very far in this life."
55   My mother had pulled the blue and white Toronto Maple Leafs sweater over my shoulders and already my arms were inside the sleeves. She pulled the sweater down and carefully smoothed all the creases in the abominable maple leaf on which, right in the middle of my chest, were written the words "Toronto Maple Leafs." I wept.
60   "I'll never wear it."
  "Why not? This sweater fits you...like a glove."
  "Maurice Richard would never put it on his back."
  "You aren't Maurice Richard. Anyway, it isn't what's on your back that counts, it's what you've got inside your head."
65   "You'll never put it in my head to wear a Toronto Maple Leafs sweater."

My mother sighed in despair and explained to me:

"If you don't keep this sweater which fits you perfectly I'll have to write to Monsieur Eaton and explain that you don't want to wear the Toronto sweater. Monsieur Eaton's an *Anglais*; he'll be insulted because he likes the Maple Leafs. And if he's insulted do you think he'll be in a hurry to answer us? Spring will be here and you won't have played a single game, just because you didn't want to wear that perfectly nice blue sweater."

So I was obliged to wear the Maple Leafs sweater. When I arrived on the rink, all the Maurice Richards in red, white and blue came up, one by one, to take a look. When the referee blew his whistle I went to take my usual position. The captain came and warned me I'd be better to stay on the forward line. A few minutes later the second line was called; I jumped onto the ice. The Maple Leafs sweater weighed on my shoulders like a mountain. The captain came and told me to wait; he'd need me later, on defense. By the third period I still hadn't played; one of the defensemen was hit in the nose with a stick and it was bleeding. I jumped on the ice: my moment had come! The referee blew his whistle; he gave me a penalty. He claimed I'd jumped on the ice when there were already five players. That was too much! It was unfair! It was persecution! It was because of my blue sweater! I struck my stick against the ice so hard it broke. Relieved, I bent down to pick up the debris. As I straightened up I saw the young vicar on skates, before me.

"My child," he said, "just because you're wearing a new Toronto Maple Leafs sweater unlike the others, it doesn't mean you're going to make the laws around here. A proper young man doesn't lose his temper. Now take off your skates and go to the church and ask God to forgive you."

Wearing my Maple Leafs sweater I went to church, where I prayed to God; I asked him to send, as quickly as possible, moths that would eat up my Toronto Maple Leafs sweater.

(1979)

*[handwritten annotation: insect/bug that eats clothes]*

## Following the Story

1. What are the team colours of the Montreal Canadiens and the Toronto Maple Leafs?
2. Excluding the goalkeeper, how many players may a team have on the ice at one time?
3. What do we learn about Maurice Richard?
4. What details does the boy provide to establish his family background?

5. Decide what these details tell you about the boy's family life.
6. Find references that show how important the Catholic Church is in this small town in Quebec.
7. What historical facts, apart from those related to hockey, can you find in this story?
8. How do the facts you located for question 7 establish the source of conflict in the story?
9. What reasons does the mother give to support her claim that she can't return the sweater?
10. Can the setting in this story be considered symbolic? Why or why not?

## Responding to the Story

1. This is a first-person narration. What sort of character is the young boy? Support your answer with details from the story.
2. What sort of characters are the mother and the young vicar? Support your answer with details from the story.
3. How would this story be changed if it were narrated from a different point of view: the mother's (limited), the vicar's (objective), or an omniscient third-person?
4. "We lived in three places—the school, the church and the skating rink." Explain how this statement provides the setting for this story.
5. Part of this boy's culture is hero-worship, in his case worship of Maurice Richard. Is hero-worship a good thing? Why or why not?
6. The conflict in this story expresses the tension between French and English Canada. The rivalry between the two professional hockey teams symbolically represents that tension. How does the narrator build the conflict to make you aware of this underlying political tension?
7. Is such intense rivalry between any sports teams socially valuable? Why or why not?
8. The climax of the story occurs when the narrator exclaims, "It was unfair! It was persecution! It was because of my blue sweater!" (line 84) What has happened? Is he correct in his opinion?
9. Can a sport actually provide the setting for "real life, real battles, real strength and real leaders"?
10. How does this story reflect its setting; how is this story about its setting?

# The Half-Closed Eyes of the Buddha and the Slowly Setting Sun

Shankar Lamichhane (Nepal) 1928–1975

*(translated from Nepali by Michael James Hutt)*

## About the Author

*Born in Kathmandu, the capital of Nepal, Shankar Lamichhane spent much of his early childhood in Varanasi, a city in Uttar Pradesh, India, where his uncle lived. As an adult, he returned to Nepal, and worked in its capital city, Kathmandu, for government and cultural agencies. He was able to pursue his real passion—writing—only part time. He published a number of short stories and essays. Devastated by an anonymous accusation of plagiarism, he stopped writing completely and became the manager of a handicrafts store in Kathmandu. He died at the age of 48.*

*Acclaimed as one of Nepal's foremost essayists, Lamichhane writes in his native language, Nepali. His writing is noted for his unrestrained passion for his country and people, lucid style, and lyrical language. His writings reflect his extensive knowledge of Nepalese history and of both Buddhist and Hindu theology and mythology, which together shape Nepalese culture. His great contributions to Nepalese literature are best exemplified by his stories about "the pulse of our reality," written in a unique style.*

## About the Story

*"The Half-Closed Eyes of the Buddha and the Slowly Setting Sun" was published in 1991 in an anthology entitled* Himalayan Voice: An Introduction to Modern Nepali Literature. *This story is very unusual because it is presented in the form of dialogue between the two narrators. However, the first narrator, the Western tourist, does not listen to the discourse of the second narrator, the Nepali tour guide. The story is set in and around Kathmandu, the capital of Nepal. The setting of Nepal is actually the subject of this story.*

*This story also refers to figures and rites in both Hindu and Buddhist theology and mythology. Ironically, it is the Western guest, not the Nepali guide, who sees himself as the expert of this knowledge as he claims, "I could take you along your ancient ways."*

## Terms Appearing in the Story

**Dakota** an airplane in commercial use between the 1940s and 1970s

**the Four Passes** the translation of Char Bhanjyang, the name of the valley in which Kathmandu, the capital of Nepal is located
**Purānas** Sanskrit word meaning ancient books
**Swyamhbūnāth** a hill near Kathmandu and a religious site
**Manjushrī** literally holy man; according to myth he drained the lake in the valley of Kathmandu by cutting through the mountains with his sword
**Chobhār** a religious site
**Kāsthamandapa** a temple, oldest building in Kathmandu
*raksi* Nepali alcoholic drink
**Newārī** ethnic group living in Nepal
**mo-mo** Tibetan meat dumpling
*stūpa* a Buddhist temple
**Ādināth** a title given to Shiva, meaning first lord
**Shiva** with Brahma and Vishnu, one of the Hindu trinity of gods
**prayer wheel** icon of a chariot wheel, signifying dharma (ethics)
*Om mani padme hum* religious chant in Sanskrit, meaning "hail to the jewel in the lotus"
**Aryan eightfold path** from a sermon by Buddha, a guide to living a good life and achieving enlightenment

Oh guide, you do not, you cannot understand the joy we Westerners feel when we first set foot upon the soil of your country!

As the Dakota° crosses the Four Passes,° we see this green valley with its geometric fields, its earthen houses of red, yellow, and white. The scent of
5　soil and mountains is in the air, and there's an age-old peacefulness in the atmosphere. You were born amongst all of this, and so perhaps you feel that the embrace of these blue hills' outspread arms confines you. But we live in the plains or beside the sea. Our vision founders on an horizon of land or sea, and so we know the affection with which the breast of these
10　hills forever clings to your sight. You have never had to suffer the feeling of insignificance that is caused by a vast distance. Perhaps we are always adrift in vastness, my friend; perhaps that is why this, your enclosure, appeals to us! Has it ever occurred to you that the half-closed eyes of the Buddha seem to welcome you, even at the airport? It is as if one acquires
15　a calmness, as if one is returning once more to a resting place.

You have always known only how to give to the West. You've given us religion and the Purānas,° images of brass and ornaments of ivory, manuscripts of palm leaves and inscriptions on copperplate. You gave us a civilization and its wisdom and garlands of jasmine flowers around our
20　necks. You have continued in your giving, ignorant of what others call

"taking," innocent of the notion of ownership. The very word *indulgence* is unknown to you. My friend, I know your history. Before I came here I spent several years in our libraries, leafing through the pages of your priceless volumes. You are a guide who will lead me down the streets and alleyways
25  of the present, but I could take you along your ancient ways. Even now I can see it clearly: the valley is filled with water, and a lotus flower blooms where Swyambhūnāth° now stands. Manjushrī° strikes with his sword at Chobhār.° I see monks and nuns receiving alms and spreading the law in the nooks and crannies of the Kāsthamandapa.° Behold the eyes of these
30  shaven-headed monks. You cannot meet their gaze! It is called the *samyak* gaze. Do you know what that means? It is perception, pure and without contamination; sight that perceives everything in its true form. I'll have just one more drink before dinner....

You live in a house like a temple, but you are unaware of its beauty, its
35  enchantment. In these wooden images, these multifarious ornamentations, these many styles, there is the flowing music of a chisel in the hands of an artist. Do you not feel it? Tell me about those happy, prosperous young artists working in the fields all day and creating beautiful images of their personal deities in their spare time, who are now covered by the dusts
40  of the past.

Once, an artist was adding the finishing touches to a wooden image when his fair, tiny wife came by, carrying her baby on her back, and poured him *raksi*° from a jug. The foam bubbled over and congealed. Is it true that it was that foam that inspired the artist to construct a roof of
45  tiles? Oh, your land is truly great, this country where so many different cultures found their home. Aryans, non-Aryans, Hindus, and Buddhists all came and obtained a rebirth here. It must be the effect of your country's soil, my friend; it was the soil that enabled all these races to flourish together here. Come, I'll drink one more small one, it's not dinnertime
50  yet....

I am greatly indebted to you for you have served me both Nepali and Newārī° food. Ah, *mo-mos*!...Just picture the scene: it is winter and an old man sits in the upper story of his house, lit only by the fire. Perhaps the smoke is filling the room like fog from floor to ceiling. Perhaps he is telling
55  his grandson about each and every Nepali item that Princess Bhrikutī took with her when King Amshuvarman sent her off to Tibet. The old lady smokes tobacco from a bamboo hookah, and, mindful of the old man, she carries on making fresh *mo-mos*. The son's wife puts some of them onto a brass plate, and the old man's words are garbled and obscured by his
60  mouthful. The grandson laughs, and the old man tries to swallow quickly,

so he burns his tongue and, unabashed, pours out a stream of ribald curses.... These are scenes that cannot be read in an old book in a library, and that is why I've had to come to Kathmandu and soak myself in its atmosphere, for which I'm greatly obliged to you.... Now, cheers once
65 again, to your great country, and to mine!

Oh, and another thing that is not to be found in any book is the smile on the faces of these people. It is a smile of welcome, as if our meeting were neither accidental nor our first. It's as if I was the farmer's eldest son, coming home after a long day's work in the fields, as if my labors had been
70 fruitful and I was content and at ease with my father. It's as if I have taken the world's most beautiful woman for my wife and have brought her along behind me, and my mother is smiling a welcome from the door. It's as if my sister's husband and I were the closest of friends and we, her brother and her husband, were coming along with our arms around one another,
75 singing songs of drunkenness. It's as if—I cannot explain; however much I try, I cannot describe it fully. That smile is full of wisdom; it is a smile from the soul, a smile peculiar to this place.... One more drink, to your Nepalese smile, that sweet smile!

And then there are the eyes. The eyes of the carved lattice windows, the
80 eyes painted on the door panels. The eyes on the *stūpas*,° the eyes of the people. And the eyes of the Himalaya, which peep out from the gaps between the hills like those of a neighbor's boy when he jumps up to see the peach tree in your garden. This is a land of eyes, a land guarded by the half-closed eyes of the Lord Buddha.

85 Even if all of the world's history books were destroyed today, your eyes would build a new culture; they would reassemble a civilization. My appetite for eyes is still not satiated. Tomorrow I shall go to a lonely place where there is a *stūpa* with eyes that are clear. There I want to see the pleasant lift of sunset reflected in the eyes of the Buddha. Show me beau-
90 tiful, full eyes, eyes without equal, eyes whose memory will make this journey of mine unforgettable.... Come, let's go to eat dinner.

Come, my guest; today I am to show you some eyes.

This is Chobhār hill, where you people come to see the cleft that was
95 made by Manjushrī's sword and the outflow of the Bāgmatī River. Today I'll take you up the hill where few of our guests ever go and no tourist's car can proceed. There (in your words) the dust of time has not yet covered the culture of the past. Do you see this worn old rock? A young village artist has drawn some birds on it. Nearby, he has sketched a temple, leaving out
100 any mention of the religion to which it belongs. Further up the hill, in the

middle of the village, stands the temple of Ādināth.° In the temple courtyard there is a shrine of Shiva,° several Buddha images, and many prayer
wheels,° inscribed *Om mani padme hum.*° You say it is a living example of
Nepalese tolerance and coexistence. Children play happily there, uncon-
105 cerned by the variety of their gods, religions, and philosophies. But my
guest, I will not take you there.

You have already seen much of such things, and you have understood
them and even preached them. Today I'll take you to a house where I feel
sure you will find the pulse of our reality. They are a farmer's family, prob-
110 ably owning a few fields here and there, where they work and sweat to pay
off half the proceeds to someone in the city. There is no smoke to fill their
upstairs room, they cook no *mo-mos* in their hearth, nor do they discuss
Bhrikutī's dowry in their winters. There is a child in the home, who is certainly no divine incarnation, either. Attacked by polio and born into a
115 poor farmer's household, the child is surely incapable of spreading the law
or of making any contribution to this earth. He has taken birth here in one
of his maker's strangest forms of creation. And moreover, my friend—oh,
the climb has tired you; would you like some filtered water from the
thermos flask?—my intention is not to show him to you as any kind of
120 symbol. Yesterday you were swept along by waves of emotion, inspired by
your "Black and White" whisky, and you urged me to show you eyes that
would forever remind you of your visit to Nepal. So I have brought you
here to show you eyes like that.

The child's whole body is useless; he cannot speak, move his hands,
125 chew his food, or even spit. His eyes are the only living parts of his body
and it is only his eyes that indicate that he is actually alive. I don't know
whether his eyes have the *samyak* gaze or not. I don't even understand the
term, but his face is certainly devoid of all emotion. His gaze is uninter-
ested, without resolution or expression; it is inactive and listless, unexer-
130 cised and lacking any measure of contemplation. (Perhaps I have begun
to speak unwittingly in the terms of the Aryan eightfold path,° which will
either be your influence or a virtue bestowed upon me by the child.)

My guest, these are the eyes you wanted. A living being accumulates
many capabilities in one lifetime. It feels happy and it smiles; it feels sad
135 and it weeps. If it feels cold, it seeks warmth, and if it is hungry, it prepares
food to eat. It seeks to learn what it doesn't already know, and it succeeds
or it fails. It has many experiences, some bitter, some sweet, and these it
relates when company, occasion, and mood seem suited. How common-
place all of these actions are! My guest, yesterday you said that we Eastern
140 peoples were always making contributions to the West, did you not? (Shall

I give you some water? Are you out of breath?) Here is a child who can nei-ther give nor take anything at all. Just put yourself in his position for a moment. You want your finger to do something, but your finger refuses. You want to speak, but speech will not come to you. Every vein, nerve, and
145 bone is powerless to heed the commands of your brain, and yet...you are alive. I know that this disease occurs in your country, too. But the ability to endure it and to maintain a total indifference in the eyes, even, perhaps, to foster the *samyak* gaze, this capacity for remaining speechless, inactive, powerless, and immobile, and yet to survive without complaint...this can
150 surely only be found in an Easterner!

Come, come closer. I have lied to his parents; I have told them that you are a doctor. Look...their faith in you shows in their eyes. There is intimacy, kindliness, and gratitude in their eyes, as if your coming here were preor-dained. That smile you described is on their faces, as if you were their
155 eldest son who has brought a life-restoring remedy across the seven seas for your brother. The old peasant woman is smiling, isn't she? It's as if she's rejoicing at the birth of her first grandchild from your wife, the beauty of the world. I know that this same smile will remain on their faces as long as you are here. I know that it will be extinguished when you turn to go.
160 Once you've gone they'll sink back into the same old darkness.

The child has a sister whose body functions properly. He watches her as she crawls around, picking up everything she comes across and putting it into her mouth, knocking over the beer, overturning the cooking stone. Just for an instant, the ambition to emulate her is reflected in his eyes, but
165 then it is reabsorbed into the same old indifference. Once his mother was scolding his sister, and a light gleamed in his eyes. I couldn't tell you to which era its vision belonged, but I realized that he wanted to speak. With a gaze devoid of language, gesture, or voice, he wanted to say, "Mother, how can you appreciate what fun it is to fall over? To crawl through the
170 green dub grass and rub the skin off your knees, to shed a couple of drops of blood like smeared tears, and graze your flesh a little. To feel pain and to cry, to call out for help. That pain would be such a sweet experience. She can rub her snot or spittle into her own grazes, or pull out the thorn that has pricked her, and throw it away. Or she could pull off a scab that has
175 healed over a buried splinter of glass or spend a few days resting under her quilt. She can climb up onto the storage jar to try to pull a picture down from the wall, and when the peg slips out and the picture falls and the glass smashes with a wonderful noise, she feels a wave of fear as she real-izes her guilt. She has grown up, learning from experience the facts that
180 fire can burn her and water makes her wet, that nettles cause blisters and

beer makes her dizzy. That if she falls she might be hurt or break a bone, that if something else falls it will probably break. That if someone dies, she is able to weep, and if someone laughs, she can laugh right back; if someone makes fun of her, she can strike them, and if someone steals from
185 her, she can steal from them. My sister, who learns and remembers each and every new word she hears, is the result of the self-sacrificing practice of thousands of years of human language. She embodies a history, a tradition, and a culture, and it is in her very ability to speak that the future is born. But not in one like me, who cannot even move his lips. In my body,
190 in its strength and gestures, an unbroken cycle of historical and human development has come to its conclusion. A long labor, a chain of events, a lengthy endeavor, and an endlessness are all at an end. The future ends and is broken abruptly."

And these are the eyes, my guest, that look at you but see nothing; this
195 is the gaze that is incapable of self-manifestation. This is beauty that is complete and has no other expression.

These are eyes surrounded by mountains; their lashes are rows of fields where rice ripens in the rains and wheat ripens in the winter. These are the eyes that welcome you, and these are eyes that build. And in these eyes
200 hides the end of life. Look! They are just as beautiful as the setting sun's reflection in the eyes of the Buddha!

(1991)

## Following the Story

1   What physical aspects of the setting does the Western tourist focus on?
2.  What physical aspects of the setting does the Nepalese guide show to the Western tourist?
3.  What cultural aspects of the setting does the Westerner focus on?
4.  What cultural aspects of the setting does the Nepalese guide show to the Western tourist?
5.  What social aspects of the setting does Westerner focus on?
6.  What social aspects of the setting does the Nepalese guide show to the Western tourist? Notice that the Nepalese narrator addresses the Westerner as "guest."
7.  What sorts of smiles greet the Western tourist in the seventh paragraph?
8.  What sorts of smiles does the Nepalese guide say the Western tourist receives?
9.  What does the Westerner claim to see in the "eyes" of Nepal?

10. How does the Nepali guide describe the expressions in the eyes that look at the Western tourist?

## Responding to the Story

1. What sort of character is the Westerner? Use details in the story to support your answer.
2. How does the Westerner think of the Nepalese culture and people?
3. What sort of character is the Nepali? Use details in the story to support your answer.
4. What does the guide think of Westerners?
5. The plot development in the first half of this story contains a series of repetitions as the Westerner drinks while waiting for dinner. What is the implication of the repeated references to alcohol?
6. The plot development in the second half of this story mirrors the first for it also contains a series of repetitions as the Nepali offers the Westerner bottled water. What is the implication of this repetition?
7. The two opposing sides in this story are clear, but what is the source of the conflict? How does the conflict relate to the setting?
8. The Westerner holds a romantic vision of Nepal based on a study of its history, culture, and religion. What attitudes are presented in this story toward this sort of education?
9. What does the Nepalese guide achieve by presenting the economic, cultural, and spiritual realities of Nepal through the paralyzed child?
10. The author intends to provoke the reader with this story. Why does he want to do that? Is he successful? Why or why not?

# War

## Luigi Pirandello (Italy) 1867–1936

*(translated from Italian by Michele Pettinati)*

### About the Author

*Born in Agrigento, Sicily, Luigi Pirandello attended the University of Palermo and the University of Rome from 1886 to 1889 and gained his doctorate in philology at the University of Bonn in Germany. While writing, he also earned his living by teaching Italian at a teacher's college in Rome from 1897 to 1922. His first significant literary*

*works were short stories published in periodicals. He wrote over 50 plays, which firmly
established his literary reputation; his novels and poetry also form an important part
of his legacy. He was awarded the Nobel Prize for Literature in 1934, two years before
his death in Rome.*

*One of the most important dramatists of the 20th century, Luigi Pirandello pur-
sued tirelessly in his plays, short stories, novels, and poems the theme of exploring the
tightly closed world of the ever-changing human personality. He began as a realistic
writer and later focused his writing on the themes of psychology and the exploration
of his characters' subconscious. Pirandello commented in 1920: "My art is full of
bitter compassion for all those who deceive themselves, but this compassion cannot
fail to be followed by the ferocious derision of destiny which condemns man to deception."*

## About the Story

*"War" was published in English in* Better Think Twice about It and Other Stories.
*Written in 1918, this story reflects on the impact of World War I (1914–1918). This
was the first war in history that involved not simply armies and navies, but whole
nations, as industrial production and civilian support for the war effort became crucial. The two sides (originally the Triple Entente of Britain, France, and Russia versus
the Triple Alliance of Germany, Austria-Hungary, and Turkey) were evenly matched
and had long been preparing for the conflict. Italy entered the war in 1915 sup-
porting the Triple Entente. However, because of the colonialist domination of much of
the world by the European countries involved, the conflict quickly became global. The
war caused death and destruction on an unprecedented scale.*

*As the passengers discuss the war, they focus on universal ideas—patriotism,
valour, suffering, and death—with which everyone can identify. In this sense, the
story goes beyond its setting of the train carriage and represents the human condition. Pirandello's work often explores individual loneliness and isolation, and this
short story presents characters who not only appear stranded in the darkened train
carriage, but are also exhausted because of lack of sleep and the strain of living
through three years of war. Pirandello is best known for his work as a playwright, and
this story could almost be a scene from a play. For the most part this story is presented
as a debate among the passengers on the train.*

    The passengers who had left Rome by the night express had had to stop
until dawn at the small station of Fabriano in order to continue their
journey by the small old-fashioned local joining the main line with
Sulmona.

5    At dawn, in a stuffy and smoky second-class carriage in which five
people had already spent the night, a bulky woman in deep mourning was

hoisted in—almost like a shapeless bundle. Behind her, puffing and moaning, followed her husband—a tiny man, thin and weakly, his face death-white, his eyes small and bright and looking shy and uneasy.

10   Having at last taken a seat he politely thanked the passengers who had helped his wife and who had made room for her; then he turned round to the woman trying to pull down the collar of her coat, and politely inquired:

"Are you all right, dear?"

The wife, instead of answering, pulled up her collar again to her eyes,
15  so as to hide her face.

"Nasty world," muttered the husband with a sad smile.

And he felt it his duty to explain to his traveling companions that the poor woman was to be pitied, for the war was taking away from her only son, a boy of twenty to whom both had devoted their entire life, even
20  breaking up their home at Sulmona to follow him to Rome, where he had to go as a student, then allowing him to volunteer for war with an assurance, however, that at least for six months he would not be sent to the front and now, all of a sudden, receiving a wire saying that he was due to leave in three days' time and asking them to go and see him off.

25   The woman under the big coat was twisting and wriggling, at times growling like a wild animal, feeling certain that all those explanations would not have aroused even a shadow of sympathy from those people who—most likely—were in the same plight as herself. One of them, who had been listening with particular attention, said:

30  "You should thank God that your son is only leaving now for the front. Mine has been sent there the first day of the war. He has already come back twice wounded and been sent back again to the front."

"What about me? I have two sons and three nephews at the front," said another passenger.

35  "Maybe, but in our case it is our *only* son," ventured the husband.

"What difference can it make? You may spoil your only son with excessive attentions, but you cannot love him more than you would all your other children if you had any. Paternal love is not like bread that can be broken into pieces and split amongst the children in equal shares. A father
40  gives *all* his love to each one of his children without discrimination, whether it be one or ten, and if I am suffering now for my two sons, I am not suffering half for each of them but double..."

"True...true..." sighed the embarrassed husband, "but suppose (of course we all hope it will never be your case) a father has two sons at
45  the front and he loses one of them, there is still one left to console him...while..."

"Yes," answered the other, getting cross, "a son left to console him but also a son left for whom he must survive, while in the case of the father of an only son if the son dies the father can die too and put an end to his dis-
50 tress. Which of the two positions is the worse? Don't you see how my case would be worse than yours?"

"Nonsense," interrupted another traveler, a fat, red-faced man with bloodshot eyes of the palest gray.

He was panting. From his bulging eyes seemed to spurt inner violence
55 of an uncontrolled vitality which his weakened body could hardly contain.

"Nonsense," he repeated, trying to cover his mouth with his hand so as to hide the two missing front teeth. "Nonsense. Do we give life to our children for our own benefit?"

The other travelers stared at him in distress. The one who had had his
60 son at the front since the first day of the war sighed: "You are right. Our children do not belong to us, they belong to the Country...."

"Bosh," retorted the fat traveler. "Do we think of the Country when we give life to our children? Our sons are born because...well, because they must be born and when they come to life they take our own life with them.
65 This is the truth. We belong to them but they never belong to us. And when they reach twenty they are exactly what we were at their age. We too had a father and mother, but there were so many other things as well...girls, cigarettes, illusions, new ties...and the Country, of course, whose call we would have answered—when we were twenty—even if father and mother
70 had said no. Now at our age, the love of our Country is still great, of course, but stronger than it is the love for our children. Is there any one of us here who wouldn't gladly take his son's place at the front if he could?"

There was a silence all around, everybody nodding as to approve.

"Why then," continued the fat man, "shouldn't we consider the feelings
75 of our children when they are twenty? Isn't it natural that at their age they should consider the love for their Country (I am speaking of decent boys, of course) even greater than the love for us? Isn't it natural that it should be so, as after all they must look upon us as upon old boys who cannot move any more and must stay at home? If Country exists, if Country is a
80 natural necessity, like bread, of which each of us must eat in order not to die of hunger, somebody must go to defend it. And our sons go, when they are twenty, and they don't want tears, because if they die, they die inflamed and happy (I am speaking, of course, of decent boys). Now, if one dies young and happy, without having the ugly sides of life, the boredom
85 of it, the pettiness, the bitterness of disillusion...what more can we ask for him? Everyone should stop crying; everyone should laugh, as I do...or at

least thank God—as I do—because my son, before dying, sent me a message saying that he was dying satisfied at having ended his life in the best way he could have wished. That is why, as you see, I do not even wear 90 mourning..."

He shook his light fawn coat as to show it; his livid lip over his missing teeth was trembling, his eyes were watery and motionless, and soon after he ended with a shrill laugh which might well have been a sob.

"Quite so...quite so..." agreed the others.

95 The woman who, bundled in a corner under her coat, had been sitting and listening had—for the last three months—tried to find in the words of her husband and her friends something to console her in her deep sorrow, something that might show her how a mother should resign herself to send her son not even to death but to a probably dangerous life. Yet not a word had 100 she found amongst the many which had been said...and her grief had been greater in seeing that nobody—as she thought—could share her feelings.

But now the words of the traveler amazed and almost stunned her. She suddenly realized that it wasn't the others who were wrong and could not understand her but herself who could not rise up to the same height of 105 those fathers and mothers willing to resign themselves, without crying, not only to the departure of their sons but even to their death.

She lifted her head, she bent over from her corner trying to listen with great attention to the details which the fat man was giving to his companions about the way his son had fallen as a hero, for his King and his 110 Country, happy and without regrets. It seemed to her that she had stumbled into a world she had never dreamt of, a world so far unknown to her and she was so pleased to hear everyone joining in congratulating that brave father who could so stoically speak of his child's death.

Then suddenly, just as if she had heard nothing of what had been said and 115 almost as if waking up from a dream, she turned to the old man, asking him:

"Then...is your son really dead?"

Everybody stared at her. The old man, too, turned to look at her, fixing his great, bulging, horribly watery light gray eyes, deep in her face. For some little time he tried to answer, but words failed him. He looked and 120 looked at her, almost as if only then—at that silly, incongruous question— he had suddenly realized at last that his son was really dead—gone for ever—for ever. His face contracted, became horribly distorted, then he snatched in haste a handkerchief from his pocket and, to the amazement of everyone, broke into harrowing, heart-rending, uncontrollable sobs.

(1918)

## Following the Story

1. What is the geographical setting of this story? How can you tell?
2. What details are given about the physical setting in this story?
3. What is the conflict in this story?
4. How does the setting influence the plot?
5. What sorts of characters are portrayed in this story?
6. How do the characters relate to their setting? ·
7. What is the narrative point of view? How can you tell?
8. What is the atmosphere in this story? Does it change at any point?
9. What is the effect of the "fat man's" speech on the other passengers?
10. What is the "dream" from which the "bundled" woman seems to awake (line 115)?


## Responding to the Story

1. What is the effect of isolating and containing these seven people in a crowded railway carriage?
2. Why is the bundled woman certain "that all those explanations would not have aroused even a shadow of sympathy" (line 26)?
3. The characters in this story remain anonymous. Does this make their discussion and feelings impersonal? Why or why not?
4. Much of this story is narrated by showing, told through dialogue. How do you think this narrative technique relates to the conflict of the story?
5. In the debate, the passengers refer to "the Country" instead of naming Italy. Does this anonymity make the issue they debate universal? Why or why not?
6. Do you agree with this statement, "We [parents] belong to them [children] but they never belong to us" (line 65)?
7. Explain how irony is used in this story.
8. Why does the narrator call the bundled woman's question "silly, incongruous"?
9. Is there anything in the story that prepared you for the dénouement?
10. When the fat man breaks into "harrowing, heart-rending, uncontrollable sobs," what is the effect on the other passengers? What was your own response to his outburst of grief?

# Unit Review

When analyzing setting, be sure to follow these guidelines:

- Identify the setting and its type.
- Determine whether the setting is unidentified, implied, sketched, or fully described.
- Identify the historical period and look for possible effects of the social, political, or economic conditions of that time in the story.
- Identify the cultural/social setting and consider its effect on the characters and the action.
- Identify the physical setting. Is the location, the time of day, or the weather unidentified or specified? How does the physical setting affect the character and the action?
- Consider whether the narrator establishes or suggests an emotional or psychological setting. What is its effect on the character and on the reader?
- Examine the story for symbolic setting and consider its effect on the story.
- Determine whether the setting is just a backdrop or influences the development of the story.

# Unit

## Literary Devices and Techniques

*There is no story written that has any value at all, however straightforward it looks and free from doubleness, double entendre, that you'd value at all if it didn't have intimations of something more than itself.*

ROBERT FROST

To create intriguing plot, characters, and narrative voices in appropriate settings, the short story writer, like the novelist, uses a variety of literary devices and techniques. These devices add texture and depth to the story and achieve special effects through artistic use of language. Therefore, to fully understand a story we need to become sensitive to the use of these literary devices and to develop an appreciation of the craftsmanship displayed in the writer's careful choice of language.

## Figures of Speech

The most common **figures of speech** are **simile**, **metaphor**, and **personification**. In their different ways these devices all turn literal meanings of language into figurative expressions by means of comparison.

Simile is a figure of speech in which two or more objects *of different kinds* are directly compared, using the two trademark introducers "like" and "as." For example, in the sentence "David is as quiet as his mother," no simile is used because son and mother are of *the same kind*—they are both people. However, we can easily recognize the use of similes in each of the following examples:

> Della's beautiful hair fell about her, rippling and shining *like a cascade of brown waters*. (O. Henry, lines 52–53)

> "Sorry, sorry, Miss Dutta, I'm clumsy *as a bear*." (Desai, line 277)

We have no trouble identifying the similes here because objects *of different kinds* are compared by using either "like" or "as."

Metaphor seems harder to recognize, as it involves an *indirect and implied comparison* that imaginatively identifies one object with another because of one or more features. Without any trademark phrase or special signal, a metaphor could take the form of a verb:

> [N]ow these five years had *telescoped* (Desai, line 58)

> Miss Dutta...raised herself on her toes to *bray* something into his ear. (Desai, line 301)

Here, in the first example, the author draws a direct comparison between the mental effect of time passing and the way a telescope becomes shorter. In the second sentence she compares the unpleasant voice of Miss Dutta, a gossipy busybody, to that of a donkey simply by using "bray" metaphorically.

A metaphor may also take the form of a noun phrase, as in *"the worm of* a husband" (Yee, line 15). Or it could appear as a clause, for example: "but they [lights on the veranda] did very little to light the lawn *which was vast, a still lake of inky grass*" (Desai, line 13). As a rule, identifying metaphor requires greater sensitivity and richer imagination on the part of the reader. Like simile, though, metaphor is used to bring concrete and familiar **images** to our mind in a new and often unusual manner, appealing to our imagination and tapping our existent reservoir of knowledge.

Personification, as the word suggests, compares an inhuman or inanimate object to a human being by granting it human form, character, or features. When we *personify* we make an implicit comparison. Among the authors we have studied so far, Jean Arasanayagam is an expert in using personification to add to the appeal of her stories. Leafing through "All Is Burning," we may spot cases of personification, such as "There would be...that rank smell of bodies through whose pores *fear had breathed*" (line 32) and "*The darkness had moved* like an open door to admit them" (line 68). When fear and darkness are endowed with life and human qualities, Arasanayagam's microcosmic picture of the deadly civil war between the Tamils and the Sinhalese that kills 250 young men on one single night becomes chillingly unforgettable.

# Images and Imagery

These figures of speech produce vivid pictures in our mind, especially when they are used in a cluster as we see in "All Is Burning": "She felt the man's breath touch the palm of her hand *like a slight vapour* [simile], *a cobweb of mist* [metaphor] *that faintly wreathed round her fingers* [personification]" (lines 208–210). Through concrete, pictorial, and sensory details, images or **imagery** (a collection of images) adds to the interest of the story and ultimately enriches our reading experience. Therefore, a full appreciation of imagery in a short story forms an essential key to a good understanding of the story and its author's message.

# Allusion

**Allusion** is a common literary device that the writer uses to appeal to the reader by referring to a well-known historical or cultural figure, work, or event. When using allusions, a writer assumes that the reader shares an established tradition and recognizes references to it. Allusions can be divided into two major categories: literary and cultural.

**Literary allusions** refer to some well-known literary figure or text in order to add to the texture and depth by association.

For example, in "The Farewell Party," Anita Desai makes two references to the well-known fairy tale "Cinderella." The first reference is made in lines 271–274, when we read, "Raman nodded and put in a few cautious words, put away his cigarettes, called a waiter to refill their glasses and *broke away before the clock struck twelve and the golden carriage turned into a pumpkin, he himself into a mouse.*"

The second allusion makes its appearance more explicitly in lines 348–349: "As if to underline *this new and Cinderella's ball-like atmosphere* of friendliness and gaiety, three pairs of neighbours now swept in...." In both cases attempts are made to draw on the reader's knowledge of the Cinderella story in order to compare the party in question to that in the popular fairy tale. Readers can see a parallel between Raman's panicky state and Cinderella's situation and a telling similarity in the fairy-tale atmosphere shared by the two parties. Thus, the use of literary allusion allows the writer to say a great deal in a few words, while generating a vivid impression for the reader.

The same comments can be made on **cultural allusions**, a blanket term that covers references to well-known historical, social, cultural, and religious events.

For example, writers of different cultural and religious backgrounds find in the Bible an inexhaustible resource of references. That is why **Biblical allusion** has become common in all kinds of literary works. "The Gift of the Magi" by

O. Henry, the first story included in this unit, contains an excellent example. As the author makes clear in the title and the last paragraph, the story hinges on an allusion to the well-known Biblical story of the magi, the three wise men who visit Jesus at the time of his birth and present him with gifts.

"Of all who give and receive gifts, such as they are wisest. Everywhere they are wisest. They are the magi" (lines 171–173). This is how O. Henry ends his "uneventful chronicle of two foolish children in a flat" with an unexpected uplifting ending. Only when the Biblical allusion that celebrates the spirit of selfless and unconditional giving is fully understood can we see Della and Jim's wisdom in "most unwisely" sacrificing for each other "the greatest treasures of their house."

In addition to the allusions to the magi and their wise gifts, the story is also interspersed with casual Biblical allusions, such as the "Queen of Sheba" and "King Solomon" in lines 47 and 49. In context, these two allusions form a parallel structure that highlights the two treasures possessed by Della and Jim with a sprinkle of O. Henry's characteristic **hyperbole** (figurative language using exaggeration). At the same time, these allusions also appeal to an audience that is assumed to share a body of knowledge.

# Irony

As a literary device, irony can be divided into three types: **verbal irony, situational irony**, and **dramatic irony**. They all depend on *contrast* of some kind.

*Verbal irony* refers to a contrast between what is said and what is meant. While it resembles **sarcasm**, which involves harshly mocking or contemptuous language, verbal irony is usually less severe in wording, yet more thought-provoking in effect.

*Situational irony* lies in a contrast between what is intended and what is accomplished. It is a literary device loved by many short story writers, for so much can be achieved, in plot, characterization, narration, and theme, when reality fails to match expectations and endeavours.

"The Americanization of Shadrach Cohen" by Bruno Lessing (pages 327–334) presents an interesting case of situational irony. Two sons, who are ashamed of their old-fashioned father, are determined to Americanize him soon after he arrives in the United States. It does not take long for them to realize, however, that "Americanization" in their father's dictionary means adhering to the old values while adapting them to the new world. When the story ends, the young men are ironically "Americanized" by the old man rather than the other way round. Hence an intriguing contrast is established between the intention and the accomplishment. Similarly, a case of situational irony, a regrettable contrast between what is intended and what is accomplished, forms the basis of the plot of "The Gift of the Magi." Also, think of the two parties described in "The Farewell Party" and "The Stolen Party." What the Ramans in one story and Rosaura in the other intend to achieve is put in sharp contrast with what they have actually achieved at the end. Situational irony is abundant in literature, just as our life is filled with it.

What is revealed in situational irony, therefore, is frequently the cosmic truth that human wishes and efforts do not always lead to the intended goals because of some uncontrollable and inexplicable factors in life. Thus it is sometimes referred to as **cosmic irony** or **irony of fate**. Shi Tiesheng, a short story writer from China, injects a strong dose of irony of fate into his story "Fate" (page 441). A tragic accident has happened to Mo Fei, a young man with a "beautiful future," and turned him into a lifetime paraplegic. It has been no one's fault; only fate is to blame. "Why why why?" Shi asks these burning, very human questions in Mo Fei's voice. "There is no why" (line 512), the same voice answers back. Is it fate, or is it what English novelist Thomas Hardy (1840–1928) calls the *unfortunate chances* that are responsible for such ironies, disappointments, and tragedies in our life? Although stories like "Fate" do not provide us with a definite answer to these questions, they make us think and wonder about some of life's profound mysteries.

*Dramatic irony* consists in a *contrast* between what a character sees or says and what the audience knows. As a literary device, it has been popular with both playwrights and fiction writers. It has also proved to be very effective both on and off stage in providing the audience/reader with palatable food for thought. For example, it is amusing for the audience to see in a **comedy** a husband flirting with the maid on stage without knowing that his wife is eavesdropping. Yet, dramatic irony is thought-provoking when a character in a **tragedy** or in a story uses words that mean one thing to him or her but another to those watching the play or reading the narrative. Like verbal and situational irony, dramatic irony helps to reveal the limitations of human knowledge and human efforts, thus heightening the value of literature.

# Symbol and Symbolism

In a literary work, a **symbol** could be a person, object, action, place, or situation *that remains itself while suggesting something else beyond itself.*

The simplest example can be found in "The Hockey Sweater" by the Canadian writer Roch Carrier (page 120). The maple leaf on his new sweater is devastating to the protagonist because it is more than a design on clothes. Rather, as the symbol for the Toronto Maple Leafs, a hockey team that is regularly trounced by the Montreal Canadiens, it symbolizes, in the boy's opinion, defeat, shame, and even betrayal. By the same token, the jade pendant (an object) in "The Jade Pendant" (page 13) is a piece of jewellery that symbolizes wealth, power, and social status. In "Prairie Widow" (page 39), Gum-may's decision to stay in the prairie and run the café on her own (an action) is symbolic of the beginning of her new life as an independent woman.

Symbols, as they appear in literary works, can be classified into two major types: **natural/conventional symbols** and **literary symbols**.

*Natural or conventional symbols* derive from nature or conventional associations that people make with various objects; they are pervasive in literature.

For example, night is a natural symbol of death whereas spring symbolizes youth and rebirth. Conventional associations attached to different objects can produce universal symbols. For instance, scales symbolize justice; a cross, Christianity; a dove, peace; the rose, beauty and love; the lion, strength and courage. Nevertheless, as conventional associations vary from culture to culture, certain symbols of this type do not carry the same meaning to people of different cultural backgrounds. To many people in the world, for example, white is the colour for weddings, as it symbolizes purity and chastity. To the Chinese and Indians, however, white is the colour for funerals as it is associated with death and ghosts. Instead of wearing white, Chinese and Indian brides are dressed in red for their wedding. Therefore, it is always advisable to have a good knowledge of the cultural background of the story when it comes to interpreting and analyzing symbols in literature.

Despite the different conventional associations in various cultures, natural or conventional symbols are mostly recognizable and understandable in their literary contexts. After all, the human race is united by the similarities we share rather than divided by our differences. That is why it is possible for readers of different cultural backgrounds to understand the symbolic meanings of fire in "All Is Burning" (page 98) and a cage in "The Cage," the second story included in this unit.

*Literary symbols* are symbols used in literary works, which the author expects the reader to be familiar with; they are not used as frequently as natural or conventional symbols. A good example can be made of the chocho vine in "The Chocho Vine" by Olive Senior (page 428). In the short story, the vine in Miss Evadney's yard functions as a symbol for her pride, her dignity, her livelihood, and her lifeline in old age. The moment the chocho vine is cut, she herself starts to tremble and wilt. If a person who has read this story says to someone who has also read the story: "gardening is now *the chocho vine* for my aging mother," that person is using a literary symbol to convey meaning.

Although such symbols work only under limited circumstances, they can be highly effective when properly used.

**Symbolism**, on the other hand, refers to *the use of symbols, especially the extensive and systematic use of symbols*, in literature. We may say in "The Cage" by Neil Bissoondath the central *symbol* is the title object "cage," and *symbolism* (the author's use of symbols) forms a very interesting aspect of the story, which portrays a young woman's struggle to be free and independent.

A symbol is similar to a metaphor only in that it is also based on an implicit or suggested comparison. However, the major differences between these two devices begin to become apparent as soon as the comparison is expanded and repeated while accumulating more associations. As Bissoondath begins his story with "For my mother, my father, not an unkind man, designed a house. For me, my father, not a kind man, designed a cage" (lines 2–4), he seems to present a metaphor, comparing a house to a cage.

This metaphorical meaning of a cage is sustained and repeated when we read a few pages later "My life became like that of the four song-birds my brother kept in bamboo cages suspended from the ceiling of his room" (lines 357–358). At this point the metaphor is intensified by the addition of the simile, through which the author draws a parallel between the protagonist and birds in cages and reinforces the central image of a cage in the story. Nonetheless, the "cage" expands beyond its mere metaphorical meaning and assumes much more profound implications when the "bird" (the young Japanese woman) not only voluntarily flies back into the "cage" after escaping from it, but also decides to decorate it with flowers for the future generations of "birds."

The cage in Bissoondath's story exemplifies how symbols and symbolism work in a short story. As a symbol, it typically appears again and again in the course of narration, calling on the reader to observe its obsessive presence and implicit significance. Normally, we cannot pinpoint the exact meanings of a symbol as we can with metaphor; hence its interpretation often requires a thorough understanding of the whole story. In this case, only when we view "the cage" in the light of what happens in the story, can we figure out what it could possibly stand for. Instead of being a simple metaphor for the father's house or for the confining patriarchal society in Japan, "the cage" most likely symbolizes the whole set of traditional Japanese values or the Japanese views on the intricate human relations in the traditional society and family.

With "the cage" thus interpreted, it becomes clear that not only the young Japanese woman, but all the other Japanese characters in the story, the father, mother, brother, and Keisuke, are also consciously or unconsciously locked in such a cage, feeling obliged to perform their assigned roles. As the protagonist sums up at the end of the story: "Tradition designed my cage. My father built it. Keisuke locked it. In returning to my father's house, I betray my mother's faith but the load is lighter on my shoulders than that of the nine generations" (lines 797–799). Obviously the cage, as a symbol, carries multiple meanings in the story. It is through symbolism that Bissoondath successfully enlarges the scope of his story and enriches its texture and implications. Imagine how much interest would be lost if we were to remove the ingenious symbolism in the story.

# Allegory

A form of extended metaphor in essence, an **allegory** refers to a story with double meanings: a surface meaning and an allegorical (underlying) meaning. An allegory is therefore a story that can be read, understood, and interpreted at two or more levels. The characters are usually personifications of abstract qualities, and the action and setting tend to be indicative of the relationships among these abstractions. The purpose of an allegory or any kind of allegorical writing may be moral, religious, political, personal, or satiric.

This anthology includes "The Wagon" by Khalida Asghar (page 176), which can be interpreted both at the surface level and at the allegorical level. At the surface level, it is a very modernistic story that devotes ample space to depicting the protagonist's mental and physical reaction to the "blood-red" sunset, the unbearable stench in the city air and his morbid obsession with the three villagers and the mysterious wagon. As a result of the unique narrative voice of a neurotic man, the story is enveloped in an aura of fantasy and hallucination. Many things don't seem to make sense at this level. We may be puzzled by questions like "Who are the three villagers?" "What did they see in the wagon?" "What happens to the protagonist in the end?"

These questions can be answered if we keep in mind the large-scale industrial modernization and nuclear proliferation that took place in the 1960s when the story was written. Viewed in such a social context, the confusing story becomes clear at the allegorical level. "I," the first-person narrator/protagonist, is nameless and therefore capable of representing any person living in a modern city plagued by insensitivity to environmental concerns. One evening on his way back to the city the man meets three villagers, personifying human conscience, curiosity, and pursuit, who alert him to the imminent danger signified by the blazing orange sunset "over the marshes of the receding Ravi" (line 10) (notice some of the key ecological terms used here). Very soon he becomes preoccupied and obsessed with the ominous sights, and before long he is acutely smitten by the "pain-filled" odour caused by senseless urbanization. His ill-fated encounter with the wagon, a carriage of all the imaginable modern evils, alienates him further from his fellow citizens and brings him to the brink of insanity. As the story ends, the man has a final encounter with human conscience (the three villagers) and totally loses touch with reality after the three villagers are turned dumb and numb by the evils of modernization carried by the wagon. Thus, "The Wagon" is at the same time a strange story about a man's obsession with three mysterious men and a hideous wagon and an allegory of modernization, environmental pollution, and nuclear proliferation and their catastrophic effect on urban dwellers.

*It is important to distinguish an allegory from a symbol.* A symbol recurs in a story and is normally so open to interpretations that we cannot easily pinpoint its exact meaning, as with "the cage" and "the chocho vine." However, an allegory requires a narrative framework that allows a structure of ideas to be represented by characters or objects in a story. To put it in computer terms, the reader need only hit the "view-changing" key to switch from the surface level to the allegorical level. Once the "view" is changed, every element at the surface level has its allegorical equivalent, *which is never the case for a symbol.* Moreover, the meaning of an allegory is relatively fixed, with none of the **ambiguity** associated with symbols.

There are also many other literary devices and techniques at the writer's disposal, but those we have just discussed are the most commonly used ones. They form part of the vocabulary of literary appreciation and study. To know *what* these devices mean, *why* they are useful to writers, and *how* they function in stories is essential to our comprehension and enhances our enjoyment of literary works in general and short stories in particular.

Now let us read the three short stories selected for this unit and appreciate how their respective writers use some of the literary devices and techniques.

# The Gift of the Magi
O. Henry (U.S.A.) 1862–1910

## About the Author

*Known as "O. Henry," a pseudonym he began to use in 1899, William Sydney Porter was born in Greensboro, North Carolina, in 1862. After leaving school at age 15, he worked as a pharmacist's assistant and a bank teller. He was convicted of embezzlement in 1898 and was imprisoned in the Ohio State Penitentiary for over three years.*

*His life experiences became a valuable resource for his short stories, which are mostly on social themes.*

*Regarded as "the master of the American short story," O. Henry wrote volumes of short, often humorous, stories with ironic twists or surprise endings in what is labelled as "the O. Henry style." He also wrote one novel,* Cabbages and Kings *(1904). By the time O. Henry died of cirrhosis of the liver in 1910, he was well on his way to being the most popular short story writer in the world. Although his fame as a writer has since declined sharply, O. Henry's short stories have been translated into at least 12 languages and gained him millions of readers all over the world.*

## About the Story

*Published in a collection of short stories set in New York City under the title of* The Four Million *in 1906, "The Gift of the Magi" is the best loved of all O. Henry's short stories. Written as a Christmas story for the New York* World *magazine section, it alludes to the well-known Biblical story of the magi in the context of the tradition of Christmas present giving. Many elements in this story are typically O. Henry: the situational irony (irony of fate), the surprise ending, and the theme celebrating traditional values and Christian love.*

## Term Appearing in the Story

**Coney Island chorus girl** a lower-class actress from Coney Island in Long Island, New York, typically known for bad taste and poor acting

One dollar and eighty-seven cents. That was all. And sixty cents of it was in pennies. Pennies saved one and two at a time by bulldozing the grocer and the vegetable man and the butcher until one's cheeks burned with the silent imputation of parsimony that such close dealing
5  implied. Three times Della counted it. One dollar and eighty-seven cents. And the next day would be Christmas.

There was clearly nothing to do but flop down on the shabby little couch and howl. So Della did it. Which instigates the moral reflection that life is made up of sobs, sniffles, and smiles, with sniffles predominating.
10  While the mistress of the home is gradually subsiding from the first stage to the second, take a look at the home. A furnished flat at $8 per week. It did not exactly beggar description, but it certainly had that word on the lookout for the mendicancy squad.

In the vestibule below was a letter-box into which no letter would go,
15 and an electric button from which no mortal finger could coax a ring. Also

appertaining thereunto was a card bearing the name "Mr. James Dillingham Young."

The "Dillingham" had been flung to the breeze during a former period of prosperity when its possessor was being paid $30 per week. Now, when the income was shrunk to $20, the letters of "Dillingham" looked blurred, as though they were thinking seriously of contracting to a modest and unassuming D. But whenever Mr. James Dillingham Young came home and reached his flat above he was called "Jim" and greatly hugged by Mrs. James Dillingham Young, already introduced to you as Della. Which is all very good.

Della finished her cry and attended to her cheeks with the powder rag. She stood by the window and looked out dully at a gray cat walking a gray fence in a gray backyard. To-morrow would be Christmas Day, and she had only $1.87 with which to buy Jim a present. She had been saving every penny she could for months, with this result. Twenty dollars a week doesn't go far. Expenses had been greater than she had calculated. They always are. Only $1.87 to buy a present for Jim. Her Jim. Many a happy hour she had spent planning for something nice for him. Something fine and rare and sterling—something just a little bit near to being worthy of the honour of being owned by Jim.

There was a pier-glass between the windows of the room. Perhaps you have seen a pier-glass in an $8 flat. A very thin and very agile person may, by observing his reflection in a rapid sequence of longitudinal strips, obtain a fairly accurate conception of his looks. Della, being slender, had mastered the art.

Suddenly she whirled from the window and stood before the glass. Her eyes were shining brilliantly, but her face had lost its colour within twenty seconds. Rapidly she pulled down her hair and let it fall to its full length.

Now, there were two possessions of the James Dillingham Youngs in which they both took a mighty pride. One was Jim's gold watch that had been his father's and his grandfather's. The other was Della's hair. Had the Queen of Sheba lived in the flat across the airshaft, Della would have let her hair hang out the window some day to dry just to depreciate Her Majesty's jewels and gifts. Had King Solomon been the janitor, with all his treasures piled up in the basement, Jim would have pulled out his watch every time he passed, just to see him pluck at his beard from envy.

So now Della's beautiful hair fell about her, rippling and shining like a cascade of brown waters. It reached below her knee and made itself almost a garment for her. And then she did it up again nervously and quickly.

55 Once she faltered for a minute and stood still while a tear or two splashed on the worn red carpet.

On went her old brown jacket; on went her old brown hat. With a whirl of skirts and with the brilliant sparkle still in her eyes, she fluttered out the door and down the stairs to the street.

60 Where she stopped the sign read: "Mme. Sofronie. Hair Goods of All Kinds." One flight up Della ran, and collected herself, panting. Madame, large, too white, chilly, hardly looked the "Sofronie."

"Will you buy my hair?" asked Della.

"I buy hair," said Madame. "Take yer hat off and let's have a sight at
65 the looks of it."

Down rippled the brown cascade.

"Twenty dollars," said Madame, lifting the mass with a practised hand.

"Give it to me quick," said Della.

Oh, and the next two hours tripped by on rosy wings. Forget the hashed
70 metaphor. She was ransacking the stores for Jim's present.

She found it at last. It surely had been made for Jim and no one else. There was no other like it in any of the stores, and she had turned all of them inside out. It was a platinum fob chain simple and chaste in design, properly proclaiming its value by substance alone and not by meretricious
75 ornamentation—as all good things should do. It was even worthy of The Watch. As soon as she saw it she knew that it must be Jim's. It was like him. Quietness and value—the description applied to both. Twenty-one dollars they took from her for it, and she hurried home with the 87 cents. With that chain on his watch Jim might be properly anxious about the time in
80 any company. Grand as the watch was, he sometimes looked at it on the sly on account of the old leather strap that he used in place of a chain.

When Della reached home her intoxication gave way a little to pru-dence and reason. She got out her curling irons and lighted the gas and went to work repairing the ravages made by generosity added to love.
85 Which is always a tremendous task, dear friends—a mammoth task.

Within forty minutes her head was covered with tiny, close-lying curls that made her look wonderfully like a truant schoolboy. She looked at her reflection in the mirror long, carefully, and critically.

"If Jim doesn't kill me," she said to herself, "before he takes a second
90 look at me, he'll say I look like a Coney Island chorus girl.° But what could I do—oh! what could I do with a dollar and eighty-seven cents?"

At 7 o'clock the coffee was made and the frying-pan was on the back of the stove hot and ready to cook the chops.

Jim was never late. Della doubled the fob chain in her hand and sat on
95 the corner of the table near the door that he always entered. Then she
heard his step on the stair away down on the first flight, and she turned
white for just a moment. She had a habit of saying little silent prayers
about the simplest everyday things and now she whispered: "Please God,
make him think I am still pretty."

100    The door opened and Jim stepped in and closed it. He looked thin and
very serious. Poor fellow, he was only twenty-two—and to be burdened
with a family! He needed a new overcoat and he was without gloves.

Jim stopped inside the door, as immovable as a setter at the scent of
quail. His eyes were fixed upon Della, and there was an expression in them
105 that she could not read, and it terrified her. It was not anger, nor surprise,
nor disapproval, nor horror, nor any of the sentiments that she had been
prepared for. He simply stared at her fixedly with that peculiar expression
on his face.

Della wriggled off the table and went for him.

110    "Jim, darling," she cried, "don't look at me that way. I had my hair cut
off and sold it because I couldn't have lived through Christmas without
giving you a present. It'll grow out again—you won't mind, will you? I just
had to do it. My hair grows awfully fast. Say 'Merry Christmas!' Jim, and
let's be happy. You don't know what a nice—what a beautiful, nice gift I've
115 got for you."

"You've cut off your hair?" asked Jim, laboriously, as if he had not
arrived at that patent fact yet even after the hardest mental labour.

"Cut it off and sold it," said Della. "Don't you like me just as well,
anyhow? I'm me without my hair, ain't I?"

120    Jim looked about the room curiously.

"You say your hair is gone?" he said, with an air almost of idiocy.

"You needn't look for it," said Della. "It's sold, I tell you—sold and gone,
too. It's Christmas Eve, boy. Be good to me, for it went for you. Maybe the
hairs of my head were numbered," she went on with a sudden serious
125 sweetness, "but nobody could ever count my love for you. Shall I put the
chops on, Jim?"

Out of his trance Jim seemed quickly to wake. He enfolded his Della. For
ten seconds let us regard with discreet scrutiny some inconsequential object
in the other direction. Eight dollars a week or a million a year—what is the
130 difference? A mathematician or a wit would give you the wrong answer.
The magi brought valuable gifts, but that was not among them. This dark
assertion will be illuminated later on.

Jim drew a package from his overcoat pocket and threw it upon the table.

135 "Don't make any mistake, Dell," he said, "about me. I don't think there's anything in the way of a haircut or a shave or a shampoo that could make me like my girl any less. But if you'll unwrap that package you may see why you had me going a while at first."

White fingers and nimble tore at the string and paper. And then an
140 ecstatic scream of joy; and then, alas! a quick feminine change to hysterical tears and wails, necessitating the immediate employment of all the comforting powers of the lord of the flat.

For there lay The Combs—the set of combs, side and back, that Della had worshipped for long in a Broadway window. Beautiful combs, pure
145 tortoise shell, with jewelled rims—just the shade to wear in the beautiful vanished hair. They were expensive combs, she knew, and her heart had simply craved and yearned over them without the least hope of possession. And now, they were hers, but the tresses that should have adorned the coveted adornments were gone.

150 But she hugged them to her bosom, and at length she was able to look up with dim eyes and a smile and say: "My hair grows so fast, Jim!"

And then Della leaped up like a little singed cat and cried, "Oh, oh!"

Jim had not yet seen his beautiful present. She held it out to him eagerly upon her open palm. The dull precious metal seemed to flash with a reflec-
155 tion of her bright and ardent spirit.

"Isn't it a dandy, Jim? I hunted all over town to find it. You'll have to look at the time a hundred times a day now. Give me your watch. I want to see how it looks on it."

Instead of obeying, Jim tumbled down on the couch and put his hands
160 under the back of his head and smiled.

"Dell," said he, "let's put our Christmas presents away and keep 'em a while. They're too nice to use just at present. I sold the watch to get the money to buy your combs. And now suppose you put the chops on."

The magi, as you know, were wise men—wonderfully wise men—who
165 brought gifts to the Babe in the manger. They invented the art of giving Christmas presents. Being wise, their gifts were no doubt wise ones, possibly bearing the privilege of exchange in case of duplication. And here I have lamely related to you the uneventful chronicle of two foolish children in a flat who most unwisely sacrificed for each other the greatest
170 treasures of their house. But in a last word to the wise of these days let it

be said that of all who give gifts these two were the wisest. Of all who give and receive gifts, such as they are wisest. Everywhere they are wisest. They are the magi.

(1906)

# Following the Story

1. How are the major characters related to one another in the story?
2. Why does Della cry at the beginning?
3. What makes Della stop crying? Is she happy with her solution?
4. What methods does the author use for characterization: telling, or showing, or in-depth presentation, or a combination of all three? Support your argument with specific examples.
5. Identify and comment on the narrative voice.
6. What is the setting of the story—where and when does it take place?
7. Find two examples of simile and explain how they work in the context.
8. Find two examples of metaphor and explain how they are effective in the context.
9. What are the major conflicts in the story?
10. Is this story developed chronologically?

# Responding to the Story

1. Why does Jim stare at Della "with that peculiar expression on his face" after he gets home? What do you think is the reason for this reaction?
2. What do you think Della would say after being told that Jim had sold his watch to buy her combs?
3. Do you find Della and Jim realistic and believable? Why or why not?
4. What would you do if you were in their situation?
5. What is revealed through the situational irony?
6. Who are the magi? How are they related to the story?
7. Why does O. Henry use a number of Biblical allusions in this story?
8. Do you like the ending? Why or why not? How would you end the story?
9. Which part of the story do you like the best, and which part do you like the least?
10. What is the story about? What have you learned from it?

# The Cage

Neil Bissoondath (Canada) 1955–

## About the Author

*Born in Trinidad, Neil (Devindra) Bissoondath came to Canada in 1973. After earning his B.A. in French at York University in 1977, he taught English and French in Toronto and became a full-time writer in 1985. In the same year,* Digging up the Mountains, *his first collection of short stories, was published and included "The Cage." His novel,* The Worlds within Her *(1998), was nominated for the Governor General's Award in 1999. He now lives in Montreal.*

*As a writer of South Asian origin and Caribbean background and a Canadian university graduate, Bissoondath has displayed in both his short stories and novels a great thematic interest in cultural alienation, displacement, and identity among new immigrants or expatriates. His fictional works are noted for their psychological and historical insights as well as for the special skills in creating characters caught in conflicts.*

## About the Story

*"The Cage" vividly depicts, through the story of a young Japanese woman, the conflicts between personal feelings and desires on the one hand and traditional values and cultural customs on the other. The ending is realistic, and yet this story exemplifies the special effect of symbolism and first-person narrative voice.*

## Terms Appearing in the Story

**Shinto** the native religious system of Japan, incorporating the belief that the Mikado (the Japanese Emperor) is the direct descendant of the sun-goddess and that implicit obedience is due to him. Many Japanese keep a Shinto shrine in the backyard to worship spirits of nature and their ancestors, among other things.

**ko-to** a Japanese musical stringed instrument played with both hands

**Samurai** a member of the military caste, a nobleman in Japanese history

**tatami** a thick mattress used to cover the Japanese-style room floor

**sashimi** thinly sliced fresh raw fish served with soy sauce and horseradish

**hara-kiri** a Japanese way of ceremonially killing oneself by cutting open the stomach when in circumstances of disgrace or under sentence of death

My father is an architect. Architects are good at designing things: stores, houses, apartments, prisons. For my mother, my father, not an unkind man, designed a house. For me, my father, not a kind man, designed a cage.

5 My father is a proud man. He traces his ancestry back nine generations. Our family name is well known in Yokohama, not only because of my father's architectural firm but also because of those nine generations: his name is my father's greatest treasure.

It is not mine.

10 At the Shinto° shrine in the backyard my father mumbles the names of his ancestors, calling on them, invoking their presence. With those names he swears, expresses pleasure, offers compliments. He knows those names better than he knows mine.

When I was small, I used to stand at the window of the living room 15 watching my father as he mumbled before the shrine. He almost always wore a grey turtleneck sweater; he suffered from asthma and said that the air that blew in off the sea, over the American warships and docks, came heavy with moisture and oil. On especially damp mornings he would return to the house with the skin under his eyes greyed and his cheeks 20 scarlet. He coughed a great deal, and I could see his chest laboring rhythmically beneath his sweater.

I often wondered why, even on the worst of mornings, with drizzle and a grey mist, he went out to the shrine: couldn't the ancestors wait a day? A few hours? Were they so demanding? One day I asked him why and he 25 just stared back at me in silence. He never answered. Maybe be couldn't. Maybe it was just something he knew deep within him, an urge he bowed to without understanding. Maybe it was to him, as to me, a mystery.

I shall never forget the day he called me Michi, the name of his father's mother. She was the person he loved best in the world, and for many years 30 after her death he would visit her grave, to cry. He called me Michi because he had simply forgotten my name. He became angry when my mother reminded him.

When I was a child he took only occasional notice of me. I was my mother's charge. He was not a bad father. He was just as much of one as 35 he was capable of being. His concerns were less immediate.

His attention grew during the teenage years, for he feared them most. When I was fifteen, I told my parents I no longer wanted to take piano lessons. I saw distress on my mother's face: she had, in her youth, before marriage, wanted to be a concert pianist. When I practised, she would often sit 40 quietly behind me, listening, saying nothing. I could feel her ears reaching

out to every key my fingers hit, every sound my touch produced. At times
I felt I was playing not for me but for her, giving her through the pain and
fatigue in my fingers a skein of memory. But music cannot be a duty. It
must come naturally. I am not a musician. I grew bored. My fingers on the
45 piano keys produced a lifeless sound. My father, admitting this, agreed to
let me stop. My father, after quietly invoking his ancestors, said it was a
bad sign. But he would agree if I accepted the *ko-to*° in place of the piano.
I agreed. It gave me my way and allowed him to assert his authority.

However, his distrust of my age continued. One day he searched among
50 my clothes and found a packet of letters. It was a modest collection, three
from girlfriends in foreign places, one from a boy I had known briefly in
school. His family had moved to Osaka and he had written me this one
letter, a friendly letter, a letter to say hello. My father ignored the letters
from my girlfriends and handed me the letter from the boy. He demanded
55 that I read it to him: a friendly letter, a silly letter; finally, a humiliating
letter. When I finished, he took the letter with him. I never saw it again. At
dinner that evening he searched my eyes for signs of crying. He saw none.
He exchanged worried glances with my mother.

I hadn't cried. Instead, I had thought; and the lesson I learned was far
60 greater than mere distrust of my father. I learnt, more than anything else,
how little of my life was my own, in my father's eyes. It was the horror of
this that prevented tears; his claim to my privacy that, finally, caused me
to regard him with eyes of ice.

I had few friends. My peers and I had little in common. They liked to talk
65 of husbands, babies, houses; boredom was my response. No simple explanation offered itself, nor did I seek one. Maybe it was my age, maybe it was
my temperament, but I accepted this situation. Often, in the middle of a
gathering of schoolmates, I would slip away home, to my room.

For there, among my school texts, was my favorite companion, a child's
70 book that had been a gift many years before from my father. It was a large
book, with hard covers and pages of a thick, velvety paper. It related the
story of the first foreigners to come to Japan. Every other page contained
an illustration, of the sea, of the ships, of the mountains of Japan, in colors
so bright they appeared edible.

75 The picture that most attracted me presented the first meeting between
foreigners and Samurai°. They stood, clusters of men, facing one another:
foreigners to the right, grotesquely bearded, drab in seafaring leathers;
Samurai to the left, resplendent in outfits of patterned and folded color.
Behind them, with purity borne only in the imagination, lay a calm, blue

80 sea tinged here and there by whitecaps of intricate lace. On the horizon, like a dark brown stain on the swept cleanliness of the sky, sat the foreigners' ship.

My father, in giving me the book, had stressed the obvious: the ugliness of the foreigners, the beauty of the Samurai. But my mind was gripped by
85 the roughness, the apparent unpredictability, of the foreigners. The Samurai were of a cold beauty; you knew what to expect of them, and in this my father saw virtue. For me, the foreigners were creatures who could have exploded with a suddenness that was like charm. Looking at them, I wondered about their houses, their food, their families. I wanted to know
90 what they thought and how they felt. This to me was the intrigue of the book, and I would spend many hours struggling with the blank my mind offered when I tried to go beyond the page before me.

I remember one day asking my father to tell me about the foreigners. He was immediately troubled. He said, "They came from Europe." But
95 what did the word "Europe" mean, I asked. Europe: to me, a word without flesh. "This is an unnecessary question," he replied, his eyes regarding the book and me with suspicion. I took the book from his hands and returned to my room.

Not long after this I showed the book to a school friend. We were both
100 about twelve years old at the time and I hoped to find in her companionship of spirit. She looked through the book and handed it back to me, saying nothing. I asked her opinion of it. She said, "It is a very pretty book." And those words, so simple, so empty, created distance between us.

The book has remained in my room ever since, safe, undisplayed.

105 At eighteen, when I graduated from high school, my parents tried to marry me off. He was an older man from my father's firm, an architect like my father. They made me wear a kimono to meet him. At first his glances were modest, but as the evening wore on he became bolder. Angered, I returned his searching gazes. He faltered. He became modest
110 once again. Finally, he left.

My behavior had not gone unnoticed. Afterwards my mother scolded me.

I said, "I do not want to marry."

My mother said, "The choice is not yours, it is not any woman's."

My father said nothing. He left the room.

115 My mother said, "You have made your father very angry."

I said, "I do not want to marry. I want to live with a man."

My mother looked at me as if I had gone mad. "We are sending you to university. You will not waste your education in such a way."

"I want to have a career."

120 "We are not giving you an education so you can work. Men want educated wives."

"I do not want to be a man's wife."

"Where are you getting such ideas? You associate with the wrong people. Such ideas are foreign to us." Then she too left the room.

125 The "wrong people" has always been one of my mother's obsessions. I remember inviting a schoolmate to my house. She met my mother. They talked. When my friend left, my mother said, "I do not think you should associate with such people." I was still obedient at the time; I never spoke to the girl again. I understood why my mother took this attitude. The girl's

130 home was in one of the poorer sections of Yokohama, her mother worked as a clerk in a department store. This was the first time my mother was too busy to drive one of my friends home. And for me, guilt came only years later, too late, as with everything in retrospect.

My mother. She once played the piano. She has a degree in opera from

135 Tokyo University. She could have had a career. Instead, she got married. She talks of her life now only to say she is happy. But what is this happiness—who can say? Not I, for I could never be happy in her situation. I maybe know too much. Yet I cannot contradict my mother. I can only say I doubt her. This self-sacrifice—she has given her all to her husband, to her

140 son, to me; she has rejected all possibility of leading her own life, of developing her talent—this self-sacrifice is not for me. She has the ability to put up with things even when she is at odds with them. I suppose this shows strength. Sometimes, though, I wonder if this is not so much strength as a simple lack of choice. My mother does not have the ability to create choice

145 where there is none.

I am, in the end, tangible proof of my mother's failure as a woman.

Once during this same summer that ushered me from high school to university my mother expressed a desire to spend the vacation in Kyoto. My father said he wished to visit Kobe; he was adamant. Later, I heard my

150 father, unaware of my presence, telling my brother to observe his handling of the situation. All along, he said, he had wanted to visit Kyoto but he would let my mother beg a little, cajole him, fawn over him; only then would he agree to visit Kyoto. My mother would think she had won a great victory. And that was the way it worked out. My mother never realized the

155 deception, and my sadness prevented me from revealing it to her. It was too, I knew, part of the game she had long ago accepted.

My mother and women like her, my father and men like him, will tell you that the man's world is in his office, the woman's in her house. But in my parents' house, designed by my father, built by him, his word is law. My mother, if she really believes in the division of domain, lives in a world of illusion.

This facility for seeing the wrong thing, asking the wrong question, already a barrier between acquaintanceship and friendship, made my relations with my brother difficult. I resented having chores to do—washing dishes, making beds, both his and mine, cleaning the house—while his only duty was to protect the family name by staying out of trouble. I resented having my telephone callers interrogated, my letters scanned, my visitors judged, while he was free to socialize with people of his own choosing. I resented the late hours he was permitted to keep while I was forced to spend my evenings practising the *ko-to*, producing music that bored me to tears and put my father in mind of his ancestors, never far out of reach. I resented my brother's freedom to choose from among the girls he knew while I could meet only those men selected by my father, always architects, always older, always pained by courtship conducted before the boss.

My brother and I have never spoken. He is as much a stranger to me as I am to him. What I know of him I do not like. He is too much like my father. They occasionally pray together at the shrine in the backyard.

I had been accepted at Tokyo University, in dietetics. This field was not my choice, but my father's. From a magazine article he had got the idea that dietetics would be a fine, harmless profession, and one easily dropped for marriage. I would have preferred literature but I had no choice. It was my father's money that afforded me an education, and his connections that brought me entry to prestigious Tokyo University.

I left for Tokyo at the end of the summer, with my mother as temporary chaperone. She settled me in and, after three days, left with the lightest of kisses. She had grown into her role, my mother, and had spent much of her time with me worrying about my father and brother. The moment she left, uncertainty became my sole companion. I was as tentative as a spider's web in wind. I avoided people, grew close to no one. My life was my books, and I emerged from chemistry and anatomy only to attend the occasional gathering organized by the dietetics department. Attendance at these "social evenings" was informally obligatory: even in the wider world, you belonged to a family and owed certain obligations. Nothing exciting ever happened at these parties. You went, you drank a little, ate a little, chatted politely, you left. Little was achieved, save homage to the concept of the group. Maybe occasionally a student would get a low grade raised a little.

It was at one of these gatherings halfway through my first year at university that I met Keisuke, a well-known Japanese poet. I had never heard of him, for my father, probably remembering the childhood incident with my story book, had proscribed literature. So at first I treated Keisuke in an offhand manner. I distrusted his name, Keisuke, a fine old traditional name; it seemed to reflect all the values my father held dear. Nor was he particularly attractive in any way. His physique was undistinguished, tending, if anything, to softness around the middle; and the whites of his eyes were scrawled by a complicated system of red veins, from lack of sleep. At one point in the evening, I heard him say that it was his habit to drop in when he could on the gatherings of the different departments. This declaration, made not to me but to a group that had politely formed around him, scared me a little. It was not something that was done and, although there was a general assent that this was a good idea, I could see the hesitation that preceded the required politeness, the easy discomfort quickly submerged in nods and smiles. And I could see, too, that Keisuke had not missed it. He looked at me and smiled: we shared a secret.

After, when he had left, there were a few whispered comments about how odd he was. One of the professors, a small, balding man, said slyly, "But he's a poet. You know what *they're* like...."

The next day at lunch in the cafeteria, Keisuke appeared at my table and sat down, without asking permission. "So," he said. "Did they find me very odd?"

Flustered at hearing the same word in his mouth as had been used to describe him the previous evening, I instinctively said, "Yes."

For a second there was silence, and then we both began laughing. Our secret, understood by a smile the evening before, was made explicit by the laughter. I became comfortable with him. He asked me to call him "Kay," and he mocked his own name, describing it with the English word "stuffy," which he had to explain to me since my English was not very good at the time.

We talked a great deal. He told me he had lived and studied in America for seven years. His father, an executive with the Panasonic Corporation, had been transferred to New Jersey when Kay was sixteen. Kay knew New York City well, and as he described it—the lights, the noise, the excitement—I wondered why he had returned, after all that time, to Japan.

He smiled at my question. "I am Japanese," he said.

I nodded, but the answer discomforted me. It was my father's explanation of too many things.

Kay and I became friends. He invited me to his apartment not far from the university. It was a small place, and cluttered. On the walls he had 240 hung framed American film posters, all at different heights so that any thought of uniformity was banished. Everywhere—on his desk, on the coffee table, on the kitchen counters—he had stacked books and magazines and papers. We would sit together in a corner on a *tatami*°, reading and talking under the yellow light of a wall-lamp.

245 I told him about my father, my mother, my brother. He showed me some of his poetry. I read it. I understood little. He asked what literature I had read. I told him about my father's prohibition on books and of his final admonition on the night before I left for Tokyo. Stay away, he had said, from books full of fine words. Kawabata, Tanizaki, Mishima would 250 not help my chemistry marks and, besides, writers always had strange ideas anyway, ideas unfit for young female minds.

Kay listened to my story in silence. Then he said, "Your father is a man full of fears." This was like revelation to me.

I confessed that I had read Mishima, for my brother had on the book 255 shelves in his room the complete works, a gift from our father. I had read them surreptitiously and, at the time, untrained, unaware, I had seized only upon the eroticism. Kay, unsurprised, explained to me what I had missed: the mingling of the sex with blood, and the brooding sense of violence. "Mishima was mad in many respects," he said. "A twentieth-260 century Samurai. His end was fitting." And now, now that I understand Mishima, I worry about my brother, and I fear him.

One evening, after a light dinner of *sashimi*° and warm sake, Kay seduced me. As I write this, I realize what an un-Japanese admission it is. It scares me a little.

265 After, lying on the *tatami*, smoking my first cigarette and enjoying the warmth and soreness that clasped my body, I felt as if I had been given a precious key, but a key to what I wasn't sure. This too Kay, lying wet next to me, understood. He suggested I read Ibsen and, in the following months as my first year of university drew to a close, he supplied translations to 270 help my shaky English through the Ibsen texts he'd studied in America. We discussed his works, among others, and the more intense our discussions became, the more I found myself articulating thoughts and ideas that would have made my father blue with rage.

Kay, one of those writers with strange ideas whom my father so feared, 275 gave me the ability to put into words what had been for me until then, ungrasped feelings. With his help, I arrived at last at a kind of self-comprehension, although confusion—guilt, Kay called it—remained. He said this was so because, although my ideas were coming into focus, their source remained hidden.

280 However, I do not want to give the impression that I always sailed smoothly. At times, especially after another of the tedious meetings with one of my father's architects—for which I was periodically called home—I felt that the seduction was less a key than a betrayal. As I sat there in my father's spare living room, serving the men, smiling at them, I felt that Kay
285 had heightened my confusion rather than diminished it. But these periods of doubt were shortlived.

The rest of my university career was uneventful. Kay and I continued to see one another from time to time but the intimacy of that first year was never repeated. He had too much work, I had too much work. At least, it
290 was the excuse we used.

I graduated as a dietitian and had no trouble finding a job in a hospital in Yokohama. I worked there for a year, in a profession not of my choosing, counting day after day the calorie intake of patients. Counting calories becomes tedious after a while and the patients soon became little more
295 than mathematical sums in my mind, defining themselves by what they could eat.

At the end of one particularly trying day, I called on a patient, an old woman, chronically ill and querulous, to discuss her rejection of prescribed food. She explained to me in a cross voice that she wanted, of all things,
300 mayonnaise on her food. I told her this was impossible. She became abusive. I became abusive. I hit her with my clipboard. She started to cry, silently, like a child, the tears filling the wrinkles and creases of her crumpled face. It was then, looking at her through my own tears, that I realized I could not continue.

305 The tedium of the job, living once more in my father's house, smiling at his architects, practising the *ko-to*, these were all taking their toll on me.

I confronted my parents with my decision. They offered an alternative. They had never been happy about my working; a working wife is in short demand. It would be better, they said, if I were to concentrate on what
310 really mattered. I was getting old, already twenty-three. In five or six years I would be considered an old maid, an also-ran in the race to the conjugal bed. I had better get cracking.

But, as usual, I had my own idea. I had managed to save a tidy sum during my year of work, money my father considered part of a future mar-
315 riage contract. In Japan, women marry not for love but for security. The man acquires a kind of maid-for-life. For a person with my ideas, marriage

means compromise, an affair not of the heart but of the bank account. Therefore, my savings compensated a bit for my advanced age and my father never failed to mention the money when one of the suitors called.

320     I, however, wanted to travel. My father said it was out of the question; neither he nor my mother could leave Yokohama at the time. I said I wanted to travel alone. My father said this was preposterous, and he called on his ancestors, all nine generations of them, to witness the madness of his daughter.

325     Kay had once said to me, "Learn from the past but never let it control you." I think it was a line from one of his poems. At that moment the line ran through my mind. If my past would not control me, I decided, then neither would my father's. I told them I was leaving. My father threatened to restrain me physically. He called my brother to help. He came. I did not
330 protest; it would have served no purpose. My father and brother were as one. Even their eyes, black circles trapped behind the same thick lenses, framed by the same black plastic, were indistinguishable. It was these eyes that I saw come at me. As they led me off between them, my mother started crying. But she said nothing. They locked me in my room and told
335 the hospital I was sick.

    For a week I lay or sat alone in my room. My mother, silent always, brought me my meals, of which I ate little. I slept a lot, tried to read, spent long hours looking at my picture book: the splendid Samurai, the bearded foreigners. At one point—I no longer remember whether it was day or
340 night; time, after a while, was of no importance—I felt myself slipping into the painting, becoming part of it. I could feel the weight of heavy sea air on my face, the soft tingle of sand beneath my feet; I could hear the broken whisper of softly tumbling surf. I was prepared to surrender myself but something—a voice, a rattle of dishes—tugged me back. For the first time
345 in my captivity, I cried. My tears fell onto the pages of my book and there the stains remain.

    They let me out after a week and I returned to work. My father had spoken to the administrator of the hospital, an old friend. Since other members of the staff had complained about the old woman's behavior, no
350 action was taken against me, save a kindly lecture on the virtues of patience.

    The next two months were, however, not easy. I was never allowed a moment to myself; my every movement was monitored, every minute accounted for. Even at work, I found out, the administrator asked discreet
355 questions about me. My father had spoken to him about more than my problems with the old woman.

My life became like that of the four song-birds my brother kept in bamboo cages suspended from the ceiling of his room. They would whistle and chirp every morning, each making its own distinct cry, sometimes
360 sounding as if in competition against one another. The birds would sing at precisely the same time every morning, demanding food. I thought they saw this ability to wake him as power, but my brother knew who controlled the food.

One day, with the sense of reserved delight he shared with our father,
365 my brother brought home a new song-bird. It was the smallest of them all, a tiny creature of a blue and a red that sparkled when brushed by the sun. But there was a problem: while the others sang, this new bird remained silent. My brother tried coaxing music our of him, in vain. He tried attacking with a stick, but the bird was unmoved. My brother first tried
370 withholding food, but later when the incentive was offered the bird ignored it, and twice he knocked over his dish, scattering the seed.

The bird uttered only one sound in his week in my brother's bedroom, a pure, shrill whistle. The cry brought my brother, my mother, and me to the room. The bird was lying on the floor of the cage. My brother opened the
375 door and poked the little body with a finger, at first gently, then more roughly. Satisfied it was dead, he picked it up by a wing, took it to the kitchen, and dropped it into the garbage can. He dusted his hands casually and returned to his breakfast. He showed no regret.

I watched my brother with horror. At that moment I hated him. I went
380 to my room and I cried, for the bird, for myself.

He replaced it that evening with a more pliant bird. This one sang easily, and it was fed.

The next day I began playing the traditional daughter. I quit my job, I never complained, I welcomed the architects, smiled at them, hinted to my
385 father of grandchildren: a game, a game for which my real personality had to be hidden away like the pregnant, unwed daughter of a rich family. It was not very difficult, for I discovered in myself a strange determination.

After two months of this, my father, watchful always, put his suspicions aside. He said to my mother, "I have exercised the power of my ancestors.
390 They cannot be resisted." Then he went to visit the grave of Michi, his father's mother.

During this period I grew closer to my mother, for she was most often my guard. One night—it turned out to be my last in my father's house— we sat talking in my room. We had turned off the lights and opened the
395 window. Above the silhouetted trees and roof tops, we could see the sky turning dark, as if expiring. As yet, no stars were visible. The night air was

cool and we could hear insects chirping and cluttering in the shrubbery outside. My mother put on a sweater over her kimono, an oddly touching sight, and folded her arms, not sternly as I had once thought, but wearily,
400 like a woman undone. We sat on the bed, I on one side, she on the other, with a great expanse between us.

I asked her, "Have you ever thought of the possibility of leading your own life?"

She sighed. "I used to think of it when I was small but I always knew it
405 would be impossible."

"Why?"

"You are playing games now." She smiled sadly. Without looking at me, she said, "Whatever happens, I am always your mother. Wherever you are, whatever you are doing, you can call me. I will help."
410 "Who can you call?"

"Your father."

"You once had friends."

"Yes, but your father comes first. Friends just..." She waved her hands, searching for words. "...just get in the way."
415 "But you haven't got any friends."

"I am content. I have all I want, all I need. Now say no more about it."

I couldn't see her face. She was all in shadow. But her voice was tender.

The next day, for the first time in many months, she left me alone, unguarded. I packed my bags and called a taxi. The night before,
420 although I hadn't known it, she had been telling me goodbye.

I had always believed I could trust none of my relatives: my father, made in the image of his ancestors; my mother, made in the image of my father; my brother, a stranger. It took me a long time to realize that my mother was my friend. I do not think she really understood me but I was
425 one of those things she put up with even though we were at odds. I hope she can one day understand my attitude but I do not expect this. I can only hope.

I spent two months in Tokyo, in an apartment lent to me by one of Kay's friends. Kay visited me from time to time. We couldn't talk. He seemed
430 uncomfortable with me and, through this, I became uncomfortable with him. We were like polite strangers. This distance, and the silences it brought with it, depressed me; and I, in turn, depressed him.

One evening, after a particularly silent dinner, I asked him to tell me exactly what was wrong.
435 He said, "Nothing." Then he closed his eyes and said, "I have not been able to write. Your mood affects me. It is not good."

I couldn't reply. There was nothing to say.

He opened his eyes, the whites red-veined, the skin around them reddened, and looked slowly around the apartment. It was very much like his,
440 the film posters, the stacks of books and magazines. He had started a style among his friends.

"There is something else, too," he finally said. "I have been wondering...well, do you think you did the correct thing in leaving your father's house?"

445    I looked at him: it was all I could do. The one person of whom I had been sure. I said. "Keisuke. Keisuke."

He left a few minutes later, after putting the dishes into the kitchen sink.

His visits grew less frequent and finally stopped altogether. Without him, I found myself enmeshed in the freedom I had sought, friendless,
450 guideless, at liberty to choose my own way. "Without him": the irony does not escape me.

I found a job, again ironically, playing the piano in a bar. I eventually moved into my own little apartment and developed a small circle of friends, all connected in one way or the other with the bar. One night the
455 owner, an overweight man who dressed in flashy American clothes, tried to pressure me into sleeping with him. I never went back to the bar and so had yet another place to avoid, another place to run from.

In Tokyo, anonymity was easy to obtain: it is not difficult to be alone in a crowd of thousands. Privacy came more easily in large, overpopulated
460 Tokyo than in the smaller, relatively slow-paced Yokohama. Tokyo, the least traditional, most western, of our cities is, for me, the safest.

But it was still Japan. I was invited to parties. Japanese parties, like marriages, are business occasions in disguise. Men go to a party to get a promotion or to clinch a deal. The women smile and serve. The men drink and
465 talk. When they have drunk enough, they talk sex and arrange package tours to Korea, where they enjoy the prostitutes of a people they detest.

I felt I had to get away. My first thought was: Europe. But I quickly realized there were yet other places I had to avoid, the usual Japanese destinations: much of Europe, much of America, especially Boston or
470 Philadelphia or New York. So I changed my money to traveller's cheques and bought a plane ticket to Toronto. It was new space. I expected nothing.

Many Japanese think of snow and bears and wonderful nature like Niagara Falls when they think of Canada. But Toronto, a big city, bigger than Tokyo, less crowded, with more trees and flowers, did not surprise me.
475 I do not know if it was Toronto or me. Probably me.

I rented a room in a big house across from a park. My landlady, Mrs. Harris, lived on the first floor with her sister, Mrs. Duncan, and her cat, Ginger. She was a small woman of about fifty, with hair too blonde for her age. "We are all widows," she said with a smile the first time I went to the
480 house. "Ginger's Tom died last week. A car, poor dear." I thought her a strange woman but she smiled often, the skin on her face stretching into congruent wrinkles.

The second floor was rented to people I never saw. But they liked rock music. Their stereo worked every day, from early morning to late at night.
485 I rarely heard the music but I was always aware of it because of the thump of the bass beneath my feet, like a beating through the worn green carpet.

The third floor was divided into two small rooms. It was one of these that I took. The ceiling followed the contours of the roof, and the walls were painted a white that reflected the little sunlight that came in through the
490 small window. The furniture was sparse: a bed, an easy chair, a table with a lamp. My window overlooked the tops of trees and, to the left, fenced-in tennis courts. Sometimes, on a clear day, I could see Lake Ontario on the horizon, a thin ribbon of blue barely distinguishable from the sky.

I did little in my first weeks in Toronto. I walked. I visited the tourist
495 sights. I learned my way around the city. The last heat of the summer exploded down from the sky every day. It exhausted me, and I spent much time sleeping. My memories of the time are dull, everything seems to have rounded corners, everything seems somehow soft.

On weekends, many people came to the park across the street, to walk,
500 to eat, to talk. I would sit at my window observing them, many forms in blue denim or shades of brown, the occasional red or yellow or purple: glimpses of lives I would never touch, for I stayed at my window.

Looking. Looking. Looking.


One hot afternoon, returning groggy from my walk, I came across my
505 third-floor neighbor sitting in the small front porch. She was a tall lady with red hair and very white skin. Perspiration slicked her forehead. She wore a thin white T-shirt and shorts. In her right hand she held an open beer bottle.

"Hello," she said as I walked up the stairs. "Hot, isn't it."
510    I said, "Yes," reaching for the doorknob. It was no cooler in the porch than it had been in the sun, only the heat was different. Out there, the sunlight burned like an open flame; here, it was like steam. I was exhausted. I did not want to deplete the last of my energy by talking. English was still a strain.

515    "It's like a goddam oven up there," she said, pushing a chair towards me. "Hell, it's like a goddam oven down here. But at least it's open."

I sat down. We had seen each other twice before but each time she had been in a hurry. I had been shy. We had just said hello.

"You from Hong Kong?" she asked.

520    "No, I am from Tokyo. I am Japanese." Across the street, the browned grass of the park cowered in the shadow of the trees.

"Oh." She sipped from her beer. "What are you doing here?"

"I plan to take English lessons." My words surprised me. It had been something to say, an excuse for being there, but as I heard myself I

525 thought it a good idea.

"Oh." Then there was silence. On the road a car sped by in a spasm of loud music.

"What do you do?" I finally asked; it took courage.

"I dance. I'm a dancer. My name is Sherry."

530    "Ballet? Jazz?"

"Table."

"Table?"

"I work in a strip joint."

"'What is 'strip joint,' please?"

535    She laughed. "It's a place where ladies like me take off their clothes. For men."

"*Hai.* Yes. I see." The heavy air wrapped itself around my skin like a steamed napkin, and for a second I smelled the oily brine of the Yokohama harbor. "Excuse me, please," I said getting up. The smell, as brief and as

540 powerful as vision, had frightened me.

She watched me open the door. "Like a goddam oven," she said.

The next day I checked the Yellow Pages for a school and went down to their office. It was on the edge of the Yorkville area, a place of expensive stores and restaurants. The sidewalks were crowded: many young people

545 with perfect hair and clothes; many old people trying to look like the young people. On one corner a young man with a clown's face juggled colored balls for a small crowd. On another, a young couple in tuxedos played violins while people hurried by.

I was uncomfortable among these people: their numbers didn't offer

550 anonymity. It was just the opposite, in fact. The people, by their dress, by their extravagance of behavior, demanded to be noticed; they were on display. I walked quickly to the office building where the school was located, into the lobby of marble that created echo in the fall of my footsteps, into the elevator that at last brought relief.

555  Behind the green door that carried only a number, a man with grey hair and glasses was sitting at a desk. In front of him were a telephone, an ashtray so full that the ashes formed a little mountain, and a messy pile of papers. He was playing Scrabble when I walked in, a rack with tiles at either side of the board. No one else was in the office; he was playing
560 against himself, right hand against left hand.

"Good morning," he said, standing up. "Can I help you?" His suit, of a dark blue, showed chalk smudges at the pockets and on the right shoulder.

"Yes, please, I wish to improve my English language."

He offered me a seat and went to another room to get coffee. The walls
565 of the office were bare; in the far corner a large climbing plant, green leaves dulled by dust, clung weakly to its wooden staff.

He returned with two Styrofoam cups of coffee. He placed one on the desk in front of me, the other on the Scrabble board. As he sat down he asked me if I was from Hong Kong. Then he told me about himself. He
570 spoke some French, some Spanish, some German. He had lived and worked in many places. He didn't like Greek food, cats, and American cigarettes. Finally, after an hour, he told me about the school and we managed to arrange private English lessons for me.

I began the following week. My teacher, a tall, nervous young man with
575 a moustache, was a student at the University of Toronto. He dressed poorly, and was so thin and white that at times, under the fluorescent light of the classroom—desk, chairs, walls bare but for the black rectangle of the chalk board—I thought I could see through him. He said he was a vegetarian.

He wanted to talk about Japan and *hara-kiri*,° although he knew
580 nothing about Japan or *hara-kiri*. We discussed food. He insisted that I, being a Japanese person, never ate bread, only rice and vegetables and raw fish and nothing else. He would not believe that I had tasted my first Big Mac in Tokyo.

At one point he said, "Ahh, yes, I understand. American imperialism."
585 "No," I replied. "Good taste."

He did not appreciate my attempt at humor. He became angry and drilled me severely on grammar and vocabulary, refusing to discuss anything.

I settled in to a routine: Classes every morning at the school; a light lunch,
590 then a walk in the afternoon; back to my hot room for a nap; dinner at a restaurant and then my room again, for homework and reading. It was an easy, uncomplicated life. For the first time I knew what it was to anticipate the next day without tension.

Sometimes I saw Sherry, my third-floor neighbor. We would exchange a
595 few words of politeness. Once she asked my opinion of a perfume she had
bought. Another time she held up to herself a new blouse. Through these
brief encounters, I grew comfortable with her, even to like her a little.

My one shadow was a nightmare. Gentle and vivid, it came again and
again, at first sporadically, later with greater frequency: my father and
600 Keisuke, both in the dress of Samurai, standing on a beach, swords
unsheathed, while behind them the sea wept with the voice of my mother.
I would awake with the sound of sobbing in my ears and I would have to
speak to myself: *I am in Toronto. I am in Toronto.*

Toronto: a place where my personality could be free, it was not a city of
605 traditions in a country of traditions. It was America, in the best implication that word held for us Japanese: bright, clean, safe, new. Life experienced without the constraints of an overwhelming past. I shall never forget
my joy when, awaking one night in a sweat from the nightmare, I realized
that here I was a young person and not almost an old maid, that by a
610 simple plane flight I had found rejuvenation.

For two months I lived with a joy I had never imagined possible, the joy
of an escape that did not demand constant confrontation with the past.

At the school, the director's hands continued to challenge one another
to Scrabble. My teacher grew thinner, shaved his moustache, grew it back,
615 added a beard. I practised grammar, vocabulary, sentence structure.

I was so comfortable I even wrote a short note to my mother, to let her
know I was all right.

Summer began signalling its end. The trees across the street lost some
of their green; the heat of the day was less severe and at night my room
620 cooled enough that I needed to cover myself with a sheet. At school, I
got a new teacher. The first had come in one morning with the shaved
head and salmon robes of a religious cult, and had spent much of one
class trying to convince me to drop English in favor of Hindi. He was
fired.

625 One evening I saw Sherry in the restaurant where I had dinner. I was
surprised, for she usually worked in the evenings.

"How's your English?" she said loudly, motioning me to her table.

"Fine, thank you. I have learnt much. How are you?" I sat down. She
had already eaten. The plate before her was empty but for smeared
630 ketchup.

"Not so great. Can't work."

"I am sorry. Are you sick?"

"Not quite. I had an operation."

"It is not serious, I hope."

635 She laughed. "No. I had a tit job."

"Pardon me, I do not understand."

"They cut my breasts open. Cleaned 'em out. Put in bags of water. Size makes money."

*"Hai.* Yes. I see." Suddenly I was no longer hungry. My eyes swept invol-
640 untarily from her face to the table.

She pushed her chair back and picked up her cigarettes. "It hurts," she said softly, a look of pain on her face. "I better go." She stood up. Her face turned into the light. I saw bags under her eyes, wrinkles I had not noticed before, and I realized I had never before seen her without makeup. The
645 light shone through her curled hair, thinning it like an old person's. "See you," she said.

"Yes, sleep well." I watched her go, feeling her take some of my joy with her.

Two weeks later, as I was doing my homework late at night, I was dis-
650 turbed by noises from Sherry's room. I put my book down and listened. At first there was nothing. Then I heard a quiet groan. I became worried. I went to my door and listened again. Another groan. I opened my door, put my head into the corridor, and said, "Sherry, what is it, please?" I listened. There was no answer, no sound. Uncertain, I closed my door and went
655 back to my books. A few minutes later, Sherry's door slammed and heavy footsteps hurried down the stairs. The front door slammed.

My door flew open. Sherry walked in slowly. She was wearing a bathrobe. "Well, little Miss Jap, you pleased with your work?" She was calm, but it was the calm of anger, the same restraint my father and my
660 brother displayed in times of emotion.

"I am sorry?" I put down my book.

"You just cost me two hundred dollars."

"I do not understand."

"'*What is it please, Sherry?*'" she mimicked me. "The john went soft on
665 me. You think I got paid? Eh? That's two hundred dollars I'm out of, lady."

"Who is John, please?"

"Jesus Christ! What are they teaching you at that school, anyways?"

I was very confused. I said, "I am sorry. Please explain."

"What are you? Some kinda moron?" Then she turned and walked back
670 to her room. Her door slammed.

I got up and closed my door. It was getting cold in the room. I shut the window and got into bed, pulling the sheet tightly up to my neck. That night my nightmare came again: my father, Keisuke, and my mother weeping like the sea.

675 When I came in from school the next day, Mrs. Harris the landlady called me into the kitchen. She was sitting at the dining table with Mrs. Duncan, Ginger the cat on her lap. The little television next to the fridge was on but the sound was turned down.

Mrs. Harris said, "About last night, my dear, I just wanted to let you 680 know it won't happen again. Sherry's gone. I asked her to leave this morning."

"What happened last night, please? I do not understand." I had tried to seek an explanation from my teacher at the school but, upon hearing the story, she had grown uneasy and talked about the English subjunctive.

685 "Oh dear," said Mrs. Harris. She glanced at Mrs. Duncan. "Well, you see, dear, she was a stripper. Do you know what that means?"

"I know. She told me." Mrs. Duncan held out a plate of cookies to me. I took one.

"And sometimes, quite often in fact I found out this morning, she 690 brought men back to her room with her. They paid her, you see. To...well, you know."

"*Hai.* Yes. I see." I understood now, with horror, the two hundred dollars.

"But she's gone now, thank God."

I went up to my room, the cookie growing moist where the tips of my 695 fingers pressed into it. The door to Sherry's room was open, the bed stripped, the dresser and table cleared of the cosmetics and perfumes Sherry collected. Beneath my feet, the neighbors' stereo beat in its steady palpitation. I felt very alone.

The weather in Toronto grew cold. The trees outside my window turned 700 gold and brown, and in one night of wind lost all sign of life. The lake in the distance became a sliver of silver beneath a heavy sky. Now, no one came to the park. The view from my window was of desolation, of bared trees and deadened grass. I rarely looked out. My afternoon walks came to an end. Instead I went directly home from school, to my room.

705 I talked from time to time with Mrs. Harris and Mrs. Duncan. They spent almost every afternoon in the kitchen. They would drink coffee and eat cookies and talk about the boyfriends they had when they were young. How different from my mother, who could never acknowledge past boyfriends and could not even have a friend to talk to.

710 At four o'clock every afternoon Mrs. Harris would put on the little television and they would smoke and look at a soap opera. Sometimes they

cried a little. I often felt, watching them blow their noses into tissues, that they were crying not for the people in the show but for themselves, for the people they might have been and the people they were. Their own lives were not so interesting as those they saw on television at four o'clock every afternoon.

I found it strange that they never told me their first names. It was as if they had lost them. One cold, rainy afternoon, an afternoon on which shadows became airborne and floated about in the air, I asked Mrs. Harris why she called herself by her husband's name.

Stroking the cat, she thought for a minute. "It's tradition, dear. Christian tradition."

"Yes, dear," Mrs. Duncan said, "it's as simple as that. It's what women have always done."

"And what do you do with your own names? Are they no longer of importance?"

"A name is a name is a name," Mrs. Harris said. She lit a cigarette and the cat leapt from her lap with a growl.

I saw that Mrs. Harris did not like my questions.

Mrs. Duncan said, "Poor Ginger. She doesn't purr any more."

Mrs. Harris said, "She's gone off her food too." There was worry in her voice.

I went to my room. Through the window, the park hunched gloomily against the rain and cold. I thought of Ginger, and of my mother and Mrs. Harris and Mrs. Duncan, and I remembered the bird that would not sing.

That night my nightmare came again, but now I sensed my own presence, and I no longer knew from whom—my mother or myself—came the sound of the weeping sea.

Two days later I received an envelope from my mother. I left it unopened for several hours: I feared it, feared what it might say and, more, what it might not. Finally, I ripped it open.

It was a short letter. In it, my mother told me that my father, on discovering my disappearance, had said nothing, had done nothing. He hadn't even called on his ancestors. She said that my father never mentions me. She then explained, briefly, the mystery of myself to me. She spoke of Michi, the idol of my father. Michi had been, my mother said, a strong and independent woman, a woman with her own ideas. She had been beaten into submission by my great-grandfather and was left, in the end, with little but her grandson, my father, as outlet for her sense of life. It was all my mother knew but she hoped the knowledge would help me.

The letter brought me once more directly before the life I had managed to ignore during these months in Toronto. It reminded me that I faced nothing here, that this life of freedom was one without foundation, that it would all inevitably end with a twenty-hour plane flight. That night I did not have my nightmare, for I did not sleep. I spent the night crying, and I could not understand why it was the memory of my father coughing before the Shinto shrine that caused me the greatest sadness.

Depression: the English word is inadequate to describe that which seized me, which took hold of my heart, my lungs, my intestines. This was more like a sickness, a sickness of the soul.

Two nights later it snowed. My coats were too thin for the climate. Instead of buying a new coat, I took out my return plane ticket.

When I arrived in Tokyo, it was raining.

I now work as a language teacher, instructing foreigners, mostly Americans, in Japanese. In return, one of them practises my English with me.

It has been over a year since I left my father's house. Since my return to Japan, I have telephoned my mother once, just to hear her voice. We both cried on the phone, but I did nor tell her where I live. Not yet.

The sea no longer weeps in my dreams. Instead, some mornings I wake up with wet cheeks and a damp pillow. I do not know why.

Or maybe I do.

There is an English expression, "No man is an island." Or woman. Expressions always contain a grain of truth and this is an expression I wish I had never learned, for it brings into too bright a light what I have come to understand: I am a woman, I am a Japanese woman—I still look to the east when I take medicine—and the ties of tradition still bind me the way they bound Michi. To understand oneself is insufficient. Keisuke has yet to realize that his precept of refusing to let the past impede the future applies, in my country, but to one sex. This is, perhaps, why I failed to understand his poetry when I first read it; it was too alien in too many ways. Keisuke to one side, my father and brother to the other, but it is always the men. For them all, the common sentence: I am Japanese.

There is, as one of my businessmen students puts it, no leadership potential in me. I do not lead, I never have. I have only practised avoidance.

Accepting my father's values would make life easier for me. But I cannot do this automatically. I am not a clock. As a first step, therefore, I

am taking a course in flower arranging, a small step, but important in its
790 own way.

For I shall, I fear, return one day soon to my father's house, to the *ko-to*, to the architects; for I have learned that the corollary of tradition's pride is tradition's guilt. Keisuke was right: I feel guilty for having betrayed my father's name and his nine generations of ancestors. Keisuke helped me
795 recognize my guilt but he did not equip me to deal with it. In this, and not in the seduction, lay the real betrayal.

Tradition designed my cage. My father built it. Keisuke locked it. In returning to my father's house, I betray my mother's faith but the load is lighter on my shoulders than that of the nine generations.

800 I shall pack away my picture book: it is a child's book. I shall save it for my children, my daughters and my sons. It is to them that I bequeath my dreams.

And in the meantime, I continue to arrange my flowers. Even a cage needs decoration.

(1985)

# Following the Story

1. How many members are there in the protagonist's family? What type of character is each of them?
2. Is the young Japanese woman a round and dynamic character? Why or why not?
3. What methods does Bissoondath use for characterization: telling, or showing, or in-depth presentation, or a combination of all? Support your argument with specific examples.
4. What are the major conflicts in the story?
5. Who is Michi? What is the importance of this character?
6. What is the protagonist's "favorite companion" from her childhood? How significant is this companion to her story?
7. Why does the protagonist distrust her father? Find any specific reasons she gives.
8. How does the protagonist get to know Keisuke (Kay)? What role does he play in her life?
9. Why does the protagonist hate her brother? What does the incident about the new song-bird show about the brother?
10. How does the protagonist relate to her mother? Find evidence in the story to support your response.

## Responding to the Story

1. Why does she say "In returning to my father's house, I betray my mother's faith"?
2. How do you feel about Keisuke (Kay)? Why does the protagonist conclude at the end that it is Keisuke who locked the cage designed by tradition and built by her father?
3. What would you do if you were in the young woman's situation?
4. Why does the protagonist have the same nightmare night after night when she is in Toronto?
5. How does the cage function as a symbol?
6. What are the possible implications of "the cage"?
7. How does this short story differ from "The Gift of the Magi" in terms of literary devices and techniques used?
8. What have you learned about Japanese society and family through reading this story?
9. Do you like the ending of the story? Why or why not?
10. How sympathetic are you to the young woman in this story and why?

---

# The Wagon

## Khalida Asghar (Pakistan) 1938–

*(translated from Urdu by Muhammad Umar Memon)*

## About the Author

*Born in Lahore (now in Pakistan), Khalida Asghar began writing fiction in her native language, Urdu, in 1963, and several of her short stories were published in the following two years. Her marriage in 1965, however, prevented her from writing for about 12 years. In 1981 she published her first book of short stories, followed by two more collections. Some of her work has appeared under her married name, Khalida Husain. She now lives in Rawalpindi, Pakistan.*

*Regarded by many as one of the preeminent modern South Asian woman writers, Khalida Asghar established her literary reputation primarily with short stories concerned with social issues, especially the issue of women's identity and status in the male-dominated, traditional Islamic society of contemporary Pakistan. Her stories are sometimes boldly experimental in both theme and technique, forcing the reader to ponder.*

# About the Story

*Written about 1963 and published as one of her early stories before her marriage, "The Wagon" can be rightly called a classic of the modern Urdu short story. It is prophetic not only in its subject (as a warning against the disastrous effects of large-scale environmental pollution caused by modernization and nuclear proliferation), but also in its style (portraying in minute detail how painfully plaguing life in a modern city can be). It is open to interpretation at more than one level. At the allegorical level, the social and moral message becomes clearer although, to some readers at least, the experience of being puzzled and confused at the surface level is a pleasure of its own kind.*

# Terms Appearing in the Story

**the Ravi River** a river that rises in the Himalayas in northwestern India and flows west into Pakistan to join the Chenab River in northeastern Pakistan
**Munna** a general word in Urdu referring to male children
**octroi post** a tax collection station on the highway or at the entrance to a city or state
**rupee** the monetary unit in India and Pakistan

In a rush to get back to the city, I quickly crossed the dirt road and walked onto the Ravi° bridge, looking indifferently at the blazing edge of the sun steadily falling into the marsh. I had a queer feeling, as though I saw something. I spun around. There they were, three of them, leaning over the
5 bridge's guard rails and gazing straight into the sunset. Their deathly concentration made me look at the sunset myself, but I found nothing extraordinary in the scene; so I looked back at them instead. Their faces, although not at all similar, still looked curiously alike. Their outfits suggested that they were well-to-do villagers, and their dust-coated shoes that they had trudged
10 for miles just to watch the sun as it set over the marshes of the receding Ravi. Impervious to the traffic on the bridge, they went on staring at the marshes which were turning a dull, deep red in the sun's last glow.

I edged closer to them. The sun had gone down completely; only a dark red stripe remained on the far horizon. Suddenly the three looked at each
15 other, lowered their heads, and silently walked away, toward the villages outside the city. For some time I stood watching their tired figures recede into the distance. Soon the night sounds coming to life in the city reminded me that it was getting late and I'd better rush home. I quickened my pace and walked on under the blue haze of the night sky, pierced here and there
20 by the blinking lights of the city ahead.

The next evening when I reached the bridge, the sunset was a few minutes away. I suddenly recalled the three men and stopped to watch the sunset even though I knew Munna° would be waiting on the front porch for sweets and Zakiya, my wife, would be ready for us to go to the movies. I couldn't budge. An inexorable force seemed to have tied me to the ground. Through almost all the previous night I'd wondered what it was about the marsh and the sunset that had engrossed those strange men so entirely.

And then, just as the blazing orange disc of the sun tumbled into the marsh, I saw the three walk up the road. They were coming from villages outside the city limits. They wore identical clothes and resembled each other in their height and gait. Again they walked up to the bridge, stood at the same spot they had the previous evening and peered into the sunset with their flaming eyes filled with a dull sadness. I watched them and wondered why, despite their diverse features, they looked so much alike. One of them, who was very old, had a long, bushy snow-white beard. The second, somewhat lighter in complexion than the other, had a face that shone like gold in the orange glow of sunset. His hair hung down to his shoulders like a fringe, and he had a scar on his forehead. The third was dark and snub-nosed.

The sun sank all the way into the marsh. As on the previous day, the men glanced at each other, let their heads drop and, without exchanging a word, went their way.

That evening I felt terribly ill at ease. In a way I regretted not asking them about their utter fascination with the sunset. What could they be looking for in the sun's fading light? — I wondered. I told Zakiya about the strange threesome. She just laughed and said, "Must be peasants, on their way to the city to have a good time."

An air of strangeness surrounded these men. Zakiya, of course, could not have known it: one really had to look at them to feel the weird aura.

The next day I waited impatiently for the evening. I walked to the bridge, expecting them to show up. And they did, just as the daylight ebbed away. They leaned over the bridge and watched the sun go down, indifferent to the sound of traffic. Their absorption in the scene made it impossible to talk to them. I waited until the sun had gone down completely and the men had started to return. This would be the time to ask them what it was they expected to find in the vanishing sun and the marshes of the receding river.

When the sun had sunk all the way, the men gave one another a sad, mute look, lowered their heads and started off. But, instead of returning to the village, they took the road to the city. Their shoes were covered with dust and their feet moved on rhythmically together.

I gathered my faltering courage and asked them, "Brothers! what village do you come from?"

65 The man with the snub nose turned around and stared at me for a while. Then the three exchanged glances, but none of them bothered to answer my question.

"What do you see over there...on the bridge?" I asked. The mystery about the three men was beginning to weigh heavily upon me now. I felt 70 as though molten lead had seeped into my legs indeed into my whole body, and that it was only a matter of time before I'd crumble to the ground reeling from a spell of dizziness.

Again they did not answer. I shouted at them in a choking voice, "Why are you always staring at the sunset?"

75 No answer.

We reached the heavily congested city road. The evening sounds grew closer. It was late October, and the air felt pleasantly cool. The sweet scent of jasmine wafted in, borne by the breeze. As we passed the octroi post,° the old man with snow-white hair suddenly spoke, "Didn't you see? Has 80 nobody in the city seen...?"

"Seen what?"

"When the sun sets, when it goes down all the way...?" asked the hoary old man, rearranging his mantle over his shoulders.

"When the sun goes down all the way?" I repeated. "What about it? 85 That happens every day!"

I said that very quickly, afraid that the slightest pause might force them back into their impenetrable silence.

"We knew that, we knew it would be that way. That's why we came. That other village, there, too..." He pointed toward the east and lowered 90 his head.

"From there we come..." said the snub-nosed man.

"From where?" I asked, growing impatient. "Please tell me clearly."

The third man peered back at me over his shoulder. The scar on his forehead suddenly seemed deeper than before. He said, "We didn't notice, nor, 95 I believe, did you. Perhaps nobody did. Because, as you say, the sun rises and sets every day. Why bother to look? And we didn't, when day after day, there, over there," he pointed in the direction of the east, "the sky became blood-red and so bright it blazed like fire even at nightfall. We just failed to notice..." He stopped abruptly, as if choking over his words. "And now 100 this redness," he resumed after a pause, "it keeps spreading from place to place. I'd never seen such a phenomenon before. Nor my elders. Nor, I believe, did they hear their elders mention anything quite like that ever happening."

Meanwhile the darkness had deepened. All I could see of my compan-
105 ions were their white flowing robes; their faces became visible only when they came directly under the pale, dim light of the lampposts. I turned around to look at the stretch of sky over the distant Ravi. I was stunned: it was glowing red despite the darkness.

"You are right," I said, to hide my puzzlement, "we really did fail to
110 notice that." Then I asked, "Where are you going?"

"To the city, of course. What would be the point of arriving there *after-wards*?"

A sudden impulse made me want to stay with them, or to take them home with me. But abruptly, they headed off on another road, and I
115 remembered I was expected home soon. Munna would be waiting on the front porch for his daily sweets and Zakiya must be feeling irritated by my delay.

The next day I stopped at the bridge to watch the sunset. I was hoping to see those three men. The sun went down completely, but they didn't
120 appear. I waited impatiently for them to show up. Soon, however, I was entranced by the sunset's last magical glow.

The entire sky seemed covered with a sheet soaked in blood, and it scared me that I was standing all alone underneath it. I felt an uncanny presence directly behind me. I spun around. There was nobody. All the
125 same, I felt sure there was someone — standing behind my back, within me, or perhaps, somewhere near.

Vehicles, of all shapes and sizes, rumbled along in the light of the street-lamps. Way back in the east, a stretch of evening sky still blazed like a winding sheet of fire, radiating heat and light far into the closing darkness.
130 I was alarmed and scurried home. Hastily I told Zakiya all I'd seen. But she laughed off the whole thing. I took her up to the balcony and showed her the red and its infernal bright glow against the dark night sky. That sobered her up a little. She thought for a while, then remarked, "We're going to have a storm any minute — I'm sure."
135 The next day in the office, as I worked, bent over my files, I heard Mujibullah ask Hafiz Ahmad, "Say, did you see how the sky glows at sunset these days? Even after it gets dark? Amazing, isn't it?"

All at once I felt I was standing alone and defenseless under that blood-sheet of a sky. I was frightened. Small drops of sweat formed on my fore-
140 head. As the evening edged closer, a strange restlessness took hold of me.

The receding Ravi, the bridge, the night sky and the sun frightened me; I wanted to walk clear out of them. And yet, I also felt irresistibly drawn toward them.

I wanted to tell my colleagues about the three peasants who in spite of
145 their distinctly individual faces somehow looked alike; about how they had come to the city accompanying this strange redness, had drawn my attention to it, and then dropped out of sight; and about how I'd searched in vain for them everywhere. But I couldn't. Mujibullah and Hafiz Ahmad, my office-mates, had each borrowed about twenty rupees° from me some
150 time ago, which they conveniently forgot to return, and, into the bargain, had stopped talking to me ever since.

On my way home when I entered the bridge, a strange fear made me walk briskly, look away from the sun, and try to concentrate instead on the street before me. But the blood-red evening kept coming right along. I
155 could feel its presence everywhere. A flock of evening birds flew overhead in a "V" formation. Like the birds, I too was returning home. Home — yes, but no longer my haven against the outside world; for the flame-colored evening came pouring in from its windows, doors, even through its walls of solid masonry.

160 I now wandered late in the streets, looking for the three peasants. I wanted to ask them where that red came from. What was to follow? Why did they leave the last settlement? What shape was it in? But I couldn't find them anywhere. Nobody seemed to care.

A few days later I saw some men pointing up to the unusual red color
165 of the evening. Before long, the whole city was talking about it. I hadn't told a soul except Zakiya. How they had found out about it was a puzzle to me. Those three peasants must be in the city — I concluded. They have got to be.

The red of evening had now become the talk of the town.
170 Chaudhri Sahib, who owns a small bookshop in Mozang Plaza, was an old acquaintance of mine. People got together at his shop for a friendly chat every evening. Often, so did I. But for some time now, since my first encounter with those mantle-wrapped oracular figures, I had been too pre-occupied with my own thoughts to go there. No matter where I went, home
175 or outside, I felt restless. At home, an inexorable urge drove me outdoors; outdoors, an equally strong urge sent me scrambling back home, where I felt comparatively safer. I became very confused about where I wanted to be. I began to feel heavy and listless.

All the same, I did go back to the bookshop once again that evening.
180 Most of the regulars had already gathered. Chaudhri Sahib asked, "What

do you think about it, fellows? Is it all due to the atomic explosions as they say? The rumor also has it that pretty soon the earth's cold regions will turn hot and the hot ones cold and the cycle of seasons will also be upset."

185     I wanted to tell them about my encounter with the three villagers but felt too shy to talk before so many people. Just then a pungent smell, the likes of which I'd never smelled before, wafted in from God knows where. My heart sank and a strange, sweet sort of pain stabbed my body. I felt nauseous, unable to decide whether it was a stench, a pungent aroma, or 190 even a wave of bitter-sweet pain. I threw the newspaper down and got up to leave.

"What's the matter?" asked Chaudhri Sahib.

"I must go. God knows what sort of smell that is."

"Smell? What smell?" Chaudhri Sahib sniffed the air.

195     I didn't care to reply and walked away. That offensive smell, the terrifying wave of pain, followed me all the way home. It made me giddy. I thought I might fall any minute. My condition frightened Zakiya, who asked, "What's the matter — you look so pale?"

"I'm all right. God knows what that smell is." I said, wiping sweat off 200 my brow, although it was the month of November.

Zakiya also sniffed the air, then said, "Must be coming from the house of Hakim Sahib. Heaven knows what strange herb concoctions they keep making day and night. Or else it's from burnt food. I burnt some today accidentally."

205     "But it seems to be everywhere...in every street and lane...throughout the city."

"Why, of course. The season's changed. It must be the smell of winter flowers," she said inattentively, and became absorbed in her knitting.

With great trepidation I again sniffed the air, but couldn't decide 210 whether the sickening odor still lingered on or had subsided. Perhaps it had subsided. The thought relieved me a bit. But there was no escape from its memory, which remained fresh in my mind, like the itching that continues for some time even after the wound has healed. The very thought that it might return gave me the chills.

215     By next morning I'd forgotten all about that rotten, suffocating smell. In the office, I found a mountain of files waiting for me. But Mujibullah and Hafiz Ahmad went on noisily discussing some movie. I couldn't concentrate on the work and felt irritated. So I decided to take a break. I called our office boy and sent him to the cafeteria for a cup of tea. Meanwhile I 220 pulled out a pack of cigarettes from my pocket and lit up.

Just then I felt a cracking blow on my head, as if I had fallen off a cliff and landed on my head, which fused everything before my eyes in a swirling blue and yellow streak. It took my numbed senses some time to realize that I was being assaulted once again by the same pain, the same
225 terrible stench. It kept coming at me in waves, and it was impossible to know its source. I found myself frantically shutting every single window in the office, while both Mujibullah and Hafiz Ahmad gawked at me uncomprehendingly.

"Let the sun in! Why are you slamming the windows?" asked Hafiz
230 Ahmad.

"The stench...the stench! My God, it's unbearable! Don't you smell it?"

Both of them raised their noses to the air and sniffed. Then Hafiz Ahmad remarked. "That's right. What sort of stench...or fragrance is that? It makes my heart sink."

235 Soon, many people were talking about the stink-waves which came in quick succession and then receded, only to renew their assault a little while later. At sundown they became especially unbearable.

Within a few weeks the stinking odor had become so oppressive that I often found it difficult to breathe. People's faces, usually quite lively and
240 fresh, now looked drained and wilted. Many complained of constant palpitation and headaches. The doctors cashed in. Intellectuals hypothesized that it must be due to nuclear blasts, which were producing strange effects throughout the world, including this foul odor in our city, which attacked people's nerves and left them in a mess. People scrambled to buy tran-
245 quilizers, which sold out instantly. Not that the supply was inadequate, but a sudden frenzy to stock up and hoard had seized people. Even sleeping pills fetched the price of rare diamonds.

I found both tranquilizers and sleeping pills useless. The stench cut sharper than a sword and penetrated the body like a laser. The only way
250 to guard against it was to get used to it — I thought; and people would do well to remember that. But I was too depressed to tell them myself. Within a few weeks, however, they themselves came to live with the stench.

Just the same, the stench struck terror in the city. People were loath to admit it, but they could not have looked more tense: their faces contorted
255 from the fear of some terrible thing happening at any moment. Nor was their fear unreasonable, as a subsequent event showed a few weeks later.

On a cold mid-December evening, I was returning home from Chaudhri Sahib's. The street was full of traffic and jostling crowds. The stores glittered with bright lights, and people went about their business as usual. Every
260 now and then a stench-wave swept in, made me giddy, and receded. I

would freeze in my stride the instant it assailed me and would start moving again as soon as it had subsided. It was the same with others. An outsider would surely have wondered why we suddenly froze, closed our eyes, stopped breathing, then took a deep breath and got started again. But that was our custom now.

That December evening I'd just walked onto the bridge when I felt as if a lance had hit me on the head. My head whirled and my legs buckled. Reeling, I clung on to a lamppost and tried to support my head with my hands. There was no lance, nor was there a hand to wield it. It was that smell — that same rotten smell — I realized with terror. In fact, it seemed that the source of the oppressive stench had suddenly moved very close to me, between my shoulder blades, near my back, immediately behind me — so close that it was impossible to think of it as apart from me.

It was then that my eyes fell on the strange carriage, rambling along in front of me. It was an oversized wagon pulled by a pair of scrawny white oxen with leather blinders over their eyes and thick ropes strung through their steaming nostrils. A wooden cage sat atop the base of the wagon, its interior hidden behind black curtains — or were they just swaying walls of darkness?

Two men, sitting outside the cage enclosure in the front of the wagon, drove the two emaciated, blindfolded animals. I couldn't make out their faces, partly because of the darkness, but partly also because they were buried in folds of cloth thrown loosely around them. Their heads drooped forward and they seemed to have dozed off, overcome by fatigue and sleep.

Behind them the interior of the curtained wagon swelled with darkness and from the heart of that darkness shot out the nauseating stench which cut sharper than a sword...Before I knew it, the wagon had creaked past me, flooding my senses with its cargo of stink. My head swirled. I jumped off the main road onto the dirt sidewalk...and vomited.

I had no idea whether the people in the city had also seen the eerie wagon. If they had, what must have they endured? I had the hardest time getting home after what I had seen. Once inside the house, I ran to my bed and threw myself on it. Zakiya kept asking me what had happened, but a blind terror sealed my lips.

A few days later a small news item appeared in the local papers. It railed against the local Municipal Office for allowing garbage carts to pass through busy streets in the evening. Not only did muck-wagons pollute the air, they also hurt the fine olfactory sense of the citizenry.

300     I took a whole week off from work. During those seven days, though hardly fit to go out and observe firsthand the plight of the city, I was nonetheless kept posted of developments by local newspapers. Groups of concerned citizens demanded that the municipal authorities keep the city clear of the muck-wagons or, if that was impossible, assign them routes
305 along less busy streets.

    On the seventh day I ventured out. A change was already visible. Wrecked by insomnia and exhaustion, people strained themselves to appear carefree and cheerful, but managed only to look painfully silly. Suddenly I recalled that in the morning I had myself looked no different in
310 the mirror.

    About this time, the number of entertainment programs and movies shot up as never before. People swarmed to box offices — often hours before a show — where they formed long lines and patiently waited to be let in, and then filed out from the entertainment still looking pale and
315 ridiculous.

    In the office, no matter how hard I tried, I couldn't concentrate on work. Intermittently, the image of the muck-wagon lumbering down the streets flashed across my mind. Was it really one of those municipal dump-carts? No. It couldn't be. Municipal dump-carts never looked like that eerie
320 wagon, with its sleepy drivers, a pair of blindfolded bony oxen, black curtains and the outrageously nauseating smell. What on earth could give off such an odd smell — at once fragrant and foul!

    An insane desire suddenly overwhelmed me: to rush up to the wagon, lift up those swaying curtains, and peek inside. I must discover the source
325 of the stench!

    Coming to the bridge my feet involuntarily slowed down. There was still some time before sunset and the waves of the pain-filled odor came faster and stronger. I leaned over the bridge, an unknown fear slowly rising in my throat. The bottomless swamp, its arms ominously outstretched,
330 seemed to be dragging me down toward it. I was afraid I might jump into the swamp, sink with the sun and become buried forever in that sprawling sheet of blood.

    I became aware of something approaching me or was I myself drawing closer to something?...Something awaited by all men — those before and
335 those after us. My whole body felt as though it was turning into a piece of granite, with no escape from the bridge, the miasma, the sun, for now they all seemed inseparable from my being. Helplessly, I looked around myself and almost dropped dead.

The three men were coming towards me from the direction of the coun-
340 tryside. As before, they were wrapped in their flowing white robes and
walked with their amazingly identical gait. I kept staring at them with
glassy eyes until they walked right up to me and stopped. The hoary old
man was crying, and his snow-white beard was drenched in tears. The
other two couldn't look up; their eyes were lowered mournfully, their teeth
345 clenched and their faces withered by a deathly pallor.

"Where were you hiding all these days?" I said between gasps and stam-
mers. "I searched for you everywhere. Tell me, please, what's happening to
the city?"

"We were waiting. Trying to hold ourselves back. We had tied ourselves
350 with ropes. Here, look!" They spread their arms before me and bared their
shoulders and backs, revealing the deep marks of the rope.

"We did not want to come..." the old man said, drowned out by a fit of
sobs.

"But there was no choice..." the second man said. Before he had fin-
355 ished, he doubled over. His companions also doubled over, as if unable to
control a sudden surge of pain. The same wave of pain-filled stench
stabbed the air about us, cutting us into halves, flooding our senses, as it
scrambled past us.

"There! Look!" said the old man, pointing in the direction of the distant
360 villages and turning deathly pale.

In the distance, I saw the wagon come up the road from behind a cloud
of dust. The drowsing coachmen had wrapped their faces because of their
nearness to the cutting stench.

A cold shiver ran through my spine. The eyes of the three men suddenly
365 became dull. They were approaching their end — perhaps.

The wagon rumbled close — the stench from it draining the blood from
our bodies — and then passed us. Its sinister, jet-black curtains, fluttering
in the gentle breeze, appeared, oddly enough, entirely motionless.

The three men ran after the wagon, caught up to it and lifted the cur-
370 tains. A split second later, a nonhuman scream burst from their gaping
mouths. They spun around and bolted toward the distant fields.

"What was it? What did you see?" I asked, running after them. But they
did not reply and kept running madly. Their eyes had frozen in a glazed
stare.

375 I followed them until we had left the city several miles behind us, then
grabbed the old man's robe and implored, "Tell me! Please tell me!"

He turned his deathly gaze and threw open his mouth. His tongue had
got stuck to his palate.

All three had become dumb.

380    My head whirled, and I collapsed. The three men continued to run, soon disappearing in the distance behind a spiraling cloud of dust. Slowly the dust settled and I returned home.

For months now I have searched in vain for those men. They have vanished without a trace. And the wagon...from that fateful evening, it too has
385  changed its route. It no longer passes through the city. After crossing the bridge, it now descends onto the dirt trail leading to villages in the countryside.

The cityfolk are no longer bothered by the slashing stench. They have become immune to it and think it has died, like an old, forgotten tale.

390    But it continues to torment my body, and day and night a voice keeps telling me, "Now, your turn! Now you shall *see!*"

And this evening I find myself on the bridge, waiting for the wagon...waiting.

(1963)

## Following the Story

1. What is the setting of the beginning of the story?
2. Is the protagonist a round and dynamic character? Why or why not?
3. How are the events arranged? Draw a chart to show the time line of the action in the story.
4. What are the major conflicts of the story?
5. When does the protagonist begin to suffer from the stench? Can you pinpoint it?
6. When does the protagonist first see the wagon? What is his reaction?
7. How do people try to explain the appearance of the wagon? Does the protagonist accept the explanation?
8. What happens when the protagonist sees the three men again?
9. What happens to the protagonist at the end?
10. Is the narrative voice in this story different from that in "The Cage"? If so, what are the major differences?

## Responding to the Story

1. If you were to describe the protagonist with five adjectives, what would be your choice of words?
2. What explanations are given in the story about the blood-red sunset? Are they reasonable? Why or why not?

3. Neither the village where the three men are from nor the city where the protagonist is living has a name. Why isn't the author specific about names of places?
4. Do you find the characters in this story realistic and believable? Why or why not?
5. Could you relate to the protagonist and his reaction to his surroundings? Give reasons for your response.
6. How do you respond to the dénouement of the story? Do you think the protagonist is out of his mind?
7. What do you think the wagon stands for?
8. Do you think the story makes sense at the surface level or only at an allegorical level? Give reasons for your answer.
9. If a few details were changed, could this story take place in North America and how believable would it be?
10. What do you think is the "unique or single effect" of this short story?

# Unit Review

When analyzing literary devices and techniques, be sure to follow these guidelines:

- Understand the concepts and definitions of key literary devices and techniques (ideally linking one example with each device/technique).
- Take note of unusual choice of words, sentence structure, repetitions, and patterns while reading. Remember: It requires careful examination (definitely more than one reading) to accomplish these tasks:
  1. Identify simile, metaphor, and personification as they appear in the story.
  2. Trace use of images and patterns of imagery.
  3. Identify allusions to other literary works and cultural, historical, political, and religious events.
  4. Identify verbal, situational, and dramatic irony.
  5. Recognize symbols and symbolism.
  6. Consider the possibility of reading the story allegorically. (Remember: Not many stories contain allegorical elements.)
- Figure out what effect the literary devices and techniques that you have identified produce in the story. Try removing them and see what is left.
- Read again to appreciate the story with an insight into how a variety of devices and techniques contribute to its interest.

# Unit 6

## Theme and Interpretation

*His theme is the universe, or something universal, but he is not necessarily going to 'say' anything about the universe; he proposes to sing, and the strangeness of the song arising in the halls of fiction is bound to give us a shock.*

E.M. FORSTER

In the previous five units we have discussed and analyzed the various elements of fiction in relation to the short story. We took apart each story in order to understand how its author created the experience we shared in reading it. When we consider the **theme** of a short story, we ask ourselves *why* and *how* that reading experience is significant to us. Identifying the theme means discovering the meaning or implication of the story and, frequently, figuring out the purpose of the author. To identify the theme or themes of a story, we now need to synthesize, or put together, the elements of fiction that we have pulled apart for analysis, and regard the story as a whole. As Edgar Allan Poe reminds us, an author writes "with deliberate care" to create a "unique or single effect" in order to "touch the soul of the reader."

When we consider the "unique or single effect" of a story, we need to remember that the theme is not the same thing as the plot or the subject. As we discussed in Unit 1, plot is the causal arrangement of the events of a story, and it alone does not allow us to examine the ideas or values conveyed by the story; that is why a plot summary is simply not enough to define theme. The theme is more than what happens in the story, and it is also more than the subject that the story explores. The theme is, in fact, the subject of the story and the light the story sheds on that subject put together.

For example, in "Salvatore" (page 106) the subject is Salvatore the protagonist, and the story simply delineates his life. In the context of the story, Salvatore is portrayed as "an ordinary Italian fisherman who possessed nothing in the world except a quality which is the rarest, the most precious and the loveliest" (lines 128–129). As the author makes clear in the narrative, however, the theme of "Salvatore" is twofold: to celebrate the extraordinary goodness among "the common run of men" and to extol the act of writing. By demonstrating as his theme that it is in the ordinary that the extraordinary exists, Maugham actually presents a profound **paradox**, the "shock" for us, as E.M. Forster calls it.

The term *theme* is often used to mean the central insight a story contains, the statement about humanity or the universal truth the author expresses and shares with the reader. The theme of a short story tends to provide a perspective or a comment on a significant experience in life. For instance, many of us have experienced culture clash, whether it be the result of emigration, social expectations, or intergenerational conflict. "The Cage" (page 154) explores this theme of culture clash from the perspective of a young Japanese woman who finds herself in conflict with a variety of cultural expectations. Writing about "The Cage," author Neil Bissoondath comments, "I grew up in a culture that restricted me, a culture that imposed its values on me and that had little regard for my personal feelings and desires. From this point of view, I identify with that Japanese girl very closely."

Bissoondath makes it clear that the short story writer wants to engage our senses, emotions, understanding, and imagination. Through the story, we share the life of another person in the hope of discovering, in the process, something about ourselves and the world around us. As the author of the UNESCO publication *Problems in Education* points out, "The person who...has never lifted the 'language curtain' behind which other people move and talk and think and feel in a way which is particular to them may not even suspect there is a way of living which is distinct from his own, let alone understand it." In discussing theme, we must lift the "language curtain" and work to understand what we find there. Unlike its literary precursors, such as the fable, which supplies the moral at the end, the short story never spells out its theme. Moreover, our response to a story, to its "shock," is completely our own.

Our interpretation of a story's theme requires us to consider all the elements of fiction to determine what experiences and ideas about life the author is communicating. To ensure that our interpretation is consistent with the form and content of the story, we have to keep in mind that every element in the story works to support and enhance the theme. A story contains the means of its own interpretation. The tools of literary analysis employed in the preceding five units enable us to support our identification of a story's theme with evidence from the story itself.

Most stories make use of more than one of these elements to explore their themes, so we must recognize and examine all of them to support our interpretation of the theme. This act of interpretation is our responsibility and essential to story reading and story writing. As the American writer Ralph Waldo Emerson (1803–1882) sums up, "'Tis the good reader that makes the good book."

First of all, how does *the point of view* reflect or reinforce the story's theme(s)? The narrative point of view of "War" (page 132) is third-person omniscient and its tone is dispassionate. The narrator simply sketches in background details and physical descriptions of the characters. Much of this story is told by showing, through the characters engaging one another in vehement debate. One of the ways the theme of this story, the tragic consequences of war, emerges is from the differences in the tone between the detached narrator and the emotional passengers. The narrative voice records the debate among the exhausted characters, who are seated on opposite sides of the second-class carriage and so physically separated. The narrator contrasts the sad silence of "the bundled woman" and the patriotic eloquence of the "fat man." This confrontation finally provides the "shock" of the ending in which the man who rationally defended death with honour on the battlefield is reduced to incoherent sobs because of his own loss.

Sometimes the theme can be *a statement by the narrator or a character* in the story. Look at this opening statement made by the first-person narrator of "The Cage": "For my mother, my father, not an unkind man, designed a house. For me, my father, not a kind man, designed a cage" (Bissoondath, lines 2–4). The narrator has succinctly depicted her dilemma. She is trapped by her father's demands and expectations: "[f]or me...my father designed a cage." Also she is alienated from her father: "For me, my father, not a kind man." However, it is clear the relationship with her mother is more complex: "[f]or my mother, my father, not an unkind man" indicates that the mother's view of the father is at odds with the narrator's and this will likely cause more tension. Finally the narrator recognizes her father's role as the provider for the family, but then makes clear that what he provides does not necessarily sustain emotional needs. "For my mother, my father...built a house." Thus, the themes of this story are, in fact, established by the narrator in its opening lines.

Also, the *arrangement of the events* in a story often offers a clue to the theme. In "The Gift of the Magi," for example, the order of the events is crucial to the dénouement of the story. A couple so loves one another that each sacrifices for the other the only treasure each possesses and of which each is proud. The wife cuts and sells her beautiful hair so that she can buy her husband a watch chain for Christmas. The husband sells his precious watch so that he can buy his wife combs for her hair. To express their mutual love, the husband and wife make sacrifices that are in vain. In fact, they are sacrifices of their vanity. The use of situational irony depends upon the ordering of the events to achieve its full impact: the demonstration of the emptiness of vanity and the celebration of love as the true gift in life.

Often recognizing *conflict(s) in a story* leads to identification of its themes. For instance, in "Look Out" (page 50) the conflict arises from the young woman's growing dissatisfaction with her role in her brother's household. Here she "looks out" for his children and for his mentally unstable wife. She feels trapped by family responsibilities, but is unable to free herself from these obligations until, perhaps, she meets the young linesman. This meeting ends suddenly when her brother returns home that evening, and her anxious response points to the theme of this story. The young woman is on the brink of independence, in the process of defining herself, her own needs. This emerging sense of self involves "looking out" for oneself and making choices for oneself, and requires her to stand up against her brother. The ambiguity of the story's ending suggests that the young woman has not yet decided whether her tears are "all for nothing."

A *character's transformation* as a result of the action is often a clue to the theme of the story. The process of coming to maturity or self-definition is a common theme in literature; a **novel** that traces this growth is called a **bildungsroman**. A short story normally focuses on a definitive moment in a character's life, so a moment of transformation, of or revelation, by a character can often point to its theme. A defining moment that creates a change or causes a character to see differently is also called an **epiphany**, a term coined in this context by James Joyce. For example, the story of "Prairie Widow" depicts Gum-may's transformation from a dependent and submissive Chinese wife to a determined and independent owner of a café in a small town in the Canadian prairies. Her moment of transformation or revelation occurs at the beginning of the story, as she leafs through old photographs and documents after her husband's death. She finally comes to the realization that she belongs in the prairies with her children. It is through this character transformation that Paul Yee, the author, extols the value of independence for this immigrant woman, conveying one important theme in his story.

Very often *literary devices and techniques* can also help to convey the theme of a story. A good example can be found in Roger Mais's symbolic use of the moon and the rain in "Look Out" to reflect the young woman's vulnerable character and her struggle to define her own identity. All the symbols form a part of the "deliberate care" with which an author "touches the soul of the reader." We have read two stories that use a cage as a central symbol. "Cages" by Guy Vanderhaege and "The Cage" by Neil Bissoondath both feature actual cages, which function symbolically to represent *things beyond themselves*. In both cases the cage, as a conventional symbol, represents the entrapment or limitation of the protagonists, which forms important themes in the stories. In the same manner, the handful of dates the young boy spews up at the end of Tayeb Salih's story symbolizes his rejection of his grandfather's outlook on life and highlights the theme of the story.

Finally we come to the essential clue to the interpretation of a story that every author offers us first: *the title*. The title of a story is carefully chosen to encapsulate the story and to captivate the reader. The title usually throws light on the theme of a story. Now let us consider a few titles we have read so far. "The Stolen Party" provokes us to question not only who the thief is in the story, but also from whom the party is stolen—both questions leading us to its theme. "Look Out" simultaneously expresses an explicit warning and describes the action of the protagonist—tying together two of the themes contained in the story. A title can be as short as one word, such as "Cages," which represents both the literal and the symbolic cages in Billy's life, highlighting the central theme of the story. On the other hand, it can be as long as "The Half-Closed Eyes of the Buddha and the Slowly Setting Sun." This title links Nepal with cultural colonialism, for the title alludes to the old saying that the sun does not set on the British empire. Finally, "The Gift of the Magi" refers to the Biblical story that underlies the theme of O. Henry's classic Christmas story.

The title of a story prepares the reader, sets up expectations and offers insight into its theme(s). It is always advisable, then, to go back to the title after reading a story and try to figure out "why this title?" and "what light does it shed on the story?" Different readers respond differently depending on the experiences, values, or ideas they bring to the reading, so they may see different themes in the same story or interpret the same theme in a different light. Whether we agree or disagree on how to interpret the theme of a short story, we should always base our reading and interpretation on the written text. Of course we can take into account the author's life, culture, and beliefs, but these are secondary sources of interpretation and add depth to our understanding. We should also keep in mind that analyzing or interpreting the theme(s) of a short story goes far beyond mere searching for emotional connections or hunting for moral messages, for a short story is not a fable. As Susan Sontag puts it so pithily, "Art is not only about something; it is something. A work of art is a thing in the world, not just a text or a commentary on the world." A good understanding of the theme (meaning) of a story depends on careful perusal of the work of art and all the elements that form the whole.

The three stories in this unit are entitled "Marriage Is a Private Affair," "Traplines," and "Swimming Lessons." Try to find out what each of these titles suggests and how it throws light on the theme(s) of the respective story. You will find that all three stories explore in their different ways parent-child relationships. That means they all deal with the same subject, but what about their themes? Are they different from one another?

---

# Marriage Is a Private Affair

Chinua Achebe (Nigeria) 1930–

## About the Author

*Born in Ogidi, Nigeria, Chinua Achebe attended University College in Ibadan, run by the University of London, and gained his B.A. in 1953. He studied broadcasting at the British Broadcasting Corporation in 1956. He was a producer for the Nigerian Broadcasting Company (NBC) in Lagos, Nigeria's capital, for 12 years. During the Nigerian civil war (1966–1970), he moved to the country's eastern region and devoted his time to writing poetry, short stories, and essays. He made several trips to the United States as a visiting professor before taking a teaching position at the University of Nigeria in Nsukka in 1976. His first novel* Things Fall Apart *(1958) was a huge success, winning him the Margaret Wrong Memorial Prize, and his fifth novel* Anthills of the Savannah *(1988) earned him a nomination for the prestigious Booker Prize.*

*Although his first language is Ibo, Chinua Achebe writes in English. Many critics regard him as the finest of the Nigerian novelists; Achebe's contributions to literature extend beyond the borders of Nigeria and post-colonial Africa. Like his novels, his short stories depict the conflict between traditional and modern values and develop the theme of "tradition versus change." Focusing on the universal qualities of human nature, Achebe's stories are appealing to many readers because of his acute vision and subtle irony. As Achebe once stated, he writes for the whole world because his "politics is concerned with universal communication across racial and cultural boundaries as a means of fostering respect for all people."*

## About the Story

*This story was originally published in* Girls at War and Other Stories *in 1972. The story takes place in Nigeria, a large country on the west coast of Africa, which has a linguistically and culturally varied population of more than 115 million people. The story is set in two locations: the first setting is Lagos, a cosmopolitan and modern city of over 6 million and the capital of Nigeria; the second setting is a small village in the countryside. This story cleverly presents the traditional, tribal way of life through cultural values held by the father, Okeke, and contrasts them with the modern approach of Nene. Caught between these two is Nnaemeka, Okeke's son, who chooses to marry Nene in spite of his father's opposition. Okeke is also a staunch Christian who turns to the Bible for guidance throughout this story; the epiphany in this story is his.*

"Have you written to your dad yet?" asked Nene one afternoon as she sat with Nnaemeka in her room at 16 Kasanga Street, Lagos.

"No. I've been thinking about it. I think it's better to tell him when I get home on leave!"

5 "But why? Your leave is such a long way off yet—six whole weeks. He should be let into our happiness now."

Nnaemeka was silent for a while, and then began very slowly as if he groped for his words: "I wish I were sure it would be happiness to him."

"Of course it must," replied Nene, a little surprised. "Why shouldn't it?"

10 "You have lived in Lagos all your life, and you know very little about people in remote parts of the country."

"That's what you always say. But I don't believe anybody will be so unlike other people that they will be unhappy when their sons are engaged to marry."

15 "Yes. They are most unhappy if the engagement is not arranged by them. In our case it's worse—you are not even an Ibo."

This was said so seriously and so bluntly that Nene could not find speech immediately. In the cosmopolitan atmosphere of the city it had always seemed to her something of a joke that a person's tribe could deter-
20 mine whom he married.

At last she said, "You don't really mean that he will object to your marrying me simply on that account? I had always thought you Ibos were kindly-disposed to other people."

"So we are. But when it comes to marriage, well, it's not quite so simple.
25 And this," he added, "is not peculiar to the Ibos. If your father were alive and lived in the heart of Ibibio-land he would be exactly like my father."

"I don't know. But anyway, as your father is so fond of you, I'm sure he will forgive you soon enough. Come on then, be a good boy and send him a nice lovely letter..."

30    "It would not be wise to break the news to him by writing. A letter will bring it upon him with a shock. I'm quite sure about that."

"All right, honey, suit yourself. You know your father."

As Nnaemeka walked home that evening he turned over in his mind different ways of overcoming his father's opposition, especially now that

35 he had gone and found a girl for him. He had thought of showing his letter to Nene but decided on second thoughts not to, at least for the moment. He read it again when he got home and couldn't help smiling to himself. He remembered Ugoye quite well, an Amazon of a girl who used to beat up all the boys, himself included, on the way to the stream, a complete

40 dunce at school.

*I have found a girl who will suit you admirably—Ugoye Nweke, the eldest daughter of our neighbor, Jacob Nweke. She has a proper Christian upbringing. When she stopped schooling some years ago her father (a man of sound judg-ment) sent her to live in the house of a pastor where she has received all the*

45 *training a wife could need. Her Sunday school teacher has told me that she reads her Bible very fluently. I hope we shall begin negotiations when you come home in December.*

On the second evening of his return from Lagos Nnaemeka sat with his father under a cassia tree. This was the old man's retreat where he went to

50 read his Bible when the parching December sun had set and a fresh, reviving wind blew on the leaves.

"Father," began Nnaemeka suddenly, "I have come to ask for forgiveness."

"Forgiveness? For what, my son?" he asked in amazement.

"It's about this marriage question."

55    "Which marriage question?"

"I can't—we must—I mean it is impossible for me to marry Nweke's daughter."

"Impossible? Why?" asked his father.

"I don't love her."

60    "Nobody said you did. Why should you?" he asked.

"Marriage today is different..."

"Look here, my son," interrupted his father, "nothing is different. What one looks for in a wife are a good character and a Christian background."

Nnaemeka saw there was no hope along the present line of argument.

65    "Moreover," he said, "I am engaged to marry another girl who has all of Ugoye's good qualities, and who…"

His father did not believe his ears. "What did you say?" he asked slowly and disconcertingly.

"She is a good Christian," his son went on; "and a teacher in a Girls'
70 School in Lagos."

"Teacher, did you say? If you consider that a qualification for a good wife I should like to point out to you, Emeka, that no Christian woman should teach. St. Paul in his letter to the Corinthians says that women should keep silence." He rose slowly from his seat and paced forwards and
75 backwards. This was his pet subject, and he condemned vehemently those church leaders who encouraged women to teach in their schools. After he had spent his emotion on a long homily he at last came back to his son's engagement, in a seemingly milder tone.

"Whose daughter is she, anyway?"
80    "She is Nene Atang."

"What!" All the mildness was gone again. "Did you say Neneataga, what does that mean?"

"Nene Atang from Calabar. She is the only girl I can marry." This was a very rash reply and Nnaemeka expected the storm to burst. But it did not.
85 His father merely walked away into his room. This was most unexpected and perplexed Nnaemeka. His father's silence was infinitely more menacing than a flood of threatening speech. That night the old man did not eat.

When he sent for Nnaemeka a day later he applied all possible ways of dissuasion. But the young man's heart was hardened, and his father even-
90 tually gave him up as lost.

"I owe it to you, my son, as a duty to show you what is right and what is wrong. Whoever put this idea into your head might as well have cut your throat. It is Satan's work." He waved his son away.

"You will change your mind, Father, when you know Nene."
95    "I shall never see her," was the reply. From that night the father scarcely spoke to his son. He did not, however, cease hoping that he would realize how serious was the danger he was heading for. Day and night he put him in his prayers.

Nnaemeka, for his own part, was very deeply affected by his father's
100 grief. But he kept hoping that it would pass away. If it had occurred to him that never in the history of his people had a man married a woman who spoke a different tongue, he might have been less optimistic. "It has never been heard," was the verdict of an old man speaking a few weeks later. In that short sentence he spoke for all of his people. This man had come with

105 others to commiserate with Okeke when news went round about his son's behavior. By that time the son had gone back to Lagos.

"It has never been heard," said the old man again with a sad shake of his head.

"What did Our Lord say?" asked another gentleman. "Sons shall rise 110 against their Fathers; it is there in the Holy Book."

"It is the beginning of the end," said another.

The discussion thus tending to become theological, Madubogwu, a highly practical man, brought it down once more to the ordinary level.

"Have you thought of consulting a native doctor about your son?" he 115 asked Nnaemeka's father.

"He isn't sick," was the reply.

"What is he then? The boy's mind is diseased and only a good herbalist can bring him back to his right senses. The medicine he requires is *Amalile*, the same that women apply with success to recapture their husbands' 120 straying affection."

"Madubogwu is right," said another gentleman. "This thing calls for medicine."

"I shall not call in a native doctor." Nnaemeka's father was known to be obstinately ahead of his more superstitious neighbors in these matters. 125 "I will not be another Mrs. Ochuba. If my son wants to kill himself let him do it with his own hands. It is not for me to help him."

"But it was her fault," said Madubogwu. "She ought to have gone to an honest herbalist. She was a clever woman, nevertheless."

"She was a wicked murderess," said Jonathan who rarely argued with 130 his neighbors because, he often said, they were incapable of reasoning. "The medicine was prepared for her husband, it was his name they called in its preparation and I am sure it would have been perfectly beneficial to him. It was wicked to put it into the herbalist's food, and say you were only trying it out."

135 Six months later, Nnaemeka was showing his young wife a short letter from his father:

It amazes me that you could be so unfeeling as to send me your wedding pic-ture. I would have sent it back. But on further thought I decided just to cut off your wife and send it back to you because I have nothing to do with her. How I 140 wish that I had nothing to do with you either.

When Nene read through this letter and looked at the mutilated picture her eyes filled with tears, and she began to sob.

"Don't cry, my darling," said her husband. "He is essentially good-natured and will one day look more kindly on our marriage." But years 145 passed and that one day did not come.

For eight years, Okeke would have nothing to do with his son, Nnaemeka. Only three times (when Nnaemeka asked to come home and spend his leave) did he write to him.

"I can't have you in my house," he replied on one occasion. "It can be 150 of no interest to me where or how you spend your leave—or your life, for that matter."

The prejudice against Nnaemeka's marriage was not confined to his little village. In Lagos, especially among his people who worked there, it showed itself in a different way. Their women, when they met at their vil-155 lage meeting, were not hostile to Nene. Rather, they paid her such excessive deference as to make her feel she was not one of them. But as time went on, Nene gradually broke through some of this prejudice and even began to make friends among them. Slowly and gradually they began to admit that she kept her home much better than most of them.

160 The story eventually got to the little village in the heart of the Ibo country that Nnaemeka and his young wife were a most happy couple. But his father was one of the few people in the village who knew nothing about this. He always displayed so much temper whenever his son's name was mentioned that everyone avoided it in his presence. By a tremendous 165 effort of will he had succeeded in pushing his son to the back of his mind. The strain had nearly killed him but he had persevered, and won.

Then one day he received a letter from Nene, and in spite of himself he began to glance through it perfunctorily until all of a sudden the expression on his face changed and he began to read more carefully.

170 *...Our two sons, from the day they learnt that they had a grandfather, have insisted on being taken to him. I find it impossible to tell them that you will not see them. I implore you to allow Nnaemeka to bring them home for a short time during his leave next month. I shall remain here in Lagos...*

The old man at once felt the resolution he had built up over so many 175 years falling in. He was telling himself that he must not give in. He tried to steel his heart against all emotional appeals. It was a reenactment of that other struggle. He leaned against a window and looked out. The sky was overcast with heavy black clouds and a high wind began to blow filling the air with dust and dry leaves. It was one of those rare occasions 180 when even Nature takes a hand in a human fight. Very soon it began to

rain, the first rain in the year. It came down in large sharp drops and was accompanied by the lightning and thunder which mark a change of season. Okeke was trying hard not to think of his two grandsons. But he knew he was now fighting a losing battle. He tried to hum a favorite hymn
185 but the pattering of large rain drops on the roof broke up the tune. His mind immediately returned to the children. How could he shut his door against them? By a curious mental process he imagined them standing, sad and forsaken, under the harsh angry weather—shut out from his house.

190    That night he hardly slept, from remorse—and a vague fear that he might die without making it up to them.

(1972)

## Following the Story

1. What is the conflict in this story?
2. What methods does the narrator use to present the characters: telling, or showing, or in-depth presentation, or a combination of all? Support your answer with details from the text.
3. What types of characters are Nene, Nnaemeka, and Okeke? Support your response with details from the text.
4. What are the qualities of a "good wife" according to Okeke?
5. What details are included to show that family ties are important to Nene and Nnaemeka?
6. Describe the narrative voice of this story.
7. How do the excerpts from the various letters help to "tell" the story?
8. Near the end of this story, the narrator comments, "It was one of those rare occasions when Nature takes a hand in a human fight" (lines 179–180). What sort of literary devices are used in this quote?
9. What impact does the climax in this story have on Okeke?
10. What causes Okeke to feel such remorse at the end of this story?

## Responding to the Story

1. What does the title of this story suggest to you?
2. Nnaemeka has chosen a "love marriage" rather than an arranged marriage. How does this choice relate to the title of the story?
3. How would you describe Okeke's personality? Use details from the text to support your response.

4. The story takes place in a modern city and in an isolated rural village. Each of these places is associated with a set of values, which create the psychological setting. How would you describe this setting?
5. What does it mean (in line 180) that "Nature takes a hand" in Okeke's life?
6. What sorts of prejudice does this story explore?
7. The story establishes a conflict between Okeke's traditional values and Nene's cosmopolitan values. What details does Achebe include to universalize this opposition and suggest it is not confined to Nigerian society?
8. How does the dénouement reflect the opening scene of this story?
9. Explain how the last sentence of this story conveys the hope of reconciliation.
10. The subject of this story is the relationship between the father and his son, but what is the theme?

---

# Traplines

Thomas King (Canada) 1943–

## About the Author

*Born in Sacramento, California, to a father of Cherokee Indian descent and a mother of German-Greek ancestry, Thomas King attended California State University at Chico where he received his B.A. and M.A. in English in 1970 and 1972 respectively. In 1986 he earned his Ph.D. in English and American Studies from the University of Utah. He worked as a photojournalist in Australia and New Zealand, a tool designer for Boeing Aircraft, and an administrator at various universities in the U.S. He was a professor of Native Studies at the University of Lethbridge, Alberta from 1979 to 1989. He then taught at the University of Minnesota before moving back to Canada in 1995 to teach at the University of Guelph. King began to publish short stories in 1987 in magazines, and his first novel* Medicine River *was published in 1990, gaining him the PEN/Josephine Miles Award. For* A Coyote Columbus Story *(1992), a children's book, he won the Governor General's Award. In 2004, he received the Trillium Award for* The Truth About Stories.

*The theme of the exclusion of aboriginals in North America from mainstream society is prevalent in King's writings. His short stories as well as his novels are noted for their humour and irony and for their innovative arrangement of events and skillful use of narrative voice. As an influential author in the Native American literary community of Canada and the United States, Thomas King entertains readers of varied* cultural backgrounds and deserves our attention. King deliberately sets his stories in the present, which he believes is "a period that is relatively free of literary monoliths and which allows for a greater latitude in the creation of characters and situations, and, more importantly, allows us [native authors] the opportunity to create for ourselves and our respective cultures both a present and a future."

## About the Story

In "Traplines," King creates a narrator through whom he can humorously present the day-to-day activities and social realities of Native life. Inadvertently, it seems, the narrator tells the recent history of his people, suggesting the importance that trapping and fishing once held in his culture, and conveying the racism they have experienced. All of this happens in the simple story of the summer in which the narrator's son graduates from high school and sets off for university. In fact, this short story is an interweaving of many stories, which are developed through the skillful use of dialogue and the narrator's self-reflection, which expresses the story's conflict. The narrator leans upon a rich oral tradition as he digresses from present to past, weaving them together to create a family history. The oral tradition that lies behind this short story is that of the North American Native peoples.

When I was twelve, thirteen at the most, and we were still living on the reserve, I asked my grandmother and she told me my father sat in the bathroom in the dark because it was the only place he could go to get away from us kids. What does he do in the bathroom, I wanted to
5  know. Sits, said my grandmother. That's it? Thinks, she said, he thinks. I asked her if he went to the bathroom, too, and she said that was adult conversation, and I would have to ask him. It seemed strange at the time, my father sitting in the dark, thinking, but rather than run the risk of asking him, I was willing to believe my grandmother's explanation.
10     At 46, I am sure it was true, though I have had some trouble convincing my son that sitting in the bathroom with the lights out is normal. He has, at eighteen, come upon language, much as a puppy comes upon a slipper. Unlike other teenagers his age who slouch in closets and basements, mute and desolate, Christopher likes to chew on conversation, toss it in the air, bang
15  it off the walls. I was always shy around language. Christopher is fearless.
       "Why do you sit in the bathroom, Dad?"
       "My father used to sit in the bathroom."
       "How many bathrooms did you have in the olden days?"
       "We lived on the reserve then. We only had the one."
20     "I thought you guys lived in a teepee or something. Where was the bathroom?"

"That was your great-grandfather. We lived in a house."

"It's a good thing we got two bathrooms," he told me.

The house on the reserve had been a government house, small and
25 poorly made. When we left and came to the city, my father took a picture
of it with me and my sister standing in front. I have the picture in a box
somewhere. I want to show it to Christopher, so he can see just how small
the house was.

"You're always bragging about that shack."

30 "It wasn't a shack."

"The one with all the broken windows?"

"Some of them had cracks."

"And it was cold, right?"

"In the winter it was cold."

35 "And you didn't have television."

"That's right."

"Jerry says that every house built has cable built in. It's a law or something."

"We didn't have cable or television."

40 " Is that why you left?"

"My father got a job here. I've got a picture of the house. You want to
see it?"

"No big deal."

"I can probably find it."

45 "No big deal."

Some of these conversations were easy. Others were hard. My conversations with my father were generally about the weather or trapping or
about fishing. That was it.

"Jerry says his father has to sit in the bathroom, too."

50 "Shower curtain was bundled up again. You have to spread it out so it
can dry."

"You want to know why?"

"Be nice if you cleaned up the water you leave on the floor."

"Jerry says it's because his father's constipated."

55 "Lawn has to be mowed. It's getting high."

"He says it's because his father eats too much junk food."

"Be nice if you cleaned the bottom of the mower this time. It's packed
with grass."

"But that doesn't make any sense, does it? Jerry and I eat junk food all
60 the time, and we're not constipated."

"Your mother wants me to fix the railing on the porch. I'm going to need your help with that."

"Are you constipated?"

Alberta wasn't much help. I could see her smiling to herself whenever Christopher started chewing. "It's because we're in the city," she said. "If we had stayed on the reserve, Christopher would be out on a trapline with his mouth shut and you wouldn't be constipated."

"Nobody runs a trapline anymore."

"My grandfather said the outdoors was good for you."

"We could have lived on the reserve, but you didn't want to."

"And he was never constipated."

"My father ran a trapline. We didn't leave the reserve until I was sixteen. Your folks have always lived in the city."

"Your father was a mechanic."

"He ran a trapline, just like his father."

"Not in the winter."

My father never remarried. After my mother died, he just looked after the four of us. He seldom talked about himself, and slowly, as my sisters and I got older, he became a mystery. He remained a mystery until his death.

"You hardly ever knew my father," I said. "He died two years after we were married."

Alberta nodded her head and stroked her hair behind her ears. "Your grandmother told me."

"She died before he did."

"My mother told me. She knew your grandmother."

"So, what did your mother tell you?"

"She told me not to marry you."

"She told me I was a damn good catch. Those were her exact words, 'damn good.'"

"She said that just to please you. She said you had a smart mouth. She wanted me to marry Sid."

"So, why didn't you marry Sid?"

"I didn't love Sid."

"What else did she say?"

"She said that constipation ran in your family."

After Christopher graduated from high school, he pulled up in front of the television and sat there for almost a month.

"You planning on going to university?" I asked him.

"I guess."

"You going to do it right away or you going to get a job?"

"I'm going to rest first."

"Seems to me, you got to make some decisions."

"Maybe I'll go in the bathroom later on and think about it."

105 "You can't just watch television."

"I know."

"You're an adult now."

Alberta called these conversations father and son talks, and you could tell the way she sharpened her tongue on "father and son" that she didn't 110 think much of them.

"You ever talk to him about important things?"

"Like what?"

"You know."

"Sure."

115 "Okay, what do you tell him?"

"I tell him what he needs to know."

"My mother talked to my sisters and me all the time. About every-thing."

"We have good conversations."

120 "Did he tell you he isn't going to college?"

"He just wants some time to think."

"Not what he told me."

I was in a book store looking for the new Audrey Thomas novel. The Ts were on the third shelf down and I had to bend over and cock my head to 125 one side in order to read the titles. As I stood there, bent over and twisted, I felt my face start to slide. It was a strange sensation. Everything that wasn't anchored to bone just slipped off the top half of my head, slopped into the lower half and just hung there like a bag of jello. When I arrived home, I got myself into the same position in front of the bathroom mirror. 130 That evening, I went downstairs and sat on the couch with Christopher and waited for a commercial.

"How about turning off the sound?"

"We going to have another talk?"

"I thought we could talk about the things that you're good at doing."

135 "I'm not good at anything."

"That's not true. You're good at computers."

"I like the games."

"You're good at talking to people. You could be a teacher."

"Teaching looks boring. Most of my teachers were boring."

140 "Times are tougher now," I said. "When your grandfather was a boy, he worked on a trapline up north. It was hard work, but you didn't need a university degree. Now you have to have one. Times are tougher."

"Mr. Johnson was the boringest of all."

"University is the key. Lot of kids go there not knowing what they want
145 to do, and, after two or three years, they figure it out. Have you applied to any universities yet?"

"Commercial's over."

"No money in watching television."

"Commercial's over."

150 Alberta caught me bent over in front of the mirror. "You lose something?"

"Mirror's got a defect in it. You can see it just there."

"At least you're not going bald."

"I talked to Christopher about university."

"My father never looked a day over 40." Alberta grinned at herself in
155 the mirror so she could see her teeth. "You know," she said, "when you stand like that, your face hangs funny."

I don't remember my father growing old. He was 56 when he died. We never had long talks about life or careers. When I was a kid—I forget how old—we drove into Medicine River to watch the astronauts land on the
160 moon. We sat in the American Hotel and watched it on the old black-and-white that Morris Rough Dog kept in the lobby. Morris told my father that they were checking the moon to see if it had any timber, water, valuable minerals or game, and, if it didn't, they planned to turn it into a reserve and move all the Cree up there. Hey, he said to my father, what's that boy
165 of yours going to be when he grows up? Beats me, said my father. Well, said Morris, there's damn little money in the hotel business and sure as hell nothing but scratch and splinters in being an Indian.

For weeks after, my father told Morris' story about the moon and the astronauts. My father laughed when he told the story. Morris had told it
170 straight-faced.

"What do you really do in the bathroom, Dad?"

"I think."

"That all?"

"Just thinking."

175 "Didn't know thinking smelled so bad."

I was in the downstairs bathroom. Christopher and Jerry were in Christopher's room. I could hear them playing video games and talking.

"My father wants me to go into business with him," said Jerry.

"Yeah."

180 "Can you see it? Me, selling cars the rest of my life?"

"Good money?"

"Sure, but what a toady job. I'd rather go to university and see what comes up."

"I'm thinking about that, too."

185 "What's your dad want you to do?" said Jerry.

It was dark in the bathroom and cool, and I sat there trying not to breathe.

"Take a guess."

"Doctor?" said Jerry. "Lawyer?"

190 "Nope."

"An accountant? My dad almost became an accountant."

"You'll never guess. You could live to be a million years old and you'd never guess."

"Sounds stupid."

195 "A trapper. He wants me to work a trapline."

"You got to be kidding."

"God's truth. Just like my grandfather."

"Your dad is really weird."

"You ought to live with him."

200 We only went fishing once. It was just before my mother died. We all got in the car and drove up to a lake just off the reserve. My dad rented a boat and took us kids out in pairs. My mother stayed on the docks and lay in the sun.

Toward the end of the day, my sisters stayed on the dock with my 205 mother, and my father and I went out in the boat alone. He had a new green tackle box he had bought at the hardware store on Saturday. Inside was an assortment of hooks and spinners and lures and a couple of red things with long trailing red-and-white skirts. He snorted and showed me a clipping that had come with the box for a lure that could actually call 210 the fish.

Used to be beaver all around here, he told me, but they've been trapped out. Do you know why the beavers were so easy to catch, he asked me. It's because they always set the trap in the same place and you always use the same bait, and pretty soon, they're gone.

215 Trapping was good money when your grandfather was here, but not now. No money in being a mechanic either. Better think of something else to do. Maybe I'll be an astronaut, I said. Have more luck trying to get pregnant, he said. Maybe I'll be a fisherman. No sir, he said. All the money's in making junk like this, and he squeezed the advertisement into a ball 220 and set it afloat on the lake.

Christopher was in front of the television when I got home from work on Friday. There was a dirty plate under the coffee table and a box of crackers sitting on the cushions.

"What do you say we get out of the house this weekend and do some-
225 thing?"

"Like what?"

"I don't know. What would you like to do?"

"We could go to that new movie."

"I meant outdoors."

230 "What's to do outdoors besides work?"

"We could go fishing."

"Fishing?"

"Sure, I used to go fishing with my father all the time."

"This one of those father, son things?"

235 "We could go to the lake and rent a boat."

"I may have a job."

"Great. Where?"

"Let you know later."

"What's the secret?"

240 "No secret. I'll just tell you later."

"What about the fishing trip?"

"Better stick around the house in case someone calls."

Christopher slumped back into the cushions and turned up the sound on the television.

245 "What about the dirty plate?"

"It's not going anywhere."

"That box is going to spill if you leave it like that."

"It's empty."

My father caught four fish that day. I caught two. He sat in the stern with 250 the motor. I sat in the bow with the anchor. When the sun dropped into the trees, he closed his tackle box and gave the starter rope a hard yank. It broke in his hand and he tumbled over backwards, the boat tipping and

slopping back and forth. Damn, he said, and he pulled himself back up on the seat. Well, son, he said, I've got a job for you, and he set the oars in the
255 locks and leaned against the motor. He looked around the lake at the trees and the mountains and the sky. And he looked at me. Try not to get me wet, he said.

Alberta was in the kitchen peeling a piece of pizza away from the box. "Christopher got a job at that new fast-food place. Did he tell you?"
260 "No. He doesn't tell me those things."

"You should talk with him more."

"I talk with him all the time."

"He needs to know you love him."

"He knows that."
265 "He just wants to be like you."

Once my sister and I were fighting, my father broke us up and sent us out in the woods to get four sticks apiece about as round as a finger. So we did. And when we brought them back, he took each one and broke it over his knee. Then he sent us out to get some more.

270 "Why don't you take him fishing?"

"I tried. He didn't want to go."

"What did you and your father do?"

"We didn't do much of anything."

"Okay, start there."

275 When we came home with the sticks, my father wrapped them all together with some cord. Try to break these, he said. We jumped on the sticks and we kicked them. We put the bundle between two rocks and hit it with a board. But the sticks didn't break. Finally, my father took the sticks and tried to break them across his knee. You kids get the idea, he
280 said. After my father went back into the house, my youngest sister kicked the sticks around the yard some more and said it was okay but she'd rather have a ball.

Christopher's job at the fast-food place lasted three weeks. After that he resumed his place in front of the television.
285 "What happened with the job?"

"It was boring."

"Lots of jobs are boring."

"Don't worry, I'll get another."

"I'm not worried," I said, and I told him about the sticks. "A stick by
290 itself is easy to break, but it's impossible to break them when they stand
together. You see what I mean."

"Chainsaw," said my son.

"What?"

"Use a chainsaw."

295 I began rowing for the docks, and my father began to sing. Then he
stopped and leaned forward as if he wanted to tell me something. Son, he
said, I've been thinking...And just then a gust of wind blew his hat off, and
I had to swing the boat around so we could get it before it sank. The hat
was waterlogged. My father wrung it out as best he could, and then he set-
300 tled in against the motor again and started singing.

My best memory of my father was that day on the lake. He lived alone,
and, after his funeral, my sisters and I went back to his apartment and
began packing and dividing the things as we went. I found his tackle box
in the closet at the back.

305 "Christopher got accepted to university."

"When did that happen?"

"Last week. He said he was going to tell you."

"Good."

"He and Jerry both got accepted. Jerry's father gave Jerry a car and
310 they're going to drive over to Vancouver and see about getting jobs before
school starts."

"Vancouver, huh?"

"Not many more chances."

"What?"

315 "For talking to your son."

Jerry came by on a Saturday, and Alberta and I helped Christopher pack
his things in the station-wagon.

"Nice car," said Alberta.

"It's a pig," said Jerry. "My father couldn't sell it because of the colour.
320 But it'll get us there."

"Bet your father and mother are going to miss you."

"My father wanted me to stick around and help with the business. Gave
me this big speech about traditions."

"Nothing wrong with traditions," Alberta said.

325     "Yeah, I guess. Look at this." Jerry held up a red metal tool box. "It's my grandfather's first tool box. My father gave it to me. You know, father to son and all that."

    "That's nice, "said Alberta.

    "I guess."

330     "Come on," said Christopher. "Couple more things and we can get going."

    Alberta put her arm around my waist and she began to poke me. Not so you could see. Just a sharp, annoying poke. "For Christ's sake," she whispered, "say something."

335     Christopher came out of the house carrying his boots and a green metal box. "All set," he said.

    "Where'd you get the box?" I asked.

    "It's an old fishing-tackle box."

    "I know."

340     "It's been sitting in the closet for years. Nobody uses it."

    "It was my father's box."

    "Yeah. It's got some really weird stuff in it. Jerry says that there's good fishing in BC."

    "That's right," said Jerry. "You should see some of those salmon."

345     "You don't fish."

    "You never took me."

    "My father gave me that box. It was his father's."

    "You never use it."

    "No, it's okay. I was going to give it to you anyway."

350     "No big deal. I can leave it here."

    "No, it's yours."

    "I'll take care of it."

    "Maybe after you get settled out there, we can come out. Maybe you and I can do some fishing."

355     "Sure."

    "Love you, honey," said Alberta and she put her arms around Christopher and held him. "I'm going to miss you. Call us if you need anything. And watch what you eat so you don't wind up like your father."

    "Sure."

360     Alberta and I stood in the yard for a while after the boys drove off. "You could have told him you loved him," she said.

    "I did. In my own way."

    "Oh, he's supposed to figure that out because you gave him that old fishing-box."

365     "That's the way my father did it."

"I thought you told me you found the box when you and your sisters were cleaning out his place."

After supper, Alberta went grocery shopping. I sat in the bathroom and imagined what my father had been going to say just before the wind took
370 his hat, something important I guessed, something I could have shared with my son.

(1991)

## Following the Story

1. What is the conflict in this story?
2. The rising action consists in a series of similar crises. How would you describe the crises?
3. What method does the narrator use to depict the characters? Support your answer with details from the text.
4. What types of character are Christopher, Alberta, and the narrator? Support your answer with details from the text.
5. Describe the narrative voice and tone in this story.
6. How do the memories of the narrator's father advance the action?
7. Much of this story is told through dialogue. How would you describe the discussions between the narrator and Christopher?
8. The story takes place in urban Canada, but this is contrasted with the narrator's childhood spent on a reserve. Explain the importance of the two settings in this story.
9. During a discussion of traditions, Jerry holds up a tool box and says, "It's my grandfather's first tool box. My father gave it to me. You know, father to son and all that" (lines 325–327). How does this relate to Christopher carrying the fishing-tackle box out of his house a few lines later?
10. List the various "traplines," actual and symbolic, you can identify in this story.

## Responding to the Story

1. How does the narrator's "sitting in the bathroom with the lights out" establish his character?
2. Explain the symbolism of the bathroom in this story.
3. In what ways is the narrator "constipated"?

4. "Christopher likes to chew on conversation, toss it in the air, bang it off walls" (lines 14–15). In what ways does the narrator demonstrate this aspect of Christopher's character?
5. Does the narrator actually talk about "important things" with his son?
6. Does Christopher know how much his father loves him? How can you tell?
7. How would you describe the relationship between father and son in this story? Support your response with details from the story.
8. Use specific examples to demonstrate the role of humour in this story.
9. How does the title of this story relate to its content?
10. The subject of this story is the relationship between the father and the son. What is its theme?

---

# Swimming Lessons

Rohinton Mistry (Canada) 1952–

## About the Author

*Born in Bombay, India, in 1952, Rohinton Mistry immigrated to Canada in 1975 after gaining a B.A. in mathematics and economics at the University of Bombay. He worked in a Toronto bank for some time and earned a B.A. at the University of Toronto in 1982. He began to write fiction in 1983 and won the short-story contest conducted by Hart House at the University of Toronto in both 1983 and 1984. His first collection of short stories,* Tales from Firozsha Baag, *published in 1987, was a finalist for the Governor General's Award for fiction. His first novel* Such a Long Journey *(1991) won a Governor General's Award, and his second novel* A Fine Balance *(1995) won the Giller Prize. He is now a full-time writer living in Brampton, Ontario.*

*As one of Canada's leading contemporary novelists, Rohinton Mistry consistently depicts in his novels the Parsi community of India, to which he himself belongs. His short stories, like his novels, skillfully attract the reader with well-crafted plot, realistic characters, and his keen observation of human conditions in both India and Canada.*

## About the Story

*When you read this story, you will see that it is actually about a young man who writes stories, and the memories the narrator has of his life in India and the incidents and people he meets in Canada are clearly part of the book he publishes and sends to his parents. The story is filled with nostalgic references to the narrator's life in*

*India, which are paralleled by his experiences in Canada. The narrator suggests he is out of his depth at times, and is able to understand and come to terms with his new life by means of his art—writing stories. These stories are written with his parents in mind at all times; in a sense they are the intended audience as much as they are characters within the story, and this complicates the point of view.*

## Terms Appearing in the Story

**kuchrawalli** glass seller

**Mamaji** grandmother

**Shiv Sena** a separatist movement

**Maharashtra** a region of India

**bundh** a general strike, a symbolic shutting down of the city

**baksheesh** tip

**Ganesh Chaturthi** festival to celebrate the god Ganesh, who appears in the form of an elephant

**kusti** a cord worn by Parsis wrapped loosely three times around the waist, taken off and used in a ceremonial hand-washing prayer; also, this ritual

**sudra** a soft muslin undershirt worn during coming-of-age ceremonies and for ceremonial purposes

**swaraj** self-rule. As Gandhi used the term in the struggle for Indian independence, it included the concepts of liberation, self-control, and non-violence.

The old man's wheelchair is audible today as he creaks by in the hallway: on some days it's just a smooth whirr. Maybe the way he slumps in it, or the way his weight rests has something to do with it. Down to the lobby he goes, and sits there most of the time, talking to people on
5 their way out or in. That's where he first spoke to me a few days ago. I was waiting for the elevator, back from Eaton's with my new pair of swimming-trunks.

'Hullo,' he said. I nodded, smiled.

'Beautiful summer day we've got.'

10 'Yes,' I said, 'it's lovely outside.'

He shifted the wheelchair to face me squarely. 'How old do you think I am?'

I looked at him blankly, and he said, 'Go on, take a guess.'

I understood the game; he seemed about seventy-five although the hair
15 was still black, so I said, 'Sixty-five?' He made a sound between a chuckle and a wheeze: 'I'll be seventy-seven next month.' Close enough.

I've heard him ask that question several times since, and everyone plays by the rules. Their faked guesses range from sixty to seventy. They pick a

lower number when he's more depressed than usual. He reminds me of
20 Grandpa as he sits on the sofa in the lobby, staring out vacantly at the
parking lot. Only difference is, he sits with the stillness of stroke victims,
while Grandpa's Parkinson's disease would bounce his thighs and legs and
arms all over the place. When he could no longer hold the *Bombay
Samachar* steady enough to read, Grandpa took to sitting on the veranda
25 and staring emptily at the traffic passing outside Firozsha Baag. Or waving
to anyone who went by in the compound: Rustomji, Nariman Hansotia in
his 1932 Mercedes-Benz, the fat ayah Jaakaylee with her shopping-bag,
the *kuchrawalli*° with her basket and long bamboo broom.

The Portuguese woman across the hall has told me a little about the old
30 man. She is the communicator for the apartment building. To gather and
disseminate information, she takes the liberty of unabashedly throwing
open her door when newsworthy events transpire. Not for Portuguese
Woman the furtive peerings from thin cracks or spyholes. She reminds me
of a character in a movie, *Barefoot in The Park* I think it was, who left empty
35 beer cans by the landing for anyone passing to stumble and give her the
signal. But PW does not need beer cans. The gutang-khutang of the elevator opening and closing is enough.

The old man's daughter looks after him. He was living alone till his
stroke, which coincided with his youngest daughter's divorce in Vancouver.
40 She returned to him and they moved into this low-rise in Don Mills. PW
says the daughter talks to no one in the building but takes good care of her
father.

Mummy used to take good care of Grandpa, too, till things became
complicated and he was moved to the Parsi General Hospital.
45 Parkinsonism and osteoporosis laid him low. The doctor explained that
Grandpa's hip did not break because he fell, but he fell because the hip,
gradually growing brittle, snapped on that fatal day. That's what osteoporosis does, hollows out the bones and turns effect into cause. It has an
unusually high incidence in the Parsi community, he said, but did not say
50 why. Just one of those mysterious things. We are the chosen people where
osteoporosis is concerned. And divorce. The Parsi community has the
highest divorce rate in India. It also claims to be the most westernized community in India. Which is the result of the other? Confusion again, of
cause and effect.

55 The hip was put in traction. Single-handed, Mummy struggled valiantly
with bedpans and dressings for bedsores which soon appeared like grim
spectres on his back. *Mamaji,*° bent double with her weak back, could give
no assistance. My help would be enlisted to roll him over on his side while

Mummy changed the dressing. But after three months, the doctor pro-
60 nounced a patch upon Grandpa's lungs, and the male ward of Parsi
General swallowed him up. There was no money for a private nursing
home. I went to see him once, at Mummy's insistence. She used to say that
the blessings of an old person were the most valuable and potent of all,
they would last my whole life long. The ward had rows and rows of beds;
65 the din was enormous, the smells nauseating, and it was just as well that
Grandpa passed most of his time in a less than conscious state.

But I should have gone to see him more often. Whenever Grandpa went
out, while he still could in the days before parkinsonism, he would bring
back pink and white sugar-coated almonds for Percy and me. Every time I
70 remember Grandpa, I remember that; and then I think; I should have
gone to see him more often. That's what I also thought when our tele-
phone-owning neighbour, esteemed by all for that reason, sent his son to
tell us the hospital had phoned that Grandpa died an hour ago.

*The postman rang the doorbell the way he always did, long and continuous;*
75 *Mother went to open it, wanting to give him a piece of her mind but thought*
*better of it, she did not want to risk the vengeance of postmen, it was so easy for*
*them to destroy letters; workers nowadays thought no end of themselves, strut-*
*ting around like peacocks, ever since all this Shiv Sena° agitation about*
*Maharashtra° for Maharashtrians, threatening strikes and Bombay bundh° all*
80 *the time, with no respect for the public; bus drivers and conductors were the*
*worst, behaving as if they owned the buses and were doing favours to commuters,*
*pulling the bell before you were in the bus, the driver purposely braking and*
*moving with big jerks to make the standees lose their balance, the conductor so*
*rude if you did not have the right change.*
85 *But when she saw the airmail envelope with a Canadian stamp her face lit up,*
*she said wait to the postman, and went in for a fifty paisa piece, a little bak-*
*sheesh° for you, she told him, then shut the door and kissed the envelope, went*
*in running, saying my son has written, my son has sent a letter, and Father*
*looked up from the newspaper and said, don't get too excited, first read it, you*
90 *know what kind of letters he writes, a few lines of empty words, I'm fine, hope*
*you are all right, your loving son—that kind of writing I don't call letter-writing.*
*Then Mother opened the envelope and took out one small page and began to*
*read silently, and the joy brought to her face by the letter's arrival began to ebb;*
*Father saw it happening and knew he was right, he said read aloud, let me also*
95 *hear what our son is writing this time, so Mother read: My dear Mummy and*
*Daddy, Last winter was terrible, we had record-breaking low temperatures all*
*through February and March, and the first official day of spring was colder than*

the first official day of winter had been, but it's getting warmer now. Looks like it will be a nice warm summer. You asked about my new apartment. It's small, but
100 not bad at all. This is just a quick note to let you know I'm fine, so you won't worry about me. Hope everything is okay at home.

After Mother put it back in the envelope, Father said everything about his life is locked in silence and secrecy, I still don't understand why he bothered to visit us last year if he had nothing to say; every letter of his has been a quick note so
105 we won't worry—what does he think we worry about, his health, in that country everyone eats well whether they work or not, he should be worrying about us with all the black market and rationing, has he forgotten already how he used to go to the ration-shop and wait in line every week; and what kind of apartment description is that, not bad at all; and if it is a Canadian weather report I need
110 from him, I can go with Nariman Hansotia from A Block to the Cawasji Framji Memorial Library and read all about it, there they get newspapers from all over the world.

The sun is hot today. Two women are sunbathing on the stretch of patchy lawn at the periphery of the parking lot. I can see them clearly from my
115 kitchen. They're wearing bikinis and I'd love to take a closer look. But I have no binoculars. Nor do I have a car to saunter out to and pretend to look under the hood. They're both luscious and gleaming. From time to time they smear lotion over their skin, on the bellies, on the inside of the thighs, on the shoulders. Then one of them gets the other to undo the
120 string of her top and spread some there. She lies on her stomach with the straps undone. I wait. I pray that the heat and haze make her forget, when it's time to turn over, that the straps are undone.

But the sun is not hot enough to work this magic for me. When it's time to come in, she flips over, deftly holding up the cups, and reties the top.
125 They arise, pick up towels, lotions, and magazines, and return to the building.

This is my chance to see them closer. I race down the stairs to the lobby. The old man says hullo. 'Down again?'

'My mailbox,' I mumble.

130 'It's Saturday,' he chortles. For some reason he finds it extremely funny. My eye is on the door leading in from the parking lot.

Through the glass panel I see them approaching. I hurry to the elevator and wait. In the dimly lit lobby I can see their eyes are having trouble adjusting after the bright sun. They don't seem as attractive as they did
135 from the kitchen window. The elevator arrives and I hold it open, inviting them in with what I think is a gallant flourish. Under the fluorescent glare

in the elevator I see their wrinkled skin, aging hands, sagging bottoms, varicose veins. The lustrous trick of sun and lotion and distance has ended.

I step out and they continue to the third floor. I have Monday night to
140 look forward to, my first swimming lesson. The high school behind the apartment building is offering, among its usual assortment of macrame and ceramics and pottery classes, a class for non-swimming adults.

The woman at the registration desk is quite friendly. She even gives me the opening to satisfy the compulsion I have about explaining my non-
145 swimming status.

'Are you from India?' she asks. I nod. 'I hope you don't mind my asking, but I was curious because an Indian couple, husband and wife, also registered a few minutes ago. Is swimming not encouraged in India?'

'On the contrary,' I say. 'Most Indians swim like fish. I'm an exception
150 to the rule. My house was five minutes walking distance from Chaupatty beach in Bombay. It's one of the most beautiful beaches in Bombay, or was, before the filth took over. Anyway, even though we lived so close to it, I never learned to swim. It's just one of those things.'

'Well,' says the woman, 'that happens sometimes. Take me, for
155 instance. I never learned to ride a bicycle. It was the mounting that used to scare me, I was afraid of falling.' People have lined up behind me. 'It's been very nice talking to you,' she says, 'hope you enjoy the course.'

The art of swimming had been trapped between the devil and the deep blue sea. The devil was money, always scarce, and kept the private swim-
160 ming clubs out of reach; the deep blue sea of Chaupatty beach was grey and murky with garbage, too filthy to swim in. Every so often we would muster our courage and Mummy would take me there to try and teach me. But a few minutes of paddling was all we could endure. Sooner or later something would float up against our legs or thighs or waists,
165 depending on how deep we'd gone in, and we'd be revulsed and stride out to the sand.

Water imagery in my life is recurring. Chaupatty beach, now the high-school swimming pool. The universal symbol of life and regeneration did nothing but frustrate me. Perhaps the swimming pool will overturn that
170 failure.

When images and symbols abound in this manner, sprawling or rolling across the page without guile or artifice, one is prone to say, how obvious, how skilless; symbols, after all, should be still and gentle as dewdrops, tiny, yet shining with a world of meaning. But what happens when, on the page
175 of life itself, one encounters the ever-moving, all-engirdling sprawl of the filthy sea? Dewdrops and oceans both have their rightful places; Nariman

Hansotia certainly knew that when he told his stories to the boys of Firozsha Baag.

The sea of Chaupatty was fated to endure the finales of life's everyday functions. It seemed that the dirtier it became, the more crowds it attracted: street urchins and beggars and beachcombers, looking through the junk that washed up. (Or was it the crowds that made it dirtier?—another instance of cause and effect blurring and evading identification.)

Too many religious festivals also used the sea as repository for their finales. Its use should have been rationed, like rice and kerosene. On Ganesh Chaturthi,° clay idols of the god Ganesh, adorned with garlands and all manner of finery, were carried in processions to the accompaniment of drums and a variety of wind instruments. The music got more frenzied the closer the procession got to Chaupatty and to the moment of immersion.

Then there was Coconut Day, which was never as popular as Ganesh Chaturthi. From a bystander's viewpoint, coconuts chucked into the sea do not provide as much of a spectacle. We used the sea, too, to deposit the leftovers from Parsi religious ceremonies, things such as flowers, or the ashes of the sacred sandalwood fire, which just could not be dumped with the regular garbage but had to be entrusted to the care of Avan Yazad, the guardian of the sea. And things which were of no use but which no one had the heart to destroy were also given to Avan Yazad. Such as old photographs.

After Grandpa died, some of his things were flung out to sea. It was high tide; we always checked the newspaper when going to perform these disposals; an ebb would mean a long walk in squelchy sand before finding water. Most of the things were probably washed up on shore. But we tried to throw them as far out as possible, then waited a few minutes; if they did not float back right away we would pretend they were in the permanent safekeeping of Avan Yazad, which was a comforting thought. I can't remember everything we sent out to sea, but his brush and comb were in the parcel, his *kusti*,° and some Kemadrin pills, which he used to take to keep the parkinsonism under control.

Our paddling sessions stopped for lack of enthusiasm on my part. Mummy wasn't too keen either, because of the filth. But my main concern was the little guttersnipes, like naked fish with little buoyant penises, taunting me with their skills, swimming underwater and emerging unexpectedly all around me, or pretending to masturbate—I think they were too young to achieve ejaculation. It was embarrassing. When I look back, I'm surprised that Mummy and I kept going as long as we did.

I examine the swimming-trunks I bought last week. Surf King, says the label, Made in Canada-Fabriqué Au Canada. I've been learning bits and pieces of French from bilingual labels at the supermarket too. These trunks are extremely sleek and streamlined hipsters, the distance from waistband to pouch tip the barest minimum. I wonder how everything will stay in place, not that I'm boastful about my endowments. I try them on, and feel the tip of my member lingers perilously close to the exit. Too close, in fact, to conceal the exigencies of my swimming lesson fantasy: a gorgeous woman in the class for non-swimmers, at whose sight I will be instantly aroused, and she, spying the shape of my desire, will look me straight in the eye with her intentions; she will come home with me, to taste the pleasures of my delectable Asian brown body whose strangeness has intrigued her and unleashed uncontrollable surges of passion inside her throughout the duration of the swimming lesson.

I drop the Eaton's bag and wrapper in the garbage can. The swimming-trunks cost fifteen dollars, same as the fee for the ten weekly lessons. The garbage bag is almost full. I tie it up and take it outside. There is a medicinal smell in the hallway; the old man must have just returned to his apartment.

PW opens her door and says, 'Two ladies from the third floor were lying in the sun this morning. In bikinis.'

'That's nice,' I say, and walk to the incinerator chute. She reminds me of Najamai in Firozsha Baag, except that Najamai employed a bit more subtlety while going about her life's chosen work.

PW withdraws and shuts her door.

*Mother had to reply because Father said he did not want to write to his son till his son had something sensible to write to him, his questions had been ignored long enough, and if he wanted to keep his life a secret, fine, he would get no letters from his father.*

*But after Mother started the letter he went and looked over her shoulder, telling her what to ask him, because if they kept on writing the same questions, maybe he would understand how interested they were in knowing about things over there; Father said go on, ask him what his work is at the insurance company, tell him to take some courses at night school, that's how everyone moves ahead over there, tell him not to be discouraged if his job is just clerical right now, hard work will get him ahead, remind him he is a Zoroastrian:* manashni, gavashni, kunashni, *better write the translation also: good thoughts, good words, good deeds—he must have forgotten what it means, and tell him to say prayers and do kusti at least twice a day.*

*Writing it all down sadly, Mother did not believe he wore his sudra° and kusti anymore, she would be very surprised if he remembered any of the prayers; when she had asked him if he needed new* sudras *he said not to take any trouble because the Zoroastrian Society of Ontario imported them from Bombay for their*
260 *members, and this sounded like a story he was making up, but she was leaving it in the hands of God, ten thousand miles away there was nothing she could do but write a letter and hope for the best.*

*Then she sealed it, and Father wrote the address on it as usual because his writing was much neater than hers, handwriting was important in the address*
265 *and she did not want the postman in Canada to make any mistake; she took it to the post office herself, it was impossible to trust anyone to mail it ever since the postage rates went up because people just tore off the stamps for their own use and threw away the letter, the only safe way was to hand it over the counter and make the clerk cancel the stamp before your own eyes.*

270 Berthe, the building superintendent, is yelling at her son in the parking lot. He tinkers away with his van. This happens every fine-weathered Sunday. It must be the van that Berthe dislikes because I've seen mother and son together in other quite amicable situations.

Berthe is a big Yugoslavian with high cheekbones. Her nationality was
275 disclosed to me by PW. Berthe speaks a very rough-hewn English, I've over-heard her in the lobby scolding tenants for late rents and leaving dirty lint screens in the dryers. It's exciting to listen to her, her words fall like rocks and boulders, and one can never tell where or how the next few will drop. But her Slavic yells at her son are a different matter, the words fly swift and
280 true, well-aimed missiles that never miss. Finally, the son slams down the hood in disgust, wipes his hands on a rag, accompanies mother Berthe inside.

Berthe's husband has a job in a factory. But he loses several days of work every month when he succumbs to the booze, a word Berthe uses
285 often in her Slavic tirades on those days, the only one I can understand, as it clunks down heavily out of the tight-flying formation of Yugoslavian sentences. He lolls around in the lobby, submitting passively to his wife's tongue-lashings. The bags under his bloodshot eyes, his stringy mous-tache, stubbled chin, dirty hair are so vulnerable to the poison-laden barbs
290 (poison works the same way in any language) emanating from deep within the powerful watermelon bosom. No one's presence can embarrass or dignify her into silence.

No one except the old man who arrives now. 'Good morning,' he says, and Berthe turns, stops yelling, and smiles. Her husband rises, positions the wheelchair at the favourite angle. The lobby will be peaceful as long as the old man is there.

It was hopeless. My first swimming lesson. The water terrified me. When did that happen, I wonder, I used to love splashing at Chaupatty, carried about by the waves. And this was only a swimming pool. Where did all that terror come from? I'm trying to remember.

Armed with my Surf King I enter the high school and go to the pool area. A sheet with instructions for the new class is pinned to the bulletin board. All students must shower and then assemble at eight by the shallow end. As I enter the showers three young boys, probably from a previous class, emerge. One of them holds his nose. The second begins to hum, under his breath: Paki Paki, smell like curry. The third says to the first two: pretty soon all the water's going to taste of curry. They leave.

It's a mixed class, but the gorgeous woman of my fantasy is missing. I have to settle for another, in a pink one-piece suit, with brown hair and a bit of a stomach. She must be about thirty-five. Plain-looking.

The instructor is called Ron. He gives us a pep talk, sensing some nervousness in the group. We're finally all in the water, in the shallow end. He demonstrates floating on the back, then asks for a volunteer. The pink one-piece suit wades forward. He supports her, tells her to lean back and let her head drop in the water.

She does very well. And as we all regard her floating body, I see what was not visible outside the pool: her bush, curly bits of it, straying out at the pink Spandex V. Tongues of water lapping against her delta, as if caressing it teasingly, make the brown hair come alive in a most tantalizing manner. The crests and troughs of little waves, set off by the movement of our bodies in a circle around her, dutifully irrigate her; the curls alternately wave free inside the crest, then adhere to her wet thighs, beached by the inevitable trough. I could watch this forever, and I wish the floating demonstration would never end.

Next we are shown how to grasp the rail and paddle, face down in the water. Between practising floating and paddling, the hour is almost gone. I have been trying to observe the pink one-piece suit, getting glimpses of her straying pubic hair from various angles. Finally, Ron wants a volunteer for the last demonstration, and I go forward. To my horror he leads the class to the deep end. Fifteen feet of water. It is so blue, and I can see the bottom. He picks up a metal hoop attached to a long wooden stick. He wants me to grasp the hoop, jump in the water, and paddle, while he

guides me by the stick. Perfectly safe, he tells me. A demonstration of how
335 paddling propels the body.

It's too late to back out; besides, I'm so terrified I couldn't find the
words to do so even if I wanted to. Everything he says I do as if in a
trance. I don't remember the moment of jumping. The next thing I know
is, I'm swallowing water and floundering, hanging on to the hoop for
340 dear life. Ron draws me to the rails and helps me out. The class
applauds.

We disperse and one thought is on my mind: what if I'd lost my grip?
Fifteen feet of water under me. I shudder and take deep breaths. This is
it. I'm not coming next week. This instructor is an irresponsible person.
345 Or he does not value the lives of non-white immigrants. I remember the
three teenagers. Maybe the swimming pool is the hangout of some racist
group, bent on eliminating all non-white swimmers, to keep their waters
pure and their white sisters unogled.

The elevator takes me upstairs. Then gutang-khutang. PW opens her
350 door as I turn the corridor of medicinal smells. 'Berthe was screaming
loudly at her husband tonight,' she tells me.

'Good for her,' I say, and she frowns indignantly at me.


The old man is in the lobby. He's wearing thick wool gloves. He wants to
know how the swimming was, must have seen me leaving with my towel
355 yesterday. Not bad, I say.

'I used to swim a lot. Very good for the circulation.' He wheezes. 'My feet
are cold all the time. Cold as ice. Hands too.'

Summer is winding down, so I say stupidly, 'Yes, it's not so warm any
more.'

360 The thought of the next swimming lesson sickens me. But as I comb
through the memories of that terrifying Monday, I come upon the straying
curls of brown pubic hair. Inexorably drawn by them, I decide to go.

It's a mistake, of course. This time I'm scared even to venture in the
shallow end. When everyone has entered the water and I'm the only one
365 outside, I feel a little foolish and slide in.

Instructor Ron says we should start by reviewing the floating technique.
I'm in no hurry. I watch the pink one-piece pull the swim-suit down
around her cheeks and flip back to achieve perfect flotation. And then
reap disappointment. The pink Spandex triangle is perfectly streamlined
370 today, nothing strays, not a trace of fuzz, not one filament, not even a sign
of post-depilation irritation. Like the airbrushed parts of glamour magazine models. The barrenness of her impeccably packaged apex is a

betrayal. Now she is shorn like the other women in the class. Why did she have to do it?

375     The weight of this disappointment makes the water less manageable, more lung-penetrating. With trepidation, I float and paddle my way through the remainder of the hour, jerking my head out every two seconds and breathing deeply, to continually shore up a supply of precious, precious air without, at the same time, seeming too anxious and losing my
380 dignity.

    I don't attend the remaining classes. After I've missed three, Ron the instructor telephones. I tell him I've had the flu and am still feeling poorly, but I'll try to be there the following week.

    He does not call again. My Surf King is relegated to an unused drawer.
385 Total losses: one fantasy plus thirty dollars. And no watery rebirth. The swimming pool, like Chaupatty beach, has produced a stillbirth. But there is a difference. Water means regeneration only if it is pure and cleansing. Chaupatty was filthy, the pool was not. Failure to swim through filth must mean something other than failure of rebirth—failure of symbolic death?
390 Does that equal success of symbolic life? death of a symbolic failure? death of a symbol? What is the equation?

*The postman did not bring a letter but a parcel, he was smiling because he knew that every time something came from Canada his baksheesh was guaranteed, and this time because it was a parcel Mother gave him a whole rupee, she was*
395 *quite excited, there were so many stickers on it besides the stamps, one for Small Parcel, another Printed Papers, a red sticker saying Insured; she showed it to Father, and opened it, then put both hands on her cheeks, not able to speak because the surprise and happiness was so great, tears came to her eyes and she could not stop smiling till Father became impatient to know and finally got up*
400 *and came to the table.*

    *When he saw it he was surprised and happy too, he began to grin, then hugged Mother saying our son is a writer, and we didn't even know it, he never told us a thing here we are thinking he is still clerking away at the insurance company, and he has written a book of stories, all these years in school and college*
405 *he kept his talent hidden, making us think he was just like one of the boys in the Baag shouting and playing the fool in the compound, and now what a surprise; then Father opened the book and began reading it, heading back to the easy chair, and Mother so excited, still holding his arm, walked with him, saying it was not fair him reading it first, she wanted to read it too, and they agreed that he*
410 *would read the first story, then give it to her so she could also read it, and they would take turns in that manner.*

*Mother removed the staples from the padded envelope in which he had mailed the book, and threw them away, then straightened the folded edges of the enve-lope and put it away safely with the other envelopes and letters she had collected*
415 *since he left.*

The leaves are beginning to fall. The only ones I can identify are maple. The days are dwindling like the leaves. I've started a habit of taking long walks every evening. The old man is in the lobby when I leave, he waves as I go by. By the time I'm back, the lobby is usually empty.

420 Today I was woken up by a grating sound outside that made my flesh crawl. I went to the window and saw Berthe raking the leaves in the parking lot. Not in the expanse of patchy lawn on the periphery, but in the parking lot proper. She was raking the black tarred surface. I went back to bed and dragged a pillow over my head, not releasing it till noon.

425 When I return from my walk in the evening, PW, summoned by the ele-vator's gutang-khutang, says, 'Berthe filled six big black garbage bags with leaves today.'

'Six bags!' I say. 'Wow!'

Since the weather turned cold, Berthe's son does not tinker with his van on
430 Sundays under my window. I'm able to sleep late.

Around eleven, there's a commotion outside. I reach out and switch on the clock radio. It's a sunny day, the window curtains are bright. I get up, curious, and see a black Olds Ninety-Eight in the parking lot, by the entrance to the building. The old man is in his wheelchair, bundled up,
435 with a scarf wound several times round his neck as though to immobilize it, like a surgical collar. His daughter and another man, the car-owner, are helping him from the wheelchair into the front seat, encouraging him with words like: that's it, easy does it, attaboy. From the open door of the lobby, Berthe is shouting encouragement too, but hers is confined to one word:
440 yah, repeated at different levels of pitch and volume, with variations on vowel-length. The stranger could be the old man's son, he has the same jet black hair and piercing eyes.

Maybe the old man is not well, it's an emergency. But I quickly scrap that thought—this isn't Bombay, an ambulance would have arrived.
445 They're probably taking him out for a ride. If he is his son, where has he been all this time, I wonder.

The old man finally settles in the front seat, the wheelchair goes in the trunk, and they're off. The one I think is the son looks up and catches me at the window before I can move away, so I wave, and he waves back.

450 In the afternoon I take down a load of clothes to the laundry room. Both machines have completed their cycles, the clothes inside are waiting to be transferred to dryers. Should I remove them and place them on top of a dryer, or wait? I decide to wait. After a few minutes, two women arrive, they are in bathrobes, and smoking. It takes me a while to realize that
455 these are the two disappointments who were sunbathing in bikinis last summer.

 'You didn't have to wait, you could have removed the clothes and carried on, dear,' says one. She has a Scottish accent. It's one of the few I've learned to identify. Like maple leaves.

460 'Well,' I say, 'some people might not like strangers touching their clothes.'

 'You're not a stranger, dear,' she says, 'you live in this building, we've seen you before.'

 'Besides, your hands are clean,' the other one pipes in. 'You can touch
465 my things any time you like.'

 Horny old cow. I wonder what they've got on under their bathrobes. Not much, I find, as they bend over to place their clothes in the dryers.

 'See you soon,' they say, and exit, leaving me behind in an erotic wake of smoke and perfume and deep images of cleavages. I start the washers
470 and depart, and when I come back later, the dryers are empty.

 PW tells me, 'The old man's son took him out for a drive today. He has a big beautiful black car.'

 I see my chance, and shoot back: 'Olds Ninety-Eight.'

 'What?'

475 'The car,' I explain, 'it's an Oldsmobile Ninety-Eight.'

 She does not like this at all, my giving her information. She is visibly nettled, and retreats with a sour face.


*Mother and Father read the first five stories, and she was very sad after reading some of them, she said he must be so unhappy there, all his stories are about*
480 *Bombay, he remembers every little thing about his childhood, he is thinking about it all the time even though he is ten thousand miles away, my poor son, I think he misses his home and us and everything he left behind, because if he likes it over there why would he not write stories about that, there must be so many new ideas that his new life could give him.*

485 *But Father did not agree with this, he said it did not mean that he was unhappy, all writers worked in the same way, they used their memories and experiences and made stories out of them, changing some things, adding some, imagining some, all writers were very good at remembering details of their lives.*

*Mother said, how can you be sure that he is remembering because he's a*
490 *writer, or whether he started to write because he is unhappy and thinks of his*
*past, and wants to save it all by making stories of it; and Father said that is not*
*a sensible question, anyway, it is now my turn to read the next story.*

The first snow has fallen, and the air is crisp. It's not very deep, about
two inches, just right to go for a walk in. I've been told that immigrants
495 from hot countries always enjoy the snow the first year, maybe for a
couple of years more, then inevitably the dread sets in, and the
approach of winter gets them fretting and moping. On the other hand,
if it hadn't been for my conversation with the woman at the swimming
registration desk, they might now be saying that India is a nation of
500 non-swimmers.

Berthe is outside, shovelling the snow off the walkway in the parking
lot. She has a heavy, wide pusher which she wields expertly.

The old radiators in the apartment alarm me incessantly. They continue
to broadcast a series of variations on death throes, and go from hot to cold
505 and cold to hot at will, there's no controlling their temperature. I speak to
Berthe about it in the lobby. The old man is there too, his chin seems to
have sunk deeper into his chest, and his face is a yellowish grey.

'Nothing, not to worry about anything,' says Berthe, dropping rough-
hewn chunks of language around me. 'Radiator no work, you tell me.
510 You feel cold, you come to me, I keep you warm,' and she opens her
arms wide, laughing. I step back, and she advances, her breasts preceding her like the gallant prows of two ice-breakers. She looks at the old
man to see if he is appreciating the act: 'You no feel scared, I keep you
safe and warm.'

515 But the old man is staring outside, at the flakes of falling snow. What
thoughts is he thinking as he watches them? Of childhood days, perhaps,
and snowmen with hats and pipes, and snowball fights, and white
Christmases, and Christmas trees? What will I think of, old in this country,
when I sit and watch the snow come down? For me, it is already too late
520 for snowmen and snowball fights, and all I will have is thoughts about
childhood thoughts and dreams, built around snowscapes and winter-
wonderlands on the Christmas cards so popular in Bombay; my snowmen
and snowball fights and Christmas trees are in the pages of Enid Blyton's
books, dispersed amidst the adventures of the Famous Five, and the Five
525 Find-Outers, and the Secret Seven. My snowflakes are even less forgettable
than the old man's, for they never melt.

It finally happened. The heat went. Not the usual intermittent coming and going, but out completely. Stone cold. The radiators are like ice. And so is everything else. There's no hot water. Naturally. It's the hot water that goes
530 through the rads and heats them. Or is it the other way around? Is there no hot water because the rads have stopped circulating it? I don't care, I'm too cold to sort out the cause and effect relationship. Maybe there is no connection at all.

I dress quickly, put on my winter jacket, and go down to the lobby. The
535 elevator is not working because the power is out, so I take the stairs. Several people are gathered, and Berthe has announced that she has telephoned the office, they are sending a man. I go back up the stairs. It's only one floor, the elevator is just a bad habit. Back in Firozsha Baag they were broken most of the time. The stairway enters the corridor outside the old
540 man's apartment, and I think of his cold feet and hands. Poor man, it must be horrible for him without heat.

As I walk down the long hallway, I feel there's something different but can't pin it down. I look at the carpet, the ceiling, the wallpaper: it all seems the same. Maybe it's the freezing cold that imparts a feeling of dif-
545 ference.

PW opens her door: 'The old man had another stroke yesterday. They took him to the hospital.'

The medicinal smell. That's it. It's not in the hallway any more.

*In the stories that he'd read so far Father said that all the Parsi families were*
550 *poor or middle-class, but that was okay; nor did he mind that the seeds for the stories were picked from the sufferings of their own lives; but there should also have been something positive about Parsis, there was so much to be proud of: the great Tatas and their contribution to the steel industry, or Sir Dinshaw Petit in the textile industry who made Bombay the Manchester of the East, or Dadabhai*
555 *Naoroji in the freedom movement, where he was the first to use the word swaraj,° and the first to be elected to the British Parliament where he carried on his campaign; he should have found some way to bring some of these wonderful facts into his stories, what would people reading these stories think, those who did not know about Parsis—that the whole community was full of cranky, bigoted*
560 *people; and in reality it was the richest, most advanced and philanthropic community in India, and he did not need to tell his own son that Parsis had a reputation for being generous and family-oriented. And he could have written something also about the historic background, how Parsis came to India from Persia because of Islamic persecution in the seventh century, and were the*

565 *descendants of Cyrus the Great and the magnificent Persian Empire. He could have made a story of all this, couldn't he?*

*Mother said what she liked best was his remembering everything so well, how beautifully he wrote about it all, even the sad things, and though he changed some of it, and used his imagination, there was truth in it.*

570 *My hope is, Father said, that there will be some story based on his Canadian experience, that way we will know something about our son's life there, if not through his letters then in his stories; so far they are all about Parsis and Bombay, and the one with a little bit about Toronto, where a man perches on top of the toilet, is shameful and disgusting although it is funny at times and did* 575 *make me laugh, I have to admit, but where does he get such an imagination from, what is the point of such a fantasy; and Mother said that she would also enjoy some stories about Toronto and the people there; it puzzles me, she said, why he writes nothing about it, especially since you say that writers use their own experience to make stories out of.*

580 *Then Father said this is true, but he is probably not using his Toronto experience because it is too early; what do you mean, too early, asked Mother and Father explained it takes a writer about ten years time after an experience before he is able to use it in his writing, it takes that long to be absorbed internally and understood, thought out and thought about, over and over again, he haunts it and it haunts him* 585 *if it is valuable enough, till the writer is comfortable with it to be able to use it as he wants; but this is only one theory I read somewhere, it may or may not be true.*

*That means, said Mother, that his childhood in Bombay and our home here is the most valuable thing in his life just now, because he is able to remember it all to write about it, and you were so bitterly saying he is forgetting where he came* 590 *from; and that may be true, said Father, but that is not what the theory means, according to the theory he is writing of these things because they are far enough in the past for him to deal with objectively, he is able to achieve what critics call artistic distance, without emotions interfering; and what do you mean emotions, said Mother, you are saying he does not feel anything for his characters, how can* 595 *he write so beautifully about so many sad things without any feelings in his heart?*

*But before Father could explain more, about beauty and emotion and inspiration and imagination, Mother took the book and said it was her turn now and too much theory she did not want to listen to, it was confusing and did not make as much sense as reading the stories, she would read them her way and Father* 600 *could read them his.*

My books on the windowsill have been damaged. Ice has been forming on the inside ledge, which I did not notice, and melting when the sun shines in. I spread them in a corner of the living room to dry out.

The winter drags on. Berthe wields her snow pusher as expertly as ever, but there are signs of weariness in her performance. Neither husband nor son is ever seen outside with a shovel. Or anywhere else, for that matter. It occurs to me that the son's van is missing, too.

The medicinal smell is in the hall again, I sniff happily and look forward to seeing the old man in the lobby. I go downstairs and peer into the mailbox, see the blue and magenta of an Indian aerogramme with Don Mills, Ontario, Canada in Father's flawless hand through the slot.

I pocket the letter and enter the main lobby. The old man is there, but not in his usual place. He is not looking out through the glass door. His wheelchair is facing a bare wall where the wallpaper is torn in places. As though he is not interested in the outside world any more, having finished with all that, and now it's time to see inside. What does he see inside, I wonder? I go up to him and say hullo. He says hullo without raising his sunken chin. After a few seconds his grey countenance faces me. 'How old to do you think I am?' His eyes are dull and glazed; he is looking even further inside than I first presumed.

'Well, let's see, you're probably close to sixty-four.'

'I'll be seventy-eight next August.' But he does not chuckle or wheeze. Instead, he continues softly, 'I wish my feet did not feel so cold all the time. And my hands.' He lets his chin fall again.

In the elevator I start opening the aerogramme, a tricky business because a crooked tear means lost words. Absorbed in this while emerging, I don't notice PW occupying the centre of the hallway, arms folded across her chest: 'They had a big fight. Both of them have left.'

I don't immediately understand her agitation. 'What...who?'

'Berthe. Husband and son both left her. Now she is all alone.'

Her tone and stance suggest that we should not be standing here talking but do something to bring Berthe's family back. 'That's very sad,' I say, and go in. I picture father and son in the van, driving away, driving across the snow-covered country, in the dead of winter, away from wife and mother; away to where? how far will they go? Not son's van nor father's booze can take them far enough. And the further they go, the more they'll remember, they can take it from me.

*All the stories were read by Father and Mother, and they were sorry when the book was finished, they felt they had come to know their son better now, yet there was much more to know, they wished there were many more stories; and this is what they mean, said Father, when they say that the whole story can never be told, the whole truth can never be known; what do you mean, they say, asked*

*Mother, who they, and Father said writers, poets, philosophers. I don't care what*
*they say, said Mother, my son will write as much or as little as he wants to, and*
645 *if I can read it I will be happy.*

*The last story they liked the best of all because it had the most in it about*
*Canada, and now they felt they knew at least a little bit, even if it was a very little*
*bit, about his day-to-day life in his apartment; and Father said if he continues to*
*write about such things he will become popular because I am sure they are inter-*
650 *ested there in reading about life through the eyes of an immigrant, it provides a*
*different viewpoint; the only danger is if he changes and becomes so much like*
*them that he will write like one of them and lose the important difference.*

The bathroom needs cleaning. I open a new can of Ajax and scour the tub.
Sloshing with mug from bucket was standard bathing procedure in the
655 bathrooms of Firozsha Baag, so my preference now is always for a shower.
I've never used the tub as yet; besides, it would be too much like Chaupatty
or the swimming pool, wallowing in my own dirt. Still, it must be cleaned.

When I've finished, I prepare for a shower. But the clean gleaming tub and
the nearness of the vernal equinox give me the urge to do something dif-
660 ferent today. I find the drain plug in the bathroom cabinet, and run the bath.

I've spoken so often to the old man, but I don't know his name. I should
have asked him the last time I saw him, when his wheelchair was facing
the bare wall because he had seen all there was to see outside and it was
time to see what was inside. Well, tomorrow. Or better yet, I can look it up
665 in the directory in the lobby: Why didn't I think of that before? It will only
have an initial and a last name, but then I can surprise him with: hullo
Mr Wilson, or whatever it is.

The bath is full. Water imagery is recurring in my life: Chaupatty beach,
swimming pool, bathtub. I step in and immerse myself up to the neck. It
670 feels good. The hot water loses its opacity when the chlorine, or whatever
it is, has cleared. My hair is still dry. I close my eyes, hold my breath, and
clunk my head. Fighting the panic, I stay under and count to thirty. I come
out, clear my lungs and breathe deeply.

I do it again. This time I open my eyes under water, and stare blindly
675 without seeing, it takes all my will to keep the lids from closing. Then I am
slowly able to discern the underwater objects. The drain plug looks different, slightly distorted; there is a hair trapped between the hole and the
plug, it waves and dances with the movement of the water. I come up,
refresh my lungs, examine quickly the overwater world of the washroom,
680 and go in again. I do it several times, over and over. The world outside the
water I have seen a lot of, it is now time to see what is inside.

The spring session for adult non-swimmers will begin in a few days at the high school. I must not forget the registration date.

The dwindled days of winter are now all but forgotten; they have grown
685 and attained a respectable span. I resume my evening walks, it's spring, and a vigorous thaw is on. The snowbanks are melting, the sound of water on its gushing, gurgling journey to the drains is beautiful. I plan to buy a book of trees, so I can identify more than the maple as they begin to bloom.

690     When I return to the building, I wipe my feet energetically on the mat because some people are entering behind me, and I want to set a good example. Then I go to the board with its little plastic letters and numbers. The old man's apartment is the one on the corner by the stairway, that makes it number 201. I run down the list, come to 201, but there are no
695 little white plastic letters beside it. Just the empty black rectangle with holes where the letters would be squeezed in. That's strange. Well, I can introduce myself to him, then ask his name.

However, the lobby was empty. I take the elevator, exit at the second floor, wait for the gutang-khutang. It does not come, the door closes noise-
700 lessly, smoothly. Berthe has been at work, or has made sure someone else has. PW's cue has been lubricated out of existence.

But she must have the ears of a cockroach. She is waiting for me. I whistle my way down the corridor. She fixes me with an accusing look. She waits till I stop whistling, then says: 'You know the old man died last
705 night.'

I cease groping for my key. She turns to go and I take a step towards her, my hand still in my trouser pocket. 'Did you know his name?' I ask, but she leaves without answering.

*Then Mother said, the part I like best in the last story is about Grandpa, where*
710 *he wonders if Grandpa's spirit is really watching him and blessing him, because you know I really told him that, I told him helping an old suffering person who is near death is the most blessed thing to do, because that person will ever after watch over you from heaven, I told him this when he was disgusted with Grandpa's urine-bottle and would not touch it, would not hand it to him even*
715 *when I was not at home.*

*Are you sure, said Father, that you really told him this, or you believe you told him because you like the sound of it, you said yourself the other day that he changes and adds and alters things in the stories but he writes it all so beautifully that it seems true, so how can you be sure; this sounds like another theory,*

720 *said Mother, but I don't care, he says I told him and I believe now I told him, so*
*even if I did not tell him then it does not matter now.*

*Don't you see, said Father, that you are confusing fiction with facts, fiction*
*does not create facts, fiction can come from facts, it can grow out of facts by com-*
*pounding, transposing, augmenting, diminishing, or altering them in any way;*
725 *but you must not confuse cause and effect, you must not confuse what really hap-*
*pened with what the story says happened, you must not loose your grasp on*
*reality, that way madness lies.*

*Then Mother stopped listening because, as she told Father so often, she was*
*not very fond of theories, and she took out her writing pad and started a letter to*
730 *her son; Father looked over her shoulder, telling her to say how proud they were*
*of him and were waiting for his next book, he also said, leave a little space for*
*me at the end, I want to write a few lines when I put the address on the envelope.*

(1987)

## Following the Story

1. What is the conflict in this story?
2. How do the italicized sections of this story contribute to the action?
3. What method does the narrator use to present the characters? Support your answer with details from the text.
4. What types of characters does the narrator encounter in his building? Support your answer with details from the text.
5. What type of character is the narrator? Support your answer with details from the text.
6. Describe the narrative voice and its tone in this story.
7. The story takes place in Toronto, which is contrasted with the narrator's childhood in India. Explain the importance of the two interwoven settings in this story.
8. How do the memories of life in India advance the action?
9. How many different swimming lessons are presented in this story?
10. What does the narrator say about "water imagery" and its meaning for him?

## Responding to the Story

1. How would you describe the narrator's personality? Support your response with details from the story.

2. What role does each of the people whom the narrator encounters in Canada play in the story?
3. In what ways does the narrator express his loneliness in Canada? Why doesn't he share this experience with his parents?
4. What sorts of disappointments does the narrator encounter? What do these disappointments indicate about the narrator?
5. How does irony function in this story?
6. The narrator attends actual swimming lessons, but the phrase also applies symbolically to his experiences in life. Explain how the title of this story relates to its content.
7. What is the relation between the dénouement and the rest of this story?
8. The subject of this story is the relationship between the narrator and his parents. What is its main theme?
9. A second theme this story explores is the relationship between experience and art, in this case writing. How does Mistry make you aware of this theme?
10. Were you as surprised as the parents to discover the narrator has become a writer? Why or why not?

# Unit Review

When analyzing theme and interpretation, be sure to follow these guidelines:

- Decide what the main theme of the story is.
- Make sure that the theme you have identified can be supported by details in the story.
- Make sure you are not simply summarizing the plot.
- Examine the point of view. Does it express or support the theme?
- Determine whether the narrator or a character makes a statement about the theme.
- Examine the arrangement of events. Does it reflect or support the theme?
- Decide how the conflict reflects or supports the theme.
- Consider whether any change(s) in the character(s) reflect or support the theme.
- Examine literary devices and techniques for their relationship to the theme.
- Determine whether the title implies the theme.
- Identify any other themes in the story.

# Part  2

## More Stories

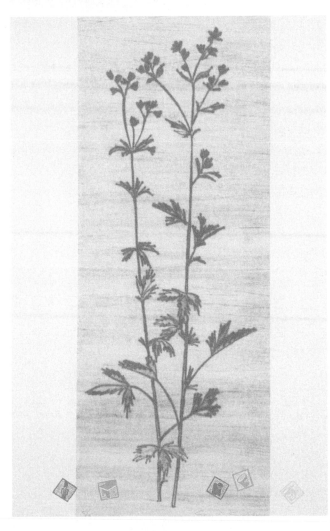

# Something to Talk about on the Way to the Funeral

Ama Ata Aidoo (Ghana) 1942–

## About the Author

*A respected Ghanian playwright, short story writer, novelist, and poet, Aidoo explores the far-reaching effects of sexism and colonialism. She was born in the Fanti town of Abeadzi Kyiakor, in the central region of Ghana. As the daughter of a chief, Aidoo was raised as aristocracy and given an extensive education, first at the University of Ghana, where she received her B.A., and then at Stanford University in the U.S. In addition to her work as a writer and educator at universities in Ghana and the U.S., Aidoo was also the Minister of Education in Ghana from 1982 to 1983. She is now a full-time writer living in Harare, Zimbabwe, with her daughter.*

*Aidoo has written two plays,* The Dilemma of a Ghost *(1964) and* Anowa *(1970), and many poems and novels. It is her short stories, however, that have earned her numerous literary awards and a large audience. As she herself has commented, "I pride myself on the fact that my stories are written to be heard, primarily." Aidoo's stories demonstrate a skillful balance of African oral techniques and Western literary conventions. Her predominant concern is the oppression of women. As shown in "Something to Talk about on the Way to the Funeral," Aidoo achieves an unusual mastery of dialogue, dramatic action, characterization, and themes through minimal narration and prevalent dialogue. As a result, each of her stories is presented as a microcosm of the inner world of women and of society, and womanhood becomes a metaphor depicting the condition of oppressed and exploited humankind in general.*

## Terms Appearing in the Story

**akatado** an item of clothing

**akwanbo** a festival

**epitsi** a cake made from plantain, a banana-like plant, that is edible when cooked

**tatare** a pancake made from plantain

**atwemo** a plain, sugared pastry drawn out in strips and fried in hot oil

**bofrot** doughnuts

**boodo** a sweet, unleavened corn bread

**boodo-ngo** a bread made from unleavened cornmeal mixed wih palm oil and baked

**sweetbad** a hard coconut pastry

**Wesleyan chapel** a Methodist church, named for its founder, John Wesley
**Stan' 7** Standard 7, or seventh grade
*whopei!* an exclamation of shock
**Ofuntumase** an area in Ghana
**cassava** a tropical plant cultivated for its edible root


...Adwoa my sister, when did you come back?

'Last night.'

Did you come specially for Auntie Araba?

'What else, my sister? I just rushed into my room to pick up my *akatado*°

5 when I heard the news. How could I remain another hour in Tarkwa after
getting such news? I arrived in the night.'

And your husband?

'He could not come. You know government-work. You must give notice
several days ahead if you want to go away for half of one day. O, and so

10 many other problems. But he will see to all that before next *Akwanbo*.°
Then we may both be present for the festival and the libation ceremony if
her family plans it for a day around that time.'

Did you hear the Bosoë dance group, practising the bread song?

'Yes. I hear they are going to make it the chief song at the funeral this

15 afternoon. It is most fitting that they should do that. After all, when the
group was formed, Auntie Araba's bread song was the first one they turned
into a Bosoë song and danced to.'

Yes, it was a familiar song in those days. Indeed it had been heard
around here for over twenty years. First in Auntie Araba's own voice with

20 its delicate thin sweetness that clung like asawa berry on the tongue: which
later, much later, had roughened a little. Then all of a sudden, it changed
again, completely. Yes, it still was a woman's voice. But it was deeper and
this time, like good honey, was rough and heavy, its sweetness within itself.

'Are you talking of when Mansa took over the hawking of the bread?'

25 Yes. That is how, in fact, that whole little quarter came to be known as
*Bosohwe*. Very often, Auntie Araba did not have to carry the bread. The
moment the aroma burst out of the oven, children began tugging at their
parents' clothes for pennies and threepences. Certainly, the first batch was
nearly always in those penny rows. Dozens of them. Of course, the children

30 always caught the aroma before their mothers did.

'Were we not among them?'

We were, my sister. We remember that on market days and other holidays, Auntie Araba's ovenside became a little market-place all by itself.
And then there was Auntie Araba herself. She always was a beautiful

35 woman. Even three months ago when they were saying that all her life was gone, I thought she looked better than some of us who claim to be in our prime. If she was a young woman at this time when they are selling beauty to our big men in the towns, she would have made something for herself.

'Though it is a crying shame that young girls should be doing that. As 40 for our big men! Hmm, let me shut my trouble-seeking mouth up. But our big men are something else too. You know, indeed, these our educated big men have never been up to much good.'

Like you know, my sister. After all, was it not a lawyer-or-a-doctor-or-something-like-that who was at the bottom of all Auntie Araba's troubles? 45 'I did not know that, my sister.'

Yes, my sister. One speaks of it only in whispers. Let me turn my head and look behind me....And don't go standing in the river telling people. Or if you do, you better not say that you heard it from me.

'How could I do that? Am I a baby?'

50 Yes, Auntie Araba was always a beauty. My mother says she really was a come-and-have-a-look type, when she was a girl. Her plaits hung at the back of her neck like the branches of a giant tree, while the skin of her arms shone like charcoal from good wood. And since her family is one of these families with always some members abroad, when Auntie Araba was 55 just about getting ready for her puberty, they sent her to go and stay at A— with some lady relative. That's where she learnt to mess around with flour so well. But after less than four years, they found she was in trouble.

'Eh-eh?'

Eh-eh, my sister. And now bring your ear nearer.

60 ....

'That lawyer-or-doctor-or-something-like-that who was the lady's husband?'

Yes.

'And what did they do about it?'

65 They did not want to spoil their marriage so they hushed up everything and sent her home quietly. Very quietly. That girl was our own Auntie Araba. And that child is Ato, the big scholar we hear of.

'Ei, there are plenty of things in the world's old box to pick up and talk about, my sister.'

70 You have said it. But be quiet and listen. I have not finished the story. If anything like that had happened to me, my life would have been ruined. Not that there is much to it now. But when Auntie Araba returned home to her mother, she was looking like a ram from the north. Big, beautiful and strong. And her mother did not behave as childishly as some

75 would in a case like this. No, she did not tear herself apart as if the world had fallen down....

'Look at how Mother Kuma treated her daughter. Rained insults on her head daily, refused to give her food and then drove her out of their house. Ah, and look at what the father of Mansa did to her too....'

80 But isn't this what I am coming to? This is what I am coming to.

'Ah-h-h...'

Anyway, Auntie Araba's mother took her daughter in and treated her like an egg until the baby was born. And then did Auntie Araba tighten her girdle and get ready to work? Lord, there is no type of dough of flour
85 they say she has not mixed and fried or baked. *Epitsi?°* *Tatare?°* *Atwemo?°* *Bofrot?°* *Boodo?°* *Boodoo-ngo?°* *Sweetbad?°* *Hei,* she went there and dashed here. But they say that somehow, she was not getting much from these efforts. Some people even say that they landed her in debts.

'But I think someone should have told her that these things are good to
90 eat but they suit more the tastes of the town-dwellers. I myself cannot see any man or woman who spends his living days on the farm, wasting his pennies on any of these sweeties which only satisfy the tongue but do not fill the stomach. Our people in the villages might buy *tatare* and *epitsi,* yes, but not the others.'

95 Like you know, my sister. This is what Auntie Araba discovered, but only after some time. I don't know who advised her to drop all those fancy foods. But she did, and finally started baking bread, ordinary bread. That turned out better for her.

'And how did she come to marry Egya Nyaako?'

100 They say that she grew in beauty and in strength after her baby was weaned. Good men and rich from all the villages of the state wanted to marry her.

'*Ei,* so soon? Were they prepared to take her with her baby?'

Yes.

105 'Hmm, a good woman does not rot.'

That is what our fathers said.

'And she chose Egya Nyaako?'

Yes. But then, we should remember that he was a good man himself.

'Yes, he was. I used to be one of those he hired regularly during the
110 cocoa harvests. He never insisted that we press down the cocoa as most of these farmers do. No, he never tried to cheat us out of our fair pay.'

Which is not what I can say of his heir!

'Not from what we've heard about him. A real mean one they say he is.'

So Auntie agreed to marry Egya Nyaako and she and her son came to
115 live here. The boy, this big scholar we now know of, went with the other
youngsters to the school the first day they started it here. In the old
Wesleyan chapel.° They say she used to say that if she never could sleep
her fill, it was because she wanted to give her son a good education.

'*Poo*, pity. And that must have been true. She mixed and rolled her
120 dough far into the night, and with the first cock-crow, got up from bed to
light her fires. Except on Sundays.'

She certainly went to church twice every Sunday. She was a good
Christian. And yet, look at how the boy turned out and what he did to her.

'Yes? You know I have been away much of the time. And I have never
125 heard much of him to respect. Besides, I only know very little.'

That is the story I am telling you. I am taking you to bird-town so I can't
understand why you insist on searching for eggs from the suburb!

'I will not interrupt you again, my sister.'

Maybe, it was because she never had any more children and therefore,
130 Ato became an only child. They say she spoilt him. Though I am not sure
I would not have done the same if I had been in her position. But they
say that before he was six years old, he was fighting her. And he continued to fight her until he became a big scholar. And then his father
came to acknowledge him as his son, and it seems that ruined him com-
135 pletely.

'Do you mean that lawyer-or-doctor-or-something-like-that man?'

Himself. They say he and his lady wife never had a male child so when
he was finishing Stan' 7° or so, he came to father him.

'*Poo*, scholars!'

140     It is a shame, my sister. Just when all the big troubles were over.

'If I had been Auntie Araba, eh, I would have charged him about a
thousand pounds for neglect.'

But Auntie Araba was not you. They say she was very happy that at last
the boy was going to know his real father. She even hoped that that would
145 settle his wild spirits. No, she did not want to make trouble. So this big man
from the city came one day with his friends or relatives and met Auntie Araba
and her relatives. It was one Sunday afternoon. In two big cars. They say some
of her sisters and relatives had sharpened their mouths ready to give him
what he deserved. But when they saw all the big men and their big cars, they
150 kept quiet. They murmured among themselves, and that was all. He told
them, I mean this new father, that he was going to send Ato to college.

'And did he?'

Yes he did. And he spoilt him even more than his mother had done. He gave him lots of money. I don't know what college he sent him to since I don't know about colleges. But he used to come here to spend some of his holidays. And every time, he left his mother with big debts to pay from his high living. Though I must add that she did not seem to mind.

'You know how mothers are, even when they have got several children.'

But, my sister, she really had a big blow when he put Mansa into trouble. Mansa's father nearly killed her.

'I hear Mansa's father is a proud man who believes that there is nothing which any man from his age group can do which he cannot do better.'

So you know. When school education came here, all his children were too old to go to school except Mansa. And he used to boast that he was only going to feel he had done his best by her when she reached the biggest college in the white man's land.

'And did he have the money?'

Don't ask me. As if I was in his pocket! Whether he had the money or not, he was certainly saying these things. But then people also knew him to add on these occasions, 'let us say it will be good, so it shall be good'. Don't laugh, my sister. Now, you can imagine how he felt when Ato did this to his daughter Mansa. I remember they reported him as saying that he was going to sue Ato for heavy damages. But luckily, Ato just stopped coming here in the holidays. But of course, his mother Auntie Araba was here. And she got something from Mansa's father. And under his very nose was Mansa's own mother. He used to go up and down ranting about some women who had no sense to advise their sons to keep their manhoods between their thighs, until they could afford the consequences of letting them loose, and other mothers who had not the courage to tie their daughters to their mats.

'O Lord.'

Yes, my sister.

'Hmm, I never knew any of these things.'

This is because you have been away in *the Mines* all the time. But me, I have been here. I am one of those who sit in that village waiting for the travellers. But also in connection with this story, I have had the chance to know so much because my husband's family house is in that quarter. I say, Mansa's father never let anyone sleep. And so about the sixth month of Mansa's pregnancy, her mother and Auntie Araba decided to do something about the situation. Auntie Araba would take Mansa in, see her through until the baby was born and then later, they would think about what to do. So Mansa went to live with her. And from that moment, people did not even know how to describe the relationship between the two. Some people said they were like

mother and daughter. Others that they were like sisters. Still more others even
said they were like friends. When the baby was born, Auntie Araba took one
195 or two of her relatives with her to Mansa's parents. Their purpose was simple.
Mansa had returned from the battlefield safe. The baby looked strong and
sound. If Mansa's father wanted her to go back to school...

'Yes, some girls do this.'

But Mansa's father had lost interest in Mansa's education.

200 'I can understand him.'

I too. So Auntie Araba said that in that case, there was no problem.
Mansa was a good girl. Not like one of these *yetse-yetse* things who think
putting a toe in a classroom turns them into goddesses. The child and
mother should go on living with her until Ato finished his education. Then
205 they could marry properly.

'Our Auntie Araba is going to heaven.'

If there is any heaven and God is not like man, my sister.

'What did Mansa's parents say?'

What else could they say? Her mother was very happy. She knew that if
210 Mansa came back to live with them she would always remind her father
of everything and then there would never be peace for anybody in the
house. They say that from that time, the baking business grew and grew
and grew. Mansa's hands pulled in money like a good hunter's gun does
with game. Auntie Araba herself became young again. She used to say
215 that if all mothers knew they would get daughters-in-law like Mansa, birth
pains would be easier to bear. When her husband Egya Nyaako died,
would she not have gone mad if Mansa was not with her? She was afraid
of the time when her son would finish college, come and marry Mansa
properly and take her away. Three years later, Ato finished college. He is a
220 teacher, as you know, my sister. The government was sending him to teach
somewhere far away from here. Then about two weeks or so before
Christmas, they got a letter from him that he was coming home.

'Ah, I am sure Mansa was very glad.'

Don't say it loudly, my sister. The news spread very fast. We teased her.
225 'These days some women go round with a smile playing round their lips
all the time. Maybe there is a bird on the neem tree behind their back door
which is giving them special good news,' we said. Auntie Araba told her
friends that her day of doom was coming upon her. What was she going
to do on her own? But her friends knew that she was also very glad. So far,
230 she had looked after her charges very well. But if you boil anything for too
long, it burns. Her real glory would come only when her son came to take
away his bride and his child.

'And the boy-child was a very handsome somebody too.'

And clever, my sister. Before he was two, he was delighting us all by imi-
tating his grandmother and his mother singing the bread-hawking song.
A week before the Saturday Ato was expected, Mansa moved back to her
parents' house.

'That was a good thing to do.'

She could not have been better advised. That Saturday, people saw her
at her bath quite early. My little girl had caught a fever and I myself had
not gone to the farm. When eleven o'clock struck, I met Mansa in the
market-place, looking like a festive dish. I asked her if what we had heard
was true, that our lord and master was coming on the market-day lorry
that afternoon. She said I had heard right.

'Maybe she was very eager to see him and could not wait in the house.'

Could you have waited quietly if you had been her?

'Oh, women. We are to be pitied.'

Tell me, my sister. I had wanted to put a stick under the story and clear
it all for you. But we are already in town.

'Yes, look at that crowd. Is Auntie Araba's family house near the mouth
of this road?'

Oh yes. Until the town grew to the big thing it is, the Twidan Abusia
house was right on the road but now it is behind about four or so other
houses. Why?

'I think I can hear singing.'

Yes, you are right.

'She is going to get a good funeral.'

That, my sister, is an answer to a question no one will ask.

'So finish me the story.'

Hmm, kinsman, when the market lorry arrived, there was no Scholar-
Teacher-Ato on it.

'No?'

No.

'What did Auntie Araba and Mansa do?'

What could they do? Everyone said that the road always has stories to
tell. Perhaps he had only missed the lorry. Perhaps he had fallen ill just on
that day or a day or so before. They would wait for a while. Perhaps he
would arrive that evening if he thought he could get another lorry, it being
a market day. But he did not come any time that Saturday or the next
morning. And no one saw him on Monday or Tuesday.

'Ohhh...'

They don't say, ohhh....We heard about the middle of the next week—I
have forgotten now whether it was the Wednesday or Thursday—that he
had come.

275 *'Eheh?'*

*Nyo.* But he brought some news with him. He could not marry Mansa.

'Oh, why? After spoiling her...'

If you don't shut up, I will stop.

'Forgive me and go on, my sister.'

280 Let us stand in this alley here—that is the funeral parlour over there. I
don't want anyone to overhear us.

'You are right.'

Chicha Ato said he could not marry Mansa because he had got another
girl into trouble.

285 *'Whopei!'°*

She had been in the college too. Her mother is a big lady and her father
is a big man. They said if he did not marry their daughter, they would
finish him....

*'Whopei!'*

290 His lawyer-father thought it advisable for him to wed that girl soon
because they were afraid of what the girl's father would do.

*'Whopei!'*

So he could not marry our Mansa.

*'Whopei!'*

295 They don't say, *Whopei,* my sister.

'So what did they do?'

Who?

'Everybody. Mansa? Auntie Araba?'

What could they do?

300 *'Whopei!'*

That was just before you came back to have your third baby, I think.

'About three years ago?'

Yes.

'It was my fourth. I had the third in Aboso but it died.'

305 Then it was your fourth. Yes, it was just before you came.

'I thought Auntie Araba was not looking like herself. But I had enough
troubles of my own and had no eyes to go prying into other people's
affairs....So that was that....'

Yes. From then on, Auntie Araba was just lost.

310 'And Mansa-ah?'

She really is like Auntie herself. She has all of her character. She too is a good woman. If she had stayed here, I am sure someone else would have married her. But she left.

'And the child?'

She left him with her mother. Haven't you seen him since you came?

'No. Because it will not occur to anybody to point him out to me until I ask. And I cannot recognise him from my mind. I do not know him at all.'

He is around, with the other schoolchildren.

'So what does Mansa do?'

When she left, everyone said she would become a whore in the city.

'*Whopei*. People are bad.'

Yes. But perhaps they would have been right if Mansa had not been the Mansa we all know. We hear Auntie Araba sent her to a friend and she found her a job with some people. They bake hundreds of loaves of bread an hour with machines.

'A good person does not rot.'

No. She sent money and other things home.

'May God bless her. And Auntie Araba herself?'

As I was telling you. After this affair, she never became herself again. She stopped baking. Immediately. She told her friends that she felt old age was coming on her. Then a few months later, they say she started getting some very bad stomach aches. She tried here, she tried there. Hospitals first, then our own doctors and their herbs. Nothing did any good.

'O our end! Couldn't the hospital doctors cut her up and find out?'

My sister, they say they don't work like that. They have to find out what is wrong before they cut people up.

'And they could not find out what was wrong with Auntie Araba?'

No. She spent whatever she had on this stomach. Egya Nyaako, as you know, had already died. So, about three months ago, she packed up all she had and came here, to squat by her ancestral hearth.

'And yesterday afternoon she died?'

Yes, and yesterday afternoon she died.

'Her spirit was gone.'

Certainly it was her son who drove it away. And then Mansa left with her soul.

'Have you ever seen Chicha Ato's lady-wife?'

No. We hear they had a church wedding. But Auntie Araba did not put her feet there. And he never brought her to Ofuntumase.°

'Maybe the two of them may come here today?'

I don't see how he can fail to come. But she, I don't know. Some of these ladies will not set foot in a place like this for fear of getting dirty.

'Hmmm....it is their own cassava!° But do you think Mansa will come and wail for Auntie Araba?'

My sister, if you have come, do you think Mansa will not?

(1988)

# Misery

## Anton Pavlovich Chekhov (Russia) 1860–1904

*(translated from Russian by Constance Garnett)*

## About the Author

*One of Russia's best-known writers, Chekhov is regarded as the father of both the modern Russian short story and of the modern Russian play. He was born in the Russian seaport town of Taganrog, near the Black Sea. Son of a grocer and grandson of a serf who had bought his family's freedom before emancipation, Chekhov was extremely familiar with the life of the poor and the unfortunate in 19th-century Russia, which he recorded objectively in his writings. He began to write stories for magazines to support himself as a medical student at Moscow University. After his graduation in 1884, he continued to write while practising medicine. By 1886 he had become so popular with readers and critics that he decided to write full time. From then on, his sporadic practice in medicine remained voluntary and charitable in nature. A man of great diligence and responsibility, Chekhov worked tirelessly for many years without paying attention to his worsening health. He married Olga Knipper, an actress in Moscow, in May 1901. Three years later, on July 2, 1904, Chekhov died of tuberculosis at age 44.*

*In his brief life Chekhov created a wealth of literary works, consisting of short stories, humorous works, novels, and plays. It is as a playwright that he has achieved most fame and influence. Among his contributions to the modern theatre are* The Seagull *(1896),* Uncle Vanya *(1899),* The Cherry Orchard *(1900), and* The Three Sisters *(1910). His short stories, collected in many anthologies and translated into different languages, are loved and noted for his ingenious handling of narrative resources and point of view as well as his focus on the mood rather than action of characters. For him the atmosphere of a story is of paramount importance, requiring both external details and psychological depictions. On that score "Misery," one of the writer's earlier stories, presents us with a perfect example.*

*The story "Misery" opens with a rhetorical question taken from a Russian folk lament.*

"To Whom Shall I Tell My Grief?"

The twilight of evening. Big flakes of wet snow are whirling lazily about the street lamps, which have just been lighted, and lying in a thin soft layer on roofs, horses' backs, shoulders, caps. Iona Potapov, the sledge-
5  driver, is all white like a ghost. He sits on the box without stirring, bent as double as the living body can be bent. If a regular snowdrift fell on him it seems as though even then he would not think it necessary to shake it

off....His little mare is white and motionless too. Her stillness, the angularity of her lines, and the stick-like straightness of her legs make her look
10 like a halfpenny gingerbread horse. She is probably lost in thought. Anyone who has been torn away from the plough, from the familiar gray landscapes, and cast into this slough, full of monstrous lights, of unceasing uproar and hurrying people, is bound to think.

It is a long time since Iona and his nag have budged. They came out of
15 the yard before dinner-time and not a single fare yet. But now the shades of evening are falling on the town. The pale light of the street lamps changes to a vivid color, and the bustle of the street grows noisier.

"Sledge to Vyborgskaya!" Iona hears. "Sledge!"

Iona starts, and through his snow-plastered eyelashes sees an officer in
20 a military overcoat with a hood over his head.

"To Vyborgskaya," repeats the officer. "Are you asleep? To Vyborgskaya!"

In token of assent Iona gives a tug at the reins which sends cakes of snow flying from the horse's back and shoulders. The officer gets into the
25 sledge. The sledge-driver clicks to the horse, cranes his neck like a swan, rises in his seat, and more from habit than necessity brandishes his whip. The mare cranes her neck, too, crooks her stick-like legs, and hesitatingly sets off....

"Where are you shoving, you devil?" Iona immediately hears shouts
30 from the dark mass shifting to and fro before him. "Where the devil are you going? Keep to the r-right!"

"You don't know how to drive! Keep to the right," says the officer angrily.

A coachman driving a carriage swears at him; a pedestrian crossing the
35 road and brushing the horse's nose with his shoulder looks at him angrily and shakes the snow off his sleeve. Iona fidgets on the box as though he were sitting on thorns, jerks his elbows, and turns his eyes about like one possessed, as though he did not know where he was or why he was there.

"What rascals they all are!" says the officer jocosely. "They are simply
40 doing their best to run up against you or fall under the horse's feet. They must be doing it on purpose.

Iona looks at his fare and moves his lips....Apparently he means to say something, but nothing comes out but a sniff.

"What?" inquires the officer.
45 Iona gives a wry smile, and straining his throat, brings out huskily: "My son..., er...my son died this week, sir."

"H'm! What did he die of?"

Iona turns his whole body round to his fare, and says:

"Who can tell! It must have been from fever....He lay three days in the
50 hospital and then he died....God's will."

"Turn round, you devil!" comes out of the darkness. "Have you gone
cracked, you old dog? Look where you are going!"

"Drive on! drive on!..."says the officer. "We shan't get there till
tomorrow going on like this. Hurry up!"

55 The sledge-driver cranes his neck again, rises in his seat, and with heavy
grace swings his whip. Several times he looks round at the officer, but the
latter keeps his eyes shut and is apparently disinclined to listen. Putting his
fare down at Vyborgskaya, Iona stops by a restaurant, and again sits huddled up on the box....Again the wet snow paints him and his horse white.
60 One hour passes, and then another.

Three young men, two tall and thin, one short and hunchbacked, come
up, railing at each other and loudly stamping on the pavement with their
galoshes.

"Cabby, to the Police Bridge!" the hunchback cries in a cracked voice.
65 "The three of us,...twenty kopecks!"

Iona tugs at the reins and clicks to his horse. Twenty kopecks is not a
fair price, but he has no thoughts for that. Whether it is a rouble or
whether it is five kopecks does not matter to him now so long as he has a
fare....The three young men, shoving each other and using bad language,
70 go up to the sledge, and all three try to sit down at once. The question
remains to be settled: Which are to sit down and which one is to stand?
After a long altercation, ill-temper, and abuse, they come to the conclusion
that the hunchback must stand because he is the shortest.

"Well, drive on," says the hunchback in his cracked voice, settling him-
75 self and breathing down Iona's neck. "Cut along! What a cap you've got,
my friend! You wouldn't find a worse one in all Petersburg...."

"He-he!...he-he!..." laughs Iona. "It's nothing to boast of!"

"Well, then, nothing to boast of, drive on! Are you going to drive like
this all the way? Eh? Shall I give you one in the neck?"

80 "My head aches," says one of the tall ones. "At the Dukmasovs' yesterday Vaska and I drank four bottles of brandy between us.

"I can't make out why you talk such stuff," says the other tall one
angrily. "You lie like a brute."

"Strike me dead, it's the truth!..."

85 "It's about as true as that a louse coughs."

"He-he!" grins Iona. "Me-er-ry gentlemen!"

"Tfoo! the devil take you!" cries the hunchback indignantly. "Will you get on, you old plague, or won't you? Is that the way to drive? Give her one with the whip. Hang it all, give it her well."

90    Iona feels behind his back the jolting person and quivering voice of the hunchback. He hears abuse addressed to him, he sees people, and the feeling of loneliness begins little by little to be less heavy on his heart. The hunchback swears at him, till he chokes over some elaborately whimsical string of epithets and is overpowered by his cough. His tall companions
95    begin talking of a certain Nadyezhda Petrovna. Iona looks round at them. Waiting till there is a brief pause, he looks round once more and says:

"This week...er...my...er...son died!"

"We shall all die,...." says the hunchback with a sigh, wiping his lips after coughing. "Come, drive on! drive on! My friends, I simply cannot
100  stand crawling like this! When will he get us there?"

"Well, you give him a little encouragement...one in the neck!"

"Do you hear, you old plague? I'll make you smart. If one stands on ceremony with fellows like you one may as well walk. Do you hear, you old dragon? Or don't you care a hang what we say?"

105  And Iona hears rather than feels a slap on the back of his neck.

"He-he!..." he laughs. "Merry gentlemen...God give you health!"

"Cabman, are you married?" asks one of the tall ones.

"I? He-he! Me-er-ry gentlemen. The only wife for me now is the damp earth....He-ho-ho!...The grave that is!...Here my son's dead and I am
110  alive....It's a strange thing, death has come in at the wrong door....Instead of coming for me it went for my son...."

And Iona turns round to tell them how his son died, but at that point the hunchback gives a faint sigh and announces that, thank God! they have arrived at last. After taking his twenty kopecks, Iona gazes for a long
115  while after the revelers, who disappear into a dark entry. Again he is alone and again there is silence for him....The misery which has been for a brief space eased comes back again and tears his heart more cruelly than ever. With a look of anxiety and suffering Iona's eyes stray restlessly among the crowds moving to and fro on both sides of the street: can he not find
120  among those thousands someone who will listen to him? But the crowds flit by heedless of him and his misery....His misery is immense, beyond all bounds. If Iona's heart were to burst and his misery to flow out, it would flood the whole world, it seems, but yet it is not seen. It has found a hiding-place in such an insignificant shell that one would not have found it with
125  a candle by daylight....

Iona sees a house-porter with a parcel and makes up his mind to address him.

"What time will it be, friend?" he asks.

"Going on for ten....Why have you stopped here? Drive on!"

130 Iona drives a few paces away, bends himself double, and gives himself up to his misery. He feels it is no good to appeal to people. But before five minutes have passed he draws himself up, shakes his head as though he feels a sharp pain, and tugs at the reins....He can bear it no longer.

"Back to the yard!" he thinks. "To the yard!"

135 And his little mare, as though she knew his thoughts, falls to trotting. An hour and a half later Iona is sitting by a big dirty stove. On the stove, on the floor, and on the benches are people snoring. The air is full of smells and stuffiness. Iona looks at the sleeping figures, scratches himself, and regrets that he has come home so early....

140 "I have not earned enough to pay for the oats, even," he thinks. "That's why I am so miserable. A man who knows how to do his work,...who has had enough to eat, and whose horse has had enough to eat, is always at ease...."

In one of the corners a young cabman gets up, clears his throat sleepily, 145 and makes for the waterbucket.

"Want a drink?" Iona asks him.

"Seems so."

"May it do you good....But my son is dead, mate....Do you hear? This week in the hospital....It's queer business...."

150 Iona looks to see the effect produced by his words, but he sees nothing. The young man has covered his head over and is already asleep. The old man sighs and scratches himself....Just as the young man had been thirsty for water, he thirsts for speech. His son will soon have been dead a week, and he has not really talked to anybody yet....He wants to talk of it prop-155 erly, with deliberation....He wants to tell how his son was taken ill, how he suffered, what he said before he died, how he died....He wants to describe the funeral, and how he went to the hospital to get his son's clothes. He still has his daughter Anisya in the country....And he wants to talk about her too....Yes, he has plenty to talk about now. His listener ought to sigh 160 and exclaim and lament....It would be even better to talk to women. Though they are silly creatures, they blubber at the first word.

"Let's go out and have a look at the mare," Iona thinks. "There is always time for sleep....You'll have sleep enough, no fear...."

He puts on his coat and goes into the stables where his mare is standing.
165 He thinks about oats, about hay, about the weather....He cannot think about his son when he is alone....To talk about him with someone is possible, but to think of him and picture him is insufferable anguish....

"Are you munching?" Iona asks his mare, seeing her shining eyes. 'There, munch away, munch away....Since we have not earned enough for
170 oats, we will eat hay....Yes,...I have grown too old to drive....My son ought to be driving, not I....He was a real coachman....He ought to have lived...."

Iona is silent for a while, and then he goes on:

"That's how it is, old girl....Kuzma Ionitch is gone....He said good-by to me....He went and died for no reason....Now, suppose you had a little colt,
175 and you were that little colt's own mother....And all at once that same little colt went and died....You'd be sorry, wouldn't you?..."

The little mare munches, listens, and breathes on her master's hands. Iona is carried away and tells her all about it.

(1886)

# The Kiss

Kate Chopin (United States) 1851–1904

## About the Author

*Catherine O'Flaherty (Kate Chopin) was born in St. Louis, Missouri. Her father, Thomas O'Flaherty, died when she was five years old, so she was raised by her mother, whose independence certainly influenced the young Kate. She enjoyed a happy childhood, and in 1868, graduated from the St. Louis Academy of the Sacred Heart, a convent school for girls of wealthy families. Thus, Kate Chopin's formative years were spent in an almost exclusively female environment; this fact no doubt influenced the themes she explored in her writing. In 1870, she married Oscar Chopin, but her husband died suddenly in 1883, leaving Kate Chopin to raise their six children alone and to manage the family business affairs. She began writing fiction in 1889, partly to support her children but also because of her own passion for reading. She composed in her family living room, surrounded by her children, working quickly and often completing a short story in a day. By 1890, she had published four short stories and a novel,* At Fault. *Chopin's short stories were well received; however, in 1899, she published what is now regarded as her finest work, a novel,* The Awakening. *This novel, like all her writing, explores a woman's response to the societal pressures of the time. The* Awakening *brought about the end of Chopin's literary career, for the American public was not prepared for a novel that dealt with a woman's personal awakening as she struggles with societal oppression and racism and her own emotional and sexual needs. The novel was denounced and banned. As a result of the negative criticism, Chopin stopped writing. She died four years later from a brain hemorrhage.*

*A voracious reader, Chopin was particularly influenced by the ideas of the American poet Walt Whitman and the technique of the French author, Guy de Maupassant, whose stories she translated from French into English. Chopin's female protagonists are concerned with self-identification. Some are self-assertive and achieve a measure of autonomy, while others simply struggle with the traditional female roles. Nevertheless, the desire for self-reliance is the theme that emerges in all her writing as she explores a woman's place in marriage and in society. Chopin described her motivation to write in this way: "Having a group of people at my disposal, I thought it might be entertaining (to myself) to throw them together and see what would happen." In "The Kiss," Chopin examines the sexual mores and marital expectations of her time.*

It was still quite light out of doors, but inside with the curtains drawn and the smouldering fire sending out a dim, uncertain glow, the room was full of deep shadows.

Brantain sat in one of these shadows; it had overtaken him and he did
5 not mind. The obscurity lent him courage to keep his eyes fastened as ardently as he liked upon the girl who sat in the firelight.

She was very handsome, with a certain fine, rich coloring that belongs to the healthy brune type. She was quite composed, as she idly stroked the satiny coat of the cat that lay curled in her lap, and she occasionally sent
10 a slow glance into the shadow where her companion sat. They were talking low, of indifferent things which plainly were not the things that occupied their thoughts. She knew that he loved her—a frank, blustering fellow without guile enough to conceal his feelings, and no desire to do so. For two weeks past he had sought her society eagerly and persistently. She
15 was confidently waiting for him to declare himself and she meant to accept him. The rather insignificant and unattractive Brantain was enormously rich; and she liked and required the entourage which wealth could give her.

During one of the pauses between their talk of the last tea and the next
20 reception the door opened and a young man entered whom Brantain knew quite well. The girl turned her face toward him. A stride or two brought him to her side, and bending over her chair—before she could suspect his intention, for she did not realize that he had not seen her visitor— he pressed an ardent, lingering kiss upon her lips.

25 Brantain slowly arose; so did the girl arise, but quickly, and the newcomer stood between them, a little amusement and some defiance struggling with the confusion in his face.

"I believe," stammered Brantain, "I see that I have stayed too long. I— I had no idea—that is, I must wish you good-bye." He was clutching his
30 hat with both hands, and probably did not perceive that she was extending her hand to him, her presence of mind had not completely deserted her; but she could not have trusted herself to speak.

"Hang me if I saw him sitting there, Nattie! I know it's deuced awkward for you. But I hope you'll forgive me this once—this very first break. Why,
35 what's the matter?"

"Don't touch me; don't come near me," she returned angrily. "What do you mean by entering the house without ringing?"

"I came in with your brother, as I often do," he answered coldly, in self-justification. "We came in the side way. He went upstairs and I came in
40 here hoping to find you. The explanation is simple enough and ought to satisfy you that the misadventure was unavoidable. But do say that you forgive me, Nathalie," he entreated, softening.

"Forgive you! You don't know what you are talking about. Let me pass. It depends upon—a good deal whether I ever forgive you."
45 At that next reception which she and Brantain had been talking about she approached the young man with a delicious frankness of manner when she saw him there.

"Will you let me speak to you a moment or two, Mr. Brantain?" she asked with an engaging but perturbed smile. He seemed extremely
50 unhappy; but when she took his arm and walked away with him, seeking a retired corner, a ray of hope mingled with the almost comical misery of his expression. She was apparently very outspoken.

"Perhaps I should not have sought this interview, Mr. Brantain; but—but, oh, I have been very uncomfortable, almost miserable since that little
55 encounter the other afternoon. When I thought how you might have mis-interpreted it, and believed things"—hope was plainly gaining the ascen-dancy over misery in Brantain's round, guileless face—"Of course, I know it is nothing to you, but for my own sake I do want you to understand that Mr. Harvy is an intimate friend of long standing. Why, we have always
60 been like cousins—like brother and sister, I may say. He is my brother's most intimate associate and often fancies that he is entitled to the same privileges as the family. Oh, I know it is absurd, uncalled for, to tell you this; undignified even," she was almost weeping, "but it makes so much difference to me what you think of—of me." Her voice had grown very low
65 and agitated. The misery had all disappeared from Brantain's face.

"Then you do really care what I think, Miss Nathalie? May I call you Miss Nathalie?" They turned into a long, dim corridor that was lined on either side with tall, graceful plants. They walked slowly to the very end of it. When they turned to retrace their steps Brantain's face was radiant and
70 hers was triumphant.

\* \* \*

Harvy was among the guests at the wedding; and he sought her out in a rare moment when she stood alone.

"Your husband," he said, smiling, "has sent me over to kiss you."

75    A quick blush suffused her face and round polished throat. "I suppose it's natural for a man to feel and act generously on an occasion of this kind. He tells me he doesn't want his marriage to interrupt wholly that pleasant intimacy which has existed between you and me. I don't know what you've been telling him," with an insolent smile, "but he has sent me 80 here to kiss you."

She felt like a chess player who, by the clever handling of his pieces, sees the game taking the course intended. Her eyes were bright and tender with a smile as they glanced up into his; and her lips looked hungry for the kiss which they invited.

85    "But, you know," he went on quietly, "I didn't tell him so, it would have seemed ungrateful, but I can tell you. I've stopped kissing women; it's dangerous."

Well, she had Brantain and his million left. A person can't have everything in this world; and it was a little unreasonable of her to expect it.

(1895)

# The Jade Peony

Wayson Choy (Canada) 1939–

## About the Author

*Wayson Choy is an award-winning Canadian author whose works have been well accepted internationally by both the common reader and literary critics. Of Chinese descent, Choy was born in Vancouver and educated at the University of British Columbia. Since 1967 he has been a professor of English at Humber College of Applied Arts and Technology in Toronto. He is also a faculty member of the Humber School for Writers. Besides teaching and writing, Mr. Choy also participates actively in various community literacy projects and AIDS groups and has been elected president of Cahoots Theatre Company in Toronto for many years.*

*Wayson Choy's novels and short stories explore and expose his vision of growing up in post-war Canadian society. His first novel,* The Jade Peony *(1995), which is about Vancouver's Chinatown during the Depression and World War II, won him the 1995 Trillium Award and the 1995 Vancouver City Book Award.* Paper Shadows: A Chinatown Childhood, *Choy's personal memoir published in 1999, was shortlisted for the 1999 Governor General's Award and named a 1999* Toronto Globe and Mail *Notable Book of the Year. While urging other people to tell "their own stories before they are lost," Wayson Choy is now working on the sequel to his best-selling novel* The Jade Peony, *which interestingly grew out of this short story published under the same title in 1979.*

When Grandmama died at 83 our whole household held its breath. She had promised us a sign of her leaving, final proof that her present life had ended well. My parents knew that without any clear sign, our own family fortunes could be altered, threatened. My stepmother
5 looked endlessly into the small cluttered room the ancient lady had occupied. Nothing was touched; nothing changed. My father, thinking that a sign should appear in Grandmama's garden, looked at the frost-killed shoots and cringed: no, that could not be it.

My two older teenage brothers and my sister, Liang, age 14, were
10 embarrassed by my parents' behavior. What would all the white people in Vancouver think of us? We were Canadians now, *Chinese-Canadians*, a hyphenated reality that my parents could never accept. So it seemed, for different reasons, we all held our breath waiting for *something*.

I was eight when she died. For days she had resisted going into the hos-
15 pital...*a cold, just a cold*...and instead gave constant instruction to my stepmother and sister on the boiling of ginseng roots mixed with bitter extract.
At night, between wracking coughs and deadly silences, Grandmama had
her back and chest rubbed with heated camphor oil and sipped a bluish
decoction of an herb called Peacock's Tail. When all these failed to abate
20 her fever, she began to arrange the details of her will. This she did with my
father, confessing finally: "I am too stubborn. The only cure for old age is
to die."

My father wept to hear this. I stood beside her bed; she turned to me.
Her round face looked darker, and the gentleness of her eyes, the thin,
25 arching eyebrows, seemed weary. I brushed the few strands of gray, brittle
hair from her face; she managed to smile at me. Being the youngest, I had
spent nearly all my time with her and could not imagine that we would
ever be parted. Yet when she spoke, and her voice hesitated, cracked, the
sombre shadows of her room chilled me.

30 Her wrinkled brow grew wet with fever, and her small body seemed even
more diminutive.

"I—I am going to the hospital, Grandson." Her hand reached out for
mine. "You know, Little Son, whatever happens I will never leave you." Her
palm felt plush and warm, the slender, old fingers boney and firm, so magi-
35 cally strong was her grip that I could not imagine how she could ever part
from me. Ever.

Her hands *were* magical. My most vivid memories are of her hands:
long, elegant fingers, with impeccable nails, a skein of fine, barely-seen
veins, and wrinkled skin like light pine. Those hands were quick when she
40 taught me, at six, simple tricks of juggling, learnt when she was a village
girl in Southern Canton; a troupe of actors had stayed on her father's farm.
One of them, "tall and pale as the whiteness of petals," fell in love with
her, promising to return. In her last years his image came back like a third
being in our two lives. He had been magician, acrobat, juggler, and some
45 of the things he taught her she had absorbed and passed on to me through
her stories and games. But above all, without realizing it then, her hands
conveyed to me the quality of their love.

Most marvellous for me was the quick-witted skill her hands revealed in
making windchimes for our birthdays: windchimes in the likeness of her
50 lost friend's only present to her, made of bits of string and scraps, in the
centre of which once hung a precious jade peony. This wondrous gift to her
broke apart years ago, in China, but Grandmama kept the jade pendant

in a tiny red silk envelope, and kept it always in her pocket, until her death.

55    These were not ordinary, carelessly made chimes, such as those you now find in our Chinatown stores, whose rattling noises drive you mad. But making her special ones caused dissension in our family, and some shame. Each one that she made was created from a treasure trove of glass fragments and castaway costume jewellery, in the same way that her first
60  windchime had been made. The problem for the rest of the family was in the fact that Grandmama looked for these treasures wandering the back alleys of Keefer and Pender Streets, peering into our neighbors' garbage cans, chasing away hungry, nervous cats and shouting curses at them.

      "All our friends are laughing at us!" Older Brother Jung said at last to
65  my father, when Grandmama was away having tea at Mrs. Lim's.

      "We are not poor," Oldest Brother Kiam declared, "yet she and Sek-Lung poke through those awful things as if—" he shoved me in frustration and I stumbled against my sister, "—they were beggars!"

      "She will make Little Brother crazy!" Sister Liang said. Without warning,
70  she punched me sharply in the back; I jumped. "You see, look how *nervous* he is!"

      I lifted my foot slightly, enough to swing it back and kick Liang in the shin. She yelled and pulled back her fist to punch me again. Jung made a menacing move towards me.

75    "Stop this, all of you!" My father shook his head in exasperation. How could he dare tell the Grand Old One, his aging mother, that what was somehow appropriate in a poor village in China, was an abomination here. How could he prevent me, his youngest, from accompanying her? If she went walking into those alley-ways alone she could well be attacked
80  by hoodlums. "She is not a beggar looking for food. She is searching for—for...."

      My stepmother attempted to speak, then fell silent. She, too, seemed perplexed and somewhat ashamed. They all loved Grandmama, but she was *inconvenient,* unsettling.

85    As for our neighbors, most understood Grandmama to be harmlessly crazy, others that she did indeed make lovely toys but for what purpose? *Why?* they asked, and the stories she told me, of the juggler who smiled at her, flashed in my head.

      Finally, by their cutting remarks, the family did exert enough pressure
90  so that Grandmama and I no longer openly announced our expeditions. Instead, she took me with her on "shopping trips," ostensibly for clothes or groceries, while in fact we spent most of our time exploring stranger and

more distant neighborhoods, searching for splendid junk: jangling pieces of a vase, cranberry glass fragments embossed with leaves, discarded glass beads from Woolworth necklaces....We would sneak them all home in brown rice sacks, folded into small parcels, and put them under her bed. During the day when the family was away at school or work, we brought them out and washed every item in a large black pot of boiling lye and water, dried them quickly, carefully, and returned them, sparkling, under her bed.

Our greatest excitement occurred when a fire gutted the large Chinese Presbyterian Church, three blocks from our house. Over the still-smoking ruins the next day, Grandmama and I rushed precariously over the blackened beams to pick out the stained glass that glittered in the sunlight. Small figure bent over, wrapped against the autumn cold in a dark blue quilted coat, happily gathering each piece like gold, she became my spiritual playmate: "There's a good one! *There!*"

Hours later, soot-covered and smelling of smoke, we came home with a Safeway carton full of delicate fragments, still early enough to steal them all into the house and put the small box under her bed. "These are special pieces," she said, giving the box a last push, "because they come from a sacred place." She slowly got up and I saw, for the first time, her hand begin to shake. But then, in her joy, she embraced me. Both of our hearts were racing, as if we were two dreamers. I buried my face in her blue quilt, and for a moment, the whole world seemed silent.

"My juggler," she said, "he never came back to me from Honan...perhaps the famine...." Her voice began to quake. "But I shall have my sacred windchime...I shall have it again."

One evening, when the family was gathered in their usual places in the parlor, Grandmama gave me her secret nod: a slight wink of her eye and a flaring of her nostrils. There was *trouble* in the air. Supper had gone badly, school examinations were due, Father had failed to meet an editorial deadline at the *Vancouver Chinese Times*. A huge sigh came from Sister Liang.

"But it is useless this Chinese they teach you!" she lamented, turning to Stepmother for support. Silence. Liang frowned, dejected, and went back to her Chinese book, bending the covers back.

"Father," Oldest Brother Kiam began, waving his bamboo brush in the air, "you must realize that this Mandarin only confuses us. We are Cantonese speakers...."

"And you do not complain about Latin, French or German in your English school?" Father rattled his newspaper, signal that his patience was ending.

"But, Father, those languages are *scientific*," Kiam jabbed his brush in the air. "We are now in a scientific, logical world."

135   Father was silent. We could all hear Grandmama's rocker.

"What about Sek-Lung?" Older Brother Jung pointed angrily at me. "He was sick last year, but this year he should have at least started Chinese school, instead of picking over garbage cans!"

"He starts next year," Father said, in a hard tone that immediately

140   warned everyone to be silent. Liang slammed her book.

Grandmama went on rocking quietly in her chair. She complimented my mother on her knitting, made a remark about the "strong beauty" of Kiam's brushstrokes which, in spite of himself, immensely pleased him. All this babbling noise was her family torn and confused in a strange land:

145   everything here was so very foreign and scientific.

The truth was, I was sorry not to have started school the year before. In my innocence I had imagined going to school meant certain privileges worthy of all my brothers' and sister's complaints. The fact that my lung infection in my fifth and sixth years, mistakenly diagnosed as TB, earned

150   me some reprieve, only made me long for school the more. Each member of the family took turns on Sunday, teaching me or annoying me. But it was the countless hours I spent with Grandmama that were my real education. Tapping me on my head she would say, "Come, Sek-Lung, we have *our* work," and we would walk up the stairs to her small crowded room.

155   There, in the midst of her antique shawls, the old ancestral calligraphy and multi-colored embroidered hangings, beneath the mysterious shelves of sweet herbs and bitter potions, we would continue doing what we had started that morning: the elaborate windchime for her death.

"I can't last forever," she declared, when she let me in on the secret of

160   this one. "It will sing and dance and glitter," her long fingers stretched into the air, pantomiming the waving motion of her ghost chimes; "My spirit will hear its sounds and see its light and return to this house and say goodbye to you."

Deftly she reached into the Safeway carton she had placed on the chair

165   beside me. She picked out a fish-shape amber piece, and with a long needle-like tool and a steel ruler, she scored it. Pressing the blade of a cleaver against the line, with the fingers of her other hand, she lifted up the glass until it cleanly *snapped* into the exact shape she required. Her hand began to tremble, the tips of her fingers to shiver, like rippling water.

170   "You see that, Little One?" She held her hand up. "That is my body fighting with Death. He is in this room now."

My eyes darted in panic, but Grandmama remained calm, undisturbed, and went on with her work. Then I remembered the glue and uncorked the jar for her. Soon the graceful ritual movements of her hand returned to her,
175 and I became lost in the magic of her task: she dabbed a cabalistic mixture of glue on one end and skillfully dropped the braided end of a silk thread into it. This part always amazed me: the braiding would slowly, *very* slowly, *unknot*, fanning out like a prized fishtail. In a few seconds the clear, homemade glue began to harden as I blew lightly over it, welding to itself
180 each separate silk strand.

Each jam-sized pot of glue was precious; each large cork had been wrapped with a fragment of pink silk. I remember this part vividly, because each cork was treated to a special rite. First we went shopping in the best silk stores in Chinatown for the perfect square of silk she required.
185 It had to be a deep pink, a shade of color blushing toward red. And the tone had to match—as closely as possible—her precious jade carving, the small peony of white and light-red jade, her most lucky possession. In the centre of this semi-translucent carving, no more than an inch wide, was a pool of pink light, its veins swirling out into the petals of the flower.
190 "This color is the color of my spirit," she said, holding it up to the window so I could see the delicate pastel against the broad strokes of sunlight. She dropped her voice, and I held my breath at the wonder of the color. "This was given to me by the young actor who taught me how to juggle. He had four of them, and each one had a centre of this rare color,
195 the color of Good Fortune." The pendant seemed to pulse as she turned it: "Oh, Sek-Lung! He had white hair and white skin *to his toes! It's true,* I saw him bathing." She laughed and blushed, her eyes softened at the memory. The silk had to match the pink heart of her pendant: the color was magical for her, to hold the unravelling strands of her memory....

200 It was just six months before she died that we really began to work on her last windchime. Three thin bamboo sticks were steamed and bent into circlets; 30 exact lengths of silk thread, the strongest kind, were cut and braided at both ends and glued to stained glass. Her hands worked on their own command, each hand racing with a life of its own: cutting, snapping,
205 braiding, knotting....Sometimes she breathed heavily and her small body, growing thinner, sagged against me. *Death,* I thought, *He is in this room,* and I would work harder alongside her. For months Grandmama and I did this every other evening, a half dozen pieces each time. The shaking in her hand grew worse, but we said nothing. Finally, after discarding hundreds,
210 she told me she had the necessary 30 pieces. But this time, because it was

a sacred chime, I would not be permitted to help her tie it up or have the joy of raising it. "Once tied," she said, holding me against my disappointment, "not even I can raise it. Not a sound must it make until I have died."

"What will happen?"

"Your father will then take the centre braided strand and raise it. He will hang it against my bedroom window so that my ghost may see it, and hear it, and return. I must say goodbye to this world properly or wander in this foreign devil's land forever."

"You can take the streetcar!" I blurted, suddenly shocked that she actually meant to leave me. I thought I could hear the clear-chromatic chimes, see the shimmering colors on the wall: I fell against her and cried, and there in my crying I knew that she would die. I can still remember the touch of her hand on my head, and the smell of her thick woolen sweater pressed against my face. "I will always be with you, Little Sek-Lung, but in a different way...you'll see."

Months went by, and nothing happened. Then one late September evening, when I had just come home from Chinese School, Grandmama was preparing supper when she looked out our kitchen window and saw a cat—a long, lean white cat—jump into our garbage pail and knock it over. She ran out to chase it away, shouting curses at it. She did not have her thick sweater on and when she came back into the house, a chill gripped her. She leaned against the door: "That was not a cat," she said, and the odd tone of her voice caused my father to look with alarm at her. "I can not take back my curses. It is too late." She took hold of my father's arm: "It was all white and had pink eyes like sacred fire."

My father started at this, and they both looked pale. My brothers and sister, clearing the table, froze in their gestures.

"The fog has confused you," Stepmother said. "It was just a cat."

But Grandmama shook her head, for she knew it was a sign. "I will not live forever," she said. "I am prepared."

The next morning she was confined to her bed with a severe cold. Sitting by her, playing with some of my toys, I asked her about the cat:

"Why did father jump at the cat with the pink eyes? He didn't see it, you did."

"But he and your mother know what it means."

"What?"

"My friend, the juggler, the magician, was as pale as white jade, and he had pink eyes." I thought she would begin to tell me one of her stories, a tale of enchantment or of a wondrous adventure, but she only paused to

250 swallow; her eyes glittered, lost in memory. She took my hand, gently opening and closing her fingers over it. "Sek-Lung," she sighed, "*he* has come back to me."

Then Grandmama sank back into her pillow and the embroidered flowers lifted to frame her wrinkled face. I saw her hand over my own, and 255 my own began to tremble. I fell fitfully asleep by her side. When I woke up it was dark and her bed was empty. She had been taken to the hospital and I was not permitted to visit.

A few days after that she died of the complications of pneumonia. Immediately after her death my father came home and said nothing to us, 260 but walked up the stairs to her room, pulled aside the drawn lace curtains of her window and lifted the windchimes to the sky.

I began to cry and quickly put my hand in my pocket for a handkerchief. Instead, caught between my fingers, was the small, round firmness of the jade peony. In my mind's eye I saw Grandmama smile and heard, 265 softly, the pink centre beat like a beautiful, cramped heart.

(1979)

# There Is No Exile

Assia Djebar (Algeria) 1936–

*(translated from French by Marjolijn de Jager)*

## About the Author

*Considered Algeria's leading female literary figure, Assia Djebar is a prolific writer of novels, poems, plays, and short stories. Born in Cherchell, Algeria to a middle-class family, Djebar not only had the privilege of receiving a better education than many Algerian women of her time, but was also the first Algerian woman to earn a scholarship to the elite École Normale Supérieure de Sèvres in Paris, France. There she studied history and took part in the Algerian students' strike of 1956 during the French-Algerian war. She adopted the pen name Djebar (meaning "intransigent" in Arabic) in 1957 when her first novel, The Mischief, was published. After a decade-long exile in Tunisia and Morocco, she returned to Algeria in 1962 when it gained its independence. In Algeria, she worked for several media institutions and taught history, literature, and film at the University of Algiers. Eventually she left Algeria and relocated to France and the United States. She is currently director of the Center for French and Francophone Studies at Louisiana State University.*

*"There Is No Exile" was written in 1959 when Djebar was an exile in Tunisia. It was not published, however, until 1980. Set against the 1954–1962 War of Independence for Algeria, the story depicts a day in the life of the Algerian community in exile. Occupying the foreground is the family of the protagonist, a 25-year-old Muslim woman. It is through them and through "the open window" of their house that the reader hears in the background the funeral cries over the death of a neighbour's young son and experiences a proposal of arranged marriage dreaded by the young woman. Nevertheless, the sombre existence at present becomes bearable for the refugees when they find comfort and hope in their nostalgic thoughts about prosperity and peace in the past and their yearning for "the day that we return to our country" in the future. Above all, their religious faith will see them through all the hardships. Djebar's portrayal of life in a special historical and political context is impressively realistic and artistic.*

## Terms Appearing in the Story

**dhor** the midday prayer (Muslims pray five times a day)
**Barberousse prison** a French-run prison in Algeria where revolutionaries were incarcerated

**Koranic verses** parts of the Koran, the Muslims' holy book, which is divided into chapters and verses
**the Cause** the Algerian War of Independence
**Ramadan** the month during which Muslims fast during the daytime

That particular morning, I'd finished the housework a little earlier, by nine o'clock. Mother had put on her veil, taken her basket; in the opening of the door, she repeated as she had been repeating every day for three years: "Not until we had been chased out of our own country did I
5 find myself forced to go out to market like a man."

"Our men have other things to do," I answered, as I'd been answering every day for three years.

"May God protect us!"

I saw Mother to the staircase, then watched her go down heavily
10 because of her legs: "May God protect us," I said again to myself as I went back in.

The cries began around ten o'clock, more or less. They were coming from the apartment next door and soon changed into shrieks. All three of us, my two sisters—Aïcha, Anissa, and I—recognized it by the way in
15 which the women received it: it was death.

Aïcha, the eldest, ran to the door, opened it in order to hear more clearly: "May misfortune stay away from us," she mumbled. "Death has paid the Smaïn family a visit."

At that moment, Mother came in. She put the basket on the floor,
20 stopped where she stood, her face distraught, and began to beat her chest spasmodically with her hands. She was uttering little stifled cries, as when she was about to get sick.

Anissa, although she was the youngest of us, never lost her calm. She ran to close the door, lifted Mother's veil, took her by the shoulders and
25 made her sit down on a mattress.

"Now don't get yourself in that state on account of someone else's misfortune," she said. "Don't forget you have a bad heart. May God shelter and keep us always."

While she repeated the phrase several more times, she went to get some
30 water and sprinkled it on Mother, who now, stretched out full length on the mattress, was moaning. Then Anissa washed her entire face, took a bottle of cologne from the wardrobe, opened it, and put it under her nostrils.

"No!" Mother said. "Bring me some lemon."

And she started to moan again.

35     Anissa continued to bustle about. I was just watching her. I've always been slow to react. I'd begun to listen to the sobs outside that hadn't ceased, would surely not cease before nightfall. There were five or six women in the Smaïn family, and they were all lamenting in chorus, each one settling, forever it seemed, into the muddled outbreak of their grief. Later, of course,
40 they'd have to prepare the meal, busy themselves with the poor, wash the body....There are so many things to do, the day of a burial.

    For now, the voices of the hired mourners, all alike without any one of them distinguishable from the other if only by a more anguished tone, were making one long, gasping chant, and I knew that it would hang over
45 the entire day like a fog in winter.

    "Who actually died over there?" I asked Mother, who had almost quieted down.

    "Their young son," she said, inhaling the lemon deeply. "A car drove over him in front of the door. I was coming home when my eyes saw him
50 twisting one last time, like a worm. The ambulance took him to the hospital, but he was already dead."

    Then she began to sigh again.

    "Those poor people," she was saying, "they saw him go out jumping with life and now they're going to bring him back in a bloodstained sheet."
55     She raised herself halfway, repeated: "jumping with life." Then she fell back down on the mattress and said nothing other than the ritual formulas to keep misfortune away. But the low voice she always used to address God had a touch of hardness, vehemence.

    "This day has an evil smell," I said, still standing in front of Mother,
60 motionlessly. "I've sensed it since this morning, but I didn't know then that it was the smell of death."

    "You have to add: May God protect us!" Mother said sharply. Then she raised her eyes to me. We were alone in the room, Anissa and Aïcha had gone back to the kitchen.
65     "What's the matter with you?" she said. "You look pale. Are you feeling sick, too?"

    "May God protect us!" I said and left the room.

    At noon, Omar was the first one home. The weeping continued. I'd attended to the meal while listening to the threnody and its modulations.
70 I was growing used to them. I thought Omar would start asking questions. But no. He must have heard about it in the street.

He pulled Aïcha into a room. Then I heard them whispering. When some important event occurred, Omar spoke first to Aïcha in this way, because she was the eldest and the most serious one. Previously, Father 75 used to do the same thing, but outside, with Omar, for he was the only son.

So there was something new; and it had nothing to do with death visiting the Smaïn family. I wasn't curious at all. Today is the day of death, all the rest becomes immaterial.

"Isn't that so?" I said to Anissa, who jumped.

80    "What's the matter now?"

"Nothing," I said without belaboring the point, for I was familiar with her always disconcerted answers whenever I'd start thinking out loud. Even this morning...

But why this sudden, blatant desire to stare at myself in a mirror, to con-
85 front my own image at some length, and to say, while letting my hair fall down my back so that Anissa would gaze upon it: "Look. At twenty-five, after having been married, after having lost my two children one after the other, having been divorced, after this exile and after this war, here I am busy admiring myself, smiling at myself like a young girl, like you..."

90    "Like me!" Anissa said, and she shrugged her shoulders.

Father came home a little late because it was Friday and he'd gone to say the prayer of *dhor*° at the mosque. He immediately asked why they were in mourning.

"Death has visited the Smaïns," I said, running toward him to kiss his
95 hand. "It has taken their young son away."

"Those poor people," he said after a silence.

I helped him get settled in his usual place, on the same mattress. Then, as I put his meal in front of him and made sure he didn't have to wait for anything, I forgot about the neighbors for a while. I liked to serve Father;
100 it was, I think, the only household task I enjoyed. Especially now. Since our departure, Father had aged a great deal. He gave too much thought to those who weren't with us, even though he never spoke of them, unless a letter arrived from Algeria and he asked Omar to read it.

In the middle of the meal I heard Mother murmur: "They can't possibly
105 feel like eating today."

"The body is still at the hospital," someone said.

Father said nothing. He rarely spoke during meals.

"I'm not really hungry," I said, getting up, to excuse myself.

The sobs outside seemed more muffled, but I could still distinguish their
110 singsong. Their gentle singsong. This is the moment, I said to myself, when
grief becomes familiar, and pleasurable, and nostalgic. This is the moment
when you weep almost voluptuously, for this gift of tears is a gift without
end. This was the moment when the bodies of my children would turn cold
fast, so fast, and when I knew it...

115 At the end of the meal, Aïcha came into the kitchen, where I was by
myself. First she went to close the windows that looked out over the neigh-
boring terraces, through which the weeping reached me. But I could still
hear it. And, oddly, it was that which made me so tranquil today, a little
gloomy.

120 "There are some women coming this afternoon to see you and to propose marriage," she began. "Father says the candidate is suitable in every
way."

Without answering, I turned my back to her and went to the window.

"Now what's your problem?" she said a little sharply.

125 "I need some air," I said and opened the window all the way, so that the
song could come in. It had already been a while since the breathing of
death had become, for me, "the song."

Aïcha remained a moment without answering. "When Father goes out,
you'll attend to yourself a little," she said at last. "These women know very
130 well that we're refugees like so many others, and that they're not going to
find you dressed like a queen. But you should look your best, nevertheless."

"They've stopped weeping," I remarked, "or perhaps they're already
tired," I said, thinking of that strange fatigue that grasps us at the depth
of our sorrow.

135 "Why don't you keep your mind on the women who're coming?" Aïcha
replied in a slightly louder voice.

Father had left. Omar too, when Hafsa arrived. Like us, she was Algerian and
we'd known her there, a young girl of twenty with an education. She was a
teacher but had been working only since her mother and she had been
140 exiled, as had so many others. "An honorable woman doesn't work outside
her home," her mother used to say. She still said it, but with a sigh of help-
lessness. One had to live, and there was no man in their household now.

Hafsa found Mother and Anissa in the process of preparing pastries, as
if these were a must for refugees like us. But her sense of protocol was
145 instinctive in Mother; an inheritance from her past life that she could not
readily abandon.

"These women you're waiting for," I asked, "who are they?"

"Refugees like us," Aïcha exclaimed. "You don't really think we'd give you away in marriage to strangers?" Then with heart and soul:
150 "Remember," she said, "the day we return to our own country, we shall all go back home, all of us, without exception."

"The day that we return," Hafsa, standing in the middle of the room, suddenly cried out, her eyes wide with dreams. "The day that we return to our country!" she repeated. "How I'd like to go back there on foot, the
155 better to feel the Algerian soil under my feet, the better to see all our women, one after the other, all the widows, and all the orphans, and finally all the men, exhausted, sad perhaps, but free—free! And then I'll take a bit of soil in my hands, oh, just a tiny handful of soil, and I'll say to them: 'See, my brothers, see these drops of blood in these grains of soil
160 in this hand, that's how much Algeria has bled throughout her body, all over her vast body, that's how much Algeria has paid for our freedom and for this, our return, with her own soil. But her martyrdom now speaks in terms of grace. So you see, my brothers.'"

"The day that we return," Mother repeated softly in the silence that fol-
165 lowed..."if God wills it."

It was then that the cries began again through the open window. Like an orchestra that brusquely starts a piece of music. Then, in a different tone, Hafsa reminded us: "I'm here for the lesson."

Aïcha pulled her into the next room.
170 During their meeting, I didn't know what to do. The windows of the kitchen and of the other two rooms looked out over the terraces. I went from one to the other, opening them, closing them, opening them again. All of this without hurrying, as if I weren't listening to the song.

Anissa caught me in my rounds.
175 "You can tell they're not Algerian," she said. "They're not even accustomed to being in mourning."

"At home, in the mountains," Mother answered, "the dead have nobody to weep over them before they grow cold."

"Weeping serves no purpose," Anissa was stoic, "whether you die in
180 your bed or on the bare ground for your country."

"What do you know about it?" I suddenly said to her. "You're too young to know."

"Soon they're going to bury him," Mother whispered.

Then she raised her head and looked at me. I had once again closed the
185 window behind me. I couldn't hear anything anymore.

"They're going to bury him this very day," Mother said again a little louder, "that's our custom."

"They shouldn't," I said. "It's a hateful custom to deliver a body to the earth when beauty still shines on it. Really quite hateful....It seems to me they're burying him while he's still shivering, still..." (but I couldn't control my voice any longer).

"Stop thinking about your children!" Mother said. "The earth that was thrown on them is a blanket of gold. My poor daughter, stop thinking about your children!" Mother said again.

"I'm not thinking about anything," I said. "No, really. I don't want to think about anything. About anything at all."

It was already four o'clock in the afternoon when they came in. From the kitchen where I was hiding, I heard them exclaim, once the normal phrases of courtesy had been uttered: "What is that weeping?"

"May misfortune stay far away from us! May God protect us!"

"It gives me goose bumps," the third one was saying. "I've almost forgotten death and tears, these days. I've forgotten them, even though our hearts are always heavy."

"That is the will of God," the second one would respond.

In a placid voice, Mother explained the reason for the mourning next door as she invited them into the only room we had been able to furnish decently. Anissa, close by me, was already making the first comments on the way the women looked. She was questioning Aïcha, who had been with Mother to welcome them. I had opened the window again and watched them exchange their first impressions.

"What are you thinking?" Anissa said, her eye still on me.

"Nothing," I said feebly; then, after a pause: "I was thinking of the different faces of fate. I was thinking of God's will. Behind that wall, there is a dead person and women going mad with grief. Here, in our house, other women are talking of marriage...I was thinking of that difference."

"Just stop 'thinking,'" Aïcha cut in sharply. Then to Hafsa, who was coming in: "You ought to be teaching *her,* not me. She spends all her time thinking. You'd almost believe she's read as many books as you have."

"And why not?" Hafsa asked.

"I don't need to learn French," I answered. "What purpose would it serve? Father has taught us all our language. 'That's all you need,' he always says."

"It's useful to know languages other than your own," Hafsa said slowly. "It's like knowing other people, other countries."

225    I didn't answer. Perhaps she was right. Perhaps you ought to learn and not waste your time letting your mind wander, like mine, through the deserted corridors of the past. Perhaps I should take lessons and study French, or anything else. But I, I never felt the need to jostle my body or my mind....Aïcha was different. Like a man: hard and hardworking. She was

230    thirty. She hadn't seen her husband in three years, who was still incarcerated in Barberousse prison,° where he had been since the first days of the war. Yet, she was getting an education and didn't settle for household work. Now, after just a few months of Hafsa's lessons, Omar no longer read her husband's infrequent letters, the few that might reach her. She managed to

235    decipher them by herself. Sometimes I caught myself being envious of her.

"Hafsa," she said, "it's time for my sister to go in and greet these ladies. Please go with her."

But Hafsa didn't want to. Aïcha insisted, and I was watching them play their little game of politeness.

240    "Does anyone know if they've come for the body yet?" I asked.

"What? Didn't you hear the chanters just now?" Anissa said.

"So that's why the weeping stopped for a moment," I said. "It's strange, as soon as some parts of the Koranic verses° are chanted, the women immediately stop weeping. And yet, that's the most painful moment, I

245    know it all too well myself. As long as the body is there in front of you, it seems the child isn't quite dead yet, can't be dead, you see?...Then comes the moment when the men get up, and that is to take him, wrapped in a sheet, on their shoulders. That's how he leaves, quickly, as on the day that he came....For me, may God forgive me, they can chant Koranic verses all

250    they want, the house is still empty after they've gone, completely empty...."

Hafsa was listening, her head leaning toward the window. With a shiver, she turned toward me. She seemed younger even than Anissa, then.

"My God," she said, emotion in her voice, "I've just turned twenty and

255    yet I've never encountered death. Never in my whole life!"

"Haven't you lost anyone in your family in this war?" Anissa asked.

"Oh yes," she said, "but the news always comes by mail. And death by mail, you see, I can't believe it. A first cousin of mine died under the guillotine as one of the first in Barberousse. Well, I've never shed a tear over

260    him because I cannot believe that he's dead. And yet he was like a brother to me, I swear. But I just can't believe he's dead, you understand?" she said in a voice already wrapped in tears.

"Those who've died for the Cause° aren't really dead," Anissa answered with a touch of pride.

265 "So, let's think of the present. Let's think about today," Aïcha said in a dry voice. "The rest is in God's hand."

There were three of them: an old woman who had to be the suitor's mother and who hastily put on her glasses as soon as I arrived; two other women, seated side by side, resembled each other. Hafsa, who'd come in behind
270 me, sat down next to me. I lowered my eyes.

I knew my part, it was one I'd played before; stay mute like this, eyes lowered, and patiently let myself be examined until the very end: it was simple. Everything is simple, beforehand, for a girl who's being married off.

275 Mother was talking. I was barely listening. I knew the themes to be developed all too well: Mother was talking about our sad state as refugees; then they'd be exchanging opinions on when the end might be announced: "...another Ramadan° to be spent away from home...perhaps this was the last one...perhaps, if God wills it! Of course, we were
280 saying the same thing last year, and the year before that....Let's not complain too much....In any event, victory is certain, all our men say the same thing. And we, we know the day of our return will come....We should be thinking of those who stayed behind....We should be thinking of those who are suffering....The Algerian people are a people whom God
285 loves....And our fighters are made of steel...." Then they'd come back to the tale of the flight, to the different means by which each one had left her soil where the fires were burning....Then they'd evoke the sadness of exile, the heart yearning for its country....And the fear of dying far from the land of one's birth....Then...."But may God be praised and may he
290 grant our prayers!"

This time it lasted a bit longer; an hour perhaps, or more. Until the time came to serve coffee. By then, I was hardly listening at all. I too was thinking in my own way of this exile, of these somber days.

I was thinking how everything had changed, how on the day of my first
295 engagement we had been in the long, bright living room of our house in the hills of Algiers; how we'd been prosperous then, we had prosperity and peace; how Father used to laugh, how he used to give thanks to God for the abundance of his home...And I, I wasn't as I was today, my soul grey, gloomy and with this idea of death beating faintly inside me since the
300 morning....Yes, I was thinking how everything had changed and that, still,

in some way everything remained the same. They were still concerned with marrying me off. And why exactly? I suddenly wondered. And why exactly? I repeated to myself, feeling something like fury inside me, or its echo. Just so I could have worries that never change whether it's peace or
305 wartime, so I could wake up in the middle of the night and question myself on what it is that sleeps in the depths of the heart of the man sharing my bed....Just so I could give birth and weep, for life never comes unaccompanied to a woman, death is always right behind, furtive, quick, and smiling at the mothers....Yes, why indeed? I said to myself.

310     Coffee had now been served. Mother was inviting them to drink.

    "We won't take even one sip," the old woman began, "before you've given us your word about your daughter."

    "Yes," the other one said, "my brother impressed upon us that we weren't to come back without your promising to give her to him as his
315 wife."

    I was listening to Mother avoid answering, have herself be begged hypocritically, and then again invite them to drink. Aïcha joined in with her. The women were repeating their request....It was all as it should be.

    The game went on a few minutes longer. Mother invoked the father's
320 authority: "I, of course, would give her to you....I know you are people of means....But there is her father."

    "Her father has already said yes to my brother," one of the two women who resembled each other replied. "The question remains only to be discussed between us."

325     "Yes," said the second one, "it's up to us now. Let's settle the question."

    I raised my head; it was then, I think, that I met Hafsa's gaze.

    There was, deep in her eyes, a strange light, surely of interest or of irony, I don't know, but you could feel Hafsa as an outsider, attentive and curious at the same time, but an outsider. I met that look.

330     "I don't want to marry," I said. "I don't want to marry," I repeated, barely shouting.

    There was much commotion in the room: Mother got up with a deep sigh; Aïcha was blushing, I saw. And the two women who turned to me, with the same slow movement of shock: "And why not?" one of them
335 asked.

    "My son," the old woman exclaimed with some arrogance, "my son is a man of science. In a few days he is leaving for the Orient."

    "Of course," Mother said with touching haste. "We know he's a scholar. We know him to have a righteous heart....Of course...."

340     "It's not because of your son," I said. "But I don't want to get married. I
see the future before my eyes, it's totally black. I don't know how to explain
it, surely it must come from God....But I see the future totally black before
my eyes!" I said again, sobbing, as Aïcha led me out of the room in silence.

Later, but why even tell the rest, except that I was consumed with shame
345 and I didn't understand. Only Hafsa stayed close to me after the women
had left.

"You're engaged," she said sadly. "Your mother said she'd give you
away. Will you accept?" and she stared at me with imploring eyes.

"What difference does it make?" I said and really thought inside myself:
350 What difference does it make? "I don't know what came over me before. But
they were all talking about the present and its changes and its misfortunes.
And I was saying to myself: of what possible use is it to be suffering like this,
far away from home, if I have to continue here as before in Algiers, to stay
home and sit and pretend....Perhaps when life changes, everything should
355 change with it, absolutely everything. I was thinking of all that," I said,
"but I don't even know if that's bad or good....You, you're smart, and you
know these things, perhaps you'll understand."

"I do understand," she said, hesitating as if she were going to start
talking and then preferred to remain silent.

360     "Open the window," I said. "It's almost dark."

She went to open it and then came back to my bed where I'd been lying
down to cry, without reason, crying for shame and fatigue all at the same
time. In the silence that followed, I was feeling distant, pondering the
night that little by little engulfed the room. The sounds from the kitchen,
365 where my sisters were, seemed to be coming from somewhere else.

Then Hafsa began to speak: "Your father," she said, "once spoke of
exile, of our present exile, and he said—oh, I remember it well, for nobody
speaks like your father—he said: 'There is no exile for any man loved by
God. There is no exile for the one who is on God's path. There are only
370 trials.'"

She went on a while, but I've forgotten the rest except that she repeated
*we* very often with a note of passion. She said that word with a peculiar
vehemence, so much so that I began to wonder toward the end whether
that word really meant the two of us alone, or rather other women, all the
375 women of our country.

To tell the truth, even if I'd known, what could I have answered? Hafsa was too knowledgeable for me. And that's what I would have liked to have told her when she stopped talking, perhaps in the expectation that I would speak.

380 But it was another voice that answered, a woman's voice that rose, through the open window, rose straight as an arrow toward the sky, that rounded itself out, spread out in its flight, a flight ample as a bird's after the storm, then came falling back down in sudden torrents.

"The other women have grown silent," I said. "The only one left to weep 385 now is the mother....Such is life," I added a moment later. "There are those who forget or who simply sleep. And then there are those who keep bumping into the walls of the past. May God take pity on them!"

"Those are the true exiles," said Hafsa.

(1959/1980)

# The Immaculate Conception Photography Gallery

Katherine Govier (Canada) 1948–

## About the Author

*Katherine Govier is an award-winning Canadian novelist and short story writer. Born on July 4, 1948 in Edmonton, Alberta, she graduated from the University of Alberta with a B.A. in 1970 and earned her M.A. from York University in Toronto in 1972. She has worked as an educator, writer-in-residence, and journalist, mainly in the Toronto area. As a professional writer, Govier has also been actively involved in a variety of social and academic activities, promoting creative writing in Canada. She now lives in Toronto with her husband and children.*

*From 1979 to 1991 she produced four novels:* Random Descent *(1979),* Going through the Motions *(1982),* Between Men *(1987), and* Hearts of Flame *(1991). So far, four collections of her short stories have been published:* Fables of Brunswick Avenue *(1985),* Before and After *(1989),* The Immaculate Conception Photography Gallery *(1994), and* The Truth Teller *(2000). Her stories, mostly set in an urban environment, are vivid and gripping, catching an array of stunning moments in Canadian life. Govier once stated that her "interest is entirely in character." To her the most challenging question in fiction writing is "how the character is created and what events flow from a human personality." As one critic rightly points out, Govier's stories are about people who cope, and they often describe rebirths and fresh starts for these characters. Sandro, the protagonist in "The Immaculate Conception Photography Gallery," is such a character, whose "fresh start" puts an end to this story, but will possibly lead to yet another wonderful story.*

Sandro named the little photography shop on St. Clair Avenue West, between Lord's Shoes and Bargain Jimmies, after the parish church in the village where he was born. He had hankered after wider horizons, the rippled brown prairies, the hard-edged mountains. But when he reached
5 Toronto he met necessity in the form of a wife and babies, and, never having seen a western sunset, he settled down in Little Italy. He photographed the brides in their fat lacquered curls and imported lace, and their quick babies in christening gowns brought over from home. Blown up to near life size on cardboard cutouts, their pictures filled the windows of his little shop.

10     Sandro had been there ten years already when he first really saw his sign, and the window. He stood still in front of it and looked. A particularly buxom bride with a lace bodice and cap sleeves cut in little scallops shimmered in a haze of concupiscence under the sign reading Immaculate Conception Photography Gallery. Sandro was not like his

15 neighbours any more, he was modern, a Canadian. He no longer went to church. As he stared, one of the street drunks shuffled into place beside him. Sandro knew them all, they came into the shop in winter. (No one ought to have to stay outside in that cold, Sandro believed.) But he especially knew Becker. Becker was a smart man; he used to be a philosopher

20 at a university.

"Immaculate Conception," said Sandro to Becker. "What do you think?"

Becker lifted his eyes to the window. He made a squeezing gesture at the breasts. "I never could buy that story," he said.

Sandro laughed, but he didn't change the sign that year or the next and

25 he got to be forty-five and then fifty and it didn't seem worth it. The Immaculate Conception Photography Gallery had a reputation. Business came in from as far away as Rosedale and North Toronto, because Sandro was a magician with a camera. He also had skill with brushes and lights and paint, he reshot his negatives, he lined them with silver, he had tricks

30 even new graduates of photography school couldn't (or wouldn't) copy.

Sandro was not proud of his tricks. They began in a gradual way, fixing stray hairs and taking wrinkles out of dresses. He did it once, then twice, then people came in asking for it. Perhaps he'd have gone on this way, with small lies, but he met with a situation that was larger than most; it

35 would have started a feud in the old country. During a very large and very expensive wedding party Tony the bridegroom seduced Alicia the bridesmaid in the basketball storage room under the floor of the parish hall. Six months later Tony confessed, hoping perhaps to be released from his vows. But the parents judged it was too late to dissolve the union: Diora was

40 used, she was no longer a virgin, there was a child coming. Tony was reprimanded, Diora consoled, the mothers became enemies, the newly-weds made up. Only Alicia remained to be dealt with. The offence became hers.

In Italy, community ostracism would have been the punishment of choice. But this was Canada, and if no one acknowledged Alicia on the

45 street, if no one visited her mother, who was heavy on her feet and forced to sit on the sofa protesting her daughter's innocence, if no one invited her father out behind to drink home-made wine, Alicia didn't care. She went off

to her job behind the till in a drugstore with her chin thrust out much as before. The inlaws perceived that the young woman could not be subdued by the old methods. This being the case, it was better she not exist at all.

Which was why Diora's mother turned up at Sandro's counter with the wedding photos. The pain Alicia had caused! she began. Diora's mother's very own miserable wages, saved these eighteen years, had paid for these photographs! She wept. The money was spent, but the joy was spoiled. When she and Diora's father looked at the row of faces flanking bride and groom there she was—Alicia, the whore! She wiped her tears and made her pitch.

"You can solve our problem, Sandro. I will get a new cake, we will all come to the parish hall. You will take the photographs again. Of course," she added, "we can't pay you again."

Sandro smiled, it was so preposterous. 'Even if I could afford to do all that work for nothing, I hate to say it, but Diora's out to here."

"Don't argue with me."

"I wouldn't be so bold," said Sandro. "But I will not take the photographs over."

The woman slapped the photographs where they lay on the counter. "You will! I don't care how you do it!" And she left.

Sandro went to the back and put his negatives on the light box. He brought out his magic solution and his razor blades and his brushes. He circled Alicia's head and shoulders in the first row and went to work. He felt a little badly, watching the bright circle of her face fade and swim, darken down to nothing. But how easily she vanished! He filled in the white spot with a bit of velvet curtain trimmed from the side.

"I'm like a plastic surgeon," he told his wife. "Take that patch of skin from the inner thigh and put it over the scar on the face. Then sand the edges. Isn't that what they do? Only it isn't a face I'm fixing, it's a memory."

His wife stood on two flat feet beside the sink. She shook the carrot she was peeling. "I don't care about Alicia," she said, "but Diora's mother is making a mistake. She is starting them off with a lie in their marriage. And why is she doing it? For her pride! I don't like this, Sandro."

"You're missing the point," said Sandro.

The next day he had another look at his work. Alicia's shoulders and the bodice of her dress were still there, in front of the chest of the uncle of the bride. He couldn't remove them; it would leave a hole in Uncle. Sandro had nothing to fill the hole, no spare male torsos in black-tie. He considered putting a head on top, but whose head? There was no such thing as a free face. A stranger would be questioned, a friend would have an alibi. Perhaps Diora's mother would not notice the black velvet space, as where a tooth had been knocked out, between the smiling faces.

Indeed she didn't but kissed his hand fervently and thanked him with tears in her eyes. "Twenty-five thousand that wedding cost me. Twenty-five thousand to get this photograph and you have rescued it."

"Surely you got dinner and a dance too?" said Sandro.

"The wedding was one day. This is forever," said Diora's mother.

"I won't do that again," said Sandro, putting the cloth over his head and looking into his camera lens to do a passport photo. In the community the doctored photograph had been examined and re-examined. Alicia's detractors enjoyed the headless shoulders as evidence of a violent punishment.

"No, I won't do that again at all," said Sandro to himself, turning aside compliments with a shake of his head. But there was another wedding. After the provolone e melone, the veal picata, the many-tiered cake topped with swans, the father of the bride drew Sandro aside and asked for a set of prints with the groom's parents removed.

"My God, why?" said Sandro.

"He's a bastard. A bad man."

"Shouldn't have let her marry his son, then," said Sandro, pulling a cigarette out of the pack in his pocket. These conversations made him nervous.

The father's weathered face was dark, his dinner-jacket did not button around his chest. He moaned and ground his lower teeth against his uppers. "You know how they are, these girls in Canada. I am ashamed to say it, but I couldn't stop her."

Sandro said nothing.

"Look, I sat here all night long, said nothing, did nothing. I don't wanna look at him for the next twenty years."

Sandro drew in a long tube of smoke.

"I paid a bundle for this night. I wanna remember it nice-like."

The smoke made Sandro nauseous. He dropped his cigarette and ground it into the floor with his toe, damning his own weakness. "So what am I going to do with the table?"

The father put out a hand like a tool, narrowed his eyes, and began to saw, where the other man sat.

"And leave it dangling, no legs?"

"So make new legs."

"I'm a photographer, not a carpenter," said Sandro. "I don't make table legs."

"Where you get legs is your problem," said the father. "I'm doing well
130 here. I've got ten guys working for me. You look like you could use some new equipment."

And what harm was it after all, it was only a photograph, said Sandro to himself. Then too there was the technical challenge. Waiting until they all got up to get their bonbonnière, he took a shot of the head table empty.
135 Working neatly with his scalpel, he cut the table from this second negative, removed the inlaws and their chairs from the first one, stuck the empty table-end onto the table in the first picture, blended over the join neatly, and printed it. Presto! Only one set of inlaws.

"I don't mind telling you, it gives me a sick feeling," said Sandro to his
140 wife. "I was there. I saw them. We had a conversation. They smiled for me. Now..." he shrugged. "An empty table. Lucky I don't go to church any more."

"Let the man who paid good money to have you do it confess, not you," she said. "A photograph is a photograph."

"That's what I thought too," said Sandro.

145 The next morning Sandro went to the Donut House, got himself a take-out coffee and stood on the street beside his window.

"Why do people care about photographs so much?" he asked Becker. Becker had newspaper stuffed in the soles of his shoes. He had on a pair of stained brown pants tied up at the waist with a paisley necktie. His bottle
150 was clutched in a paper bag gathered around the neck.

"You can put them on your mantel," said Becker. "They don't talk back."

"Don't people prefer life?" said Sandro.

"People prefer things," said Becker.

"Don't they want their memories to be true?"

155 "No," said Becker.

"Another thing. Are we here just to get our photograph taken? Do we have a higher purpose?"

Becker pulled one of the newspapers out of his shoe. There were Brian and Mila Mulroney having a gloaty kiss. They were smeared by muddy
160 water and depressed by the joint in the ball of Becker's foot.

"I mean real people," said Sandro. "Have we no loyalty to the natural?"

"These are existential questions, Sandro," said Becker. "Too many more of them and you'll be out here on the street with the rest of us."

Sandro drained the coffee from his cup, pitched it in the bin painted
165 "Keep Toronto Clean" and went back into his gallery. The existential questions nagged. But he did go out and get the motor drive for the camera. In

the next few months he eradicated a pregnancy from a wedding photo, added a daughter-in-law who complained of being left out of the Christmas shots, and made a groom taller. Working in the darkroom, he
170 was hit by vertigo. He was on a slide, beginning a descent. He wanted to know what the bottom felt like.

After a year of such operations a man from the Beaches came in with a tiny black and white photo of a long-lost brother. He wanted it coloured and fitted into a family shot around a picnic table on Centre Island.

175 "Is this some kind of joke?" said Sandro. It was the only discretion he practised now: he wanted to talk about it before he did it.

"No. I'm going to send it to Mother. She thinks Christopher wrote us all off."

"Did he?" said Sandro.

180 "Better she should not know."

Sandro neglected to ask if Christopher was fat or thin. He ended up taking a medium-sized pair of shoulders from his own cousin and propping them up behind a bush, with Christopher's head on top. Afterward, Sandro lay sleepless in his bed. Suppose that in the next few months Christopher
185 should turn up dead, say murdered. Then Mother would produce the photograph stamped Immaculate Conception Photography Gallery, 1816 St. Clair Avenue West. Sandro would be implicated. The police might come.

"I believe adding people is worse than taking them away," he said to his wife.

190 "You say yes to do it, then you do it. You think it's wrong, you say no."

"Let me try this on you, Becker," said Sandro the next morning. "To take a person out is only half a lie. It proves nothing except that he was not in that shot. To add a person is a whole lie: it proves that he was there, when he was not."

195 "You haven't proven a thing, you're just fooling around with celluloid. Have you got a buck?" said Becker.

"It is better to be a murderer than a creator. I am playing God, outplaying God at His own game." He was smarter than Becker now. He knew it was the photographs that lasted, not the people. In the end the proof was
200 in the proof. Though he hadn't prayed in thirty years, Sandro began to pray. It was like riding a bicycle: he got the hang of it again instantly. "Make me strong," he prayed, "strong enough to resist the new equipment that I might buy, strong enough to resist the temptation to expand the gallery, to buy a house in the suburbs. Make me say no to people who
205 want alterations."

But Sandro's prayers were not answered. When people offered him money to dissolve an errant relative, he said yes. He said yes out of curiosity. He said yes out of a desire to test his skills. He said yes out of greed. He said yes out of compassion. "What is the cost of a little happiness?" he said. "Perhaps God doesn't count photographs. After all, they're not one of a kind."

Sandro began to be haunted, in slow moments behind the counter in the Immaculate Conception, by the faces of those whose presence he had tampered with. He kept a file—Alicia the lusty bridesmaid, Antonia and Marco, the undesired inlaws. Their heads, their shoes and their hands, removed from the scene with surgical precision, he saved for the moment when, God willing, a forgiving relative would ask him to replace them. But the day did not come. Sandro was not happy.

"Becker," he said, for he had a habit now of buying Becker a coffee first thing in the morning and standing out if it was warm, or in if it was cold, for a chat. "Becker, let's say it's a good service I'm doing. It makes people happy, even if it tells lies."

"Sandro," said Becker, who enjoyed his coffee, "these photographs, doctored by request of the subjects, reflect back the lives they wish to have. The unpleasant bits are removed, the wishes are added. If you didn't do it, someone else would. Memory would. It's a service."

"It's also money," said Sandro. He found Becker too eager to make excuses now. He liked him better before.

"You're like Tintoretto, painting in his patron, softening his greedy profile, lifting the chin of his fat wife. It pays for the part that's true art."

"Which part is that?" said Sandro, but Becker didn't answer. He was still standing there when Diora came in. She'd matured, she'd gained weight, and her twins, now six years old, were handsome and strong. Sandro's heart flew up in his breast. Perhaps she had made friends with Alicia, perhaps Diora had come to have her bridesmaid reinstated.

"The long nightmare is over," said Diora. "I've left him."

The boys were running from shelf to shelf lifting up the photographs with their glass frames and putting them down again. Sandro watched them with one eye. He knew what she was going to say.

"I want you to take him out of those pictures," she said.

"You'd look very foolish as a bride with no groom," he said severely.

"No, no, not those," she said. "I mean the kids' birthday shots."

They had been particularly fine, those shots, taken only two weeks ago, Tony tall and dark, Diora and the children radiant and blond.

245 "Be reasonable, Diora," he said. "I never liked him myself. But he balances the portrait. Besides, he was there."

"He was not there!" cried Diora. Her sons went on turning all the pictures to face the walls. "He was never there. He was running around, in his heart he was not with me. I was alone with my children."

250 "I'll take another one," said Sandro. "Of you and the boys. Whenever you like. This one stays like it is."

"We won't pay."

"But Diora," said Sandro, "everyone knows he's their father."

"They have no father," said Diora flatly.

255 "It's immaculate conception," said Becker gleefully.

But Diora did not hear. "It's our photograph, and we want him out. You do your job. The rest of it's none of your business." She put one hand on the back of the head of each of her twins and marched them out the door.

Sandro leaned on his counter idly flipping the pages of a wedding 260 album. He had a vision of a great decorated room, with a cake on the table. Everyone had had his way, the husband had removed the wife, the wife the husband, the bridesmaid her parents, and so forth. There was no one there.

"We make up our lives out of the people around us," he said to Becker. 265 "When they don't live up to standard, we can't just wipe them out."

"Don't ask me," said Becker. "I just lit out for the streets. Couldn't live up to a damn thing." Then he too went out the door.

"Lucky bugger," said Sandro.

Alone, he went to his darkroom. He opened his drawer of bits and 270 pieces. His disappeared ones, the inconvenient people. His body parts, his halves of torsos, tips of shiny black shoes. Each face, each item of clothing punctured him a little. He looked at his negatives stored in drawers. They were scarred, pathetic things. I haven't the stomach for it, not any more, thought Sandro.

275 As he walked home, St. Clair Avenue seemed very fine. The best part was, he thought, there were no relationships. Neither this leaning drunk nor that window-shopper was so connected to any other as to endanger his, or her, existence. The tolerance of indifference, said Sandro to himself, trying to remember it so that he could tell Becker.

280 But Sandro felt ill at ease in his own home, by its very definition a dangerous and unreliable setting. His wife was stirring something, with her lips tight together. His children, almost grown up now, bred secrets as they looked at television. He himself only posed in the doorway, looking for hidden seams and the faint hair-lines of an airbrush.

285     That night he stood exhausted by his bed. His wife lay on her side with one round shoulder above the sheet. Behind her on the wall was the photo he'd taken of their village before he left Italy. He ought to reshoot it, take out that gas station and clean up the square a little. His pillow had an indentation, as if a head had been erased. He slept in a chair.

290     In the morning he went down to the shop. He got his best camera and set up a tripod on the sidewalk directly across the street. He took several shots in the solid bright morning light. He locked the door and placed the CLOSED sign in the window. In the darkroom he developed the film, floating the negatives in the pungent fluid until the row of shop fronts

295 came through clearly, the flat brick faces, the curving concrete trim, the two balls on the crowns. Deftly he dissolved each brick of his store, the window and the sign. Deftly he reattached each brick of the store on the west side to the bricks of the store to the east.

    I have been many things in my life, thought Sandro, a presser of shut-

300 ters, a confessor, a false prophet. Now I am a bricklayer, and a good one. He taped the negatives together and developed them. He touched up the join and then photographed it again. He developed this second negative and it was perfect. Number 1812, Lord's Shoes, joined directly to 1820, Bargain Jimmies: the Immaculate Conception Photography Gallery at

305 1816 no longer existed. Working quickly, because he wanted to finish before the day was over, he blew it up to two feet by three feet. He cleared out his window display of brides and babies and stood up this new photo-graph—one of the finest he'd ever taken, he thought. Then he took a couple of cameras and a bag with the tripod and some lenses. He turned

310 out the light, pulling the door shut behind him, and began to walk west.

(1994)

# Arthur

Bruce (William) Hunter (Canada) 1952–

## About the Author

*Bruce Hunter is a Canadian writer whose poetry and short stories have been enter-*
*taining a wide range of audience over the past 20 years. Born in Calgary, Alberta,*
*Hunter received a bachelor's degree in fine arts at York University in 1983 and*
*attended the Banff School of Fine Arts from 1984 to 1987. He has worked as a con-*
*struction worker, janitor, landscape gardener, educator, and freelance writer. He*
*teaches in the School of Computer Studies, Seneca College of Applied Arts and*
*Technology in Toronto, and lives in Stratford, Ontario.*

*Several collections of Bruce Hunter's poetry have been published, including*
Benchmark *(1982),* The Beekeeper's Daughter *(1986), and* Light against Light.
*His short stories have been published in magazines such as* Canadian Fiction *and*
Canadian Forum, *collected in* Country Music Country *(1996), and frequently*
*anthologized. Having had some first-hand knowledge of blue-collar labour earlier in*
*his life, Hunter once proclaimed: "Both my fiction and poetry are written from the*
*point of view of working people, which is less an overt political statement than an*
*attempt to present the history and lives of the people I've lived and worked with*
*without sentimentality and with as much craft and skill as I can muster." Indeed,*
*such a unique point of view constitutes one of the most intriguing aspects of stories*
*like "Arthur."*

"You'll be alright. Bundle up good." My mother yanked my scarf tied
bank robber style at the back of my raised hood.

My education, at nine and a half, was not complete in her eyes. Each
day contained a verse of inspiration from her worn copy of *One Day at a*
5 *Time* and some other crucial instruction usually in the form of a story
about the weather, people, my dog or whatever else sprang to her mind.

Today it was twenty below zero, not quite Thirty Below, that mystical
number where several threes collided in a deadly freeze as she told me
once: "At thirty below with a thirty mile per hour wind, exposed flesh
10 freezes in thirty seconds. That's fifty below by the chill factor." Later,
among the piles of magazines under her bed I found the copy of *Reader's*
*Digest*, and there it was, between "Life's Like That" and "Laughter's the Best
Medicine"—"Chill Factor—the *Real* Temperature."

"Last year," she said, "a little girl in Altadore had to have a fireman
15 pour boiling water on her tongue because she didn't listen to her mother."
She turned and got the grocery money from the counter.

I wondered what this had to do with going out to the store at twenty
below. As I stood in the landing in my duffle coat, sucking in all the warm
air I could through my scarf, the mittens she'd knitted dangled at my
20 sleeves, with the cord that kept them a pair tugging at the back of my neck
and my scarf choking the front. I was embarrassed by that string she
insisted on adding.

Nine and a half is a cruel age when you start to notice you have mitten
strings and others don't. And even if you hadn't, other kids were only too
25 happy to point it out for you as they had my old pants with the new elastic
waist: "Smarty pants, smarty pants," they'd hollered, the cry ringing in my
ears for weeks. I didn't even try to explain what her effort to extend the life
of outgrown pants had cost me as she fished them out of the bottom of the
closet.

30 "Never, ever, put your tongue on metal when it's this cold. Not on the
fence, anything. The fire department couldn't do a thing and there she
stood with her tongue on the aluminum door until they put boiling water
on it."

It had never occurred to me, until now, to put my tongue, lips or any-
35 thing else for that matter on the big aluminum door with the curly cues
and our family initial proudly hanging in the centre. She gave me the grocery note for Mr. Waterfield which I tucked into one mitt and the change
wrapped tightly in a five dollar bill I dropped into the toe of the other.

"Hurry back, and I'll make us some lunch," she said, giving my scarf one
40 final tug and my back a warm pat as she held open the screen door. I was
glad to be getting out. My mother was lonely all the long winter, and happy
to have me there about the house, but the holidays were wearing on and I
was tiring of her loneliness. I wanted to be outside again, going to school
and talking to my friends. But only my father and I had heavy winter
45 clothing which was a luxury then. She had to wait until my father could
drive her, or those rare days when the Chinook winds, ripe with the punky
heat of spring, blew down from the Rocky Mountains and turned the streets
to slush for a day or two in January or February. Then she got out.

Outside, the road and sidewalk were one thick grey arch of frozen
50 packed snow that crunched and creaked dully under me, as I picked up
each overboot with the shoe inside slipping up and down generating a
little warmth with each step. The hood of my coat was drawn tight over

my toque pulled down to my eyebrows and the scarf covered my cheeks. Only my eyes and the top of my nose poked through the narrow band that
55 remained.

It was eight long blocks to Waterfield's General Store in the cluster of buildings on the main road that ran parallel to the C.P.R. tracks. Through the small slit on my hood, I could see all the way there down an eight block long tunnel of ice and packed snow. For good reason no one else was
60 out today even though only a few more days remained of Christmas holidays. The chimneys above the houses on each side of the long street had tall feathers of smoke rising from them. There was no wind but the cold was heavy and solid. No sounds carried out from the nearby houses and even the creaking of my boots on the snow was absorbed quickly into the
65 frozen air as if I'd never been there.

I trudged slowly like a bandaged-up alien with the huge boots on my feet and one arm swinging off tempo with the money in the toe of my mitt throwing itself ahead and the cold began to cut my breath into smaller and shorter gasps. The tears in my eyes had begun to ice and I rubbed my
70 eyelashes with my mitts to keep them apart. My scarf was now thick with frozen breath, rendering it stiff as my mother's laundry banging and clattering on the clothes line in the wind until she stacked it like thin sheets of plywood in her basket. I pulled down my scarf to take in air which in turn seared my throat. Ice crystals were growing slowing up the drawstring of
75 my hood as they had already on the power lines over my head. The store was still four blocks away: it was now as far back home as it was ahead. I trudged. I felt my brain freezing and I thought of the girl from Altadore and boiling water; I couldn't imagine it hurting at all.

Outside Waterfield's General Store, the Seven-Up thermometer stood
80 with the red line at -23 Fahrenheit and the windows with the Black Cat decals and the huge red Coca-Cola saucer were frosted nearly to the top. Inside, the warmth of the ripe banana and chewing gum air was sharp and immediate. Tom Waterfield looked down from his newspaper spread open on the counter and stared over his half-frame glasses he wore on the
85 end of his nose that made him look always sceptical and deserving of an answer like a teacher.

"Cold out there Tom. Come right in and get warm."

I liked Tom Waterfield not just because we had the same first name but because he treated me like we were equals almost, although I knew we
90 weren't. He didn't call me Tommy like almost everybody else, including my father.

I tore off my mitts and handed him the note. I didn't really need one for the groceries but you had to be sixteen to buy tobacco or cigarettes or you needed a note. I emptied out the five and change onto the linoleum
95 counter top.

"What else ya got here?" he read, taking down a green can of Export A with the dancing kilted lady on the front.

"Two Cream of Tomato. And Chicken Gumbo. One bread. You get that will ya."

100 When Tom wasn't busy like today he filled your order, but if he was busy, you helped yourself except for the tobacco and the candy he kept down behind the counter in a little window. And he didn't tolerate long decisions on whether you wanted one banana bubble gum cigar or ten Mojoes for your nickel.

105 "No, bottom shelf, bottom, right there," he pointed me down the big section of red and white cans that took up most of the canned goods section.

"There ya are. Small Velveeta from the dairy case and that does her."

A small stack of groceries had risen on the counter. We were running low; the last of the turkey soup had run out and it would be three more
110 days before the weekend and my father would be home early enough to take us in the car to the new Safeway's on the other side of town.

"That's..." he jabbed the figures into the adding machine buttons, pulled the crank quickly three times for the total and tore off the tape, "six dollars and thirty-two cents."

115 He counted out the change on the counter, sweeping it into the cup of his hand.

"Close. Mom's keeping good track of the money. Six fifty."

I was glad. I hated having to take something back because there wasn't enough money and sometimes there wasn't.

120 "Thirty three, four, five, forty, and fifty," he counted, handing me three pennies, a nickel and a dime. I quickly considered the possibilities here.

"I better get matches," I said. "One book please. And two caramels."

This was my tip and the matches were for her. I drove a hard bargain.

My hands felt all pins and needles and the tips of my fingers burned like
125 they were matches. I'd pulled my hood and my scarf down but still I'd started to sweat and the rough yarn of the mitten cord cut into my neck.

Tom folded over the bag after placing the bread gently on top. I wanted to stay and get warm, but I also felt funny just waiting in the store not buying anything else and getting all sweaty and itchy.

130　　As I put the bag down by the door the change rattled in the bottom, and I pulled my hood and scarf back up and shoved my mittens into my sleeves. Then I sucked in one last lungful of warm sweet banana air and scooped up the bag. As I leaned on the outside door, I had to shove it open against the wind and the inner door clicked securely behind me.

135　　At first it wasn't too bad. The chewy caramel warmed my cheeks as long as I didn't have to open my mouth to breathe. But two blocks later, the wind opened my sleeves and filled my hood freezing my hair and raising goose bumps on my arms. I looked back at the big blue panel truck with the block heater cord running into the store. Waterfields also delivered gro-
140　ceries. But my mother was too proud to ask and I was her son.

　　A bit of caramel squirted out and stuck to the side of my face, gluing my frozen scarf to my cheek. My hands ached. The bag was getting heavier and I shifted it from one arm to the other. As I put it down to rest, tears started down my cheek and I couldn't see our house even after the wind
145　died. Now I couldn't go back; I couldn't go forward.

　　I picked up the bag and walked a few more feet and put it down again, this time almost dropping it. No sounds came from the nearby houses. No one looked out. I hated my mother. I hated where we lived, this dumb street, Waterfield's. Then the wind started again.

150　　Suddenly, I felt something on my shoulder and heard a muffled sound above and beside me.

　　"Here, let me." A man I didn't recognize in an army parka and a huge brown toque with a pom-pom on top lifted the bag with one hand.

　　"That way?" he nodded ahead. "I'll carry, you lead."

155　　Hope goes a long way towards warmth. Instantly I felt better.

　　"Didn't catch your name. Mine's Arthur."

　　"Tom," I said, wiping the frozen goo from my cheek.

　　The wind gusted again and we shouldered into it. All I could see was that he was tall and thin-legged but his long stride made me throw my
160　boots ahead of me more quickly now and I puffed to keep up with him. The wind dropped and rose again, picking up the thin loose layer of snow off the park beside us. The ice crystals grazed my nose like cold sand and an old Christmas tree rolled down the road like a tumbleweed.

　　"Woo, whiteout!" he shouted over the wind.

165　　I halted for a moment. He turned and waited, then put his free hand on my back as I caught up with him.

　　"Best we not stop. Too damned cold." My father always said Goddamn.

It had not occurred to me just then who Arthur might be. Out here in the middle of the day. In a snowstorm. All the men were away at work.
170 Besides he was doing what I couldn't. But as we passed the red fire callbox mounted on the telephone pole that marked our street, I was starting to worry, but I was too afraid to stare, which would mean having to run and risk falling.

I did anyway. What was my mother going to say? One of her instruc-
175 tions had been about talking to strangers. Not talking to strangers.

"I can carry it from here," I looked up. All I could see through my thin band of sight, was the toque and the turned-up collar of the green parka that I now noticed was missing its hood. He also had no gloves and he kept shifting the bag from one hand to the other which he warmed in his
180 pocket. There was something familiar about him now that I hadn't real-ized earlier. Then a chill that had nothing to do with the weather ran up my spine.

"Don't you worry buddy. I'll take you right home. C'mon, too cold to stop." I could hear the shiver in his voice, but he kept walking.
185 Half a mile back down the tracks from Waterfield's was an old railway hotel that the Salvation Army ran as a hostel for single men. The hosties, as people called them, rode the freights or the city buses out to our edge of town. Out behind the hostel on the far bank of the irrigation canal in a grove of poplar was a hobo jungle where the men stayed when their time
190 was up. Sometimes the police had to go in and get a body and there were always stories of fights and stabbings. Under no circumstances were we to go near the tracks or the canal.

No one sat beside them on the bus. Some people even got up, shoving, cursing and sat somewhere else or stood up all the way home if one sat
195 beside them. Some were old and surly, talking to themselves or singing gut-tural songs. Others were young and smart-alecky, talking in loud voices and looking right in the eyes of people who tried to ignore them. All of them wore Sally Ann clothing, dark old coats, usually dress coats that looked funny on a bum. Most of them had bad breath with booze on it. And
200 B.O. The bus drivers had to tell them to shut up or throw them off the bus.

One driver even pulled over between stops once, after they all got off at the hostel, took out a rag and began furiously wiping the hand rails and backs of seats where they'd sat.

"God-damned swine," he'd glared at me. I nodded in agreement, afraid.
205 As we neared my house I started to want him gone. What if he wouldn't go. I knew my mother would be mad. Somehow I had failed her.

As Arthur and I turned up our walk, my mother's face was visible in a small clear circle of glass surrounded by a square-edged halo of frost that filled the picture window.

210 I wanted to turn and tell him, this no longer needed stranger, to go away. This is my house, mister. Thanks but you can leave now. I knew it was too late. Arthur must have seen her first because he handed me the bag and turned away. But my mother's face disappeared from the window, the front door opened and she stuck her head out. I knew she'd shoo him

215 away after what she'd said about strangers.

"Thank god. I just called Tom Waterfield. I was so worried when the wind picked up."

She turned to Arthur while she took the bag from me and stopped him.

"Thank you very much."

220 Arthur nodded to her and started back down the walk. I was relieved. But my mother stood watching.

"Wait. You must come in."

He paused a moment, confused, but then came up the steps behind me, a little too quickly, I thought. Right then I hated my mother for sending

225 me. And even more I hated her for letting this man into our house. I hadn't asked for his help.

"Let me take your coat," she put it over her arm the way she did for good company and then undid my scarf, "You get out of those clothes and I'll put some soup on. What's your friend's name?"

230 He's not my friend, I thought.

"Arthur." I fidgeted with the toggles on my boots.

"Arthur, I'm Edna," she said, leaving off her last name. Maybe he didn't have a last name and she didn't want him to feel bad.

"Welcome to our home. Tom will show you where the washroom is." My

235 mother was using her best company voice and manners. We usually called it the bathroom.

He spent a long time washing. I went in after he finished and ran warm water over my hands which made the skin feel as if it was shrinking and too tight for my fingers, but it warmed me up fast. I checked the medicine

240 cabinet to see if anything was missing. My father's Gillette safety razor was still there, his chipped shaving mug and fragrant bushy shaving brush. The Noxzema, the Aspirin, the styptic pencil my father used for his shaving cuts and his Wildroot hair cream. At Cubs, we'd learned Kim's Game where we had to memorize a table full of objects, leave the room

245 and then come back to identify what item was missing. I'd never been

good at it, but everything looked like it was here. I heard my mother's laughter and when I came out, he was standing in the kitchen doorway smiling and talking to her.

My mother hustled us into the dining room and Arthur didn't say much, 250 but he seemed grateful to be out of the cold.

"You don't have to, ma'am."

My mother seemed glad to have the company and she flew between the kitchen stove and counter and rushed in with a plateful of long fingers of white bread sliced into dunkers for the soup heating on the stove.

255 "No bother. It won't take long at all," she called out cheerfully from the kitchen.

With the wire cheese cutter she slapped the thick slices of Velveeta onto the bread and flipped it onto the waffle iron to grill. The margarine sizzled and smoked with each slap.

260 Sitting across the table, Arthur still had on his toque and he looked ridiculous. I wondered why my mother hadn't said anything. I was never allowed to wear a hat at the table. His face was very red and creased but his voice was young, maybe even younger than my father's. His eyebrows were like two bushy blonde shelves on his forehead and his grey eyes 265 pierced whenever they looked into mine. Slowly I was warming up, but when I blew my nose, there was a strange and familiar smell.

B.O.—body odour. And then the smell of urine and campfire smoke. My mother had warned me about B.O. Good hygiene, she'd say. Arthur had B.O. and B.O. was a hostie smell.

270 Most of them had the same red face and smelled so bad you tried not to breathe if they sat beside you on the bus. And now one of them was sitting in my father's chair in a stupid toque, stinking up our house and about to eat our food while mother was treating him like good company.

Then, I realized what was missing from the medicine cabinet: my 275 father's old straight razor that he kept hidden behind all his other things. I wanted to jump up and check. Instead I looked down at the bowl of soup my mother placed in front of me. Cream of Tomato soup. I thought of the story of Sweeny Todd our cubmaster had told us one wintry night when we were alone in a cabin at Camp Gardiner. My throat felt bare naked and 280 cold. I swallowed hard.

Arthur had three bowls of soup and four grilled sandwiches. My mother just kept on bringing them and he never said no. I could hardly finish one bowl. After lunch, Arthur got up suddenly from the table and I nearly jumped. He reached for the knife at my mother's plate while she was in the

285 kitchen making coffee. We'd all be dead, I thought. Downed with a dull knife, Melmac plates and bowls everywhere and our throats slit ear to ear like Sweeny Todd's victims and warm blood gurgling out of us like Campbell's Cream of Tomato soup.

"Don't bother," my mother called out, "Tom will clean up. Tom." She
290 seemed unaware of any reason to fear him, this man with my father's razor in his pocket. I could see the rectangular outline of its case lying horizontally in his pants pocket as he stood up.

He stacked the knife on my mother's plate and put them on top of mine. But I knew it was a ploy. I took the dishes from the table out to the kitchen
295 and went to go off to the bathroom. I wondered how to get my mother alone and tell her. And the telephone hung on the wall between her in the kitchen and him in the dining room.

"Take these out to the table will you?" she stopped me with two mugs and a plate of cookies.

300 "You smoke, don't you, Arthur?" my mother asked from the kitchen.

"If you don't mind." He shifted in his chair as he answered.

Even though my mother hadn't exactly asked me to join them, I wasn't letting him out of my sight. When she came back into the dining room she brought her long cigarette roller, an ashtray and the can of Export A.

305 "Help yourself to the coffee and cookies. I'll roll us a few cigarettes."

"You like Johnny Cash?" Arthur pointed to the stack of albums leaning against the flip top record player. She only had four of his albums.

"You too?" she said more than asked, preoccupied with the quick flip of white paper and tobacco into long white pencils that rolled out on the
310 table.

"I like him—he plays mouth organ good too."

My mother corrected me if I said good when I meant well. But I was more worried about his free hand which rested on the pant pocket where the razor was.

315 Then my mother evened out the long white cigarettes and reached into the pocket of her house dress. She took out my father's razor, pulled open its case, carefully unfolded the shiny blade out of the ivory handle and expertly nicked each long cigarette into regular sizes. She'd had it all along.

320 "That does the trick," she said. "Nothing else in the house quite this sharp." Then she used a match head to tuck the loose strands of tobacco back into the cut ends.

"Don't tell your father," she said, giving me a nod.

That still didn't satisfy me. It just meant he brought his own knife. I didn't take my eyes off him for a second. But they both ignored me as he held a match out to her. Her cigarette sputtered and flared the way rollies do. She inhaled deeply and then exhaled through her nostrils filling the air with a cloud of thick rich smoke.

"Would you like to hear something?"

"You got Orange Blossom Special?" he asked.

My mother slipped the album from its jacket and set the needle onto the record.

It was then Arthur made his move. Catching us off guard, he reached into his pocket. My father's razor lay closed at the other end of the table. We were defenceless. I put my hands over my eyes. This was it.

I heard a spit-wet wheeze and then a low metallic wail. I looked through my fingers. On the table in front of him was a cardboard box with the lettering:

M. HOHNER
MARINE BAND HARMONICA

Great. Sometimes you'd see the hosties out in front of the Cecil Hotel or the Queens with a hat or a cigar box. The odd one was okay; most just made noise.

While Arthur wasn't great, he wasn't awful either. He wailed in the right places, cupping his hands closed and open for the train whistle parts. His Adam's apple bobbed and his cheeks puffed and sucked as he made the click, click, cluck sound of the wheels. My mother, meanwhile, picked up the coffee spoons and cupped one inside the other with her forefinger acting as a spring and tapped them in the palm of her other hand to keep the beat as she sang the chorus. Actually neither of them sounded bad.

My mother laughed when the song was finished. I'd never heard her sing or laugh this freely with my father. I knew it was wrong, but I couldn't say a thing to my father because if I hadn't needed help none of this would have happened.

"You got any more songs Arthur?" my mother asked while she poured him more coffee.

Instead of answering, Arthur began to cough, deep racking ones full of spit he wiped from his mouth with the paper napkin from the cookie plate. Each time he coughed, his body rocked forward almost lifting him from the chair.

"Are you alright?" My mother stood over him with the coffee pot still in her hand. We were both worried now. I wondered about my father coming home to a dead bum in his chair.

"I'm fine," he finally said, wiping his mouth and gulping some coffee 365 which seemed to settle him down. "But I better go."

This time my mother didn't stop him. And as he stood in the doorway, puffing on his parka, she pressed a handful of rollies into his and gave him a pair of gloves my father never wore. As he turned out the door, he looked at me and then nodded to my mother.

370     "Bye Tom. Thank you."

After he left, my mother latched the aluminum door shut as it banged with the wind. I went to the front window and watched him cut across the park towards the hostel. The needles of the Christmas tree jabbed my elbow as I made a squeaky circle in the frost, my finger going round and 375 round until there was a small clear hole. I watched him appear and reappear in the gusts of snow-filled wind until I could no longer see him, this man for whom my mother sang and laughed, and the small opening I'd made closed, covered with my frozen breath. In the kitchen, the tap filled the sink with water; the radio was silent, as was my mother who neither 380 sang nor laughed.

(1996)

# Cranes

## Hwang Sunwŏn (Korea) 1915–

*(translated from Korean by Peter H. Lee)*

## About the Author

*Hwang Sunwŏn is one of the most influential novelists and short story writers in Korea. (Note that Hwang is the family name. For Korean, Chinese, and Japanese names, we place the family name first, as in the original language. You may also see the name in the opposite order.) Born in 1915 near Pyongyang in what is now North Korea, Hwang graduated from Waseda University in Japan with a degree in English literature in 1939. After Korea was liberated from Japanese rule in 1945 and divided at the 38th parallel into two sections, Hwang and his family moved from the northern part to the southern part. He taught high school briefly and then taught Korean literature at Kyung Hee University in Seoul from 1957 to 1993.*

*Two volumes of Hwang's poetry were published in his university days, and since then he has produced seven novels and more than one hundred short stories in the seven decades of his literary career. His most successful novel,* Trees on the Cliff *(1960), demonstrates an ambitious effort to combine Western influence and native tradition in modern Korean literature. Yet it is his short stories that have earned him the title of a consummate writer of 20th-century Korea. All his stories balance a lyrical humanism with superior craftsmanship. As the author of some of modern Korea's best-known stories, such as "Cranes" (1953) and "A Shadow Solution" (1984), Hwang displays a mastery of narrative techniques, vivid artistic imagination, and profound insights into human personality and relations as they are put to the test.*

## Terms Appearing in the Story

**Thirty-eighth Parallel** the border between North Korea and South Korea
**wen** cyst or skin blemish

T he northern village lay snug beneath the high, bright autumn sky, near the border at the Thirty-eighth Parallel.° White gourds lay one against the other on the first floor of an empty farmhouse. Any village elders who passed by extinguished their bamboo pipes first, and the chil-
5 dren, too, turned back some distance off. Their faces were marked with fear.

As a whole, the village showed little damage from the war, but it still did not seem like the same village Sŏngsam had known as a boy.

At the foot of a chestnut grove on the hill behind the village he stopped
10 and climbed a chestnut tree. Somewhere far back in his mind he heard the old man with a wen° shout, "You bad boy, climbing up my chestnut tree again!"

The old man must have passed away, for he was not among the few village elders Sŏngsam had met. Holding onto the trunk of the tree, Sŏngsam
15 gazed up at the blue sky for a time. Some chestnuts fell to the ground as the dry clusters opened of their own accord.


A young man stood, his hands bound, before a farmhouse that had been converted into a Public Peace Police office. He seemed to be a stranger, so Sŏngsam went up for a closer look. He was stunned: this young man was
20 none other than his boyhood playmate, Tŏkchae.

Sŏngsam asked the police officer who had come with him from Ch'ŏn-t'ae for an explanation. The prisoner was the vice-chairman of the Farmers' Communist League and had just been flushed out of hiding in his own house, Sŏngsam learned.
25 Sŏngsam sat down on the dirt floor and lit a cigarette.

Tŏkchae was to be escorted to Ch'ŏngdan by one of the peace police.

After a time, Sŏngsam lit a new cigarette from the first and stood up.

"I'll take him with me."

Tŏkchae averted his face and refused to look at Sŏngsam. The two left
30 the village.

Sŏngsam went on smoking, but the tobacco had no flavor. He just kept drawing the smoke in and blowing it out. Then suddenly he thought that Tŏkchae, too, must want a puff. He thought of the days when they had shared dried gourd leaves behind sheltering walls, hidden from the adults'
35 view. But today, how could he offer a cigarette to a fellow like this?

Once, when they were small, he went with Tŏkchae to steal some chestnuts from the old man with the wen. It was Sŏngsam's turn to climb the tree. Suddenly the old man began shouting. Sŏngsam slipped and fell to the ground. He got chestnut burrs all over his bottom, but he kept on run-
40 ning. Only when the two had reached a safe place where the old man could not overtake them did Sŏngsam turn his bottom to Tŏkchae. The burrs hurt so much as they were plucked out that Sŏngsam could not keep tears from welling up in his eyes. Tŏkchae produced a fistful of chestnuts

from his pocket and thrust them into Sŏngsam's....Sŏngsam threw away
45 the cigarette he had just lit, and then made up his mind not to light
another while he was escorting Tŏkchae.

They reached the pass at the hill where he and Tŏkchae had cut fodder for
the cows until Sŏngsam had to move to a spot near Ch'ŏnt'ae, south of the
Thirty-eighth Parallel, two years before the liberation.

50     Sŏngsam felt a sudden surge of anger in spite of himself and shouted,
"So how many have you killed?"

For the first time, Tŏkchae cast a quick glance at him and then looked
away.

"You! How many have you killed?" he asked again.

55     Tŏkchae looked at him again and glared. The glare grew intense, and
his mouth twitched.

"So you managed to kill quite a few, eh?" Sŏngsam felt his mind
clearing itself, as if some obstruction had been removed. "If you were vice-
chairman of the Communist League, why didn't you run? You must have
60 been lying low with a secret mission."

Tŏkchae did not reply.

"Speak up. What was your mission?"

Tŏkchae kept walking. Tŏkchae was hiding something, Sŏngsam
thought. He wanted to take a good look at him, but Tŏkchae kept his face
65 averted.

Fingering the revolver at his side, Sŏngsam went on: "There's no need to
make excuses. You're going to be shot anyway. Why don't you tell the
truth here and now?"

"I'm not going to make any excuses. They made me vice-chairman of
70 the League because I was a hardworking farmer, and one of the poorest. If
that's a capital offense, so be it. I'm still what I used to be—the only thing
I'm good at is tilling the soil." Alter a short pause, he added, "My old man
is bedridden at home. He's been ill almost half a year." Tŏkchae's father was
a widower, a poor, hardworking farmer who lived only for his son. Seven
75 years ago his back had given out, and he had contracted a skin disease.

"Are you married?"

"Yes," Tŏkchae replied after a time.

"To whom?"

"Shorty."

80     "To Shorty?" How interesting! A woman so small and plump that she
knew the earth's vastness, but not the sky's height. Such a cold fish! He and
Tŏkchae had teased her and made her cry. And Tŏkchae had married her!

"How many kids?"

"The first is arriving this fall, she says."

85 Sŏngsam had difficulty swallowing a laugh that he was about to let burst forth in spite of himself. Although he had asked how many children Tŏkchae had, he could not help wanting to break out laughing at the thought of the wife sitting there with her huge stomach, one span around. But he realized that this was no time for joking.

90 "Anyway, it's strange you didn't run away."

"I tried to escape. They said that once the South invaded, not a man would be spared. So all of us between seventeen and forty were taken to the North. I thought of evacuating, even if I had to carry my father on my back. But Father said no. How could we farmers leave the land behind 95 when the crops were ready for harvesting? He grew old on that farm depending on me as the prop and mainstay of the family. I wanted to be with him in his last moments so I could close his eyes with my own hand. Besides, where can farmers like us go, when all we know how to do is live on the land?"

100 Sŏngsam had had to flee the previous June. At night he had broken the news privately to his father. But his father had said the same thing: Where could a farmer go, leaving all the chores behind? So Sŏngsam had left alone. Roaming about the strange streets and villages in the South, Sŏngsam had been haunted by thoughts of his old parents and the young 105 children, who had been left with all the chores. Fortunately, his family had been safe then, as it was now.

They had crossed over a hill. This time Sŏngsam walked with his face averted. The autumn sun was hot on his forehead. This was an ideal day for the harvest, he thought.

110 When they reached the foot of the hill, Sŏngsam gradually came to a halt. In the middle of a field he spied a group of cranes that resembled men in white, all bent over. This had been the demilitarized zone along the Thirty-eighth Parallel. The cranes were still living here, as before, though all the people were gone.

115 Once, when Sŏngsam and Tŏkchae were about twelve, they had set a trap here, without anybody else knowing, and caught a crane, a Tanjŏng crane. They had tied the crane up, even binding its wings, and paid it daily visits, patting its neck and riding on its back. Then one day they overheard the neighbors whispering: someone had come from Seoul with a permit 120 from the governor-general's office to catch cranes as some kind of specimens. Then and there the two boys had dashed off to the field. That they

would be found out and punished had no longer mattered; all they cared about was the fate of their crane. Without a moment's delay, still out of breath from running, they untied the crane's feet and wings, but the bird
125  could hardly walk. It must have been weak from having been bound.

The two held the crane up. Then, suddenly, they heard a gunshot. The crane fluttered its wings once or twice and then sank back to the ground.

The boys thought their crane had been shot. But the next moment, as another crane from a nearby bush fluttered its wings, the boys' crane
130  stretched its long neck, gave out a whoop, and disappeared into the sky. For a long while the two boys could not tear their eyes away from the blue sky into which their crane had soared.

"Hey, why don't we stop here for a crane hunt?" Sŏngsam said suddenly. Tŏkchae was dumbfounded.
135  "I'll make a trap with this rope; you flush a crane over here."

Sŏngsam had untied Tŏkchae's hands and was already crawling through the weeds.

Tŏkchae's face whitened. "You're sure to be shot anyway"—these words flashed through his mind. Any instant a bullet would come flying from
140  Sŏngsam's direction, Tŏkchae thought.

Some paces away, Sŏngsam quickly turned toward him.

"Hey, how come you're standing there like a dummy? Go flush a crane!"

Only then did Tŏkchae understand. He began crawling through the weeds.
145  A pair of Tanjŏng cranes soared high into the clear blue autumn sky, flapping their huge wings.

(1953)

# A White Heron

Sarah Orne Jewett (U.S.A.) 1849–1909

## About the Author

*Sarah Orne Jewett is regarded as one of the best American writers in the "local colour movement" during the last half of the 19th century. Born in South Berwick, Maine, she graduated from Berwick Academy in 1866 and received an honorary doctorate from Bowdoin College in 1901. She began to submit short stories to magazines under the pseudonyms A.D. Eliot, Alice Eliot, and Sarah C. Sweet in 1867 and continued to write until her death in 1909.*

*Sarah Orne Jewett wrote several novels, including her masterpieces* Deephaven *(1877) and* The Country of the Pointed Firs *(1896), numerous short stories and poems, and one volume of history. Nevertheless, she is best known for her sketches about provincial life in New England during the 1800s. Seeking to preserve the rural past of her native Maine through her works, Jewett demonstrated great talent for faithful depiction of ordinary characters and local culture in her predominantly New England settings, as well as for her romantic approach to realistic situations. "A White Heron," considered by many her best short story, exemplifies Jewett's lyrical observations of the natural landscape and her indignant response to human insensitivity and destruction of nature. As a writer, Jewett was more concerned with the emotional impact of human action and experience than with action-filled plot. Jewett makes use of local dialect in the dialogue of this story.*

## Term Appearing in the Story

**bangeing** scrounging

## 1

The woods were already filled with shadows one June evening, just before eight o'clock, though a bright sunset still glimmered faintly among the trunks of the trees. A little girl was driving home her cow, a
5 plodding, dilatory, provoking creature in her behavior, but a valued companion for all that. They were going away from the western light, and striking deep into the dark woods, but their feet were familiar with the path, and it was no matter whether their eyes could see it or not.

There was hardly a night the summer through when the old cow could be
10 found waiting at the pasture bars; on the contrary it was her greatest pleasure to hide herself away among the high huckleberry bushes, and

though she wore a loud bell she had made the discovery that if one stood perfectly still it would not ring. So Sylvia had to hunt for her until she found her,
and call Co'! Co'! with never an answering Moo, until her childish patience
15  was quite spent. If the creature had not given good milk and plenty of it, the
case would have seemed very different to her owners. Besides, Sylvia had all
the time there was, and very little use to make of it. Sometimes in pleasant
weather it was a consolation to look upon the cow's pranks as an intelligent
attempt to play hide and seek, and as the child had no playmates she lent
20  herself to this amusement with a good deal of zest. Though this chase had
been so long that the wary animal herself had given an unusual signal of
her whereabouts, Sylvia had only laughed when she came upon Mistress
Moolly at the swamp-side, and urged her affectionately homeward with a
twig of birch leaves. The old cow was not inclined to wander farther, she even
25  turned in the right direction for once as they left the pasture, and stepped
along the road at a good pace. She was quite ready to be milked now, and
seldom stopped to browse. Sylvia wondered what her grandmother would say
because they were so late. It was a great while since she had left home at half
past five o'clock, but everybody knew the difficulty of making this errand a
30  short one. Mrs. Tilley had chased the horned torment too many summer
evenings herself to blame any one else for lingering, and was only thankful
as she waited that she had Sylvia, nowadays, to give such valuable assistance. The good woman suspected that Sylvia loitered occasionally on her
own account; there never was such a child for straying about out-of-doors
35  since the world was made! Everybody said that it was a good change for a
little maid who had tried to grow for eight years in a crowded manufacturing
town, but, as for Sylvia herself, it seemed as if she never had been alive at all
before she came to live at the farm. She thought often with wistful compassion of a wretched dry geranium that belonged to a town neighbor.
40      "'Afraid of folks,'" old Mrs. Tilley said to herself, with a smile, after she
had made the unlikely choice of Sylvia from her daughter's houseful of
children, and was returning to the farm. "'Afraid of folks,' they said! I
guess she won't be troubled no great with 'em up to the old place!" When
they reached the door of the lonely house and stopped to unlock it, and the
45  cat came to purr loudly, and rub against them, a deserted pussy, indeed,
but fat with young robins, Sylvia whispered that this was a beautiful place
to live in, and she never should wish to go home.

The companions followed the shady woodroad, the cow taking slow steps,
and the child very fast ones. The cow stopped long at the brook to drink,
50  as if the pasture were not half swamp, and Sylvia stood still and waited,

letting her bare feet cool themselves in the shoal water, while the great twilight moths struck softly against her. She waded on through the brook as the cow moved away, and listened to the thrushes with a heart that beat fast with pleasure. There was a stirring in the great boughs overhead. They

55 were full of little birds and beasts that seemed to be wide-awake, and going about their world, or else saying goodnight to each other in sleepy twitters. Sylvia herself felt sleepy as she walked along. However, it was not much farther to the house, and the air was soft and sweet. She was not often in the woods so late as this, and it made her feel as if she were a part of the

60 gray shadows and the moving leaves. She was just thinking how long it seemed since she first came to the farm a year ago, and wondering if everything went on in the noisy town just the same as when she was there; the thought of the great red-faced boy who used to chase and frighten her made her hurry along the path to escape from the shadow of the trees.

65 Suddenly this little woods-girl is horror-stricken to hear a clear whistle not very far away. Not a bird's whistle, which would have a sort of friendliness, but a boy's whistle, determined, and somewhat aggressive. Sylvia left the cow to whatever sad fate might await her, and stepped discreetly aside into the bushes, but she was just too late. The enemy had discovered her, and called

70 out in a very cheerful and persuasive tone, "Halloa, little girl, how far is it to the road?" and trembling Sylvia answered almost inaudibly, "A good ways."

She did not dare to look boldly at the tall young man, who carried a gun over his shoulder, but she came out of her bush and again followed the cow, while he walked alongside.

75 "I've been hunting for some birds," the stranger said kindly, "and I have lost my way, and need a friend very much. Don't be afraid," he added gallantly. "Speak up and tell me what your name is, and whether you think I can spend the night at your house, and go out gunning early in the morning."

Sylvia was more alarmed than before. Would not her grandmother con-

80 sider her much to blame? But who could have foreseen such an accident as this? It did not appear to be her fault, and she hung her head as if the stem of it were broken, but managed to answer, "Sylvy," with much effort when her companion again asked her name.

Mrs. Tilley was standing in the doorway when the trio came into view

85 The cow gave a loud moo by way of explanation.

"Yes, you'd better speak up for yourself, you old trial! Where'd she tuck herself away this time, Sylvy?" Sylvia kept an awed silence; she knew by instinct that her grandmother did not comprehend the gravity of the situation. She must be mistaking the stranger for one of the farmer-lads of the

90 region.

The young man stood his gun beside the door, and dropped a heavy game-bag beside it; then he bade Mrs. Tilley good-evening, and repeated his wayfarer's story, and asked if he could have a night's lodging.

"Put me anywhere you like," he said. "I must be off early in the
95 morning, before day; but I am very hungry, indeed. You can give me some milk at any rate, that's plain."

"Dear sakes, yes," responded the hostess, whose long slumbering hospitality seemed to be easily awakened. "You might fare better if you went out the main road a mile or so, but you're welcome to what we've got. I'll milk
100 right off, and you make yourself at home. You can sleep on husks or feathers," she proffered graciously "I raised them all myself." There's good pasturing for geese just below here towards the ma'sh. Now step round and set a plate for the gentleman, Sylvy!" And Sylvia promptly stepped. She was glad to have something to do, and she was hungry herself.

105 It was a surprise to find so clean and comfortable a little dwelling in this New England wilderness. The young man had known the horrors of its most primitive housekeeping, and the dreary squalor of that level of society which does not rebel at the companionship of hens. This was the best thrift of an old-fashioned farmstead, though on such a small scale
110 that it seemed like a hermitage. He listened eagerly to the old woman's quaint talk, he watched Sylvia's pale face and shining gray eyes with ever growing enthusiasm, and insisted that this was the best supper he had eaten for a month; then, afterward, the new-made friends sat down in the doorway together while the moon came up.

115 Soon it would be berry-time, and Sylvia was a great help at picking. The cow was a good milker, though a plaguy thing to keep track of, the hostess gossiped frankly, adding presently that she had buried four children, so that Sylvia's mother, and a son (who might be dead) in California were all the children she had left. "Dan, my boy, was a great hand to go gunning,"
120 she explained sadly, "I never wanted for pa'tridges or gray squer'ls while he was to home. He's been a great wand'rer, I expect, and he's no hand to write letters. There, I don't blame him, I'd ha' seen the world myself if it had been so I could.

"Sylvia takes after him," the grandmother continued affectionately,
125 after a minute's pause. "There ain't a foot o' ground she don't know her way over, and the wild creatur's counts her one o' themselves. Squer'ls she'll tame to come an' feed right out o' her hands, and all sorts o' birds. Last winter she got the jay-birds to bangeing° here, and I believe she'd 'a' scanted herself of her own meals to have plenty to throw out amongst 'em,
130 if I hadn't kep' watch. Anything but crows, I tell her, I'm willin' to help

support,—though Dan he went an' tamed one o' them that did seem to have reason same as folks. It was round here a good spell after he went away. Dan an' his father they didn't hitch,—but he never held up his head ag'in after Dan dared him an' gone off."

135 The guest did not notice this hint of family sorrows in his eager interest in something else.

"So Sylvy knows all about birds, does she?" he exclaimed, as he looked round at the little girl who sat, very demure but increasingly sleepy, in the moonlight. "I am making a collection of birds myself. I have been at it ever
140 since I was a boy." (Mrs. Tilley smiled.) "There are two or three very rare ones I have been hunting for these five years. I mean to get them on my own ground if they can be found."

"Do you cage 'em up?" asked Mrs. Tilley doubtfully, in response to this enthusiastic announcement.

145 "Oh, no, they're stuffed and preserved, dozens and dozens of them," said the ornithologist, "and I have shot or snared every one myself. I caught a glimpse of a white heron three miles from here on Saturday, and I have followed it in this direction. They have never been found in this district at all. The little white heron, it is," and he turned again to look at
150 Sylvia with the hope of discovering that the rare bird was one of her acquaintances.

But Sylvia was watching a hop-toad in the narrow footpath.

"You would know the heron if you saw it," the stranger continued eagerly "A queer tall white bird with soft feathers and long thin legs. And
155 it would have a nest perhaps in the top of a high tree, made of sticks, something like a hawk's nest."

Sylvia's heart gave a wild beat; she knew that strange white bird, and had once stolen softly near where it stood in some bright green swamp grass, away over at the other side of the woods. There was an open place where the
160 sunshine always seemed strangely yellow and hot, where tall, nodding rushes grew, and her grandmother had warned her that she might sink in the soft black mud underneath and never be heard of more. Not far beyond were the salt marshes and beyond those was the sea, the sea which Sylvia wondered and dreamed about, but never had looked upon, though its great
165 voice could often be heard above the noise of the woods on stormy nights.

"I can't think of anything I should like so much as to find that heron's nest," the handsome stranger was saying. "I would give ten dollars to anybody who could show it to me," he added desperately, "and I mean to spend my whole vacation hunting for it if need be. Perhaps it was only
170 migrating, or had been chased out of its own region by some bird of prey."

Mrs. Tilley gave amazed attention to all this, but Sylvia still watched the toad, not divining, as she might have done at some calmer time, that the creature wished to get to its hole under the doorstep, and was much hindered by the unusual spectators at that hour of the evening. No amount of thought, that night, could decide how many wished-for treasures the ten dollars, so lightly spoken of, would buy.

The next day the young sportsman hovered about the woods, and Sylvia kept him company, having lost her first fear of the friendly lad, who proved to be most kind and sympathetic. He told her many things about the birds and what they knew and where they lived and what they did with themselves. And he gave her a jack-knife, which she thought as great a treasure as if she were a desert-islander. All day long he did not once make her troubled or afraid except when he brought down some unsuspecting singing creature from its bough. Sylvia would have liked him vastly better without his gun; she could not understand why he killed the very birds he seemed to like so much. But as the day waned, Sylvia still watched the young man with loving admiration. She had never seen anybody so charming and delightful; the woman's heart, asleep in the child, was vaguely thrilled by a dream of love. Some premonition of that great power stirred and swayed these young foresters who traversed the solemn woodlands with soft-footed silent care. They stopped to listen to a bird's song; they pressed forward again eagerly, parting the branches,—speaking to each other rarely and in whispers; the young man going first and Sylvia following, fascinated, a few steps behind, with her gray eyes dark with excitement.

She grieved because the longed-for white heron was elusive, but she did not lead the guest, she only followed, and there was no such thing as speaking first. The sound of her own unquestioned voice would have terrified her,—it was hard enough to answer yes or no when there was need of that. At last evening began to fall, and they drove the cow home together, and Sylvia smiled with pleasure when they came to the place where she heard the whistle and was afraid only the night before.

## 2

Half a mile from home, at the farther edge of the woods, where the land was highest, a great pine-tree stood, the last of its generation. Whether it was left for a boundary mark, or for what reason, no one could say; the woodchoppers who had felled its mates were dead and gone long ago, and a whole forest of sturdy trees, pines and oaks and maples, had grown again. But the stately head of this old pine towered above them all and

210 made a landmark for sea and shore miles and miles away. Sylvia knew it well. She had always believed that whoever climbed to the top of it could see the ocean; and the little girl had often laid her hand on the great rough trunk and looked up wistfully at those dark boughs that the wind always stirred, no matter how hot and still the air might be below. Now she
215 thought of the tree with a new excitement, for why, if one climbed it at break of day, could not one see all the world, and easily discover whence the white heron flew, and mark the place and find the hidden nest?

What a spirit of adventure, what wild ambition! What fancied triumph and delight and glory for the later morning when she could make known
220 the secret! It was almost too real and too great for the childish heart to bear.

All night the door of the little house stood open, and the whippoorwills came and sang upon the very step. The young sportsman and his old hostess were sound asleep, but Sylvia's great design kept her broad awake and watching. She forgot to think of sleep. The short summer night seemed
225 as long as the winter darkness, and at last when the whippoorwills ceased, and she was afraid the morning would after all come too soon, she stole out of the house and followed the pasture path through the woods, hastening toward the open ground beyond, listening with a sense of comfort and companionship to the drowsy twitter of a half-awakened bird, whose
230 perch she had jarred in passing. Alas, if the great wave of human interest which flooded for the first time this dull little life should sweep away the satisfactions of an existence heart to heart with nature and the dumb life of the forest!

There was the huge tree asleep yet in the paling moonlight, and small
235 and hopeful Sylvia began with utmost bravery to mount to the top of it, with tingling, eager blood coursing the channels of her whole frame, with her bare feet and fingers, that pinched and held like bird's claws to the monstrous ladder reaching up, up, almost to the sky itself. First she must mount the white oak tree that grew alongside, where she was almost lost
240 among the dark branches and the green leaves heavy and wet with dew; a bird fluttered off its nest, and a red squirrel ran to and fro and scolded pettishly at the harmless housebreaker. Sylvia felt her way easily. She had often climbed there, and knew that higher still one of the oak's upper branches chafed against the pine trunk, just where its lower boughs were
245 set close together. There, when she made the dangerous pass from one tree to the other, the great enterprise would really begin.

She crept out along the swaying oak limb at last, and took the daring step across into the old pine-tree. The way was harder than she thought; she must reach far and hold fast, the sharp dry twigs caught and held her

250 and scratched her like angry talons, the pitch made her thin little fingers clumsy and stiff as she went round and round the tree's great stem, higher and higher upward. The sparrows and robins in the woods below were beginning to wake and twitter to the dawn, yet it seemed much lighter there aloft in the pine-tree, and the child knew that she must hurry if her
255 project were to be of any use.

The tree seemed to lengthen itself out as she went up, and to reach farther and farther upward. It was like a great main-mast to the voyaging earth; it must truly have been amazed that morning through all its ponderous frame as it felt this determined spark of human spirit creeping and climbing from
260 higher branch to branch. Who knows how steadily the least twigs held themselves to advantage this light, weak creature on her way! The old pine must have loved his new dependent. More than all the hawks, and bats, and moths, and even the sweet-voiced thrushes, was the brave, beating heart of the solitary gray-eyed child. And the tree stood still and held away the winds
265 that June morning while the dawn grew bright in the east.

Sylvia's face was like a pale star, if one had seen it from the ground when the last thorny bough was past, and she stood trembling and tired, but wholly triumphant, high in the tree-top. Yes, there was the sea with the dawning sun making a golden dazzle over it, and toward that glorious east
270 flew two hawks with slow-moving pinions. How low they looked in the air from that height when before one had only seen them far up, and dark against the blue sky. Their gray feathers were soft as moths; they seemed only a little way from the tree, and Sylvia felt as if she too could go flying away among the clouds. Westward, the woodlands and farms reached
275 miles and miles into the distance; here and there were church steeples, and white villages; truly it was a vast and awesome world.

The birds sang louder and louder. At last the sun came up bewilderingly bright. Sylvia could see the white sails of ships out at sea, and the clouds that were purple and rose-colored and yellow at first began to fade away
280 Where was the white heron's nest in the sea of green branches, and was this wonderful sight and pageant of the world the only reward for having climbed to such a giddy height? Now look down again, Sylvia, where the green marsh is set among the shining birches and dark hemlocks; there where you saw the white heron once you will see him again; look, look! a
285 white spot of him like a single floating feather comes up from the dead hemlock and grows larger, and rises, and comes close at last, and goes by the landmark pine with steady sweep of wing and outstretched slender

neck and crested head. And wait! wait! do not move a foot or a finger, little girl, do not send an arrow of light and consciousness from your two eager eyes, for the heron has perched on a pine bough not far beyond yours, and cries back to his mate on the nest, and plumes his feathers for the new day!

The child gives a long sigh a minute later when a company of shouting catbirds comes also to the tree, and vexed by their fluttering and lawlessness the solemn heron goes away. She knows his secret now, the wild, light, slender bird that floats and wavers, and goes back like an arrow presently to his home in the green world beneath. Then Sylvia, well satisfied, makes her perilous way down again, not daring to look far below the branch she stands on, ready to cry sometimes because her fingers ache and her lamed feet slip. Wondering over and over again what the stranger would say to her, and what he would think when she told him how to find his way straight to the heron's nest.

"Sylvy, Sylvy!" called the busy old grandmother again and again, but nobody answered, and the small husk bed was empty, and Sylvia had disappeared.

The guest waked from a dream, and remembering the day's pleasure hurried to dress himself that it might sooner begin. He was sure from the way the shy little girl looked once or twice yesterday that she had at least seen the white heron, and now she must really be persuaded to tell. Here she comes now, paler than ever, and her worn old frock is torn and tattered, and smeared with pine pitch. The grandmother and the sportsman stand in the door together and question her, and the splendid moment has come to speak of the dead hemlock-tree by the green marsh.

But Sylvia does not speak after all, though the old grandmother fretfully rebukes her, and the young man's kind appealing eyes are looking straight in her own. He can make them rich with money; he has promised it, and they are poor now. He is so well worth making happy, and he waits to hear the story she can tell.

No, she must keep silence! What is it that suddenly forbids her and makes her dumb? Has she been nine years growing, and now, when the great world for the first time puts out a hand to her, must she thrust it aside for a bird's sake? The murmur of the pine's green branches is in her ears, and she remembers how the white heron came flying through the golden air and how they watched the sea and the morning together, and Sylvia cannot speak; she cannot tell the heron's secret and give its life away.

325 Dear loyalty, that suffered a sharp pang as the guest went away disappointed later in the day, that could have served and followed him and loved him as a dog loves! Many a night Sylvia heard the echo of his whistle haunting the pasture path as she came home with the loitering cow. She forgot even her sorrow at the sharp report of his gun and the piteous sight
330 of thrushes and sparrows dropping silent to the ground, their songs hushed and their pretty feathers stained and wet with blood. Were the birds better friends than their hunter might have been,—who can tell? Whatever treasures were lost to her, woodlands and summer-time, remember! Bring your gifts and graces and tell your secrets to this lonely country child!

(1886)

# Cowboys and Indians

Basil Johnston (Canada) 1929–

## About the Author

*Basil Johnston is a highly respected Canadian writer of Ojibway origin. Born on the Parry Sound Indian Reserve in Ontario, he graduated from Loyola College in Montreal in 1954 and received his secondary school teaching certificate from Ontario College of Education in 1962. His early career spanned a variety of occupations, including hunting, fishing, trapping, farming, and working in the lumbering and mining indus-tries. He taught history at a Toronto high school before he joined the staff of the Royal Ontario Museum. Johnston is now a member of the ethnology department of the Royal Ontario Museum. He is vice-chairman of the Ontario Geographic Names Board and serves on the Canadian Council for Native Business. He has also been a con-sultant on native studies for the Ontario Ministry of Education. He now lives in Richmond Hill, Ontario.*

*Basil Johnston is the author of many short stories, essays, articles, poems, and books, including several guides for teaching and learning the Ojibway language. His most popular book,* Moose Meat Point *(1978), is a collection of 22 short stories set on a fictional reserve, Moose Meat Point near Blunder Bay. "Cowboys and Indians," a wry oral story, first appeared in* The Ontario Indian *in 1981. It exemplifies Johnston's unique sense of humour, laconic style, and dramatic wit. Demonstrating an undying interest in Ojibway traditions, customs, and relationships on and off the reserve, Basil Johnston's works present an impressive testimony to the rich cultural heritage of his people.*

Hollywood grew fast and big. By the 1930s there were many studios employing many actors in the production of many motion pictures. Within the same few years as the studios got bigger, techniques improved; as techniques improved so did the quality of acting; and as acting got
5 better, so did the range and variety of themes enlarge. And of course viewers' tastes became more refined and discriminating, requiring of Hollywood and the studios more authenticity and less artificiality in their productions.

And the studios were willing to oblige.
10 It was decided by the producer and director of a major studio planning a western picture with either Hoot Gibson, Tom Mix, or Ken Maynard as the principal star, to hire real Indians to take part in the production. With

real Indians the advantages were obvious. Besides lending authenticity to the motion picture, Indians represented a substantial saving. Their natural
15 pigmentation would reduce expenses in cosmetics and make-up artistics, their natural horsemanship would save time and expenses usually incurred in training greenhorns to ride; their possession of herds of ponies would save time and outlay in the rental and feeding of horses; and their natural talent for art would obviate the need for anthropologists to act as
20 consultants in authenticating Indian art and design. The only expense to be incurred was the fee of $2.00 per day for movie extras.

Management calculated that 500 Indians along with 500 horses were needed for no more than two days to shoot an attack upon a wagon-train. The producer and the director also decided that there would be substantial
25 savings by establishing the location of the filming near an Indian reservation somewhere in the west.

Inquiries, preliminary and cursory, made of historians and the Bureau of Indian Affairs in Washington indicated that the Crow Indians of Montana, having retained their traditions and still owning large herds of
30 horses, would be best suited for a motion picture of the kind planned by the studio. Besides, the terrain in the area was genuine honest-to-goodness Indian country, excellent for camera work.

Negotiations with the Bureau of Indian Affairs for permission to treat with the Crows for their services as actors and for the provision of horses
35 began at once. Permission was granted by Washington; and the Crows were more than willing to take part.

Crew and cast arrived by train in Billings, Montana. Anxious to get started and to finish shooting the siege of a wagon-train in as short a time as possible, the producer and director sent a limousine to the reservation
40 to fetch the chief.

Over a meal with the chief and his retinue of councillors and hangers-on. the producer, portly and bald, beneath a cloud of smoke produced by a fat cigar, informed the chief that it was a great privilege to work with the Crows and that it was an honour and a distinction for his studio to set
45 precedent in the entire industry by being the first to use real, live, honest-to-goodness Indians in a motion picture. For the Crows, it would mean fame and national recognition...and money...$2.00 a day for those taking part; $1.00 per day for those providing horses, and $1.00 per day for those providing art work and the loan of teepees.
50 An interpreter translated for the chief.

The producer smiled and blew a cloud of smoke out of the side of his mouth. The Crow responded "How! How! How!"

"It shouldn't take long chief, three or four days...no more. A day to get ready and two or three to film the scene. We don't want to interfere too much in your affairs, you've probably got a lot to do and...we are working under a pretty tight schedule."

The interpreter relayed this information to the chief.

"Now chief. We want 500 warriors; 500 horses; bows and arrows and...maybe fifty or so rifles...feathers, head-dresses, buckskin jackets, and...buck-skin leggings...and four or five people who can paint designs on horses and put make-up on warriors." The producer continued, "The scene itself will be easy. The warriors will attack the wagon-train at day-break. It shouldn't take more than half an hour. Very easy, really don't need any rehearsals. My colleague will tell you what to do. Probably the easiest two bucks you'll ever make...cash as soon as the scene's shot. Can you get all this stuff by tomorrow night, chief?" And the producer flicked ashes from his fat cigar.

The interpreter prattling in Crow to his chief and councillors pounded the table, slashed the air, shrugged his shoulders to emphasize his message to his listeners, who looked dumbfounded. Nevertheless they injected a "How! How!" frequently enough into the discourse to intimate some understanding.

The chief said something.

"How many horses?"

"500, the producer might even settle for 450."

The interpreter addressed his chief who shook his head grunting "How!"

"Ain't got 500 horses," the interpreter said sadly.

"450?"

"Ain't dat many on de reservation."

"300?"

"No, not dat many: not like long time ago."

"Well! How many have you got?" the producer asked, his face pinching into worried lines and his voice losing its cheer and vitality.

"Maybe 10...20...an' not very good dem."

"Keeee...rice...!" And the producer bit a chunk of cigar, crushing the other end in the ashtray. "Are there any horses around here?"

"Yeah. Ranchers and farmers got dem."

To his assistant, the producer instructed "Get 500 horses by tomorrow evening. We have to shoot that scene next morning with the Indians charging down the slope."

The interpreter whispered to his chief who shook his head.

"Say, mister," the interpreter addressed the producer, "how about saddles?"

"Saddles?" the word erupted.

"Yeah, saddles."

95 There was a moment of cosmic silence. "Saddles!" the producer repeated mouthing the word in disbelief. "What do you mean...saddles! You're all going to ride bare-back. This film is going to be authentic...who ever heard of Indians riding on saddles...supposed to be the finest horsemen in the world."

The interpreter stiffened in fright at the thought that he might be one of 100 the warriors to ride bare-back, and he hung his head.

"Don't know how to ride...us. Forgot how...long time ago...Need saddles...might fall off an' git hurt...us."

"This is incredible!...unbelievable!...no horses!...can't ride!..." the producer gasped as he sank into the chair. "Keeeeee-rice."

105 Hope waning from his brow and voice, the producer tried "You still got bows an' arrows?"

The interpreter slouched even lower "No! Got none of dem t'ings, us."

"Buckskin outfits?"

"No." another shameful shrug.

110 "Moccasins?"

"Some," a little brighter.

"Head-dresses?"

"Maybe two, three—very old dem."

"Teepees?"

115 "No more—live in houses us."

"Anyone know Indian designs...you know—war paint for warriors...and horses?"

"Don't t'ink so...everybody forgot."

The producer groaned. "This is astounding...I can't believe it...No 120 horses...can't ride...no teepees...no buckskin...no...no moccasins...no...no head-dresses...and...probably not even loin-cloths..." and he was quivering. "It boggles the mind."

"What do we do?" the director asked.

For several moments the producer assessed the circumstances, and pos-125 sessing an analytical mind he stated what needed to be done.

"With all our crew and cast here, and with our wagon-train and cannon and horses, we can't very well go back now. We'll have to train these Indians to ride. Now...Adams," the producer's assistant. "I want you to get on the line right away. Get a guy who knows something about Indians, 130 from the Bureau of Indian Affairs. I want you to get maybe a dozen chiefs' outfits; and 500 loincloths, bows an' arrows for everyone, about a dozen head-dresses and moccasins...everything we need to make these Indians...*Indians*. Is that clear? And get those horses by tomorrow night."

"Yes sir!"

135 "In the meantime, I'll call the studio office for more money. Let's get movin'."

The assistant went out.

"How long we gotta stay in this miserable God-forsaken cow-town?" Ken Maynard inquired.

140 "Coupla weeks...maybe."

Ken Maynard groaned.

"Now!" directing his cigar at the interpreter and his remarks to the chief, the producer said, "Tell the chief to get 500 young men to learn to ride bare-back, an' to learn fast."

145 The interpreter apprised his chief of the message. The chief responded.

"He say $2.00 a day!"

"Keeee-rice! Tell him, okay."

Two mornings later, 500 horses borrowed and rented from the local ranchers were delivered to the Indian reservation. 500 Crows began prac-
150 tising the art of horsemanship at once, and in earnest. And while it is true that many Crows shied away from the horses, just as many horses shied away from the Crows, so that there was much anxious circling of horses around Indians and Indians around horses, pulling, and jerking midst the clamour of pleas "Whoa! Whoa! Steady there Nellie! Easy there!" all in
155 Crow, and the horses perhaps because they were unfamiliar with Crow refusing to "whoa." Eventually, horses and Crows overcame their mutual distrust and suspicions and animosities to enable the Indians to mount their beasts.

There were of course some casualties, a few broken legs, sprained
160 ankles, cracked ribs, and bruised behinds suffered by the novices on the first day. But by the third day most of the young men, while not accomplished equestrians, were able to ride passably well; that is, they fell off their mounts less often.

With the arrival of the equipment, bows and arrows, head-dresses, moc-
165 casins, loin-cloths, shipped by express from Washington, one day was set aside for the Crow warriors to practise shooting arrows from bows, first from a standing position and then from horseback. There were a few more casualties but nothing serious.

Along with the equipment came twelve make-up artists accompanied
170 by an anthropologist to advise the artists in war-paint designs and to
instruct the Crow in war-whooping. Twelve immense pavilions were
erected, outside of each billboards bearing symbols and markings representative of warrior war-paint and horse-paint designs. Each Indian
having selected the design that best suited his taste and his horse entered
175 a pavilion where he and his steed were painted, emerging at the other end
of the massive tent looking very fierce and ready for war.

The movie moguls decided that they would film the siege of the wagon-
train at 5 a.m. regardless of the readiness of the Indians. "So what if a few
Red-skins fall off their horses...be more realistic."

180 As planned and according to script ten Crows, dressed in white buckskin
heavily beaded and wearing war-bonnets to represent leadership, along
with 450 warriors wearing only loin-cloths and armed with bows and
arrows were assembled in a shallow depression unseen from the wagon-
train. The horses pawed the ground and snorted and whinnied, while the
185 director, producer, assorted assistants, and camera-men waited for the sun
to cast its beams upon the wagon-train. When that critical moment
occurred, signalled by an assistant with a wave of an arm, the director
shouted "Action! Cameras roll!"

450 Indians on 450 horses erupted over the lip of the valley a 'hoopin'
190 an' a hollerin', their savage war-cries splitting the air while 1800 hooves
thundered down the slope, shaking the earth. Wagon-train passengers
spilled out of covered-wagons, splashed up from blankets, seized rifles,
yelling "Injuns! Injuns!" and hurled themselves behind boxes and crates
and barrels and began firing. At one end of the valley, Ken Maynard on
195 his white charger waited for his cue; at the other end fifty cavalrymen
waited to charge to the rescue, Bang! Bang! Bang! The Crows, a 'hoopin'
an' a hollerin' were riding round and round the wagon-train, firing their
arrows into the covered wagons and into boxes and crates and barrels.
Bang! Bang! Bang! Round and round rode the Crows.

200 "Cut! Cut! Cut!" everyone was shouting. "Cut! Cut! Cut!" everyone was
waving his arms. Cut! Cut! Cut! 450 Crows, yelling whoa! whoa! whoa!
brought their steeds to a halt.

The director, also on a horse, was livid with rage. He almost choked
"Somebody's gotta die; when you're shot, you fall off your horse and die.
205 Don't you understand?"

The Indians nodded and grunted "How! How!"

The director in disgust rode off leaving the cast and crew to repair 3000
to 4000 punctures and perforations inflicted by arrows on the canvas of

the covered wagons. Six members of the cast suffering injuries from stray
210 arrows needed medical attention. The Indians, with the arrows they had
recovered, retired to the reservation to mend their weapons.

Just before sun-up next day there was a final admonition. "Get it done
right this time!" The warriors responded "How! How!"

At the hand signal, "Action! Cameras roll!" were uttered.

215 450 Indians on 450 horses boiled over the lip of the valley, a 'hoopin'
an' a hollerin', their savage war cries rending the peace, while 1800
hooves pounded down the slope convulsing the ground. Wagon-train
patrons scurried out of covered wagons, sprang from blankets, seized their
rifles, yelling "Injuns! Injuns!" and dove behind boxes and crates and bar-
220 rels and began firing. Bang! Bang! Bang!

Seventy-five of the Crows, a 'hoopin' an' a hollerin' fell off their horses.
Bang! Bang! Bang! 200 more Crows, a 'hoopin' an' a hollerin' spun off
their mounts. Bang! Bang! Bang! The rest pitched off their steeds which
fled in all directions.

225 "Cut! Cut! Cut!" everyone was shouting. 450 Crows suspended their
moanin' an' a groanin' an' a rollin' on the ground, even though many
had sustained real injuries, to listen to and to watch the director.

There was a torrent of curses, sulphuric glares, which eventually subsided into mutterings, the gist of which was relayed by the interpreter to
230 the chiefs and warriors "that not everyone should have fallen off his
horse." To this the chief replied $2.00.

The scene was re-enacted the next day without incident. After the
shooting there were hand-shakes all around; and expressions of admiration tendered by Ken Maynard to the Crows for the speed with which they
235 had developed horsemanship, remarking that "it must be in-bred."

Crew and cast were celebrating over wine and whiskey, cheese and
crackers, when the film editor summoned the director. "Come here and
look at these," he said, thrusting a magnifying glass to his superior. The
director held the film strip against the light; he applied the magnifying
240 glass to the stills.

"Sun-glasses! Keeee-rice...sun-glasses...those damned Indians. Keeee-
rice...what next..."

When told, the producer kicked a chair after hurling a bottle into a
corner: for close to ten minutes he cursed Indians. But it was useless, the
245 scene had to be shot again.

Horses and Indians had to be recalled and reassembled for retakes for
which the good chief demanded $2.00 for his people. It took another week
before the wagon-train siege was filmed to the satisfaction of the producer

and his director. In the interim there were two days of rain, one filming
250 aborted by several Crows wearing watches, an extra filming of a prairie
fire ignited by Ken Maynard that miscarried because several Crow warriors, supposedly dead, moved to avoid getting burned during a critical
segment of the filming. When the first real epic of "Cowboys and Indians"
was finally done, the Crows were jubilant, indebted to their chief for the
255 prosperity and lasting renown that he exacted during difficult times. The
producer and director, cast and crew, departed in disquiet over having
exceeded their budget.

But whatever doubts the producer and the director might have entertained were more than vindicated by reviews of the film in which the
260 horsemanship of the Crow was acclaimed and the genius of the producer
for his vision and for his foresight in using Indians in motion pictures.

(1981)

# Immortality

## Kawabata Yasunari (Japan) 1899–1972

*(translated from Japanese by J. Martin Holman)*

## About the Author

*Kawabata Yasunari is one of Japan's most celebrated writers; in 1968 he became the first Japanese author to receive the Nobel Prize in literature. (Note that Kawabata is the family name. You may also see the name as Yasunari Kawabata.) Born in Osaka, Kawabata lost both parents in the first three years of his life and his sister, grandmother, and grandfather by the time he was 16. These deaths proved to be traumatic and led to what he called the "orphan's disposition" that marked his life and work. He received a degree in English literature from Tokyo Imperial University in 1920 and a degree in Japanese literature from the same university in 1924. He worked as a novelist, short story writer, literary critic, and translator until he committed suicide in 1972.*

*Kawabata's writings are known for their expressions of the traditional beauty and aesthetic values of Japan as well as for his intriguing and somewhat enigmatic characters. In addition to his prize-winning novels, he also created between 1921 and 1972 nearly 150 short stories that can "fit into the palm of one's hand" (known as "palm-of-the-hand" stories). These stories contain brief sketches of human experience portrayed with poetic intricacy and lyrical imagery and express the writer's favourite themes of loneliness, alienation, the meaninglessness and fleeting nature of human passion, aging, and death. These gemlike stories, such as "Immortality," catch readers' imagination and lead them through the labyrinth of life, death, confusion, misunderstanding, and eternal love.*

## Term Appearing in the Story

**hakama** loose trousers tied at the waist with a cord and worn with a kimono

An old man and a young girl were walking together.

There were a number of curious things about them. They nestled close together like lovers, as if they did not feel the sixty years' difference in their ages. The old man was hard of hearing. He could not understand most of
5 what the girl said. The girl wore maroon *hakama*° with a purple-and-white kimono in a fine arrow pattern. The sleeves were rather long. The old man was wearing clothes like those a girl would wear to pull weeds from a rice

field, except that he wore no leggings. His tight sleeves and trousers gathered at the ankles looked like a woman's. His clothes hung loose at his thin
10 waist.

They walked across a lawn. A tall wire net stood in front of them. The lovers did not seem to notice that they would run into it if they kept walking. They did not stop, but walked right through the net as a spring breeze might blow through it.

15 After they passed through, the girl noticed the net. "Oh." She looked at the man. "Shintarō, did you pass through the net, too?"

The old man did not hear, but he grabbed the wire net. "You bastard. You bastard," he said as he shook it. He pulled too hard, and in a moment, the huge net moved away from him. The old man staggered and fell
20 holding onto it.

"Watch out, Shintarō! What happened?" The girl put her arms around him and propped him up.

"Let go of the net...Oh, you've lost so much weight," the girl said.

The old man finally stood up. He heaved as he spoke. "Thank you." He
25 grasped the net again, but this time lightly, with only one hand. Then in the loud voice of a deaf person he said, "I used to have to pick up balls from behind a net day after day. For seventeen long years."

"Seventeen years is a long time?...It's short."

"They just hit the balls as they pleased. They made an awful sound
30 when they struck the wire net. Before I got used to it, I'd flinch. It's because of the sound of those balls that I became deaf."

It was a metal net to protect the ball boys at a golf driving range. There were wheels on the bottom so they could move forward and back and right and left. The driving range and golf course next to it were separated by
35 some trees. Originally it had been a grove of all kinds of trees, but they had been cut until only an irregular row remained.

The two walked on, the net behind them.

"What pleasant memories it brings back to hear the sound of the ocean." Wanting the old man to hear these words, the girl put her mouth
40 to his ear. "I can hear the sound of the ocean."

"What?" The old man closed his eyes. "Ah, Misako. It's your sweet breath. Just as it was long ago."

"Can't you hear the sound of the ocean? Doesn't it bring back fond memories?"

45 "The ocean...Did you say the ocean? Fond memories? How could the ocean, where you drowned yourself, bring back fond memories?"

"Well, it does. This is the first time I've been back to my hometown in fifty-five years. And you've come back here, too. This brings back memories." The old man could not hear, but she went on. "I'm glad I drowned myself. That way I can think about you forever, just as I was doing at the moment I drowned myself. Besides, the only memories and reminiscences I have are those up to the time I was eighteen. You are eternally young to me. And it's the same for you. If I hadn't drowned myself and you came to the village now to see me, I'd be an old woman. How disgusting. I wouldn't want you to see me like that."

The old man spoke. It was a deaf man's monologue. "I went to Tokyo and failed. And now, decrepit with age, I've returned to the village. There was a girl who grieved that we were forced to part. She had drowned herself in the ocean, so I asked for a job at a driving range overlooking the ocean. I begged them to give me the job...if only out of pity."

"This area where we are walking is the woods that belonged to your family."

"I couldn't do anything but pick up balls. I hurt my back from bending over all the time...But there was a girl who had killed herself for me. The rock cliffs were right beside me, so I could jump even if I were tottering. That's what I thought."

"No. You must keep living. If you were to die, there wouldn't be anyone on earth who would remember me. I would die completely." The girl clung to him. The old man could not hear, but he embraced her.

"That's it. Let's die together. This time...You came for me, didn't you."

"Together? But you must live. Live for my sake, Shintarō." She gasped as she looked over his shoulder. "Oh, those big trees are still there. All three...just like long ago." The girl pointed, so the old man turned his eyes toward the trees.

"The golfers are afraid of those trees. They keep telling us to cut them down. When they hit a ball, they say it curves to the right as though sucked in by the magic of those trees."

"Those golfers will die in due time—long before those trees. Those trees are already hundreds of years old. Those golfers talk that way, but they don't understand the life span of a man," the girl said.

"Those are trees my ancestors have looked after for hundreds of years, so I had the buyer promise not to cut the trees when I sold the land to him."

"Let's go." The girl tugged at the old man's hand. They tottered toward the great trees.

The girl passed easily through the tree trunk. The old man did the same.

"What?" The girl stared at the old man and marveled. "Are you dead too, Shintarō? Are you? When did you die?"

He did not answer.

90 "You *have* died...Haven't you? How strange I didn't meet you in the world of the dead. Well, try walking through the tree trunk once more to test whether you're dead or alive. If you are dead we can go inside the tree and stay."

They disappeared inside the tree. Neither the old man nor the young
95 girl appeared again.

The color of evening began to drift onto the small saplings behind the great trees. The sky beyond turned a faint red where the ocean sounded.

(1963)

# The Americanization of Shadrach Cohen

Bruno Lessing (U.S.A.) 1870–1940

## About the Author

*Bruno Lessing is the pseudonym for Rudolph Edgar Block, who is best remembered as an author of short stories about life in the ghetto on the East Side of New York at the end of the 19th and the beginning of the 20th century. Born in New York on December 6, 1870, he began to report for the* New York Sun *while attending City College of New York. Then he became Sunday editor for the* New York Recorder *and also a reporter for the* New York World. *After graduating from CCNY, he worked as a comics-supplements editor for the Hearst syndicate for 28 years. His first collection of stories,* Children of Men, *was published in 1903, and his second collection,* With the Best Intention, *appeared in 1914. He died in Arizona on April 29, 1940.*

*Bruno Lessing captures in his stories the pathos of hardships and the subtle humour found in everyday life in New York's Jewish community. His terse style is vaguely reminiscent of Chekhov's. Though mostly set against the background of Jewish life, Lessing's stories often deal with universal themes. "The Americanization of Shadrach Cohen," collected in* Children of Men, *exemplifies Lessing's emphasis on traditional values as well as his superb sense of irony in life. Both verbal irony and situational irony are effectively used to highlight the theme in this story.*

## Term Appearing in the Story

**Shadchen** a match maker

There is no set rule for the turning of the worm; most worms, however, turn unexpectedly. It was so with Shadrach Cohen.

He had two sons. One was named Abel and the other Gottlieb. They had left Russia five years before their father, had opened a store on Hester Street
5 with the money he had given them. For reasons that only business men would understand they conducted the store in their father's name—and, when the business began to prosper and they saw an opportunity of investing further capital in it to good advantage, they wrote to their dear father to come to this country.

10 "We have a nice home for you here," they wrote. "We will live happily together."

Shadrach came. With him he brought Marta, the serving-woman who had nursed his wife until she died, and whom, for his wife's sake, he had taken into the household. When the ship landed he was met by two
15 dapper-looking young men, each of whom wore a flaring necktie with a diamond in it. It took him some time to realize that these were his two sons. Abel and Gottlieb promptly threw their arms around his neck and welcomed him to the new land. Behind his head they looked at each other in dismay. In the course of five years they had forgotten that their father
20 wore a gaberdine—the loose, baglike garment of the Russian Ghetto—and had a long, straggling grey beard and ringlets that came down over his ears—that, in short, he was a perfect type of the immigrant whose appearance they had so frequently ridiculed. Abel and Gottlieb were proud of the fact that they had become Americanized. And they frowned at Marta.

25 "Come, father," they said. "Let us go to a barber, who will trim your beard and make you look more like an American. Then we will take you home with us."

Shadrach looked from one to the other in surprise.

"My beard?" he said; "what is the matter with my beard?"

30 "In this city," they explained to him, "no one wears a beard like yours except the newly landed Russian Jews."

Shadrach's lips shut tightly for a moment. Then he said:

"Then I will keep my beard as it is. I am a newly landed Russian Jew."

His sons clenched their fists behind their backs and smiled at him amiably.
35 After all, he held the purse-strings. It was best to humour him.

"What shall we do with Marta?" they asked. "We have a servant. We will not need two."

"Marta," said the old man, "stays with us. Let the other servant go. Come, take me home: I am getting hungry."

40 They took him home, where they had prepared a feast for him. When he bade Marta sit beside him at the table Abel and Gottlieb promptly turned and looked out of the window. They felt that they could not conceal their feelings. The feast was a dismal affair. Shadrach was racking his brains to find some explanation that would account for the change that
45 had come over his sons. They had never been demonstrative in their affection for him, and he had not looked for an effusive greeting. But he realized immediately that there was a wall between him and his sons; some change had occurred; he was distressed and puzzled. When the meal was over Shadrach donned his praying cap and began to recite the grace after
50 meals. Abel and Gottlieb looked at each other in consternation. Would they have to go through this at every meal? Better—far better—to risk their

father's displeasure and acquaint him with the truth at once. When it came to the response Shadrach looked inquiringly at his sons. It was Abel who explained the matter:

55  "We—er—have grown out of—er—that is—er—done away with—er— sort of fallen into the habit, don't you know, of leaving out the prayer at meals. It's not quite American!"

Shadrach looked from one to the other. Then, bowing his head, he went on with his prayer.

60  "My sons," he said, when the table had been cleared. "It is wrong to omit the prayer after meals. It is part of your religion. I do not know anything about this America or its customs. But religion is the worship of Jehovah, who has chosen us as His children on earth, and that same Jehovah rules supreme over America even as He does over the country that 65 you came from."

Gottlieb promptly changed the subject by explaining to him how badly they needed more money in their business. Shadrach listened patiently for a while, then said:

"I am tired after my long journey. I do not understand this business that 70 you are talking about. But you may have whatever money you need. After all, I have no one but you two." He looked at them fondly. Then his glance fell upon the serving-woman, and he added, quickly:

"And Marta."

"Thank God," said Gottlieb, when their father had retired, "he does not 75 intend to be stingy."

"Oh, he is all right," answered Abel. "After he gets used to things he will become Americanized like us."

To their chagrin, however, they began to realize, after a few months, that their father was clinging to the habits and customs of his old life with 80 a tenacity that filled them with despair. The more they urged him to abandon his ways the more eager he seemed to become to cling to them. He seemed to take no interest in their business affairs, but he responded, almost cheerfully, to all their requests for money. He began to feel that this, after all, was the only bond between him and his sons. And when they had 85 pocketed the money, they would shake their heads and sigh.

"Ah, father, if you would only not insist upon being so old-fashioned!" Abel would say.

"And let us fix you up a bit," Gottlieb would chime in.

"And become more progressive—like the other men of your age in this 90 country."

"And wear your beard shorter and trimmed differently."

"And learn to speak English."

Shadrach never lost his temper; never upbraided them. He would look from one to the other and keep his lips tightly pressed together. And when
95  they had gone he would look at Marta and would say:

"Tell me what you think, Marta. Tell me what you think."

"It is not proper for me to interfere between father and sons," Marta would say. And Shadrach could never induce her to tell him what she thought. But he could perceive a gleam in her eyes and observed a certain
100  nervous vigor in the way she cleaned the pots and pans for hours after these talks, that fell soothingly upon his perturbed spirit.

As we remarked before, there is no rule for the turning of the worm. Some worms, however, turn with a crash. It was so with Shadrach Cohen.

Gottlieb informed his father that he contemplated getting married.

105  "She is very beautiful," he said. "The affair is all in the hands of the Shadchen."°

His father's face lit up with pleasure.

"Gottlieb," he said, holding out his hand, "God bless you! It's the very best thing you could do. Marta, bring me my hat and coat. Come, Gottlieb.
110  Take me to see her. I cannot wait a moment. I want to see my future daughter-in-law at once. How happy your mother would be if she were alive to-day!"

Gottlieb turned red and hung back.

"I think, father," he said, "you had better not go just yet. Let us wait a
115  few days until the Shadchen has made all the arrangements. She is an American girl. She—she won't—er—understand your ways—don't you know? And it may spoil everything."

Crash! Marta had dropped an iron pot that she was cleaning. Shadrach was red in the face with suppressed rage.

120  "So!" he said. "It has come to this. You are ashamed of your father!" Then he turned to the old servant:

"Marta," he said, "to-morrow we become Americanized—you and I."

There was an intonation in his voice that alarmed his son.

"You are not angry—" he began, but with a fierce gesture his father cut
125  him short.

"Not another word. To bed! Go to bed at once."

Gottlieb was dumbfounded. With open mouth he stared at his father. He had not heard that tone since he was a little boy.

"But, father—" he began.

130    "Not a word. Do you hear me? Not a word will I listen to. In five minutes if you are not in bed you go out of this house. Remember, this is my house."

Then he turned to Abel. Abel was calmly smoking a cigar.

"Throw that cigar away," his father commanded, sternly.

Abel gasped and looked at his father in dismay.

135    "Marta, take that cigar out of his mouth and throw it into the fire. If he objects he goes out of the house."

With a smile of intense delight Marta plucked the cigar from Abel's unresisting lips, and incidentally trod heavily upon his toes. Shadrach gazed long and earnestly at his sons.

140    "To-morrow, my sons," he said, slowly, "you will begin to lead a new life."

In the morning Abel and Gottlieb, full of dread forebodings, left the house as hastily as they could. They wanted to get to the store to talk matters over. They had hardly entered the place, however, when the figure of their father loomed up in the doorway. He had never been in the place
145 before. He looked around him with great satisfaction at the many evidences of prosperity which the place presented. When he beheld the name "Shadrach Cohen, Proprietor" over the door he chuckled. Ere his sons had recovered from the shock of his appearance a pale-faced clerk, smoking a cigarette, approached Shadrach, and in a sharp tone asked:

150    "Well, sir, what do you want?" Shadrach looked at him with considerable curiosity. Was he Americanized, too? The young man frowned impatiently.

"Come, come! I can't stand here all day. Do you want anything?"

Shadrach smiled and turned to his sons.

"Send him away at once. I don't want that kind of young man in my
155 place." Then turning to the young man, upon whom the light of revelation had quickly dawned, he said, sternly:

"Young man, whenever you address a person who is older than you, do it respectfully. Honour your father and your mother. Now go away as fast as you can. I don't like you."

160    "But, father," interposed Gottlieb, "we must have someone to do his work."

"Dear me," said Shadrach, "is that so? Then, for the present, you will do it. And that young man over there—what does he do?"

"He is also a salesman."

165    "Let him go. Abel will take his place."

"But, father, who is to manage the store? Who will see that the work is properly done?"

"I will," said the father. "Now, let us have no more talking. Get to work."

Crestfallen, miserable, and crushed in spirit, Abel and Gottlieb began
170 their humble work while their father entered upon the task of familiarizing
himself with the details of the business. And even before the day's work
was done he came to his sons with a frown of intense disgust.

"Bah!" he exclaimed. "It is just as I expected. You have both been
making as complete a mess of this business as you could without ruining
175 it. What you both lack is sense. If becoming Americanized means
becoming stupid, I must congratulate you upon the thoroughness of your
work. To-morrow I shall hire a manager to run this store. He will arrange
your hours of work. He will also pay you what you are worth. Not a cent
more. How late have you been keeping this store open?"
180 "Until six o'clock," said Abel.

"H'm! Well, beginning to-day, you both will stay here until eight o'clock.
Then one of you can go. The other will stay until ten. You can take turns.
I will have Marta send you some supper."

To the amazement of Abel and Gottlieb the business of Shadrach Cohen
185 began to grow. Slowly it dawned upon them that in the mercantile realm
they were as children compared with their father. His was the true money-
maker spirit; there was something wonderful in the swiftness with which
he grasped the most intricate phases of trade; and where experience failed
him some instinct seemed to guide him aright. And gradually, as the busi-
190 ness of Shadrach Cohen increased, and even the sons saw vistas of prosperity beyond their wildest dreams, they began to look upon their father
with increasing respect. What they had refused to the integrity of his character, to the nobility of his heart, they promptly yielded to the shrewdness
of his brain. The sons of Shadrach Cohen became proud of their father. He,
195 too, was slowly undergoing a change. A new life was unfolding itself before
his eyes, he became broader-minded, more tolerant, and, above all, more
flexible in his tenets. Contact with the outer world had quickly impressed
him with the vast differences between his present surroundings and his old
life in Russia. The charm of American life, of liberty, of democracy,
200 appealed to him strongly. As the field of his business operations widened
he came more and more in contact with American business men, from
whom he learned many things—principally the faculty of adaptability.
And as his sons began to perceive that all these business men whom, in

former days, they had looked upon with feelings akin to reverence, seemed
to show to their father an amount of deference and respect which they had
never evinced toward the sons, their admiration for their father increased.

And yet it was the same Shadrach Cohen.

From that explosive moment when he had rebelled against his sons he
demanded from them implicit obedience and profound respect. Upon that
point he was stern and unyielding. Moreover, he insisted upon a strict
observance of every tenet of their religion. This, at first, was the bitterest
pill of all. But they soon became accustomed to it. When life is light and
free from care, religion is quick to fly; but when the sky grows dark and life
becomes earnest, and we feel its burden growing heavy upon our shoulders, then we welcome the consolation that religion brings, and we cling
to it. And Shadrach Cohen had taught his sons that life was earnest. They
were earning their bread by the sweat of their brow. No prisoner, with
chain and ball, was subjected to closer supervision by his keeper than were
Gottlieb and Abel.

"You have been living upon my charity," their father said to them: "I
will teach you how to earn your own living."

And he taught them. And with the lesson they learned many things;
learned the value of discipline, learned the beauty of filial reverence,
learned the severe joy of the earnest life.

One day Gottlieb said to his father:

"May I bring Miriam to supper to-night? I am anxious that you should
see her."

Shadrach turned his face away so that Gottlieb might not see the joy
that beamed in his eyes.

"Yes, my son," he answered. "I, too, am anxious to see if she is worthy
of you."

Miriam came, and in a stiff, embarrassed manner Gottlieb presented her
to his father. The girl looked in surprise at the venerable figure that stood
before her—a picture of a patriarch from the Pentateuch, with a long, straggling beard, and ringlets of hair falling over the ears, and clad in the long
gaberdine of the Russian Ghettos. And she saw a pair of grey eyes bent
keenly upon her—eyes of shrewdness, but soft and tender as a woman's—
the eyes of a strong man with a kind heart. Impulsively she ran toward him
and seized his hands. And, with a smile upon her lips, she said:

"Will you not give me your blessing?"

When the evening meal had ended, Shadrach donned his praying cap, and with bowed head intoned the grace after meals:

"We will bless Him from whose wealth we have eaten!" And in fervent tones rose from Gottlieb's lips the response:

245     "Blessed be He!"


(1903)

# Black Walls

## Liu Xinwu (China) 1942–

*(translated from Chinese by Alice Childs)*

## About the Author

*Liu Xinwu (Liu is the family name) is a renowned novelist and short story writer. Born in Sichuan, China in 1942, Liu graduated from a teacher's college in 1961. He taught Chinese in a middle school in Beijing until 1976, when he became an editor in a Beijing publishing house. He had tried his hand at writing stories at age 16, but did not become a full-time writer until his short stories "The Form Teacher" and "I Love Every Leaf in Green" won the first prize in the national short story competition successively in 1978 and 1979. Liu now lives with his family in Beijing.*

*"Black Walls," like most of Liu Xinwu's short stories, depicts ordinary city people in their urban environment. Written in 1982, the story is evidently set at a time not long after the end of the so-called "Great Proletarian Cultural Revolution," which ran from 1966 to 1977. Many references are made to events that took place in the decade-long political turmoil; for example, Mr. Zhao had been the deputy-in-charge of "the Workers' Propaganda Team" in a song and dance troupe ten years earlier, and his wife had been the head of a "socialist neighbourhood committee." More importantly, the twisted mentality fostered by the "Revolution," which senselessly advocated uniformity and condemned any form of individuality and originality, is fully exposed and exhibited in the story. In every sense, the "courtyard in an alley" where the story is set represents a literary microcosm of the narrow-minded and intrusive society that categorically stifles differences no matter how harmless they may seem. Thanks to Liu's adroit artistry and gentle humour, the story presents a **satire** that keeps the reader involved enough to enjoy the tale, yet detached enough to appreciate its moral.*

Summertime. Sunday.

A courtyard in an alley. Three fruit trees, five or six households.

Early morning. 7:30 a.m.

The room at the eastern end of the courtyard is the Zhous'. Actually there
5 is just one certain Mr Zhou, about thirty years old, who lives there on his own.
One might assume that he has never been married, though he uses a basin
with a large, red double happiness design. One might also assume that he
had been married and divorced but then why does he lower his head, study
the ground and walk off in the other direction when he sees an unmarried
10 woman in the courtyard? He only recently moved in and his work unit has a
long and complicated name so his neighbours have not been able to work out

exactly what he does for a living. By reckoning on their fingers they can work out that at his age, having been sent to the countryside for eight years, he can only have been working for about seven years at the most. Consequently, the
15 amount of money in his monthly wage packet is not interesting enough to keep them guessing for long. Since he moved in he has never caused any trouble. He never drops in on anyone, nor does he receive any guests. When he meets neighbours in the courtyard they may first ask him: 'How are you?' He will reply neither shyly nor arrogantly: 'I'm very well, thank you'; or he
20 may first ask the neighbour: 'Finished for the day?', and the neighbour will reply: 'Lord no! I'm just sitting in the cool breeze awhile'. But he will not stop and chat. Sometimes when he goes to the communal tap in the courtyard to fetch water, wash his clothes, or wash some rice and he bumps into a neighbour, of course they have to say something to each other. He only speaks
25 when forced to reply to a question. If he answers, he will not follow it with another question. The other families who have lived in the courtyard a long time cannot say that they like him, nor that they dislike him.

He was busy very early one morning. First he moved everything out of his room, then he mixed some sort of liquid in a large wash basin. He must
30 have borrowed a foot operated spray gun yesterday. Clearly, he was going to paint his room.

This began as nothing out of the ordinary. When the neighbours bumped into him at the communal tap, they asked him: 'Are you painting your room today?' 'Yes, yes I am.' Then they asked him politely, 'Do you
35 need some help?' He thanked them: 'I've got a spray gun so it should be an easy job! Thank you anyway.' After collecting the water he calmly walked away. A calling cicada was hiding in the umbrella-like crown of a scholar tree whose trunk was only as wide as the mouth of a bowl. The noise was getting louder, hut they had all grown accustomed to it and so
40 did not find it annoying anymore.

7:46 a.m.

'Chi — chi — chi...'

It was a new sound but it was clear what it was. Zhou had started spraying his room.
45 7:55 a.m.

Several of the young people from the courtyard had the day off and went out one by one. Naturally they were all dressed up in the latest fashions, each one different from the next. One girl, a meat cutter during the week, was wearing imitation jewel earrings and cream coloured high-
50 heels. As she left the courtyard, she opened a blue-flowered, nylon, automatic umbrella. There was also a young man who worked in the foundry's

workshop. On his upper half, he was wearing an Indiana State University T-shirt, printed in English. On his legs, he wore grey corduroy hunting trousers originally made for export. He put on a pair of large-framed,
55 purple sunglasses as he walked out, pushing a small-wheeled bicycle. A second girl hurried out of the courtyard. She studied business management at the local branch of the university. She was wearing a pale green dress, loose at the waist, which she had made herself, and was carrying a round, rattan hand-bag. The events which followed may have occurred because
60 they all went out, but it is hard to say if things would have been different if they had not done so, as there was still one young person who remained behind the entire time. This young man sold glassware in the local market and was enjoying a day off. After breakfast, he lay on his bed, reading *The Lamp Without Light.* When his mother called him to join in the following
65 events, he smiled, lay back down and continued to read his book.

8:15 a.m.

The atmosphere in the courtyard was heating up. It is not quite correct to say 'in the courtyard'; it would be better to say 'in the room'. It was not in every room, but it was in the north room in the middle of the courtyard.
70 That was where the Zhao family lived. Mr Zhao was fifty-six years old. He had retired early so his second daughter could take over his job. Soon after his retirement, he went to another work unit to 'fill in' for a time. Recently, that unit began making cutbacks, leaving Mr Zhao out of work. Currently, he was trying to arrange another job in a different work unit.

75 Several of the neighbours gathered at his house. They told Mr Zhao the news: Mr Zhou was not spraying his walls white but black! He was actually spraying his walls black! They did not know what kind of paint he was using but it was black as ink! Pitch black!

Mr Zhao was both astounded and strangely pleased at the same time.
80 Ten years before, he had been the deputy-in-charge of the Workers' Propaganda Team in a song and dance troupe. At that time when some 'activists' came to inform him about some 'new trends', his manner and tone were just as they were now. Mrs Zhao felt much as her husband did. Eight years before she had been the head of a 'socialist neighbourhood
85 committee'. Once when some people told her about the remains of a reactionary slogan written at the base of the wall behind the date tree, the atmosphere was much as it was now. Who could guess that something would happen to bring the dead issues of a decade or so ago back to life again?

90 'That's just not right,' Mr Zhao proclaimed.

'How dreadful,' said Mrs Zhao indignantly.

8:25 a.m.

'Ch — chi — chi...'

Mr Zhou was still spraying his room.

95 Newsflash: He had sprayed the ceiling black, too!

Mr Zhao asked them all to sit down, giving the room the feeling of a meeting hall. Meetings can take on all forms: at some, everyone is bored; at others, only you are interested; at still others, it is you who is bored. Mr Zhao enjoyed the present meeting. He put forward the motion: 'In this sort 100 of situation we should inform the police as soon as possible.'

If this were eight or ten years ago, this would not have been a mere proposal but a conclusive decision; not just a man giving his own opinion, but a leader's directive.

But, this was the present, not the past. Tall, thin Mr Qian went so far as 105 to immediately oppose him, saying 'As I see it, we shouldn't go to the authorities...that is, we have no basis. What can we tell the police?'

Mr and Mrs Zhao both stared hard at him. They were both thinking: Damn tailor! Years ago when he was an entrepreneur he never dared to open his mouth, much less oppose our suggestions, but now he does some 110 private business at home, buys a colour television and his whole tone of voice changes.

Mr Qian sat up straight and began fervently expressing his opinion: 'Brother Zhou may be suffering from a recurring illness. There are such diseases; I've read about them in the paper. Sufferers have been known to 115 behave strangely under stressful conditions...Young Zhou was airing his quilt outside his front door last Sunday. Perhaps no one noticed but the quilt cover was made of bright red silk while the underside was duller red. Really, very odd! So I say we should not go to the police but fetch a doctor instead. Although I have heard that traditional medicines don't work on 120 these kinds of illnesses, it would not hurt to consult him.'

Not many people responded to Mr Qian's words because as he talked they could not help gazing out of the window, through the shade of the scholar tree, to where they could see 'Brother Zhou'. Perfectly calm and collected, he continued to spray his walls. Faintly, they could hear him hum- 125 ming a song. Was this the manner of a sick person?

Mr Sun, who was sitting by the door, passed his little finger through his thinning hair and suggested: 'Shouldn't we just go and ask him why he is spraying his walls black? If he can't give a good reason, we can just forbid him—no, advise him not to—yes, advise him not to do it any more.'

130 Another neighbour, Mrs Li, who was sitting in the middle of the crowd, took the opportunity to say, 'Why don't you go and ask him for us.'

Everyone agreed to this suggestion.

8:36 a.m.

When Mr Sun made his suggestion he thought it would naturally be Mr
135 and Mrs Zhao who would confront Mr Zhou. He never imagined it would
be he who would be sent to ask. He regretted sitting by the door. For the
past thirty years, he had worked in a primary school in charge of general
affairs. He had not taught a class in his life. Consequently, he had picked
up many of the mannerisms of a teacher but, now faced with a situation
140 where he had to straighten his back and go to investigate a 'strange phenomenon', he felt as though he had been forced to the front of a podium
to deliver a speech. His hands and knees shook uncontrollably and he was
completely tongue tied.

8:37a.m.

145 'Chi — chi — chi...' The spraying continued.

'Bzzzzzzz...' Inside the room, they continued talking in hushed voices.

Mr Sun flicked the long nail of the little finger on his left hand and
stared at the tips of his shoes. He was not willing to go to question 'Brother
Zhou'. How could he ever face them again if he received a brash refusal?
150 How could he explain such a failure? What if the idiot said something
incriminating? Should he report it directly and be responsible for the
unknown consequences, or should he keep the information to himself and
risk being accused of protecting Mr Zhou? And what if some evidence
came to light in the future...

155 He gave it tremendous thought. Beads of sweat broke out on his forehead as he said, 'Maybe...maybe Mr Zhao could go and ask instead?'

As no one else wanted the job, everyone agreed and said in chorus, 'Yes!
Let Mr Zhao go!"

Mr Zhao did not make any immediate move, but waited for them to
160 stop urging and start pleading with him. Only then did he abruptly stand
up and declare, 'I'll go and ask!' He turned and left the room.

Everyone gazed out the window and watched the receding figure of Mr
Zhao walking straight towards Mr Zhou's front door. They all listened
attentively, hoping to catch a part of the conversation. All they could hear
165 was the incessant call of the cicadas, high in the scholar tree.

8:41 a.m.

Ashen-faced, Mr Zhao returned to the room and reported, 'That rascal
says he will come and explain to me when he has finished. I knew he
would pull some trick. He doesn't respect us, his neighbours.'
170 Mrs Zhao pointed out of the window and said, 'That's the man come to
read the water meter, isn't it? He'll go and look in Mr Zhou's room! He'll

probably spread all kinds of rumours about black paint and our courtyard, and give us all a bad name!'

Mrs Li, whose job was fluffing cotton into quilts, had a very placid nature and so put forward an explanation to make them all feel better, 'Perhaps the black paint is just the undercoat. When it's dry he'll spray a top coat of white paint.'

8:43 a.m.

'Chi — chi — chi...' The noise from the spray gun continued. Looking towards the room all they could see was blackness. No one really believed Mrs Li's explanation. The more Mrs Li looked, the more she could not help despairing.

What could one say? Black walls! In this very courtyard! Mr Zhou is not afraid of doing evil things himself, but he should not get others involved.

8:45 a.m.

Everyone in the room agreed about one thing: he should not spray his walls black! How could anyone spray his walls and ceiling black? Most people would not dare even think of such a thing. He did not just think about it, he actually did it! Extraordinary! Weird! Half-mad! Reactionary!

Mr Zhao still thought the police should be informed. Just as he was about to go and do so, he had second thoughts: The police station is not the same as it was eight or ten years ago (at that time there was not a police station but a 'group to smash the leaders of the judicial and public security institutions'. It was in the same courtyard as the present-day police station). Today the police are not as extreme nor do they think themselves as important as in the past. They always talk about 'going by the book' but once you start doing things 'by the book' then problems like the black wall dilemma will drag on and possibly never be resolved. Mr Zhao hesitated. He felt strongly about it and really did want to report it. It was a responsibility he could not shirk, a duty he had to take quick action to deal with. Could he be doing it for his own good? But what possible benefit could come of reporting it?

Mrs Zhao realized what her husband must be feeling and felt very bitter. How different it was eight or ten years ago! Her husband was actually suffering now because he lacked any real skills, and could only work as an assistant or warehouse watchman. Was it because he had not tried to learn a trade? Certainly not. For the past thirty odd years he had been transferred to work in various campaigns. The campaigns had come and gone, so now he had no way of earning a living. Formerly all his pride had come from his political sensitivity. Now he had a chance to display this talent, but his eyes, wrinkled face and the corners of his mouth showed hesitancy. Why was it? What was all this exertion for today? Could it be just for the good of his own family?

More and more, Mr Zhao believed that 'Brother Zhou' was suffering
215 from a recurring illness. He admitted that what he had just been thinking was wrong. Traditional doctors were unable to treat this sort of illness. Could he not just let the doctor take his pulse? Not really. He would still have to get a Western doctor. But doctors didn't make house calls nowadays. It would be extremely difficult. Who could persuade him to go to the
220 out-patients department?

Mrs Li wanted to go home and get her lump of a son to stop reading his novels and think of what to do. Perhaps he could bring Mr Zhou to his senses, and even help spray the walls white again. White is so nice! Why should anyone want anything different?

225 Mr Sun wanted to go home but was too embarrassed to make the move. In this sort of situation a person ought to make clear his position on the matter, so in the future he could not be accused of 'sitting on the fence'. Of course a person should not leave it so that in any future situation he could not be accused of having played a part in a 'misjudged case'. Ideally one
230 would avoid any sort of criticism in the past, present or future. He had already shown enough 'intention' to go to Mr Zhou's, so he should now make an early retreat. But it would be hard to slip out without being noticed...

8:48 a.m.

235 Mr Zhao had a grandson affectionately known as 'Little Button' who was not much more than ten years old. At the start of all this he had been painting in the back room. At length, he came and leaned on the doorway between the two rooms, curiously listening to the adults' discussion. He thought the room crowded, muggy, hot and disordered. Why did adults
240 have to torment themselves like this?

Once again they began to discuss the matter and once again the atmos-phere heated up. Little Button stood before his grandfather, turned his head and asked: 'Grandpa, what are you all doing?'

Mr Zhao said to him firmly, 'Off with you! Go and play! There's nothing
245 for you here!'

Little Button was not convinced and thought to himself: Are you angry with Uncle Zhou for spraying his walls? Uncle Zhou is a very nice man. He's such fun. Once he called me to his room. He took some pieces of card from a drawer. The pieces were of every colour under the sun and were as big as the *Evening News*. He kept changing them and pressed them up to my eyes so that all I could see was that colour. Then he asked: 'Do you like it or not? Does it feel hot or cold? Dry or wet? Pleasant or nasty to smell? Does it make you want to go to sleep or go out and play? What does it make you think of? Or does it make you think nothing at all? Does it make you feel frightened or calm? Does it make you thirsty or not? Do you want to go on looking at it or not? He jotted down every reply that I made. See how much fun he is! If you don't believe me, go over to his place and see for yourselves!'

Little Button thought this far, then raised his head and said loudly, 'Grandpa, you still haven't finished your discussion. You must be awfully tired. Can I say something now?'

There was nothing for it but for everyone to stop talking. They all looked at him.

Mr Zhao waved his hands as if he had been wronged and said, 'Right, right! Go ahead!'

Little Button asked: 'When Uncle Zhou has finished his room, will he go from door to door spraying everyone else's rooms as well?'

8:49 a.m.

Everyone went blank.

8:50 a.m.

Mr Zhao blurted out: 'I'm sure he'd dare!' Mrs Zhao echoed, 'He'll try! Mrs Li and Mr Sun said at once, 'He wouldn't, he'd never...' Mr Qian thought carefully before saying, 'He doesn't look like a troublemaker. His illness only seems to recur in his own home...'

8:51.30 a.m.

Little Button turned round, blinked his round, black eyes, blacker even than the walls, shining black. He smiled innocently and said in a shrill voice: 'So that's settled! Uncle Zhou is spraying the walls of his own room, and it has nothing to do with us, so what are you all going on about?'

8:52 a.m.

Everyone went silent.

The 'chi — chi — chi...' of the wall spraying drifted over, mingling with the sound of the cicadas, becoming even more pronounced.

(1982)

# The New Year's Sacrifice

## Lu Xun (China) 1881–1936

*(translated from Chinese by Gladys Yang and Yang Xianyi)*

## About the Author

*Lu Xun (also spelt as Lu Hsun), pseudonym of Zhou Shuren, is regarded as the father of modern Chinese literature. His first story, "A Madman's Diary" (1918), was considered the first story written in modern Chinese. Born into an impoverished but educated family of the gentry in Shaoxing, China in 1881, he received a traditional education before attending Jiangnan Naval Academy in 1898 and the School of Railway and Mines in 1899 in Nanjing. In 1902, he went to Japan where he studied the Japanese language and then medicine at Sendai Provincial Medical School. In 1906 he dropped out before graduation to devote himself entirely to writing. He returned to China in 1909. He worked as a school teacher (1910–11), a civil servant in the Ministry of Education in Beijing (1912–26), and a university professor at different Chinese universities (1920–27). A founding member of several leftist organizations such as the League of Left-wing Writers, Lu Xun was a leading advocate for intellectual and artistic freedom and civil rights in China. He died of tuberculosis on October 19, 1936.*

*Lu Xun wrote a large number of essays on various topics, ranging from literature, philosophy, and ethics to politics and international affairs. These essays, together with his stories, were collected and published in 20 volumes in 1938, two years after his death. His stories were published in three collections, respectively entitled* Call to Arms *(1923),* Wandering *(1926), and* Old Tales Retold *(1935). Written in clear and cogent language, Lu Xun's stories are imbued with his sympathy for the oppressed and the exploited as well as his indignation against what he called the "man-eating-man" social system. Taken from* Wandering, *"The New Year's Sacrifice," written in 1924, depicts the miserable life and death of a village woman who falls prey to the inhuman feudalistic system. Named after her first husband, Hsiang Liu's wife is never allowed to have her own identity. Naturally she becomes useless when the men in her life, her two husbands and her son, have left the world. The narration is filled with detailed observations, and the unique narrative tone is especially noteworthy.*

## Terms Appearing in the Story

**old calendar** the Chinese lunar calendar
**imperial college** the highest institute of learning in the Ching dynasty

**Kang Yu-wei** a famous reformer who lived from 1858 to 1927 and advocated constitutional monarchy
**Chen Tuan** a hermit at the beginning of the 10th century
***Kang Hsi's Dictionary*** a Chinese dictionary compiled under the auspices of Emperor Kang Hsi, who reigned from 1662 to 1722
***Commentaries on the Four Books*** Confucian classics
**"Ghosts and spirits are properties of Nature"** a Confucian saying
**ten years younger than she** in old China it used to be common in country districts for young women to be married to boys of ten or eleven. The bride's labour could then be exploited by her husband's family.
**money for his wedding** in old China, because of the labour value of the peasant woman, the man's family virtually bought the wife
**two this New Year** it was the custom in China to reckon a child as one year old at birth, and to add another year to his age at New Year

New Year's Eve of the old calendar° seems after all more like the real New Year's Eve; for, to say nothing of the villages and towns, even in the air there is a feeling that New Year is coming. From the pale, lowering evening clouds issue frequent flashes of lightning, followed by a rumbling
5 sound of firecrackers celebrating the departure of the Hearth God; while, nearer by, the firecrackers explode even more violently, and before the deafening report dies away the air is filled with a faint smell of powder. It was on such a night that I returned to Luchen, my native place. Although I call it my native place, I had had no home there for some time, so I had
10 to put up temporarily with a certain Mr. Lu, the fourth son of his family. He is a member of our clan, and belongs to the generation before mine, so I ought to call him "Fourth Uncle." An old student of the imperial college° who went in for Neo-Confucianism, I found him very little changed in any way, simply slightly older, but without any moustache as yet. When we
15 met, after exchanging a few polite remarks he said I was fatter, and after saying that immediately started a violent attack on the revolutionaries. I knew this was not meant personally, because the object of the attack was still Kang Yu-wei.° Nevertheless, conversation proved difficult, so that in a short time I found myself alone in the study.
20 The next day I got up very late, and after lunch went out to see some relatives and friends. The day after I did the same. None of them was greatly changed, simply slightly older; but every family was busy preparing for "the sacrifice." This is the great end-of-year ceremony in

Luchen, when people reverently welcome the God of Fortune and solicit
25 good fortune for the coming year. They kill chickens and geese and buy
pork, scouring and scrubbing until all the women's arms turn red in the
water. Some of them still wear twisted silver bracelets. After the meat is
cooked some chopsticks are thrust into it at random, and this is called the
"offering." It is set out at dawn when incense and candles are lit, and they
30 reverently invite the God of Fortune to come and partake of the offering.
Only men can be worshippers, and after the sacrifice they naturally continue to let off firecrackers as before. This happens every year, in every
family, provided they can afford to buy the offering and firecrackers; and
this year they naturally followed the old custom.

35     The day grew overcast. In the afternoon it actually started to snow, the
biggest snow-flakes as large as plum blossom petals fluttered about the sky;
and this, combined with the smoke and air of activity, made Luchen appear
in a ferment. When I returned to my uncle's study the roof of the house was
already white with snow. The room also appeared brighter, the great red
40 rubbing hanging on the wall showing up very clearly the character for
Longevity written by the Taoist saint Chen Tuan.° One of a pair of scrolls
had fallen down and was lying loosely rolled up on the long table, but the
other was still hanging there, bearing the words: "By understanding reason
we achieve tranquillity of mind." Idly, I went to turn over the books on the
45 table beneath the window, but all I could find was a pile of what looked like
an incomplete set of *Kang Hsi's Dictionary,*° a volume of Chiang Yung's *Notes
to Chu Hsi's Philosophical Writings* and a volume of *Commentaries on the Four
Books.*° At all events, I made up my mind to leave the next day.

Besides, the very thought of my meeting with Hsiang Lin's Wife the day
50 before made me uncomfortable. It happened in the afternoon. I had been
visiting a friend in the eastern part of the town. As I came out I met her by
the river, and seeing the way she fastened her eyes on me I knew very well
she meant to speak to me. Of all the people I had seen this time at Luchen
none had changed as much as she: her hair, which had been streaked with
55 white five years before, was now completely white, quite unlike someone
in her forties. Her face was fearfully thin and dark in its sallowness, and
had moreover lost its former expression of sadness, looking as if carved out
of wood. Only an occasional flicker of her eyes showed she was still a living
creature. In one hand she carried a wicker basket, in which was a broken
60 bowl, empty; in the other she held a bamboo pole longer than herself, split
at the bottom: it was clear she had become a beggar.

I stood still, waiting for her to come and ask for money.

"You have come back?" she asked me first.

"Yes."

65 "That is very good. You are a scholar, and have travelled too and seen a lot. I just want to ask you something." Her lustreless eyes suddenly gleamed.

I never guessed she would talk to me like this. I stood there taken by surprise.

70 "It is this." She drew two paces nearer, and whispered very confidentially: "After a person dies, does he turn into a ghost or not?"

As she fixed her eyes on me I was seized with foreboding. A shiver ran down my spine and I felt more nervous than during an unexpected examination at school, when unfortunately the teacher stands by one's side.

75 Personally, I had never given the least thought to the question of the existence of spirits. In this emergency how should I answer her? Hesitating for a moment, I reflected: "It is the tradition here to believe in spirits, yet she seems to be sceptical — perhaps it would be better to say she hopes: hopes that there is immortality and yet hopes that there is not. Why increase the

80 sufferings of the wretched? To give her something to look forward to, it would be better to say there is.

"There may be, I think," I told her hesitantly.

"Then, there must also be a Hell?"

"What, Hell?" Greatly startled, I could only try to evade the question.

85 "Hell? According to reason there should be one too — but not necessarily. Who cares about it anyway?..."

"Then will all the people of one family who have died see each other again?"

"Well, as to whether they will see each other again or not...." I realized

90 now that I was a complete fool; for all my hesitation and reflection I had been unable to answer her three questions. Immediately I lost confidence and wanted to say the exact opposite of what I had previously said. "In this case...as a matter of fact, I am not sure....Actually, regarding the question of ghosts, I am not sure either."

95 In order to avoid further importunate questions, I walked off, and beat a hasty retreat to my uncle's house, feeling exceedingly uncomfortable. I thought to myself: "I am afraid my answer will prove dangerous to her. Probably it is just that when other people are celebrating she feels lonely by herself, but could there be another reason? Could she have had some pre-

100 monition? If there is another reason, and as a result something happens, then, through my answer, I shall be held responsible to a certain extent." Finally, however, I ended by laughing at myself, thinking that such a chance

meeting could have no great significance, and yet I was taking it so to heart; no wonder certain educationalists called me a neurotic. Moreover I had dis- 105 tinctly said, "I am not sure," contradicting my previous answer; so that even if anything did happen, it would have nothing at all to do with me.

"I am not sure" is a most useful phrase.

Inexperienced and rash young men often take it upon themselves to solve people's problems for them or choose doctors for them, and if by any 110 chance things turn out badly, they are probably held to blame; but by simply concluding with this phrase "I am not sure," one can free oneself of all responsibility. At this time I felt even more strongly the necessity for such a phrase, since even in speaking with a beggar woman there was no dispensing with it.

115 However, I continued to feel uncomfortable, and even after a night's rest my mind kept running on this, as if I had a premonition of some untoward development. In that oppressive snowy weather, in the gloomy study, this discomfort increased. It would be better to leave: I should go back to town the next day. The boiled shark's fins in the Fu Hsing Restaurant used to cost 120 a dollar for a large portion, and I wondered if this cheap and delicious dish had increased in price or not. Although the friends who had accompanied me in the old days had scattered, even if I was alone the shark's fins still had to be tasted. At all events, I made up my mind to leave the next day.

After experiencing many times that things which I hoped would not 125 happen and felt should not happen invariably did happen, I was desperately afraid this would prove another such case. And, indeed, strange things did begin to happen. Towards evening I heard talking — it sounded like a discussion — in the inner room; but soon the conversation ended, and all I heard was my uncle saying loudly as he walked out: "Not earlier 130 nor later, but just at this time — sure sign of a bad character!"

At first I felt astonished, then very uncomfortable, thinking these words must refer to me. I looked outside the door, but no one was there. I contained myself with difficulty till their servant came in before dinner to brew a pot of tea, when at last I had a chance to make some enquiries.

135 "With whom was Mr. Lu angry just now?" I asked

"Why, still with Hsiang Lin's Wife," he replied briefly.

"Hsiang Lin's Wife? How was that?" I asked again.

"She's dead."

"Dead?" My heart suddenly missed a beat. I started, and probably 140 changed colour too. But since he did not raise his head, he was probably quite unaware of how I felt. Then I controlled myself, and asked:

"When did she die?"

"When? Last night, or else today, I'm not sure."

"How did she die?"

145    "How did she die? Why, of poverty of course." He answered placidly and, still without having raised his head to look at me, went out.

However, my agitation was only short-lived, for now that something I had felt imminent had already taken place, I no longer had to take refuge in my "I'm not sure," or the servant's expression "dying of poverty" for com-
150 fort. My heart already felt lighter. Only from time to time something still seemed to weigh on it. Dinner was served, and my uncle solemnly accompanied me. I wanted to ask about Hsiang Lin's Wife, but knew that although he had read, "Ghosts and spirits are properties of Nature,"° he had retained many superstitions, and on the eve of this sacrifice it was out of the question
155 to mention anything like death or illness. In case of necessity one could use veiled allusions, but unfortunately I did not know how to, so although questions kept rising to the tip of my tongue, I had to bite them back. From his solemn expression I suddenly suspected that he looked on me as choosing not earlier nor later but just this time to come and trouble him, and that I
160 was also a bad character; therefore to set his mind at rest I told him at once that I intended to leave Luchen the next day and go back to the city. He did not press me greatly to stay. So we quietly finished the meal.

In winter the days are short and, now that it was snowing, darkness already enveloped the whole town. Everybody was busy beneath the lamp-
165 light, but outside the windows it was very quiet. Snow-flakes fell on the thickly piled snow, as if they were whispering, making me feel even more lonely. I sat by myself under the yellow gleam of the vegetable oil lamp and thought, "This poor woman, abandoned by people in the dust as a tiresome and worn-out toy, once left her own imprint in the dust, and those who
170 enjoy life must have wondered at her for wishing to prolong her existence; but now at least she has been swept clear by eternity. Whether spirits exist or not I do not know; but in the present world when a meaningless existence ends, so that someone whom others are tired of seeing is no longer seen, it is just as well, both for the individual concerned and for others." I
175 listened quietly to see if I could hear the snow falling outside the window, still pursuing this train of thought, until gradually I felt less ill at ease.

Fragments of her life, seen or heard before, now combined to form one whole.

She did not belong to Luchen. One year at the beginning of winter, when
180 my uncle's family wanted to change their maidservant, Old Mrs. Wei brought her in and introduced her. Her hair was tied with white bands, she

wore a black skirt, blue jacket and pale green bodice, and was about twenty-six, with a pale skin but rosy cheeks. Old Mrs. Wei called her Hsiang Lin's Wife, and said that she was a neighbour of her mother's
185 family, and because her husband was dead she wanted to go out to work. My uncle knitted his brows and my aunt immediately understood that he disapproved of her because she was a widow. She looked very suitable, though, with big strong feet and hands, and a meek expression; and she had said nothing but showed every sign of being tractable and hard-
190 working. So my aunt paid no attention to my uncle's frown, but kept her. During the period of probation she worked from morning till night, as if she found resting dull, and she was so strong that she could do a man's work; accordingly on the third day it was settled, and each month she was to be paid five hundred cash.

195  Everybody called her Hsiang Lin's Wife. They did not ask her her own name; but since she was introduced by someone from Wei Village who said she was a neighbour, presumably her name was also Wei. She was not very talkative, only answering when other people spoke to her, and her answers were brief. It was not until a dozen days or so had passed that they learned
200 little by little that she still had a severe mother-in-law at home and a younger brother-in-law more than ten years old, who could cut wood. Her husband, who had been a woodcutter too, had died in the spring. He had been ten years younger than she.° This little was all that people learned from her.

205  The days passed quickly. She worked as hard as ever; she would eat anything, and did not spare herself.

Everybody agreed that the Lu family had found a very good maidservant, who really got through more work than a hard-working man. At the end of the year she swept, mopped, killed chickens and geese and sat up
210 to boil the sacrificial meat, single-handed, so the family did not have to hire extra help. Nevertheless she, on her side, was satisfied; gradually the trace of a smile appeared at the corner of her mouth. She became plumper and her skin whiter.

New Year was scarcely over when she came back from washing rice by
215 the river looking pale, and said that in the distance she had just seen a man wandering on the opposite bank who looked very like her husband's cousin, and probably he had come to look for her. My aunt, much alarmed, made detailed enquiries, but failed to get any further information. As soon as my uncle learned of it he frowned and said, "This is bad.
220 She must have run away from her husband's family."

Before long this inference that she had run away was confirmed.

About a fortnight later, just as everybody was beginning to forget what had happened, Old Mrs. Wei suddenly called, bringing with her a woman in her thirties who, she said, was the maidservant's mother-in-law.
225 Although the woman looked like a villager, she behaved with great self-possession and had a ready tongue in her head. After the usual polite remarks she apologized for coming to take her daughter-in-law home, saying there was a great deal to be done at the beginning of spring, and since there were only old people and children at home they were short-
230 handed.

"Since it is her mother-in-law who wants her to go back, what is there to be said?" was my uncle's comment.

Thereupon her wages were reckoned up. They amounted to one thousand seven hundred and fifty cash, all of which she had left with her mis-
235 tress without using a single coin. My aunt gave the entire amount to her mother-in-law. The latter also took her clothes, thanked Mr. and Mrs. Lu and went out. By this time it was already noon.

"Oh, the rice! Didn't Hsiang Lin's Wife go to wash the rice?" my aunt exclaimed some time later. Probably she was rather hungry, so that she
240 remembered lunch.

Thereupon everybody set about looking for the rice basket. My aunt went first to the kitchen, then to the hall, then to the bedroom; but not a trace of it was to be seen anywhere. My uncle went outside, but could not find it either; only when he went right down to the riverside did he see it, set down
245 fair and square on the bank, with a bundle of vegetables beside it.

Some people there told him that a boat with a white awning had moored there in the morning, but since the awning covered the boat completely they did not know who was inside, and before this incident no one had paid any attention to it. But when Hsiang Lin's Wife came to wash
250 rice, two men looking like country people jumped off the boat just as she was kneeling down and seizing hold of her carried her on board. After several shouts and cries, Hsiang Lin's Wife became silent: they had probably stopped her mouth. Then two women walked up, one of them a stranger and the other Old Mrs. Wei. When the people who told this story tried to
255 peep into the boat they could not see very clearly, but Hsiang Lin's Wife seemed to be lying bound on the floor of the boat.

"Disgraceful! Still..." said my uncle.

That day my aunt cooked the midday meal herself, and my cousin Ah Niu lit the fire.

260 After lunch Old Mrs. Wei came again.

"Disgraceful!" said my uncle.

"What is the meaning of this? How dare you come here again!" My aunt, who was washing dishes, started scolding as soon as she saw her. "You recommended yourself, and then plotted to have her carried off, causing all this stir. What will people think? Are you trying to make a laughing-stock of our family?"

"Aiya, I was really taken in! Now I have come specially to clear up this business. When she asked me to find her work, how was I to know that she had left home without her mother-in-law's consent? I am very sorry, Mr. Lu, Mrs. Lu. Because I am so old and foolish and careless, I have offended my patrons. However, it is lucky for me that your family is always so generous and kind, and unwilling to be hard on your inferiors. This time I promise to find you someone good to make up for my mistake."

"Still..." said my uncle.

Thereupon the business of Hsiang Lin's Wife was concluded, and before long it was also forgotten.

Only my aunt, because the maidservants taken on afterwards were all lazy or fond of stealing food, or else both lazy and fond of stealing food, with not a good one in the lot, still often spoke of Hsiang Lin's Wife. On such occasions she would always say to herself, "I wonder what has become of her now?" meaning that she would like to have her back. But by the following New Year she too gave up hope.

The New Year's holiday was nearly over when Old Mrs. Wei, already half tipsy, came to pay her respects, and said it was because she had been back to Wei Village to visit her mother's family and stayed a few days that she had come late. During the course of conversation they naturally came to speak of Hsiang Lin's Wife.

"She?" said Mrs. Wei cheerfully. "She is in luck now. When her mother-in-law dragged her home, she had already promised her to the sixth son of the Ho family in Ho Village. Not long after she reached home they put her in the bridal chair and sent her off."

"Aiya! What a mother-in-law!" exclaimed my aunt in amazement.

"Ah, madam, you really talk like a great lady! We country folk, poor women, think nothing of that. She still had a younger brother-in-law who had to be married. And if they hadn't found her a husband, where would they have found the money for his wedding?° But her mother-in-law is a clever and capable woman, who knows how to drive a good bargain, so she married her off into the mountains. If she had married her to someone in the same village, she wouldn't have got so much money; but since very

300 few women are willing to marry someone living deep in the mountains, she got eighty thousand cash. Now the second son is married, the presents only cost her fifty thousand, and after paying the wedding expenses she still has over ten thousand left. Just think, doesn't this show she knows how to drive a good bargain?..."

305 "But was Hsiang Lin's Wife willing?"

"It wasn't a question of being willing or not. Of course anyone would have protested. They just tied her up with a rope, stuffed her into the bridal chair, carried her to the man's house, put on the bridal headdress, performed the ceremony in the hall and locked them in their room; and that 310 was that. But Hsiang Lin's Wife is quite a character. I heard she really put up a great struggle, and everybody said she was different from other people because she had worked in a scholar's family. We go-betweens, madam, see a great deal. When widows remarry, some cry and shout, some threaten to commit suicide, some when they have been carried to the 315 man's house won't go through the ceremony, and some even smash the wedding candlesticks. But Hsiang Lin's Wife was different from the rest. They said she shouted and cursed all the way, so that by the time they had carried her to Ho Village she was completely hoarse. When they dragged her out of the chair, although the two chair-bearers and her young 320 brother-in-law used all their strength, they couldn't force her to go through the ceremony. The moment they were careless enough to loosen their grip — gracious Buddha! — she threw herself against a corner of the table and knocked a big hole in her head. The blood poured out; and although they used two handfuls of incense ashes and bandaged her with two pieces of 325 red cloth, they still couldn't stop the bleeding. Finally it took all of them together to get her shut up with her husband in the bridal chamber, where she went on cursing. Oh, it was really dreadful!" She shook her head, cast down her eyes and said no more.

"And after that what happened?" asked my aunt.

330 "They said the next day she still didn't get up," said Old Mrs. Wei, raising her eyes.

"And after?"

"After? She got up. At the end of the year she had a baby, a boy, who was two this New Year.° These few days when I was at home some people 335 went to Ho Village, and when they came back they said they had seen her and her son, and that both mother and baby are fat. There is no mother-in-law over her, the man is a strong fellow who can earn a living, and the house is their own. Well, well, she is really in luck."

After this even my aunt gave up talking of Hsiang Lin's Wife.

340     But one autumn, two New Years after they heard how lucky Hsiang Lin's Wife had been, she actually reappeared on the threshold of my uncle's house. On the table she placed a round bulb-shaped basket, and under the eaves a small roll of bedding. Her hair was still wrapped in white bands, and she wore a black skirt, blue jacket and pale green bodice. But her skin
345  was sallow and her cheeks had lost their colour; she kept her eyes downcast, and her eyes, with their tear-stained rims, were no longer bright. Just as before, it was Old Mrs. Wei, looking very benevolent, who brought her in, and who explained at length to my aunt:

      "It was really a bolt from the blue. Her husband was so strong, nobody
350  could have guessed that a young fellow like that would die of typhoid fever. First he seemed better, but then he ate a bowl of cold rice and the sickness came back. Luckily she had the boy, and she can work, whether it is chopping wood, picking tea-leaves or raising silkworms; so at first she was able to carry on. Then who could believe that the child, too, would be
355  carried off by a wolf? Although it was nearly the end of spring, still wolves came to the village — how could anyone have guessed that? Now she is all on her own. Her brother-in-law came to take the house, and turned her out; so she has really no way open to her but to come and ask help from her former mistress. Luckily this time there is nobody to stop her, and you
360  happen to be wanting a new servant, so I have brought her here. I think someone who is used to your ways is much better than a new hand...

      "I was really stupid, really..." Hsiang Lin's Wife raised her listless eyes to say. "I only knew that when it snows the wild beasts in the glen have nothing to eat and may come to the villages; I didn't know that in spring
365  they came too. I got up at dawn and opened the door, filled a small basket with beans and called our Ah Mao to go and sit on the threshold and shell the beans. He was very obedient and always did as I told him: he went out. Then I chopped wood at the back of the house and washed the rice, and when the rice was in the pan and I wanted to boil the beans I called Ah
370  Mao, but there was no answer; and when I went out to look, all I could see was beans scattered on the ground, but no Ah Mao. He never went to other families to play; and in fact at each place where I went to ask, there was no sign of him. I became desperate, and begged people to go to look for him. Only in the afternoon, after looking everywhere else, did they go to
375  look in the glen and see one of his little shoes caught on a bramble. 'That's bad,' they said, 'he must have met a wolf.' And sure enough when they went further in there he was, lying in the wolf's lair, with all his entrails eaten away, his hand still tightly clutching that little basket...." At this point she started crying, and was unable to complete the sentence.

380     My aunt had been undecided at first, but by the end of this story the rims of her eyes were rather red. After thinking for a moment she told her to take the round basket and bedding into the servants' quarters. Old Mrs. Wei heaved a long sigh as if relieved of a great burden. Hsiang Lin's Wife looked a little more at ease than when she first came and, without having

385 to be told the way, quietly took away her bedding. From this time on she worked again as a maidservant in Luchen.

    Everybody still called her Hsiang Lin's Wife.

    However, she had changed a great deal. She had not been there more than three days before her master and mistress realized that she was not

390 as quick as before. Since her memory was much worse, and her impassive face never showed the least trace of a smile, my aunt already expressed herself very far from satisfied. When the woman first arrived, although my uncle frowned as before, because they invariably had such difficulty in finding servants he did not object very strongly, only secretly warned my

395 aunt that while such people may seem very pitiful they exert a bad moral influence. Thus although it would be all right for her to do ordinary work she must not join in the preparations for sacrifice; they would have to prepare all the dishes themselves, for otherwise they would be unclean and the ancestors would not accept them.

400     The most important event in my uncle's household was the ancestral sacrifice, and formerly this had been the busiest time for Hsiang Lin's Wife; but now she had very little to do. When the table was placed in the centre of the hall and the curtain fastened, she still remembered how to set out the winecups and chopsticks in the old way.

405     "Hsiang Lin's Wife, put those down!" said my aunt hastily. "I'll do it!"

    She sheepishly withdrew her hand and went to get the candlesticks.

    "Hsiang Lin's Wife, put those down!" cried my aunt hastily again. "I'll fetch them."

    After walking round several times without finding anything to do,

410 Hsiang Lin's Wife could only go hesitantly away. All she did that day was to sit by the stove and feed the fire.

    The people in the town still called her Hsiang Lin's Wife, but in a different tone from before; and although they talked to her still, their manner was colder. She did not mind this in the least, only, looking straight in front

415 of her, she would tell everybody her story, which night or day was never out of her mind.

    "I was really stupid, really," she would say. "I only knew that when it snows the wild beasts in the glen have nothing to eat and may come to the villages; I didn't know that in spring they came too. I got up at dawn and

420 opened the door, filled a small basket with beans and called our Ah Mao to
go and sit on the threshold and shell them. He was very obedient and always
did as I told him: he went out. Then I chopped wood at the back of the house
and washed the rice, and when the rice was in the pan and I wanted to boil
the beans I called Ah Mao, but there was no answer; and when I went out to
425 look, all I could see was beans scattered on the ground, but no Ah Mao. He
never went to other families to play; and in fact at each place where I went
to ask, there was no sign of him. I became desperate, and begged people to
go to look for him. Only in the afternoon, after looking everywhere else, did
they go to look in the glen and see one of his little shoes caught on a bramble.
430 'That's bad,' they said, 'he must have met a wolf.' And sure enough when
they went further in there he was, lying in the wolf's lair, with all his entrails
eaten away, his hand still tightly clutching that small basket...." At this point
she would start crying and her voice would trail away.

This story was rather effective, and when men heard it they often
435 stopped smiling and walked away disconcerted, while the women not only
seemed to forgive her but their faces immediately lost their contemptuous
look and they added their tears to hers. There were some old women who
had not heard her speaking in the street, who went specially to look for
her, to hear her sad tale. When her voice trailed away and she started to
440 cry, they joined in, shedding the tears which had gathered in their eyes.
Then they sighed, and went away satisfied, exchanging comments.

She asked nothing better than to tell her sad story over and over again,
often gathering three or four hearers. But before long everybody knew it by
heart, until even in the eyes of the most kindly, Buddha fearing old ladies
445 not a trace of tears could be seen. In the end, almost everyone in the town
could recite her tale, and it bored and exasperated them to hear it.

"I was really stupid, really..." she would begin.

"Yes, you only knew that in snowy weather the wild beasts in the mountains had nothing to eat and might come down to the villages." Promptly
450 cutting short her recital, they walked away.

She would stand there open-mouthed, looking at them with a dazed
expression, and then go away too, as if she also felt disconcerted. But she
still brooded over it, hoping from other topics such as small baskets, beans
and other people's children, to lead up to the story of her Ah Mao. If she
455 saw a child of two or three, she would say, "Oh dear, if my Ah Mao were
still alive, he would be just as big...."

Children seeing the look in her eyes would take fright and, clutching the
hems of their mothers' clothes, try to tug them away. Thereupon she would
be left by herself again, and finally walk away disconcerted. Later every-

460 body knew what she was like, and it only needed a child present for them
to ask her with an artificial smile, "Hsiang Lin's Wife, if your Ah Mao were
alive, wouldn't he be just as big as that?"

She probably did not realize that her story, after having been turned
over and tasted by people for so many days, had long since become stale,
465 only exciting disgust and contempt; but from the way people smiled she
seemed to know that they were cold and sarcastic, and that there was no
need for her to say any more. She would simply look at them, not
answering a word.

In Luchen people celebrate New Year in a big way: preparations start
470 from the twentieth day of the twelfth month onwards. That year my
uncle's household found it necessary to hire a temporary manservant, but
since there was still a great deal to do they also called in another maidservant, Liu Ma, to help. Chickens and geese had to be killed; but Liu Ma
was a devout woman who abstained from meat, did not kill living things,
475 and would only wash the sacrificial dishes. Hsiang Lin's Wife had nothing
to do but feed the fire. She sat there, resting, watching Liu Ma as she
washed the sacrificial dishes. A light snow began to fall.

"Dear me, I was really stupid," began Hsiang Lin's Wife, as if to herself,
looking at the sky and sighing.

480 "Hsiang Lin's Wife, there you go again," said Liu Ma, looking at her
impatiently. "I ask you: that wound on your forehead, wasn't it then you
got it?"

"Uh, huh," she answered vaguely.

"Let me ask you: what made you willing after all?"

485 "Me?"

"Yes. What I think is, you must have been willing; otherwise...."

"Oh dear, you don't know how strong he was."

"I don't believe it. I don't believe he was so strong that you really
couldn't keep him off. You must have been willing, only you put the blame
490 on his being so strong."

"Oh dear, you...you try for yourself and see." She smiled.

Liu Ma's lined face broke into a smile too, making it wrinkled like a
walnut; her small beady eyes swept Hsiang Lin's Wife's forehead and fastened on her eyes. As if rather embarrassed, Hsiang Lin's Wife immediately
495 stopped smiling, averted her eyes and looked at the snowflakes.

"Hsiang Lin's Wife, that was really a bad bargain," continued Liu Ma
mysteriously. "If you had held out longer or knocked yourself to death, it
would have been better. As it is, after living with your second husband for
less than two years, you are guilty of a great crime. Just think: when you

500 go down to the lower world in future, these two men's ghosts will fight over you. To which will you go? The King of Hell will have no choice but to cut you in two and divide you between them. I think, really…"

Then terror showed in her face. This was something she had never heard in the mountains.

505 "I think you had better take precautions beforehand. Go to the Tutelary God's Temple and buy a threshold to be your substitute, so that thousands of people can walk over it and trample on it, in order to atone for your sins in this life and avoid torment after death."

At the time Hsiang Lin's Wife said nothing, but she must have taken 510 this to heart, for the next morning when she got up there were dark circles beneath her eyes. After breakfast she went to the Tutelary God's Temple at the west end of the village, and asked to buy a threshold. The temple priests would not agree at first, and only when she shed tears did they give a grudging consent. The price was twelve thousand cash.

515 She had long since given up talking to people, because Ah Mao's story was received with such contempt; but news of her conversation with Liu Ma that day spread, and many people took a fresh interest in her and came again to tease her into talking. As for the subject, that had naturally changed to deal with the wound on her forehead.

520 "Hsiang Lin's Wife, I ask you: what made you willing after all that time?" one would cry.

"Oh, what a pity, to have had this knock for nothing," another looking at her scar would agree.

Probably she knew from their smiles and tone of voice that they were 525 making fun of her, for she always looked steadily at them without saying a word, and finally did not even turn her head. All day long she kept her lips tightly closed, bearing on her head the scar which everyone considered a mark of shame, silently shopping, sweeping the floor, washing vegetables, preparing rice. Only after nearly a year did she take from my aunt 530 her wages which had accumulated. She changed them for twelve silver dollars, and asking for leave went to the west end of the town. In less time than it takes for a meal she was back again, looking much comforted, and with an unaccustomed light in her eyes. She told my aunt happily that she had bought a threshold in the Tutelary God's Temple.

535 When the time came for the ancestral sacrifice at the winter equinox, she worked harder than ever, and seeing my aunt take out the sacrificial utensils and with Ah Niu carry the table into the middle of the hall, she went confidently to fetch the winecups and chopsticks.

"Put those down, Hsiang Lin's Wife!" my aunt called out hastily.

540    She withdrew her hand as if scorched, her face turned ashen-grey, and instead of fetching the candlesticks she just stood there dazed. Only when my uncle came to burn incense and told her to go, did she walk away. This time the change in her was very great, for the next day not only were her eyes sunken, but even her spirit seemed broken. Moreover she became very

545    timid, not only afraid of the dark and shadows, but also of the sight of anyone. Even her own master or mistress made her look as frightened as a little mouse that has come out of its hole in the daytime. For the rest, she would sit stupidly, like a wooden statue. In less than half a year her hair began to turn grey, and her memory became much worse, reaching a

550    point when she was constantly forgetting to go and prepare the rice.

"What has come over Hsiang Lin's Wife? It would really have been better not to have kept her that time." My aunt would sometimes speak like this in front of her, as if to warn her.

However, she remained this way, so that it was impossible to see any

555    hope of her improving. They finally decided to get rid of her and tell her to go back to Old Mrs. Wei. While I was at Luchen they were still only talking of this; but judging by what happened later, it is evident that this was what they must have done. Whether after leaving my uncle's household she became a beggar, or whether she went first to Old Mrs. Wei's

560    house and later became a beggar, I do not know.

I was woken up by firecrackers exploding noisily close at hand, saw the glow of the yellow oil lamp as large as a bean, and heard the splutter of fireworks as my uncle's household celebrated the sacrifice. I knew that it was nearly dawn. I felt bewildered, hearing as in a dream the confused

565    continuous sound of distant crackers which seemed to form one dense cloud of noise in the sky, joining the whirling snow-flakes to envelop the whole town. Wrapped in this medley of sound, relaxed and at ease, the doubt which had preyed on me from dawn to early night was swept clean away by the atmosphere of celebration, and I felt only that the saints of

570    heaven and earth had accepted the sacrifice and incense and were all reeling with intoxication in the sky, preparing to give the people of Luchen boundless good fortune.

(1924)

# Zaabalawi

Naguib Mahfouz (Egypt) 1911–

*(translated from Arabic by Denys Johnson-Davies)*

## About the Author

*Naguib Mahfouz is regarded as one the finest writers in Arabic and has received many awards from his own country, Egypt, for his work. In recognition of the quality of his skills, he was awarded the Nobel Prize in Literature in 1988, becoming the first Arab writer to be so recognized. In honouring Mahfouz with this award, the Swedish Academy noted that Mahfouz was an author "who, through works rich in nuance— now clear-sightedly realistic, now evocatively ambiguous—has formed an Arabian narrative art that applies to all mankind." Born in Gamaliya, a district of Cairo, Mahfouz uses this location for many of his stories, presenting a microcosm of Egyptian society. In 1934 he graduated from the University of Cairo with a degree in philosophy and continued with post-graduate work there for another year before beginning a career as a civil servant in a variety of cultural offices for the Egyptian government. He is also affiliated with the Egyptian newspaper* Al-Ahram *as a journalist.*

*Mahfouz published his first novel in 1939 and has so far produced 32 novels and 13 collections of short stories. Three of his recent works ("Respected Sir," "Wedding Song," and "The Search") were published together in one volume in 2001. Sixteen of his novels, including the acclaimed* Miramar *(1967) have been made into movies. Mahfouz is justly famous for his Cairo Trilogy (1956–1957), novels that reflect the social conditions and political realities of his homeland. In the sixties, Mahfouz's style underwent a change, leading him to experiment with symbolism and allegory. While Mahfouz has been celebrated for his realistic representation of the political, social, religious, and personal issues confronting the modern Egyptian, he has also met with criticism; in 1994, he was stabbed by Islamic extremists in an attempt to assassinate him. "Zaabalawi" traces an intensely personal journey, one that exemplifies a search for God, for the meaning of life.*

## Terms Appearing in the Story

**Mouski** a market in Cairo
**dervishes** religious ascetics in Islam
**Lesser Bairam** an Islamic holy feast

$F$inally I became convinced that I had to find Sheikh Zaabalawi. The first time I had heard of his name had been in a song:

*What's wrong with the world, O Zaabalawi?*
*They've turned it upside down and made it insipid.*

5   It had been a popular song in my childhood and one day it had occurred to me—in the way children have of asking endless questions—to ask my father about him.

"Who is Zaabalawi, father?"

He had looked at me hesitantly as though doubting my ability to under-
10  stand the answer. However, he had replied:

"May his blessing descend upon you, he's a true saint of God, a remover of worries and troubles. Were it not for him I would have died miserably—"

In the years that followed I heard him many a time sing the praises of his good saint and speak of the miracles he performed. The days passed
15  and brought with them many illnesses from each one of which I was able, without too much trouble and at a cost I could afford, to find a cure, until I became afflicted with that illness for which no one possesses a remedy. When I had tried everything in vain and was overcome by despair, I remembered by chance what I had heard in my childhood: Why, I asked
20  myself, should I not seek out Sheikh Zaabalawi? I recollected that my father had said that he had made his acquaintance in Khan Gaafar at the house of Sheikh Kamar, one of those sheikhs who practiced law in the religious courts, and I therefore took myself off to his house. Wishing to make sure that he was still living there, I made enquiries of a vendor of beans
25  whom I found in the lower part of the house.

"Sheikh Kamar!" he said, looking at me in amazement. "He left the quarter ages ago. They say he's now living in Garden City and has his office in al-Azhar Square."

I looked up the office address in the telephone book and immediately
30  set off to the Chamber of Commerce Building where it was located. On asking to see him I was ushered into a room just as a beautiful woman with a most intoxicating perfume was leaving it. The man received me with a smile and motioned me towards a fine leather-upholstered chair. My feet were conscious of the costly lushness of the carpet despite the thick
35  soles of my shoes. The man wore a lounge suit and was smoking a cigar; his manner of sitting was that of someone well satisfied both with himself

and his worldly possessions. The look of warm welcome he gave me left no doubt in my mind that he thought me a prospective client, and I felt acutely embarrassed at encroaching upon his valuable time.

40    "Welcome!" he said, prompting me to speak.

"I am the son of your old friend Sheikh Ali al-Tahtawi," I answered so as to put an end to my equivocal position.

A certain languor was apparent in the glance he cast at me; the languor was not total in that he had not as yet lost all hope in me.

45    "God rest his soul," he said. "He was a fine man."

The very pain that had driven me to go there now prevailed upon me to stay.

"He told me," I continued, "of a devout saint named Zaabalawi whom he met at Your Honor's. I am in need of him, sir, if he be still in the land 50 of the living."

The languor became firmly entrenched in his eyes and it would have come as no surprise to me if he had shown the door to both me and my father's memory.

"That," he said in the tone of one who has made up his mind to termi-55 nate the conversation, "was a very long time ago and I scarcely recall him now."

Rising to my feet so as to put his mind at rest regarding my intention of going, I asked:

"Was he really a saint?"

60    "We used to regard him as a man of miracles."

"And where could I find him today?" I asked, making another move towards the door.

"To the best of my knowledge he was living in the Birgawi Residence in al-Azhar," and he applied himself to some papers on his desk with a res-65 olute movement that indicated he wouldn't open his mouth again. I bowed my head in thanks, apologized several times for disturbing him and left the office, my head so buzzing with embarrassment that I was oblivious to all sounds around me.

I went to the Birgawi Residence which was situated in a thickly popu-70 lated quarter. I found that time had so eaten into the building that nothing was left of it save an antiquated facade and a courtyard which, despite it being supposedly in the charge of a caretaker, was being used as a rubbish dump. A small insignificant fellow, a mere prologue to a man, was using the covered entrance as a place for the sale of old books on the-75 ology and mysticism.

On asking him about Zaabalawi he peered at me through narrow, inflamed eyes and said in amazement:

"Zaabalawi! Good heavens, what a time ago that was! Certainly he used to live in this house when it was livable in, and many was the time 80 he would sit with me talking of bygone days and I would be blessed by his holy presence. Where, though, is Zaabalawi today?"

He shrugged his shoulders sorrowfully and soon left me to attend to an approaching customer. I proceeded to make enquiries of many shop-keepers in the district. While I found that a large number of them had 85 never even heard of him, some, though recalling nostalgically the pleasant times they had spent with him, were ignorant of his present whereabouts, while others openly made fun of him, labeled him a char-latan, and advised me to put myself in the hands of a doctor—as though I had not already done so. I therefore had no alternative but to return dis-90 consolately home.

With the passing of the days like motes in the air my pains grew so severe that I was sure I would not be able to hold out much longer. Once again I fell to wondering about Zaabalawi and clutching at the hopes his venerable name stirred within me. Then it occurred to me to seek the help 95 of the local Sheikh of the district; in fact, I was surprised I hadn't thought of this to begin with. His office was in the nature of a small shop except that it contained a desk and a telephone, and I found him sitting at his desk wearing a jacket over his striped *galabia*. As he did not interrupt his conversation with a man sitting beside him, I stood waiting till the man 100 had gone. He then looked up at me coldly. I told myself that I should win him over by the usual methods, and it wasn't long before I had him cheer-fully inviting me to sit down.

"I'm in need of Sheikh Zaabalawi," I answered his enquiry as to the pur-pose of my visit.

105 He gazed at me with the same astonishment as that shown by those I had previously encountered.

"At least," he said, giving me a smile that revealed his gold teeth, "he is still alive. The devil of it is, though, he has no fixed abode. You might well bump into him as you go out of here, on the other hand you might 110 spend days and months in fruitless search of him."

"Even you can't find him!"

"Even I! He's a baffling man, but I thank the Lord that he's still alive!"

He gazed at me intently, and murmured:

"It seems your condition is serious."

115     "Very!"

"May God come to your aid! But why don't you go about it rationally?"

He spread out a sheet of paper on the desk and drew on it with unexpected speed and skill until he had made a full plan of the district showing all the various quarters, lanes, alleyways, and squares. He looked at it
120 admiringly and said, "These are dwelling houses, here is the Quarter of the Perfumers, here the Quarter of the Coppersmiths, the Mouski° the Police, and Fire Stations. The drawing is your best guide. Look carefully in the cafes, the places where the dervishes° perform their rites, the mosques and prayer-rooms, and the Green Gate, for he may well be concealed among
125 the beggars and be indistinguishable from them. Actually, I myself haven't seen him for years, having been somewhat preoccupied with the cares of the world and was only brought back to those most exquisite times of my youth by your enquiry."

I gazed at the map in bewilderment. The telephone rang and he took
130 up the receiver.

"Take it," he told me, generously. "We're at your service."

Folding up the map, I left and wandered off through the quarter, from square to street to alleyway, making enquiries of everyone I felt was familiar with the place. At last the owner of a small establishment for
135 ironing clothes told me:

"Go to the calligrapher Hassanein in Umm al-Ghulam—they were friends."

I went to Umm al-Ghulam where I found old Hassanein working in a deep, narrow shop full of signboards and jars of color. A strange smell, a
140 mixture of glue and perfume, permeated its every corner. Old Hassanein was squatting on a sheepskin rug in front of a board propped against the wall: in the middle of it he had inscribed the word "Allah" in silver lettering. He was engrossed in embellishing the letters with prodigious care. I stood behind him, fearful to disturb him or break the inspiration that
145 flowed to his masterly hand. When my concern at not interrupting him had lasted some time, he suddenly enquired with unaffected gentleness:

"Yes?"

Realizing that he was aware of my presence, I introduced myself.

"I've been told that Sheikh Zaabalawi is your friend and I'm looking for
150 him," I said.

His hand came to a stop. He scrutinized me in astonishment.

"Zaabalawi! God be praised!" he said with a sigh.

"He is a friend of yours, isn't he?" I asked eagerly.

"He was, once upon a time. A real man of mystery: he'd visit you so
155 often that people would imagine he was your nearest and dearest, then
would disappear as though he'd never existed. Yet saints are not to be
blamed."

The spark of hope went out with the suddenness of a lamp by a power-
cut.

160 "He was so constantly with me," said the man, "that I felt him to be a
part of everything I drew. But where is he today?"

"Perhaps he is still alive?"

"He's alive, without a doubt. He had impeccable taste and it was due to
him that I made my most beautiful drawings."

165 "God knows," I said, in a voice almost stifled by the dead ashes of hope,
"that I am in the direst need of him and no one knows better than you of
the ailments in respect of which he is sought."

"Yes—yes. May God restore you to health. He is, in truth, as is said of
him, a man, and more—

170 Smiling broadly, he added: "And his face is possessed of an unforgettable beauty. But where is he?"

Reluctantly I rose to my feet, shook hands and left. I continued on my way
eastwards and westwards through the quarter, enquiring about him from
everyone who, by reason of age or experience, I felt was likely to help me.
175 Eventually I was informed by a vendor of lupine that he had met him a short
while ago at the house of Sheikh Gad, the well-known composer. I went to
the musician's house in Tabakshiyya where I found him in a room tastefully
furnished in the old style, its walls redolent with history. He was seated on a
divan, his famous lute lying beside him, concealing within itself the most
180 beautiful melodies of our age, while from within the house came the sound
of pestle and mortar and the clamor of children. I immediately greeted him
and introduced myself, and was put at my ease by the unaffected way in
which he received me. He did not ask, either in words or gesture, what had
brought me, and I did not feel that he even harbored any such curiosity.
185 Amazed at his understanding and kindness, which boded well, I said:

"O Sheikh Gad, I am an admirer of yours and have long been
enchanted by the renderings of your songs."

"Thank you," he said with a smile.

"Please excuse my disturbing you," I continued timidly, "but I was told
190 that Zaabalawi was your friend and I am in urgent need of him."

"Zaabalawi!" he said, frowning in concentration, "You need him? God
be with you, for who knows, O Zaabalawi, where you are?"

"Doesn't he visit you?" I asked eagerly.

"He visited me some time ago. He might well come now; on the other
hand I mightn't see him till death!"

I gave an audible sigh and asked:

"What made him like that?"

He took up his lute. "Such are saints or they would not be saints," he
said laughing.

"Do those who need him suffer as I do?"

"Such suffering is part of the cure!"

He took up the plectrum and began plucking soft strains from the
strings. Lost in thought, I followed his movements. Then, as though
addressing myself, I said:

"So my visit has been in vain!"

He smiled, laying his cheek against the side of the lute.

"God forgive you," he said, "for saying such a thing of a visit that has
caused me to know you and you me!"

I was much embarrassed and said apologetically:

"Please forgive me; my feelings of defeat made me forget my manners!"

"Do not give in to defeat. This extraordinary man brings fatigue to all
who seek him. It was easy enough with him in the old days when his place
of abode was known. Today, though, the world has changed and after
having enjoyed a position attained only by potentates, he is now pursued
by the police on a charge of false pretenses. It is therefore no longer an
easy matter to reach him, but have patience and be sure that you will do
so."

He raised his head from the lute and skillfully led into the opening bars
of a melody. Then he sang:

*I make lavish mention, even though I blame myself, of those I have loved,*
*For the words of lovers are my wine.*

With a heart that was weary and listless I followed the beauty of the
melody and the singing.

"I composed the music to this poem in a single night," he told me when
he had finished. "I remember that it was the night of the Lesser Bairam.°
He was my guest for the whole of that night and the poem was of his
choosing. He would sit for a while just where you are, then would get up
and play with my children as though he were one of them. Whenever I
was overcome by weariness or my inspiration failed me he would punch

230 me playfully in the chest and joke with me, and I would bubble over with melodies and thus I continued working till I finished the most beautiful piece I have ever composed."

"Does he know anything about music?"

"He was the epitome of things musical. He had an extremely beautiful
235 speaking voice and you had only to hear him to want to burst into song. His loftiness of spirit stirred within you—"

"How was it that he cured those diseases before which men are power-less?"

"That is his secret. Maybe you will learn it when you meet him."

240 But when would that meeting occur? We relapsed into silence and the hubbub of children once more filled the room.

Again the Sheikh began to sing. He went on repeating the words "and I have a memory of her" in different and beautiful variations until the very walls danced in ecstasy. I expressed my wholehearted admiration and he
245 gave me a smile of thanks. I then got up and asked permission to leave and he accompanied me to the outer door. As I shook him by the hand he said, "I hear that nowadays he frequents the house of Hagg Wanas al-Damanhouri. Do you know him?"

I shook my head, a modicum of renewed hope creeping into my heart.

250 "He is a man of private means," he told me, "who from time to time visits Cairo, putting up at some hotel or other. Every evening, though, he spends at the Negma Bar in Alfi Street."

I waited for nightfall and went to the Negma Bar. I asked a waiter about Hagg Wanas and he pointed to a corner which was semi-secluded because
255 of its position behind a large pillar with mirrors on its four sides. There I saw a man seated alone at a table with a bottle three-quarters empty and another empty one in front of him; there were no snacks or food to be seen and I was sure that I was in the presence of a hardened drinker. He was wearing a loosely flowing silk *galabia* and a carefully wound turban; his
260 legs were stretched out towards the base of the pillar, and as he gazed into the mirror in rapt contentment the sides of his face, rounded and hand-some despite the fact that he was approaching old age, were flushed with wine. I approached quietly till I stood but a few feet away from him. He did not turn towards me, or give any indication that he was aware of my
265 presence.

"Good evening, Mr. Wanas," I said with amiable friendliness.

He turned towards me abruptly as though my voice had roused him from slumber and glared at me in disapproval. I was about to explain what had brought me to him when he interrupted me in an almost imperative

270 tone of voice which was none the less not devoid of an extraordinary gentleness:

"First, please sit down, and, second, please get drunk!"

I opened my mouth to make my excuses but, stopping up his ears with his fingers, he said:

275 "Not a word till you do what I say."

I realized that I was in the presence of a capricious drunkard and told myself that I should go along with him at least halfway.

"Would you permit me to ask one question?" I said with a smile, sitting down.

280 Without removing his hands from his ears he indicated the bottle.

"When engaged in a drinking bout like this I do not allow any conversation between myself and another unless, like me, he is drunk, otherwise the session loses all propriety and mutual comprehension is rendered impossible."

285 I made a sign indicating that I didn't drink.

"That's your look-out," he said offhandedly. "And that's my condition!"

He filled me a glass which I meekly took and drank. No sooner had it settled in my stomach than it seemed to ignite. I waited patiently till I had grown used to its ferocity, and said:

290 "It's very strong, and I think the time has come for me to ask you about—"

Once again, however, he put his fingers in his ears.

"I shan't listen to you until you're drunk!"

He filled up my glass for the second time. I glanced at it in trepidation;
295 then, overcoming my innate objection, I drank it down at a gulp. No sooner had it come to rest inside me than I lost all willpower. With the third glass I lost my memory and with the fourth the future vanished. The world turned round about me and I forgot why I had gone there. The man leaned towards me attentively but I saw him—saw everything—as a mere
300 meaningless series of colored planes. I don't know how long it was before my head sank down on to the arm of the chair and I plunged into deep sleep. During it I had a beautiful dream the like of which I had never experienced. I dreamed that I was in an immense garden surrounded on all sides by luxuriant trees and the sky was nothing but stars seen between the
305 entwined branches, all enfolded in an atmosphere like that of sunset or a sky overcast with cloud. I was lying on a small hummock of jasmine petals which fell upon me like rain, while the lucent spray of a fountain unceasingly sprinkled my head and temples. I was in a state of deep contentedness, of ecstatic serenity. An orchestra of warbling and cooing played in

310 my ear. There was an extraordinary sense of harmony between me and
my inner self, and between the two of us and the world, everything being
in its rightful place without discord or distortion. In the whole world there
was no single reason for speech or movement, for the universe moved in a
rapture of ecstasy. This lasted but a short while. When I opened my eyes
315 consciousness struck at me like a policeman's fist and I saw Wanas al-
Damanhouri regarding me with concern. In the bar only a few drowsy
people were left.

"You have slept deeply," said my companion; "you were obviously
hungry for sleep."

320    I rested my heavy head in the palms of my hands. When I took them
away in astonishment and looked down at them I found that they glistened with drops of water.

"My head's wet," I protested.

"Yes, my friend tried to rouse you," he answered quietly.

325    "Somebody saw me in this state?"

"Don't worry, he is a good man. Have you not heard of Sheikh
Zaabalawi?"

"Zaabalawi!" I exclaimed, jumping to my feet.

"Yes," he answered in surprise. "What's wrong?"

330    "Where is he?"

"I don't know where he is now. He was here and then he left."

I was about to run off in pursuit but found I was more exhausted than
I had imagined. Collapsed over the table, I cried out in despair:

"My sole reason for coming to you was to meet him. Help me to catch
335 up with him or send someone after him."

The man called a vendor of prawns and asked him to seek out the
Sheikh and bring him back. Then he turned to me.

"I didn't realize you were afflicted. I'm very sorry—"

"You wouldn't let me speak," I said irritably.

340    "What a pity! He was sitting on this chair beside you the whole time. He
was playing with a string of jasmine petals he had round his neck, a gift
from one of his admirers, then, taking pity on you, he began to sprinkle
some water on your head to bring you round."

"Does he meet you here every night?" I asked, my eyes not leaving the
345 doorway through which the vendor of prawns had left.

"He was with me tonight, last night and the night before that, but
before that I hadn't seen him for a month."

"Perhaps he will come tomorrow," I answered with a sigh.

"Perhaps.

350   "I am willing to give him any money he wants."

Wanas answered sympathetically:

"The strange thing is that he is not open to such temptations, yet he will cure you if you meet him."

"Without charge?"

355   "Merely on sensing that you love him."

The vendor of prawns returned, having failed in his mission.

I recovered some of my energy and left the bar, albeit unsteadily. At every street corner I called out, "Zaabalawi!" in the vague hope that I would be rewarded with an answering shout. The street boys turned con-

360 temptuous eyes on me till I sought refuge in the first available taxi.

The following evening I stayed up with Wanas al-Damanhouri till dawn, but the Sheikh did not put in an appearance. Wanas informed me that he would be going away to the country and wouldn't be returning to Cairo until he'd sold the cotton crop.

365   I must wait, I told myself; I must train myself to be patient. Let me content myself with having made certain of the existence of Zaabalawi, and even of his affection for me, which encourages me to think that he will be prepared to cure me if a meeting between us takes place.

Sometimes, however, the long delay wearied me. I would become beset

370 by despair and would try to persuade myself to dismiss him from my mind completely. How many weary people in this life know him not or regard him as a mere myth! Why, then, should I torture myself about him in this way?

No sooner, however, did my pains force themselves upon me than I

375 would again begin to think about him, asking myself as to when I would be fortunate enough to meet him. The fact that I ceased to have any news of Wanas and was told he had gone to live abroad did not deflect me from my purpose; the truth of the matter was that I had become fully convinced that I had to find Zaabalawi.

380   Yes, I have to find Zaabalawi.


(1965)

# Tuesday Siesta

Gabriel Garcia Marquez (Colombia) 1928–

*(translated from Spanish by S.J. Bernstein)*

## About the Author

*Gabriel Garcia Marquez was awarded the Nobel Prize in 1982, but his works, in particular his novel* One Hundred Years of Solitude *(1967), had already earned him international acclaim as one of the greatest living storytellers. He had received numerous awards in his homeland and internationally. Marquez was born in Aracataca, Colombia in 1928 and attended the Universidad Nacional de Colombia and the Universidad de Cartagena before becoming a journalist in1947. He has worked for a number of South American newspapers as an international reporter. He helped form the Prensa Latina news agency in1959 and founded Fundacion Habeas in 1979. He is a well-respected journalist who still writes a weekly syndicated column. He has written many articles, plays, short stories, and novels, including the remarkable* Love in the Time of Cholera. *Marquez is a popular author; in fact, his Nobel citation states: "Each new work of his is received by critics and readers as an event of world importance, is translated into many languages and published as quickly as possible in large editions."*

*Marquez's style is often referred to as magic realism. It is a rich blend of fact, fantasy, and fable. His "stream of consciousness" has been compared to a whirlpool presenting a fictional world in which anything is possible. Always political, Marquez explores a human reality that at times seems hallucinatory or irrational with tenderness and ironic humour. Of his writing he says, "It always amuses me that the biggest praise for my work comes for the imagination while the truth is there is not a single line in all my work that does not have a basis in reality." This reality can be seen in "Tuesday Siesta," in which Marquez bewilders the reader as the mother and daughter try to make sense of the death of their family member and the menace of the reaction to that death builds steadily.*

The train emerged from the quivering tunnel of sandy rocks, began to cross the symmetrical, interminable banana plantations, and the air became humid and they couldn't feel the sea breeze any more. A stifling blast of smoke came in the car window. On the narrow road parallel to the
5 railway there were oxcarts loaded with green bunches of bananas. Beyond the road, in uncultivated spaces set at odd intervals there were offices with

electric fans, red-brick buildings, and residences with chairs and little white tables on the terraces among dusty palm trees and rosebushes. It was eleven in the morning, and the heat had not yet begun.

10  "You'd better close the window," the woman said. "Your hair will get full of soot."

The girl tried to, but the shade wouldn't move because of the rust.

They were the only passengers in the lone third-class car. Since the smoke of the locomotive kept coming through the window, the girl left her
15  seat and put down the only things they had with them: a plastic sack with some things to eat and a bouquet of flowers wrapped in newspaper. She sat on the opposite seat, away from the window, facing her mother. They were both in severe and poor mourning clothes.

The girl was twelve years old, and it was the first time she'd ever been
20  on a train. The woman seemed too old to be her mother, because of the blue veins on her eyelids and her small, soft, and shapeless body, in a dress cut like a cassock. She was riding with her spinal column braced firmly against the back of the seat, and held a peeling patent-leather handbag in her lap with both hands. She bore the conscientious serenity of someone
25  accustomed to poverty.

By twelve the heat had begun. The train stopped for ten minutes to take on water at a station where there was no town. Outside, in the mysterious silence of the plantations, the shadows seemed clean. But the still air inside the car smelled like untanned leather. The train did not pick up speed. It
30  stopped at two identical towns with wooden houses painted bright colors. The woman's head nodded and she sank into sleep. The girl took off her shoes. Then she went to the washroom to put the bouquet of flowers in some water.

When she came back to her seat, her mother was waiting to eat. She
35  gave her a piece of cheese, half a corn-meal pancake, and a cookie, and took an equal portion out of the plastic sack for herself. While they ate, the train crossed an iron bridge very slowly and passed a town just like the ones before, except that in this one there was a crowd in the plaza. A band was playing a lively tune under the oppressive sun. At the other side of town the
40  plantations ended in a plain which was cracked from the drought.

The woman stopped eating.

"Put on your shoes," she said.

The girl looked outside. She saw nothing but the deserted plain, where the train began to pick up speed again, but she put the last piece of cookie
45  into the sack and quickly put on her shoes. The woman gave her a comb.

"Comb your hair," she said.

The train whistle began to blow while the girl was combing her hair. The woman dried the sweat from her neck and wiped the oil from her face with her fingers. When the girl stopped combing, the train was passing the outlying houses of a town larger but sadder than the earlier ones.

"If you feel like doing anything, do it now," said the woman. "Later, don't take a drink anywhere even if you're dying of thirst. Above all, no crying."

The girl nodded her head. A dry, burning wind came in the window, together with the locomotive's whistle and the clatter of the old cars. The woman folded the plastic bag with the rest of the food and put it in the handbag. For a moment a complete picture of the town, on that bright August Tuesday, shone in the window. The girl wrapped the flowers in the soaking-wet newspapers, moved a little farther away from the window, and stared at her mother. She received a pleasant expression in return. The train began to whistle and slowed down. A moment later it stopped.

There was no one at the station. On the other side of the street, on the sidewalk shaded by the almond trees, only the pool hall was open. The town was floating in the heat. The woman and the girl got off the train and crossed the abandoned station—the tiles split apart by the grass growing up between—and over to the shady side of the street.

It was almost two. At that hour, weighted down by drowsiness, the town was taking a siesta. The stores, the town offices, the public school were closed at eleven, and didn't reopen until a little before four, when the train went back. Only the hotel across from the station, with its bar and pool hall, and the telegraph office at one side of the plaza stayed open. The houses, most of them built on the banana company's model, had their doors locked from inside and their blinds drawn. In some of them it was so hot that the residents ate lunch in the patio. Others leaned a chair against the wall, in the shade of the almond trees, and took their siesta right out in the street.

Keeping to the protective shade of the almond trees, the woman and the girl entered the town without disturbing the siesta. They went directly to the parish house. The woman scratched the metal grating on the door with her fingernail, waited a moment, and scratched again. An electric fan was humming inside. They did not hear the steps. They hardly heard the slight creaking of a door, and immediately a cautious voice, right next to the metal grating: "Who is it?" The woman tried to see through the grating.

"I need the priest," she said.

"He's sleeping now."

"It's an emergency," the woman insisted.

Her voice showed a calm determination.

The door was opened a little way, noiselessly, and a plump, older woman appeared, with very pale skin and hair the color of iron. Her eyes

90  seemed too small behind her thick eye-glasses.

"Come in," she said, and opened the door all the way.

They entered a room permeated with an old smell of flowers. The woman of the house led them to a wooden bench and signaled them to sit down. The girl did so, but her mother remained standing, absent-mind-

95  edly, with both hands clutching the handbag. No noise could be heard above the electric fan.

The woman of the house reappeared at the door at the far end of the room. "He says you should come back after three," she said in a very low voice. "He just lay down five minutes ago."

100  "The train leaves at three-thirty," said the woman.

It was a brief and self-assured reply, but her voice remained pleasant, full of undertones. The woman of the house smiled for the first time.

"All right," she said.

When the far door closed again, the woman sat down next to her

105  daughter. The narrow waiting room was poor, neat, and clean. On the other side of the wooden railing which divided the room, there was a work-table, a plain one with an oilcloth cover, and on top of the table a primitive typewriter next to a vase of flowers. The parish records were beyond. You could see that it was an office kept in order by a spinster.

110  The far door opened and this time the priest appeared, cleaning his glasses with a handkerchief. Only when he put them on was it evident that he was the brother of the woman who had opened the door.

"How can I help you?" he asked.

"The keys to the cemetery," said the woman.

115  The girl was seated with the flowers in her lap and her feet crossed under the bench. The priest looked at her, then looked at the woman, and then through the wire mesh of the window at the bright, cloudless sky.

"In this heat," he said. "You could have waited until the sun went down."

120  The woman moved her head silently. The priest crossed to the other side of the railing, took out of the cabinet a notebook covered in oilcloth, a wooden penholder, and an inkwell, and sat down at the table. There was more than enough hair on his hands to account for what was missing on his head.

125  "Which grave are you going to visit?" he asked.

"Carlos Centeno's," said the woman.

"Who?"

"Carlos Centeno," the woman repeated.

The priest still did not understand.

130     "He's the thief who was killed here last week," said the woman in the same tone of voice. "I am his mother."

The priest scrutinized her. She stared at him with quiet self-control, and the Father blushed. He lowered his head and began to write. As he filled the page, he asked the woman to identify herself, and she replied unhesi-
135 tatingly, with precise details, as if she were reading them. The Father began to sweat. The girl unhooked the buckle of her left shoe, slipped her heel out of it, and rested it on the bench rail. She did the same with the right one.

It had all started the Monday of the previous week, at three in the
140 morning, a few blocks from there. Rebecca, a lonely widow who lived in a house full of odds and ends, heard above the sound of the drizzling rain someone trying to force the front door from the outside. She got up, rummaged around in her closet for an ancient revolver that no one had fired since the days of Colonel Aureliano Buendía, and went into the living
145 room without turning on the lights. Orienting herself not so much by the noise at the lock as by a terror developed in her by twenty-eight years of loneliness, she fixed in her imagination not only the spot where the door was but also the exact height of the lock. She clutched the weapon with both hands, closed her eyes, and squeezed the trigger. It was the first time
150 in her life that she had fired a gun. Immediately after the explosion, she could hear nothing except the murmur of the drizzle on the galvanized roof. Then she heard a little metallic bump on the cement porch, and a very low voice, pleasant but terribly exhausted: "Ah, Mother." The man they found dead in front of the house in the morning, his nose blown to
155 bits, wore a flannel shirt with colored stripes, everyday pants with a rope for a belt, and was barefoot. No one in town knew him.

"So his name was Carlos Centeno," murmured the Father when he finished writing.

"Centeno Ayala," said the woman. "He was my only boy."

160     The priest went back to the cabinet. Two big rusty keys hung on the inside of the door; the girl imagined, as her mother had when she was a girl and as the priest himself must have imagined at some time, that they were Saint Peter's keys. He took them down, put them on the open notebook on the railing, and pointed with his forefinger to a place on the page
165 he had just written, looking at the woman.

"Sign here."

The woman scribbled her name, holding the handbag under her arm. The girl picked up the flowers, came to the railing shuffling her feet, and watched her mother attentively.

170 The priest sighed.

"Didn't you ever try to get him on the right track?"

The woman answered when she finished signing.

"He was a very good man."

The priest looked first at the woman and then at the girl, and realized
175 with a kind of pious amazement that they were not about to cry. The woman continued in the same tone:

"I told him never to steal anything that anyone needed to eat, and he minded me. On the other hand, before, when he used to box, he used to spend three days in bed, exhausted from being punched."

180 "All his teeth had to be pulled out," interrupted the girl.

"That's right," the woman agreed. "Every mouthful I ate those days tasted of the beatings my son got on Saturday nights."

"God's will is inscrutable," said the Father.

But he said it without much conviction, partly because experience had
185 made him a little skeptical and partly because of the heat. He suggested that they cover their heads to guard against sunstroke. Yawning, and now almost completely asleep, he gave them instructions about how to find Carlos Centeno's grave. When they came back, they didn't have to knock. They should put the key under the door; and in the same place, if they
190 could, they should put an offering for the Church. The woman listened to his directions with great attention, but thanked him without smiling.

The Father had noticed that there was someone looking inside, his nose pressed against the metal grating, even before he opened the door to the street. Outside was a group of children. When the door was opened wide,
195 the children scattered. Ordinarily, at that hour there was no one in the street. Now there were not only children. There were groups of people under the almond trees. The Father scanned the street swimming in the heat and then he understood. Softly, he closed the door again.

"Wait a moment," he said without looking at the woman. His sister
200 appeared at the far door with a black jacket over her nightshirt and her hair down over her shoulders. She looked silently at the Father.

"What was it?" he asked.

"The people have noticed," murmured his sister.

"You'd better go out by the door to the patio," said the Father.

205 "It's the same there," said his sister. "Everybody is at the windows."

The woman seemed not to have understood until then. She tried to look into the street through the metal grating. Then she took the bouquet of flowers from the girl and began to move toward the door. The girl followed her.

210 "Wait until the sun goes down," said the Father.

"You'll melt," said his sister, motionless at the back of the room. "Wait and I'll lend you a parasol."

"Thank you," replied the woman. "We're all right this way."

She took the girl by the hand and went into the street.

(1962)

# Abandoned

Guy de Maupassant (France) 1850–1893

(translated from French by Albert M. C. McMaster)

## About the Author

Guy de Maupassant is one of the most acclaimed writers of the short story in the world. He is the acknowledged master of the French short story. He was probably born at the Chateau de Miromesniel near Dieppe. His family background was aristocratic, and through his mother he was introduced to many of the great writers of the time: Gustav Flaubert, Émile Zola, Ivan Turgenev, Algernon Swinburn, and Henry James, all of whom were interested in literary naturalism and psychology. Maupassant served in the French army during the Franco-Prussian War (1870), interrupting his studies in law school to do so. From 1872–80, Maupassant worked as a civil servant, first in the Ministry of Maritime Affairs and later at the Ministry of Education. However, he had little interest in bureaucracy and devoted himself to writing and to womanizing. During this time, Maupassant contracted syphilis; this disease eventually caused his mental illness. In January 1892, Maupassant attempted suicide by cutting his throat, and he was committed to an asylum in Passy. He died here on July 6, 1893.

In his short literary life, Maupassant wrote more than 300 short stories, six novels, three travel books, and an anthology of poetry. He also worked as a reporter and columnist. He was fascinated by human psychology, and wrote a number of horror stories reflecting his interest in abnormal psychology. His plots have influenced writers such as Stephen King and filmmakers such as John Ford, Luis Bunuel, and Oliver Stone. His short stories are based on simple, mundane occurrences that reveal the hidden and unexpected in his characters; Maupassant is justly famous for the twist in the dénouement of his stories. However, it is his precise and balanced style that has made him one of the most admired and influential short story writers. His tone is usually objective, based on meticulous observation of others (and here his photographic memory must have served him well), and his cynical assessment of events. Many of his stories deal with the tragedies of daily life, but Guy de Maupassant handles these with a characteristically sympathetic humour. He says his writing isn't concerned with "telling a story or entertaining us or touching our hearts but at forcing us to think and understand the deep, hidden meaning of events." While his stories achieve his stated aim, they also demonstrate his ability to achieve that which he claims he hasn't set out to do: tell a story convincingly, entertain his audience, and touch hearts. "Abandoned" is a story that succeeds in all this.

"**I** really think you must be mad, my dear, to go for a country walk in such weather as this. You have had some very strange notions for the last two months. You drag me to the seaside in spite of myself, when you have never once had such a whim during all the forty-four years that we have been
5 married. You chose Fécamp, which is a very dull town, without consulting me in the matter, and now you are seized with such a rage for walking, you who hardly ever stir out on foot, that you want to take a country walk on the hottest day of the year. Ask d'Apreval to go with you, as he is ready to gratify all your whims. As for me, I am going back to have a nap."

10    Madame de Cadour turned to her old friend and said:

"Will you come with me, Monsieur d'Apreval?"

He bowed with a smile, and with all the gallantry of former years:

"I will go wherever you go," he replied.

"Very well, then, go and get a sunstroke," Monsieur de Cadour said; and
15 he went back to the Hôtel des Bains to lie down for an hour or two.

As soon as they were alone, the old lady and her old companion set off, and she said to him in a low voice, squeezing his hand:

"At last! at last!"

"You are mad," he said in a whisper. "I assure you that you are mad.
20 Think of the risk you are running. If that man—"

She started.

"Oh! Henri, do not say *that man*, when you are speaking of him."

"Very well," he said abruptly, "if our son guesses anything, if he has any suspicions, he will have you, he will have us both in his power. You have
25 got on without seeing him for the last forty years. What is the matter with you to-day?"

They had been going up the long street that leads from the sea to the town, and now they turned to the right, to go to Etretat. The white road stretched in front of him, then under a blaze of brilliant sunshine, so they
30 went on slowly in the burning heat. She had taken her old friend's arm, and was looking straight in front of her, with a fixed and haunted gaze, and at last she said:

"And so you have not seen him again, either?"

"No, never."

35    "Is it possible?"

"My dear friend, do not let us begin that discussion again. I have a wife and children and you have a husband, so we both of us have much to fear from other people's opinion."

She did not reply; she was thinking of her long past youth and of many
40 sad things that had occurred. She had been married as girls are married; she

hardly knew her betrothed, who was a diplomatist, and later, she lived the same life with him that all women of the world live with their husbands. But Monsieur d'Apreval, who was also married, loved her with a profound passion, and while Monsieur de Cadour was absent in India, on a political mis-

45 sion for a long time, she succumbed. Could she possibly have resisted, have refused to give herself? Could she have had the strength and courage not to have yielded, as she loved him also? No, certainly not; it would have been too hard; she would have suffered too much! How cruel and deceitful life is! Is it possible to avoid certain attacks of fate, or can one escape from one's des-

50 tiny? When a solitary, abandoned woman, without children and with a careless husband, always escapes from the passion which a man feels for her, as she would escape from the sun, in order to live in darkness until she dies?

How well she recalled all the details of their early friendship, his smiles, the way he used to linger, in order to watch her until she was indoors.

55 What happy days they were, the only really delicious days she had ever enjoyed, and how quickly they were over!

And then—her discovery—of the penalty she paid! What anguish!

Of that journey to the South, that long journey, her sufferings, her constant terror, that secluded life in the small, solitary house on the shores of the

60 Mediterranean, at the bottom of a garden, which she did not venture to leave. How well she remembered those long days which she spent lying under an orange tree, looking up at the round, red fruit, amid the green leaves. How she used to long to go out, as far as the sea, whose fresh breezes came to her over the wall, and whose small waves she could hear lapping on

65 the beach. She dreamed of its immense blue expanse sparkling under the sun, with the white sails of the small vessels, and a mountain on the horizon. But she did not dare to go outside the gate. Suppose anybody had recognized her unshapely as she was, and showing her disgrace by her expanded waist.

And those days of waiting, those last days of misery and expectation! The

70 impending suffering, and then that terrible night! What misery she had endured, and what a night it was! How she had groaned and screamed! She could still see the pale face of her lover, who kissed her hand every moment, and the clean-shaven face of the doctor and the nurse's white cap.

And what she felt when she heard the child's feeble cries, that wail, that

75 first effort of a human's voice!

And the next day! the next day! the only day of her life on which she had seen and kissed her son; for, from that time, she had never even caught a glimpse of him.

And what a long, void existence hers had been since then, with the thought

80 of that child always, always floating before her. She had never seen her son,

that little creature that had been part of herself, even once since then; they had taken him from her, carried him away, and had hidden him. All she knew was that he had been brought up by some peasants in Normandy, that he had become a peasant himself, had married well, and that his father,
85 whose name he did not know, had settled a handsome sum of money on him.

How often during the last forty years had she wished to go and see him and to embrace him! She could not imagine to herself that he had grown! She always thought of that small human atom which she had held in her arms and pressed to her bosom for a day.

90 How often she had said to M. d'Apreval: "I cannot bear it any longer; I must go and see him."

But he had always stopped her and kept her from going. She would be unable to restrain and to master herself; their son would guess it and take advantage of her, blackmail her; she would be lost.

95 "What is he like?" she said.

"I do not know. I have not seen him again, either."

"Is it possible? To have a son and not to know him; to be afraid of him and to reject him as if he were a disgrace! It is horrible."

They went along the dusty road, overcome by the scorching sun, and
100 continually ascending that interminable hill.

"One might take it for a punishment," she continued; "I have never had another child, and I could no longer resist the longing to see him, which has possessed me for forty years. You men cannot understand that. You must remember that I shall not live much longer, and suppose I should
105 never see him, never have seen him!...Is it possible? How could I wait so long? I have thought about him every day since, and what a terrible existence mine has been! I have never awakened, never, do you understand, without my first thoughts being of him, of my child. How is he? Oh, how guilty I feel toward him! Ought one to fear what the world may say in a
110 case like this? I ought to have left everything to go after him, to bring him up and to show my love for him. I should certainly have been much happier, but I did not dare, I was a coward. How I have suffered! Oh, how those poor, abandoned children must hate their mothers!"

She stopped suddenly, for she was choked by her sobs. The whole valley
115 was deserted and silent in the dazzling light and the overwhelming heat, and only the grasshoppers uttered their shrill, continuous chirp among the sparse yellow grass on both sides of the road.

"Sit down a little," he said.

She allowed herself to be led to the side of the ditch and sank down with
120 her face in her hands. Her white hair, which hung in curls on both sides of

her face, had become tangled. She wept, overcome by profound grief, while he stood facing her, uneasy and not knowing what to say, and he merely murmured: "Come, take courage."

She got up.

125 "I will," she said, and wiping her eyes, she began to walk again with the uncertain step of an elderly woman.

A little farther on the road passed beneath a clump of trees, which hid a few houses, and they could distinguish the vibrating and regular blows of a blacksmith's hammer on the anvil; and presently they saw a wagon
130 standing on the right side of the road in front of a low cottage, and two men shoeing a horse under a shed.

Monsieur d' Apreval went up to them.

"Where is Pierre Benedict's farm?" he asked.

"Take the road to the left, close to the inn, and then go straight on; it is
135 the third house past Poret's. There is a small spruce fir close to the gate; you cannot make a mistake."

They turned to the left. She was walking very slowly now, her legs threatened to give way, and her heart was beating so violently that she felt as if she should suffocate, while at every step she murmured, as if in
140 prayer:

"Oh! Heaven! Heaven!"

Monsieur d'Apreval, who was also nervous and rather pale, said to her somewhat gruffly:

"If you cannot manage to control your feelings, you will betray yourself
145 at once. Do try and restrain yourself."

"How can I?" she replied. "My child! When I think that I am going to see my child."

They were going along one of those narrow country lanes between farmyards, that are concealed beneath a double row of beech trees at
150 either side of the ditches, and suddenly they found themselves in front of a gate, beside which there was a young spruce fir.

"This is it," he said.

She stopped suddenly and looked about her. The courtyard, which was planted with apple trees, was large and extended as far as the small
155 thatched dwelling house. On the opposite side were the stable, the barn, the cow house and the poultry house, while the gig, the wagon and the manure cart were under a slated outhouse. Four calves were grazing under the shade of the trees and black hens were wandering all about the enclosure.

All was perfectly still; the house door was open, but nobody was to be
160 seen, and so they went in, when immediately a large black dog came out

of a barrel that was standing under a pear tree, and began to bark furiously.

There were four bee-hives on boards against the wall of the house.

Monsieur d'Apreval stood outside and called out:

165　"Is anybody at home?"

Then a child appeared, a little girl of about ten, dressed in a chemise and a linen petticoat, with dirty, bare legs and a timid and cunning look. She remained standing in the doorway, as if to prevent any one going in.

"What do you want?" she asked.

170　"Is your father in?"

"No."

"Where is he?"

"I don't know."

"And your mother?"

175　"Gone after the cows."

"Will she be back soon?"

"I don't know."

Then suddenly the lady, as if she feared that her companion might force her to return, said quickly:

180　"I shall not go without having seen him."

"We will wait for him, my dear friend."

As they turned away, they saw a peasant woman coming toward the house, carrying two tin pails, which appeared to be heavy and which glistened brightly in the sunlight.

185　She limped with her right leg, and in her brown knitted jacket, that was faded by the sun and washed out by the rain, she looked like a poor, wretched, dirty servant.

"Here is mamma," the child said.

When she got close to the house, she looked at the strangers angrily and

190 suspiciously, and then she went in, as if she had not seen them. She looked old and had a hard, yellow, wrinkled face, one of those wooden faces that country people so often have.

Monsieur d'Apreval called her back.

"I beg your pardon, madame, but we came in to know whether you

195 could sell us two glasses of milk."

She was grumbling when she reappeared in the door, after putting down her pails.

"I don't sell milk," she replied.

"We are very thirsty," he said, "and madame is very tired. Can we not

200 get something to drink?"

The peasant woman gave them an uneasy and cunning glance and then she made up her mind.

"As you are here, I will give you some," she said, going into the house, and almost immediately the child came out and brought two chairs, which
205 she placed under an apple tree, and then the mother, in turn, brought out two bowls of foaming milk, which she gave to the visitors. She did not return to the house, however, but remained standing near them, as if to watch them and to find out for what purpose they had come there.

"You have come from Fécamp?" she said.

210 "Yes," Monsieur d'Apreval replied, "we are staying at Fécamp for the summer."

And then, after a short silence, he continued:

"Have you any fowls you could sell us every week?"

The woman hesitated for a moment and then replied:

215 "Yes, I think I have. I suppose you want young ones?"

"Yes, of course."

"'What do you pay for them in the market?"

D'Apreval, who had not the least idea, turned to his companion:

"What are you paying for poultry in Fécamp, my dear lady?"

220 "Four francs and four francs fifty centimes," she said, her eyes full of tears, while the farmer's wife, who was looking at her askance, asked in much surprise:

"Is the lady ill, as she is crying?"

He did not know what to say, and replied with some hesitation:

225 "No—no—but she lost her watch as we came along, a very handsome watch, and that troubles her. If anybody should find it, please let us know."

Mother Benedict did not reply, as she thought it a very equivocal sort of answer, but suddenly she exclaimed:

230 "Oh, here is my husband!"

She was the only one who had seen him, as she was facing the gate. D'Apreval started and Madame de Cadour nearly fell as she turned round suddenly on her chair.

A man bent nearly double, and out of breath, stood there, ten-yards
235 from them, dragging a cow at the end of a rope. Without taking any notice of the visitors, he said:

"Confound it! What a brute!"

And he went past them and disappeared in the cow house.

Her tears had dried quickly as she sat there startled, without a word and
240 with the one thought in her mind, that this was her son, and D'Apreval, whom the same thought had struck very unpleasantly, said in an agitated voice:

"Is this Monsieur Benedict?"

"Who told you his name?" the wife asked, still rather suspiciously.

"The blacksmith at the corner of the highroad," he replied, and then
245 they were all silent, with their eyes fixed on the door of the cow house, which formed a sort of black hole in the wall of the building. Nothing could be seen inside, but they heard a vague noise, movements and foot-steps and the sound of hoofs, which were deadened by the straw on the floor, and soon the man reappeared in the door, wiping his forehead, and
250 came toward the house with long, slow strides. He passed the strangers without seeming to notice them and said to his wife:

"Go and draw me a jug of cider; I am very thirsty."

Then he went back into the house, while his wife went into the cellar and left the two Parisians alone.
255 "Let us go, let us go, Henri," Madame de Cadour said, nearly distracted with grief, and so d'Apreval took her by the arm, helped her to rise, and sustaining her with all his strength, for he felt that she was nearly fainting, he led her out, after throwing five francs on one of the chairs.

As soon as they were outside the gate, she began to sob and said,
260 shaking with grief:

"Oh! oh! is that what you have made of him?"

He was very pale and replied coldly:

"I did what I could. His farm is worth eighty thousand francs, and that is more than most of the sons of the middle classes have."
265 They returned slowly, without speaking a word. She was still crying; the tears ran down her cheeks continually for a time, but by degrees they stopped, and they went back to Fécamp, where they found Monsieur de Cadour waiting dinner for them. As soon as he saw them, he began to laugh and exclaimed:
270 "So my wife has had a sunstroke, and I am very glad of it. I really think she has lost her head for some time past!"

Neither of them replied, and when the husband asked them, rubbing his hands:

"Well, I hope that, at least, you have had a pleasant walk?"
275 Monsieur d'Apreval replied:

"A delightful walk, I assure you; perfectly delightful."

(1884)

# A Garden of Her Own

Shani Mootoo (Canada) 1958–

## About the Author

*Shortly after Shani Mootoo was born in Ireland, her parents moved to Trinidad, where she was raised. Now a resident of Vancouver, Mootoo is a multimedia artist and videomaker as well as a respected writer. Her novel* Cereus Blooms at Night *(1996) was nominated for several awards: the 1997 Giller Prize, the Chapters/Books in Canada First Novel Award, and the Ethel Wilson Fiction Prize. Her other publications are* Out on Mainstreet *(1993) and* The Predicament of Or *(2001). Many of her protagonists are, like Mootoo herself, women of Indian descent from the Caribbean.*

*Her stories in* Out on Mainstreet, *like her novels, explore relationships against a backdrop of differences—differences of race, culture, gender, and sexual orientation. Mootoo's writing has been praised for its "deft design of vivid and sensuous scenes" and for presenting "a memorable lesson in the value of love, whatever guise it may wear." The protagonist of "A Garden of her Own" is faced with a life that is without love, so she creates a passion to give her life meaning. This search for a better life, for a more meaningful existence in a world that is often hostile is a unifying theme in Mootoo's writing. In "A Garden of Her Own," Vijai expresses her need for creativity and personal growth in her little garden on the balcony.*

A north-facing balcony meant that no sunlight would enter there. A deep-in-the-heart-of-the-forest green pine tree, over-fertilized opulence extending its midriff, filled the view from the balcony.

There was no window, only a glass sliding door which might have let
5 fresh air in and released second- or third-hand air and the kinds of odours that build phantoms in stuffy apartments. But it remained shut. Not locked, but stuck shut from decades of other renters' black, oily grit and grime which had collected in the grooves of the sliding door's frame.

Vijai knew that it would not budge up, down or sideways. For the
10 amount of rent the husband paid for this bachelor apartment, the landlord could not be bothered. She opened the hallway door to let the cooking lamb fat and garlic smells drift out into the hallway. She did not want them to burrow into the bed sheets, into towels and clothes crammed into the dented cream-coloured metal space-saver cupboard that she had to
15 share with the husband. It was what all the other renters did too; everyone's years of oil—sticky, burnt, over-used, rancid oil—and of garlic,

onions and spices formed themselves into an impenetrable nose-singeing, skin-stinging presence that lurked menacingly in the hall. Instead of releasing the lamb from the husband's apartment, opening the door
20 allowed this larger phantom to barge its way in.

Vijai, engulfed, slammed the door shut. She tilted her head to face the ceiling and breathed in hard, searching for air that had no smell, no weight. The husband was already an hour late for dinner. She paced the twelve strides, back and forth, from the balcony door to the hall door, glancing
25 occasionally at the two table settings, stopping to straighten his knife, his fork, the napkin, the flowers, his knife, his fork, the napkin, the flowers. Her arms and legs tingled weakly and her intestines filled up with beads of acid formed out of unease and fear. Seeing a smear of her fingerprint on the husband's knife, she picked it up and polished it on her T-shirt until it gleamed
30 brilliantly, and she saw in it her mother's eyes looking back at her.

Sunlight. I miss the sunlight—yellow light and a sky ceiling miles high. Here the sky sits on my head, heavy grey with snow and freezing rain. I miss being able to have doors and windows opened wide, never shut except sometimes in the rainy season. Rain, rain, pinging on, winging off
35 the galvanized tin roof. But always warm rain. No matter how much it rained, it was always warm.

And what about the birds? Flying in through the windows how often? Two, three times a week? Sometimes even twice in a single day. In the shimmering heat you could see them flying slowly, their mouths wide open
40 as if crying out soundlessly. They would actually be flicking their tongues at the still air, gulping and panting, looking for a window to enter and a curtain rod to land on to cool off. But once they had cooled off and were ready to fly off again, they could never seem to focus on the window to fly through and they would bang themselves against the walls and the light
45 shade until they fell, panicked and stunned. I was the one who would get the broom and push it gently up toward one of these birds after it looked like it had cooled off, and prod, prod, prod until it hopped onto the broom and then I would lower it and reach from behind and cup the trembling in my hand. I can, right now, feel the life, the heat in the palm of my hand
50 from the little body, and the fright in its tremble. I would want to hold on to it, even think of placing it in a cage and looking after it, but something always held me back. I would put my mouth close to its ears and whisper calming shh shh shhhhs, and then take it, pressed to my chest, out the back door and open my hand and wait for it to take its time fluffing out
55 right there in my open hand before flying away.

But here? There are hardly any birds here, only that raucous, aggressive old crow that behaves as if it owns the scraggly pine tree it sits in across the street. This street is so noisy! Every day, all day and all night long, even on Sundays, cars whiz by, ambulances and fire trucks pass screaming, and 60 I think to myself thank goodness it couldn't be going for anyone I know. I don't know anyone nearby.

Too much quiet here, too shut off. Not even the sound of children playing in the street, or the sound of neighbours talking to each other over fences, conversations floating in through open windows, open bricks. Here 65 even when doors are open people walk down hallways with their noses straight ahead, making a point of not glancing to even nod hello.

Oh! This brings all kinds of images to my mind: the coconut tree outside my bedroom brushing, scraping, swishing against the wall. Green-blue iridescent lizards clinging, upside down, to the ceiling above my bed.

70 And dinner time. Mama's voice would find me wherever I was. "Vijai, go and tell Cheryl to put food on the table, yuh father comin home just now." Standing in one place, at the top of her meagre voice she would call us one by one: "Bindra, is dinner time. Bindra, why you so harden, boy? Dinner gettin cold. Turn off that TV right now! Shanti, come girl, leave 75 what you doin and come and eat. Vashti, go and tell Papa dinner ready, and then you come and sit down." Sitting down, eating together. Talking together. Conversations with no boundaries, no false politeness, no need to impress Mama or Papa.

But that's not how it was always. Sometimes Papa didn't come home till 80 long after suppertime. Mama would make us eat but she would wait for him. Sometimes he wouldn't come for days, and she would wait for him then too.

But there were always flowers from the garden on the table. Pink and yellow gerberas, ferns, ginger lilies. That was your happiness, eh Mama? 85 the garden, eh? And when there were blossoms you and I would go outside together. You showed me how to angle the garden scissors so that the plant wouldn't hurt for too long. We would bring in the bundle of flowers and greenery with their fresh-cut garden smell and little flying bugs and spiders, and you would show me how to arrange them for a centrepiece or a 90 corner table or a floor piece. The place would look so pretty! Thanks for showing that to me, Mama.

Mama, he's never brought me any flowers. Not even a dandelion.

I don't want him to ask how much these cost. Don't ask me who sent them. No one sent them; I bought them myself. With my own money. My 95 own money.

He's never given me anything. Only money for groceries.

Late. Again.

I jabbed this lamb with a trillion little gashes and stuffed a clove of
garlic in each one with your tongue, your taste buds in mind. I spent half
100   the day cooking this meal and you will come late and eat it after the juices
have hardened to a candle-wax finish, as if it were nothing but a
microwave dinner.

I want a microwave oven.

Mama, why did you wait to eat? If I were to eat now would you, Papa,
105   he think I am a bad wife? Why did you show me this, Mama?

I must not nag.

Vijai remained sleeping until the fan in the bathroom woke her. It sputtered raucously, like an airplane engine starting up, escalating in time to
fine whizzing, lifting off into the distance.

110   Five-thirty, Saturday morning.

She had fretted through most of the night, twisting, arching her body,
drawing her legs up to her chest, to the husband's chest, rolling, and
nudging him, hoping that he would awaken to pull her body into his and
hold her there. She wanted to feel the heat of his body along the length of
115   hers, his arms pressing her to him. Or his palm placed flat on her lower
belly, massaging, touching her. He responded to her fidgeting once and she
moved closer to encourage him, but he turned his naked back to her and
continued his guttural exhaling, inhaling, sounding exactly like her
father.

120   Eventually Vijai's eyes, burning from salty tears that had spilled and
dampened the pillow under her cheek, fluttered shut and she slept, deep
and dreamless, until the fan awakened her.

When the sound of the shower water snapping at the enamel tub was
muffled against his body, she pulled herself over to lie in and smell his
125   indentation in the tired foam mattress. She inhaled, instead, the history of
the mattress: unwashed hair, dying skin, old and rancid sweat—not the
smell she wanted to nestle in. Neither would the indentation cradle her;
she could feel the protruding shape of the box-spring beneath the foam.

She debated whether to get up and thanklessly make his toast and tea, or
130   pretend not to have awakened, the potential for blame nagging at her. She
slid back to her side of his bed, the other side of the line that he had drawn
down the middle with the cutting edge of his outstretched hand. Vijai

pulled her knees to her chest and hugged them. When the shower stopped she hastily straightened herself out and put her face inside the crack between the bed and the rough wall. Cold from the wall transferred itself onto her cheek, and layers upon layers of human smells trapped behind cream-coloured paint pierced her nostrils.

Vijai was aware of the husband's every move as she lay in his bed. Water from the kitchen tap pounded the sink basin, then attacked the metal floor of the kettle, gradually becoming muffled and high-pitched as the kettle filled up. He always filled it much more than was necessary for one cup of tea, which he seldom drank. The blow dryer. First on the highest setting, then dropped two notches to the lowest, and off. The electric razor. Whizzing up and down his cheek, circling his chin, the other cheek, grazing his neck. Snip, snip and little dark half-moon hair from his nostrils and his sideburns cling to the rim of the white sink basin. Wiping up, scrubbing, making spotless these areas, and others, before he returns, are her evidence that she is diligent, that she is, indeed, her mother's daughter.

At this point in the routine she always expects a handsome aftershave cologne to fill the little bachelor apartment, to bring a moment of frivolity and romance into the room. In one favourite version of her memories, this is what normally happened in her parents' bedroom at precisely this point. But the husband would only pat on his face a stinging watery liquid with the faintest smell of lime, a smell that evaporated into nothingness the instant it touched his skin.

She held herself tensely, still in the crack between the bed and the wall, as he made his way into the dark corner that he called the bedroom. The folding doors of the closet squeaked open. A shirt slid off a hanger, leaving it dangling and tinkling against the metal rod. Vijai heard the shirt that she had ironed (stretched mercilessly tight across the ironing board, the tip of the iron with staccato spurts of steam sniffing out the crevice of every seam, mimicking the importance with which her mother had treated this task) being pulled against his body and his hands sliding down the stiff front as he buttoned it.

Then there was a space empty of his sounds. The silence made the walls of her stomach contract like a closed-up accordion. Her body remained rigid. Her heart sounded as if it had moved right up into her ears, thundering methodically, and that was all that she could hear. She struggled with herself to be calm so that she could know where he was and what he was doing. Not knowing made her scalp want to unpeel itself. Then, the bed sagged as he kneeled on it, leaned across and brushed his mouth on the back of her head. His full voice had no regard for her sleep or the time of morning. He said, "Happy Birthday. I left twenty dollars on the table for you. Buy yourself a present."

175 The thundering subsided and her heart rolled and slid, rolled and slid, down, low down, and came to rest between her thighs. She turned over with lethargic elegance, as if she were just waking up, stretching out her back like a cat, but the apartment door was already being shut and locked from the outside.

180 The streets here are so wide! I hold my breath as I walk across them, six lanes wide. What if the light changes before I get to the other side? You have to walk so briskly, not only when you're crossing a wide street but even on the sidewalk. Otherwise people pass you and then turn back and stare at you, shaking their heads. And yet I remember Mama telling us
185 that fast walking, hurrying, was very unladylike.

I yearn for friends. My own friends, not his, but I'm afraid to smile at strangers. So often we huddled up in Mama's big bed and read the newspapers about things that happened to women up here—we read about women who suddenly disappeared and months later their corpses would
190 be found, having been raped and dumped. And we also read about serial murders. The victims were almost always women who had been abducted from the street by strangers in some big North American city. Mama and Papa warned me, when I was leaving to come up here, not to make eye contact with strangers because I wouldn't know whose eyes I might be
195 looking into or what I was encouraging, unknowingly. It's not like home, they said, where everybody knows everybody.

No bird sounds—there are not quite so many different kinds of birds here. Yes, Papa, yes, I can just hear you saying to stop this nonsense, all this thinking about home, that I must think of here as my home now, but I
200 haven't yet left you and Mama. I know now that I will never fully leave, nor will I ever truly be here. You felt so close, Papa, when you phoned this morning and asked like you have every past year, how was the birthday girl. You said that in your office you often look at the calendar pictures of autumn fields of bales of hay, lazy rivers meandering near brick-red farm-
205 houses, and country roads with quaint white wooden churches with red steeples, and you think that that's what my eyes have already enjoyed.

"It's all so beautiful, Papa," I said, and knowing you, you probably heard what I wasn't saying. Thanks for not pushing further. I couldn't tell you that he is working night and day to "make it," to "get ahead," to live
210 like the other men he works with. That he is always thinking about this,

and everything else is frivolous right now, so we haven't yet been for that drive in the country to see the pictures in the calendars pinned on the wall above your desk. He doesn't have time for dreaming, but I must dream or else I find it difficult to breathe.

215  At home the fence around our house and the garden was the furthest point that I ever went to on my own. From the house, winding in and out of the dracaenas and the philodendrons that I planted with Mama many Julys ago, feeling the full, firm limbs of the poui, going as far as the hibiscus and jasmine fence, and back into the house again. Any further away from the
220  house than that and the chauffeur would be driving us! And now? Just look at me! I am out in a big city on my own. I wish you all could see me. I wish we could be doing this together.

Papa, you remember, don't you, when you used to bring home magazines from your office and I would flip through them quickly looking for
225  full-page pictures of dense black-green tropical mountains, or snow-covered bluish-white ones? Ever since those first pictures I have dreamt of mountains, of touching them with the palms of my hands, of bicycling in them, and of hiking. Even though I never canoed on a river or a big lake with no shores, I know what it must feel like! I can feel what it is to ride
230  rapids like they do in National Geographic magazines. Cold river spray and drenchings, sliding, tossing, crashing! I still dream of bicycling across a huge continent. I used to think, if only I lived in North America! But here I am, in this place where these things are supposed to happen, in the midst of so much possibility, and for some reason my dreams seem even further
235  away, just out of reach. It's just not quite as simple as being here.

This land stretches on in front of me, behind me and forever. My back feels exposed, naked, so much land behind, and no fence ahead.

Except that I must cook dinner tonight.

What if I just kept walking and never returned! I could walk far way, to
240  another province, change my name, cut my hair. After a while I would see my face on a poster in a grocery store, along with all the other missing persons. The problem is that then I wouldn't even be able to phone home and speak with Mama or Papa or Bindra and Vashti without being tracked and caught, and then who knows what.

245  Well, this is the first birthday I've ever spent alone. But next time we speak on the phone I will be able to tell you that I went for a very long walk. Alone.

I think I will do this every day—well, maybe every other day, and each time I will go a new route and a little further. I will know this place in order to own it, but still I will never really leave you.

250     Mama, Papa, Vashti, Bindra, Shanti,
    Mama, Papa, Vashti, Bindra, Shanti.
    Mama. Papa. Vashti. Bindra. Shanti.

Twenty-four years of Sundays, of eating three delightfully noisy, lengthy meals together, going to the beach or for long drives with big pots of rice,
255 chicken and peas, and chocolate cake, singing "Michael Row Your Boat Ashore," and "You Are My Sunshine," doing everything in tandem with her brother and sisters and Mama and Papa. This particular characteristic of Sundays was etched deeply in her veins. (Not all Sundays were happy ones but recently she seems to have forgotten that.)
260     It would be her twenty-fourth Sunday here, the twenty-fourth week of marriage.
    The only Sunday since the marriage that the husband had taken off and spent in his apartment was six weeks ago, and since he needed to spend that day alone Vijai agreed to go to the library for at least three
265 hours. Before she left the house she thought she would use the opportunity to take down recipes for desserts, but once she began walking down the street she found herself thinking about rivers and mountains. She bypassed the shelves with all the cooking books and home-making maga-zines and found herself racing toward valleys, glaciers, canoeing, rapids
270 and the like. She picked up a magazine about hiking and mountaineering, looked at the equipment advertisements, read incomprehensible jargon about techniques for climbing.
    After about forty minutes, not seeing herself in any of the magazines, she became less enthusiastic, and eventually frustrated and bored. She
275 looked at her watch every fifteen minutes or so and then she started watching the second hand go around and counting each and every second in her head. When three hours had passed she remembered that she had said at least three hours, and she walked home slowly, stopping to window-shop and checking her watch until an extra twenty minutes had passed.
280     The strength of her determination that they not spend this Sunday apart warded off even a hint of such a suggestion from the husband. What she really wanted to do was to go for the long drive up to a glacier in the nearby mountains. That way she would have him to herself for at least five hours. But he had worked several twelve-hour shifts that week and needed
285 to rest in his apartment.
    She went to the grocery store, to the gardening section, and bought half a dozen packages of flower seeds, half a dozen packages of vegetable seeds, bags of soil, fertilizer, a fork and spade, a purple plastic watering can, and

a score of nursery trays. She brought it all home in a taxi. Enough to keep
290  her busy and in his apartment for an entire Sunday. She was becoming
adept at finding ways to get what she wanted.

He never asked and Vijai did not tell that from her allowance she had
paid a man from the hardware store to come over and fix the balcony
sliding door. She stooped on the balcony floor scooping earth into nursery
295  trays. He sat reading the newspaper, facing the balcony in his big sagging
gold armchair that he had bought next-door at a church basement sale for
five dollars. She was aware that he was stealing glances at her as she bent
over her garden-in-the-making.

I wore this shirt, no bra, am stopping, bending over here to reveal my
300  breasts to you. *Look at them! Feel something!*

I might as well be sharing this apartment with a brother, or a roommate.

She feels his hands on her waist, leading her from behind to the edge of his
bed. Her body is crushed under his as he slams himself against her, from
behind, grunting. She holds her breath, taut against his weight and the
305  pain, but she will not disturb his moment. She hopes that the next
moment will be hers. She waits with the bed sheet pulled up to her chin.
The toilet flushes and, shortly after, she hears newspaper pages being
turned in the sagging five-dollar gold armchair.

Later, deep-sleep breathing and low snoring from the bedroom fills the
310  apartment, dictating her movements. She sits on the green-and-yellow
shag carpet, leaning against the foot of the husband's armchair, in front
of the snowy black-and-white television watching a French station turned
down low enough not to awaken him. Something about listening to a language that she does not understand comforts her, gives her companion-
315  ship in a place where she feels like a foreigner. She is beginning to be able
to repeat advertisements in French.

(1993)

# How I Met My Husband

Alice Munro (Canada) 1931–

## About the Author

*Alice Munro, one of Canada's most celebrated authors, is an acknowledged master of the short story. In 2001, Alice Munro was given the Rea Award for lifetime achievement for her contributions to the short story genre. Her work has not only earned her respect and praise, but also many literary awards, for she has been acknowledged as an expert short story writer ever since her first collection of short stories,* Dance of the Happy Shades and Other Stories *(1968). This book won the Governor General's Literary Award, as did* Who Do You Think You Are? *(1978),* The Beggar Maid *(1979), and* The Progress of Love *(1986). Her best-known collection,* Lives of Girls and Women *(1971), won the Canadian Bestseller's award and was adapted as a CBC series.* The Love of a Good Woman *(1998) and* Hateship, Friendship, Courtship, Loveship, Marriage *(2001) were both nominated for the national Book Critics Award for Fiction.*

*Born and raised in Wingham, Ontario, Munro usually writes about characters living in small towns in southwestern Ontario. Their everyday experiences are the subject of Munro's stories, yet she makes them appear extraordinary because of her acute empathy, understanding, and exploration of human relationships. Critics celebrate Munro's seemingly effortless, conversational tone, her simple, controlled diction and the moral and emotional depth she conveys in her pictures of life. She doesn't judge her characters, and by offering no resolution to her stories, Munro enables her readers to draw their own conclusions. In the words of one reviewer, she possesses "an exhilarating ability to make the readers see the familiar with fresh insight and compassion." So it is in "How I Met My Husband," as Edie discovers she likes "for people to think what pleases them and makes them happy."*

We heard the plane come over at noon, roaring through the radio news, and we were sure it was going to hit the house, so we all ran out into the yard. We saw it come in over the treetops, all red and silver, the first close-up plane I ever saw. Mrs. Peebles screamed.

5   "Crash landing," their little boy said. Joey was his name.

"It's okay," said Dr. Peebles. "He knows what he's doing." Dr. Peebles was only an animal doctor, but had a calming way of talking, like any doctor.

This was my first job—working for Dr. and Mrs. Peebles, who had
10  bought an old house out on the Fifth Line, about five miles out of town. It
was just when the trend was starting of town people buying up old farms,
not to work them but to live on them.

We watched the plane land across the road, where the fairgrounds used
to be. It did make a good landing field, nice and level for the old race track,
15  and the barns and display sheds torn down now for scrap lumber so there
was nothing in the way. Even the old grandstand bays had burned.

"All right," said Mrs. Peebles, snappy as she always was when she got
over her nerves. "Let's go back in the house. Let's not stand here gawking
like a set of farmers."

20  She didn't say that to hurt my feelings. It never occurred to her.

I was just setting the dessert down when Loretta Bird arrived, out of
breath, at the screen door.

"I thought it was going to crash into the house and kill youse all!"

She lived on the next place and the Peebleses thought she was a coun-
25  trywoman, they didn't know the difference. She and her husband didn't
farm, he worked on the roads and had a bad name for drinking. They had
seven children and couldn't get credit at the HiWay Grocery. The Peebleses
made her welcome, not knowing any better, as I say, and offered her
dessert.

30  Dessert was never anything to write home about, at their place. A dish
of Jell-O or sliced bananas or fruit out of a tin. "Have a house without a
pie, be ashamed until you die," my mother used to say, but Mrs. Peebles
operated differently.

Loretta Bird saw me getting the can of peaches.

35  "Oh, never mind," she said. "I haven't got the right kind of a stomach
to trust what comes out of those tins, I can only eat home canning."

I could have slapped her. I bet she never put down fruit in her life.

"I know what he's landed here for," she said. "He's got permission to use
the fairgrounds and take people up for rides. It costs a dollar. It's the same
40  fellow who was over at Palmerston last week and was up the lakeshore
before that. I wouldn't go up, if you paid me."

"I'd jump at the chance," Dr. Peebles said. "I'd like to see this neighbor-
hood from the air."

Mrs. Peebles said she would just as soon see it from the ground. Joey said
45  he wanted to go and Heather did, too. Joey was nine and Heather was
seven.

"Would you, Edie?" Heather said.

I said I didn't know. I was scared, but I never admitted that, especially in front of children I was taking care of.

50    "People are going to be coming out here in their cars raising dust and trampling your property, if I was you I would complain." Loretta said. She hooked her legs around the chair rung and I knew we were in for a lengthy visit. After Dr. Peebles went back to his office or out on his next call and Mrs. Peebles went for her nap, she would hang around me while I was
55 trying to do the dishes. She would pass remarks about the Peebleses in their own house.

   "She wouldn't find time to lay down in the middle of the day, if she had seven kids like I got."

   She asked me did they fight and did they keep things in the dresser
60 drawer not to have babies with. She said it was a sin if they did. I pretended I didn't know what she was talking about.

   I was fifteen and away from home for the first time. My parents had made the effort and sent me to high school for a year, but I didn't like it. I was shy of strangers and the work was hard, they didn't make it nice for
65 you or explain the way they do now. At the end of the year the averages were published in the paper, and mine came out at the very bottom, 37 percent. My father said that's enough and I didn't blame him. The last thing I wanted, anyway, was to go on and end up teaching school. It happened the very day the paper came out with my disgrace in it, Dr. Peebles
70 was staying at our place for dinner, having just helped one of the cows have twins, and he said I looked smart to him and his wife was looking for a girl to help. He said she felt tied down, with the two children, out in the country. I guess she would, my mother said, being polite, though I could tell from her face she was wondering what on earth it would be like to have
75 only two children and no barn work, and then to be complaining.

   When I went home I would describe to them the work I had to do, and it made everybody laugh. Mrs. Peebles had an automatic washer and dryer, the first I ever saw. I have had those in my own home for such a long time now it's hard to remember how much of a miracle it was to me, not having
80 to struggle with the wringer and hang up and haul down. Let alone not having to heat water. Then there was practically no baking. Mrs. Peebles said she couldn't make pie crust, the most amazing thing I ever heard a woman admit. I could, of course, and I could make light biscuits and a white cake and dark cake, but they didn't want it, she said they watched
85 their figures. The only thing I didn't like about working there, in fact, was

feeling half hungry a lot of the time. I used to bring back a box of dough-nuts made out at home, and hide them under my bed. The children found out, and I didn't mind sharing, but I thought I better bind them to secrecy.

The day after the plane landed Mrs. Peebles put both children in the car
90 and drove over to Chesley, to get their hair cut. There was a good woman then at Chesley for doing hair. She got hers done at the same place, Mrs. Peebles did, and that meant they would be gone a good while. She had to pick a day Dr. Peebles wasn't going out into the country, she didn't have her own car. Cars were still in short supply then, after the war.

95    I loved being left in the house alone, to do my work at leisure. The kitchen was all white and bright yellow, with fluorescent lights. That was before they ever thought of making the appliances all different colors and doing the cupboards like dark old wood and hiding the lighting. I loved light. I loved the double sink. So would anybody new-come from washing
100 dishes in a dishpan with a rag-plugged hole on an oilcloth-covered table by light of a coal-oil lamp. I kept everything shining.

The bathroom too. I had a bath in there once a week. They wouldn't have minded if I took one oftener, but to me it seemed like asking too much, or maybe risking making it less wonderful. The basin and the tub
105 and the toilet were all pink, and there were glass doors with flamingoes painted on them, to shut off the tub. The light had a rosy cast and the mat sank under your feet like snow, except that it was warm. The mirror was three-way. With the mirror all steamed up and the air like a perfume cloud, from things I was allowed to use, I stood up on the side of the tub
110 and admired myself naked, from three directions. Sometimes I thought about the way we lived out at home and the way we lived here and how one way was so hard to imagine when you were living the other way. But I thought it was still a lot easier, living the way we lived at home, to pic-ture something like this, the painted flamingoes and the warmth and the
115 soft mat, than it was anybody knowing only things like this to picture how it was the other way. And why was that?

I was through my jobs in no time, and had the vegetables peeled for supper and sitting in cold water besides. Then I went into Mrs. Peebles' bedroom. I had been in there plenty of times, cleaning, and I always took
120 a good look in her closet, at the clothes she had hanging there. I wouldn't have looked in her drawers, but a closet is open to anybody. That's a lie. I would have looked in drawers, but I would have felt worse doing it and been more scared she could tell.

Some clothes in her closet she wore all the time, I was quite familiar
125 with them. Others she never put on, they were pushed to the back. I was
disappointed to see no wedding dress. But there was one long dress I could
just see the skirt of, and I was hungering to see the rest. Now I took note of
where it hung and lifted it out. It was satin, a lovely weight on my arm,
light bluish-green in color, almost silvery. It had a fitted, pointed waist and
130 a full skirt and an off-the-shoulder fold hiding the little sleeves.

Next thing was easy. I got out of my own things and slipped it on. I was
slimmer at fifteen than anybody would believe who knows me now and
the fit was beautiful. I didn't, of course, have a strapless bra on, which was
what it needed, I just had to slide my straps down my arms under the
135 material. Then I tried pinning up my hair, to get the effect. One thing led
to another. I put on rouge and lipstick and eyebrow pencil from her dresser.
The heat of the day and the weight of the satin and all the excitement
made me thirsty, and I went out to the kitchen, got-up as I was, to get a
glass of ginger ale with ice cubes from the refrigerator. The Peebleses drank
140 ginger ale, or fruit drinks, all day, like water, and I was getting so I did too.
Also there was no limit on ice cubes, which I was so fond of I would even
put them in a glass of milk.

I turned from putting the ice tray back and saw a man watching me
through the screen. It was the luckiest thing in the world I didn't spill the
145 ginger ale down the front of me then and there.

"I never meant to scare you. I knocked but you were getting the ice out,
you didn't hear me."

I couldn't see what he looked like, he was dark the way somebody is
pressed up against a screen door with the bright daylight behind them. I
150 only knew he wasn't from around here.

"I'm from the plane over there. My name is Chris Watters and what I
was wondering was if I could use that pump."

There was a pump in the yard. That was the way the people used to get
their water. Now I noticed he was carrying a pail.

155 "You're welcome," I said. "I can get it from the tap and save you
pumping." I guess I wanted him to know we had piped water, didn't pump
ourselves.

"I don't mind the exercise." He didn't move, though, and finally he said,
"Were you going to a dance?"

160 Seeing a stranger there had made me entirely forget how I was dressed.

"Or is that the way ladies around here generally get dressed up in the
afternoon?"

I didn't know how to joke back then. I was too embarrassed.

"You live here? Are you the lady of the house?"

165  "I'm the hired girl."

Some people change when they find that out, their whole way of looking at you and speaking to you changes, but his didn't.

"Well, I just wanted to tell you you look very nice. I was so surprised when I looked in the door and saw you. Just because you looked so nice

170  and beautiful."

I wasn't even old enough then to realize how out of the common it is, for a man to say something like that to a woman, or somebody he is treating like a woman. For a man to say a word like *beautiful.* I wasn't old enough to realize or to say anything back, or in fact to do anything but

175  wish he would go away. Not that I didn't like him, but just that it upset me so, having him look at me, and me trying to think of something to say.

He must have understood. He said good-bye, and thanked me, and went and started filling his pail from the pump. I stood behind the Venetian blinds in the dining room, watching him. When he had gone, I went into

180  the bedroom and took the dress off and put it back in the same place. I dressed in my own clothes and took my hair down and washed my face, wiping it on Kleenex, which I threw in the wastebasket.

The Peebleses asked me what kind of man he was. Young, middle-aged, short, tall? I couldn't say.

185  "Good-looking?" Dr. Peebles teased me.

I couldn't think a thing but that he would be coming to get his water again, he would be talking to Dr. or Mrs. Peebles, making friends with them, and he would mention seeing me that first afternoon, dressed up. Why not mention it? He would think it was funny. And no idea of the

190  trouble it would get me into.

After supper the Peebleses drove into town to go to a movie. She wanted to go somewhere with her hair fresh done. I sat in my bright kitchen wondering what to do, knowing I would never sleep. Mrs. Peebles might not fire me, when she found out, but it would give her a different feeling about me

195  altogether. This was the first place I ever worked but I already had picked up things about the way people feel when you are working for them. They like to think you aren't curious. Not just that you aren't dishonest, that isn't enough. They like to feel you don't notice things, that you don't think or wonder about anything but what they liked to eat and how they liked

200  things ironed, and so on. I don't mean they weren't kind to me, because

they were. They had me eat my meals with them (to tell the truth I expected to, I didn't know there were families who don't) and sometimes they took me along in the car. But all the same.

I went up and checked on the children being asleep and then I went out.
205 I had to do it. I crossed the road and went in the old fairgrounds gate. The plane looked unnatural sitting there, and shining with the moon. Off at the far side of the fairgrounds where the bush was taking over, I saw his tent.

He was sitting outside it smoking a cigarette. He saw me coming.

210 "Hello, were you looking for a plane ride? I don't start taking people up till tomorrow." Then he looked again and said, "Oh, it's you. I didn't know you without your long dress on."

My heart was knocking away, my tongue was dried up. I had to say something. But I couldn't. My throat was closed and I was like a deaf-and-
215 dumb.

"Did you want a ride? Sit down. Have a cigarette."

I couldn't even shake my head to say no, so he gave me one.

"Put it in your mouth or I can't light it. It's a good thing I'm used to shy ladies."

220 I did. It wasn't the first time I had smoked a cigarette, actually. My girl-friend out home, Muriel Lowe, used to steal them from her brother.

"Look at your hand shaking. Did you just want to have a chat, or what?"

In one burst I said, "I wisht you wouldn't say anything about that
225 dress."

"What dress? Oh, the long dress."

"It's Mrs. Peebles'."

"Whose? Oh, the lady you work for? She wasn't home so you got dressed up in her dress, eh? You got dressed up and played queen. I don't
230 blame you. You're not smoking the cigarette right. Don't just puff. Draw it in. Did anybody ever show you how to inhale? Are you scared I'll tell on you? Is that it?"

I was so ashamed at having to ask him to connive this way I couldn't nod. I just looked at him and he saw yes.

235 "Well I won't. I won't in the slightest way mention it or embarrass you. I give you my word of honor."

Then he changed the subject, to help me out, seeing I couldn't even thank him.

"What do you think of this sign?"

240      It was a board sign lying practically at my feet.

     SEE THE WORLD FROM THE SKY. ADULTS $1.00, CHILDREN 50¢. QUALIFIED PILOT.

     "My old sign was getting pretty beat up, I thought I'd make a new one. That's what I've been doing with my time today."

245      The lettering wasn't all that handsome, I thought. I could have done a better one in half an hour.

     "I'm not an expert at sign making."

     "It's very good," I said.

     "I don't need it for publicity, word of mouth is usually enough. I turned
250 away two carloads tonight. I felt like taking it easy. I didn't tell them ladies were dropping in to visit me."

     Now I remembered the children and I was scared again, in case one of them had waked up and called me and I wasn't there.

     "Do you have to go so soon?"

255      I remembered some manners. "Thank you for the cigarette."

     "Don't forget. You have my word of honor."

     I tore off across the fairgrounds, scared I'd see the car heading home from town. My sense of time was mixed up, I didn't know how long I'd been out of the house. But it was all right, it wasn't late, the children were
260 asleep. I got in my bed myself and lay thinking what a lucky end to the day, after all, and among things to be grateful for I could be grateful Loretta Bird hadn't been the one who caught me.

     The yard and borders didn't get trampled, it wasn't as bad as that. All the same it seemed very public, around the house. The sign was on the fair-
265 grounds gate. People came mostly after supper but a good many in the afternoon, too. The Bird children all came without fifty cents between them and hung on the gate. We got used to the excitement of the plane coming in and taking off, it wasn't excitement anymore. I never went over, after that one time, but would see him when he came to get his water. I would be out on
270 the steps doing sitting-down work, like preparing vegetables, if I could.

     "Why don't you come over? I'll take you up in my plane."

     "I'm saving my money," I said, because I couldn't think of anything else.

     "For what? For getting married?"

275      I shook my head.

     "I'll take you up for free if you come sometime when it's slack. I thought you would come, and have another cigarette."

I made a face to hush him, because you never could tell when the children would be sneaking around the porch, or Mrs. Peebles herself listening
280  in the house. Sometimes she came out and had a conversation with him. He told her things he hadn't bothered to tell me. But then I hadn't thought to ask. He told her he had been in the war, that was where he learned to fly a plane, and how he couldn't settle down to ordinary life, this was what he liked. She said she couldn't imagine anybody liking such a thing.
285  Though sometimes, she said, she was almost bored enough to try anything herself, she wasn't brought up to living in the country. It's all my husband's idea, she said. This was news to me.

"Maybe you ought to give flying lessons," she said.

"Would you take them?"

290  She just laughed.

Sunday was a busy flying day in spite of it being preached against from two pulpits. We were all sitting out watching. Joey and Heather were over on the fence with the Bird kids. Their father had said they could go, after their mother saying all week they couldn't.

295  A car came down the road past the parked cars and pulled up right in the drive. It was Loretta Bird who got out, all importance, and on the driver's side another woman got out, more sedately. She was wearing sunglasses.

"This is a lady looking for the man that flies the plane," Loretta Bird
300  said. "I heard her inquire in the hotel coffee shop where I was having a Coke and I brought her out."

"I'm sorry to bother you," the lady said. "I'm Alice Kelling, Mr. Watters' fiancée."

This Alice Kelling had on a pair of brown and white checked slacks and
305  a yellow top. Her bust looked to me rather low and bumpy. She had a worried face. Her hair had had a permanent, but had grown out, and she wore a yellow band to keep it off her face. Nothing in the least pretty or even young-looking about her. But you could tell from how she talked she was from the city, or educated, or both.

310  Dr. Peebles stood up and introduced himself and his wife and me and asked her to be seated.

"He's up in the air right now, but you're welcome to sit and wait. He gets his water here and he hasn't been yet. He'll probably take his break about five."

315  "That is him, then?" said Alice Kelling, wrinkling and straining at the sky.

"He's not in the habit of running out on you, taking a different name?" Dr. Peebles laughed. He was the one, not his wife, to offer iced tea. Then she sent me into the kitchen to fix it. She smiled. She was wearing sun-
320 glasses too.

"He never mentioned his fiancée," she said.

I loved fixing iced tea with lots of ice and slices of lemon in tall glasses. I ought to have mentioned before, Dr. Peebles was an abstainer, at least around the house, or I wouldn't have been allowed to take the place. I had
325 to fix a glass for Loretta Bird too, though it galled me, and when I went out she had settled in my lawn chair, leaving me the steps.

"I knew you was a nurse when I first heard you in that coffee shop."

"How would you know a thing like that?"

"I get my hunches about people. Was that how you met him, nursing?"
330 "Chris? Well yes. Yes, it was."

"Oh, were you overseas?" said Mrs. Peebles.

"No, it was before he went overseas. I nursed him when he was sta-tioned at Centralia and had a ruptured appendix. We got engaged and then he went overseas. My, this is refreshing, after a long drive."
335 "He'll be glad to see you," Dr. Peebles said. "It's a rackety kind of life, isn't it, not staying one place long enough to really make friends."

"Youse've had a long engagement," Loretta Bird said.

Alice Kelling passed that over. "I was going to get a room at the hotel, but when I was offered directions I came on out. Do you think I could
340 phone them?"

"No need," Dr. Peebles said. "You're five miles away from him if you stay at the hotel. Here, you're right across the road. Stay with us. We've got rooms on rooms, look at this big house."

Asking people to stay, just like that, is certainly a country thing, and
345 maybe seemed natural to him now, but not to Mrs. Peebles, from the way she said, oh yes, we have plenty of room. Or to Alice Kelling, who kept protesting, but let herself be worn down. I got the feeling it was a tempta-tion to her, to be that close. I was trying for a look at her ring. Her nails were painted red, her fingers were freckled and wrinkled. It was a tiny
350 stone. Muriel Lowe's cousin had one twice as big.

Chris came to get his water, late in the afternoon just as Dr. Peebles had predicted. He must have recognized the car from a way off. He came smiling.

"Here I am chasing after you to see what you're up to," called Alice
355 Kelling. She got up and went to meet him and they kissed, just touched, in front of us.

"You're going to spend a lot on gas that way," Chris said.

Dr. Peebles invited Chris to stay for supper, since he had already put up the sign that said: NO MORE RIDES TILL 7 P.M. Mrs. Peebles wanted it
360 served in the yard, in spite of the bugs. One thing strange to anybody from the country is this eating outside. I had made a potato salad earlier and she had made a jellied salad, that was one thing she could do, so it was just a matter of getting those out, and some sliced meat and cucumbers and fresh leaf lettuce. Loretta Bird hung around for some time saying,
365 "Oh, well, I guess I better get home to those yappers," and, "It's so nice just sitting here, I sure hate to get up," but nobody invited her, I was relieved to see, and finally she had to go.

That night after rides were finished Alice Kelling and Chris went off somewhere in her car. I lay awake till they got back. When I saw the car
370 lights sweep my ceiling I got up to look down on them through the slats of my blind. I don't know what I thought I was going to see. Muriel Lowe and I used to sleep on her front veranda and watch her sister and her sister's boy friend saying good night. Afterward we couldn't get to sleep, for longing for somebody to kiss us and rub against us and we would talk
375 about suppose you were out in a boat with a boy and he wouldn't bring you in to shore unless you did it, or what if somebody got you trapped in a barn, you would have to, wouldn't you, it wouldn't be your fault. Muriel said her two girl cousins used to try with a toilet paper roll that one of them was a boy. We wouldn't do anything like that; just lay and
380 wondered.

All that happened was that Chris got out of the car on one side and she got out on the other and they walked off separately—him toward the fairgrounds and her toward the house. I got back in bed and imagined about me coming home with him, not like that.

385 Next morning Alice Kelling got up late and I fixed a grapefruit for her the way I had learned and Mrs. Peebles sat down with her to visit and have another cup of coffee. Mrs. Peebles seemed pleased enough now, having company. Alice Kelling said she guessed she better get used to putting in a day just watching Chris take off and come down, and Mrs. Peebles said she
390 didn't know if she should suggest it because Alice Kelling was the one with the car, but the lake was only twenty-five miles away and what a good day for a picnic.

Alice Kelling took her up on the idea and by eleven o'clock they were in the car, with Joey and Heather and a sandwich lunch I had made. The
395 only thing was that Chris hadn't come down, and she wanted to tell him where they were going.

"Edie'll go over and tell him," Mrs. Peebles said. "There's no problem."

Alice Kelling wrinkled her face and agreed.

"Be sure and tell him we'll be back by five!"

400    I didn't see that he would be concerned about knowing this right away, and I thought of him eating whatever he ate over there, alone, cooking on his camp stove, so I got to work and mixed up a crumb cake and baked it, in between the other work I had to do; then, when it was a bit cooled, wrapped it in a tea towel. I didn't do anything to myself but take off my

405 apron and comb my hair. I would like to have put some makeup on, but I was too afraid it would remind him of the way he first saw me, and that would humiliate me all over again.

He had come and put another sign on the gate: NO RIDES THIS P.M. APOLOGIES. I worried that he wasn't feeling well. No sign of him outside

410 and the tent flap was down. I knocked on the pole.

"Come in," he said, in a voice that would just as soon have said *Stay out.* I lifted the flap.

"Oh, it's you. I'm sorry. I didn't know it was you."

He had been just sitting on the side of the bed, smoking. Why not at

415 least sit and smoke in the fresh air?

"I brought a cake and hope you're not sick," I said.

"Why would I be sick? Oh—that sign. That's all right. I'm just tired of talking to people. I don't mean you. Have a seat." He pinned back the tent flap. "Get some fresh air in here."

420    I sat on the edge of the bed, there was no place else. It was one of those foldup cots, really: I remembered and gave him his fiancée's message.

He ate some of the cake. "Good."

"Put the rest away for when you're hungry later."

"I'll tell you a secret. I won't be around here much longer."

425    "Are you getting married?"

"Ha ha. What time did you say they'd be back?"

"Five o'clock."

"Well, by that time this place will have seen the last of me. A plane can get further than a car." He unwrapped the cake and ate another piece of

430 it, absent-mindedly.

"Now you'll be thirsty."

"There's some water in the pail."

"It won't be very cold. I could bring some fresh. I could bring some ice from the refrigerator."

435    "No," he said. "I don't want you to go. I want a nice long time of saying good-bye to you."

He put the cake away carefully and sat beside me and started those little kisses, so soft, I can't ever let myself think about them, such kindness in his face and lovely kisses, all over my eyelids and neck and ears, all over, then
440 me kissing back as well as I could (I had only kissed a boy on a dare before, and kissed my own arms for practice) and we lay back on the cot and pressed together, just gently, and he did some other things, not bad things or not in a bad way. It was lovely in the tent, that smell of grass and hot tent cloth with the sun beating down on it, and he said, "I wouldn't do you
445 any harm for the world." Once, when he had rolled on top of me and we were sort of rocking together on the cot, he said softly, "Oh, no," and freed himself and jumped up and got the water pail. He splashed some of it on his neck and face, and the little bit left, on me lying there.

"That's to cool us off, miss."

450 When we said good-bye I wasn't at all sad, because he held my face and said, "I'm going to write you a letter. I'll tell you where I am and maybe you can come and see me. Would you like that? Okay then. You wait." I was really glad I think to get away from him, it was like he was piling presents on me I couldn't get the pleasure of till I considered them alone.

455 No consternation at first about the plane being gone. They thought he had taken somebody up, and I didn't enlighten them. Dr. Peebles had phoned he had to go to the country, so there was just us having supper, and then Loretta Bird thrusting her head in the door and saying, "I see he's took off."

460 "What?" said Alice Kelling, and pushed back her chair.

"The kids come and told me this afternoon he was taking down his tent. Did he think he'd run through all the business there was around here? He didn't take off without letting you know, did he?"

"He'll send me word," Alice Kelling said. "He'll probably phone tonight.
465 He's terribly restless, since the war."

"Edie, he didn't mention to you, did he?" Mrs. Peebles said. "When you took over the message?"

"Yes," I said. So far so true.

"Well why didn't you say?" All of them were looking at me. "Did he say
470 where he was going?"

"He said he might try Bayfield," I said. What made me tell such a lie? I didn't intend it.

"Bayfield, how far is that?" said Alice Kelling.

Mrs. Peebles said, "Thirty, thirty-five miles."

475 "That's not far. Oh, well, that's really not far at all. It's on the lake, isn't it?"

You'd think I'd be ashamed of myself, setting her on the wrong track. I did it to give him more time, whatever time he needed. I lied for him, and also, I have to admit, for me. Women should stick together and not do
480 things like that. I see that now, but didn't then. I never thought of myself as being in any way like her, or coming to the same troubles, ever.

She hadn't taken her eyes off me. I thought she suspected my lie.

"When did he mention this to you?"

"Earlier."

485 "When you were over at the plane?"

"Yes."

"You must've stayed and had a chat." She smiled at me, not a nice smile. "You must've stayed and had a little visit with him."

"I took a cake," I said, thinking that telling some truth would spare me
490 telling the rest.

"We didn't have a cake," said Mrs. Peebles rather sharply.

"I baked one."

Alice Kelling said, "That was very friendly of you."

"Did you get permission," said Loretta Bird. "You never know what these
495 girls'll do next," she said. "It's not they mean harm so much, as they're ignorant."

"The cake is neither here nor there," Mrs. Peebles broke in. "Edie, I wasn't aware you knew Chris that well."

I didn't know what to say.

500 "I'm not surprised," Alice Kelling said in a high voice. "I knew by the look of her as soon as I saw her. We get them at the hospital all the time." She looked hard at me with her stretched smile. "Having their babies. We have to put them in a special ward because of their diseases. Little country tramps. Fourteen and fifteen years old. You should see the babies they
505 have, too."

"There was a bad woman here in town had a baby that pus was running out of its eyes," Loretta Bird put in.

"Wait a minute," said Mrs. Peebles. "What is this talk? Edie. What about you and Mr. Watters? Were you intimate with him?"

510 "Yes," I said. I was thinking of us lying on the cot and kissing, wasn't that intimate? And I would never deny it.

They were all one minute quiet, even Loretta Bird.

"Well," said Mrs. Peebles. "I am surprised. I think I need a cigarette. This is the first of any such tendencies I've seen in her," she said, speaking to Alice Kelling, but Alice Kelling was looking at me.

"Loose little bitch." Tears ran down her face. "Loose little bitch, aren't you? I knew as soon as I saw you. Men despise girls like you. He just made use of you and went off, you know that, don't you? Girls like you are just nothing, they're just public conveniences, just filthy little rags!"

"Oh, now," said Mrs. Peebles.

"Filthy," Alice Kelling sobbed. "Filthy little rags!"

"Don't get yourself upset," Loretta Bird said. She was swollen up with pleasure at being in on this scene. "Men are all the same."

"Edie, I'm very surprised," Mrs. Pebbles said. "I thought your parents were so strict. You don't want to have a baby, do you?"

I'm still ashamed of what happened next. I lost control, just like a six-year-old, I started howling. "You don't get a baby from just doing that!"

"You see. Some of them are that ignorant," Loretta Bird said.

But Mrs. Peebles jumped up and caught my arms and shook me.

"Calm down. Don't get hysterical. Calm down. Stop crying. Listen to me. Listen, I'm wondering if you know what being intimate means. Now tell me. What did you think it meant?"

"Kissing," I howled.

She let go. "Oh, Edie. Stop it. Don't be silly. It's all right. It's all a misunderstanding. Being intimate means a lot more than that. Oh, I *wondered.*"

"She's trying to cover up, now," said Alice Kelling. "Yes. She's not so stupid. She sees she got herself in trouble."

"I believe her," Mrs. Peebles said. "This is an awful scene."

"Well there is one way to find out," said Alice Kelling, getting up. "After all, I am a nurse."

Mrs. Peebles drew a breath and said, "No. No. Go to your room, Edie. And stop that noise. This is too disgusting."

I heard the car start in a little while. I tried to stop crying, pulling back each wave as it started over me. Finally I succeeded, and lay heaving on the bed.

Mrs. Peebles came and stood in the doorway.

"She's gone," she said. "That Bird woman too. Of course, you know you should never have gone near that man and that is the cause of all this trouble. I have a headache. As soon as you can, go and wash your face in cold water and get at the dishes and we will not say any more about this."

Nor we didn't. I didn't figure out till years later the extent of what I had been saved from. Mrs. Peebles was not very friendly to me afterward, but she was fair. Not very friendly is the wrong way of describing what she was.

555 She had never been very friendly. It was just that now she had to see me all the time and it got on her nerves, a little.

As for me, I put it all out of my mind like a bad dream and concentrated on waiting for my letter. The mail came every day except Sunday, between one-thirty and two in the afternoon, a good time for me because Mrs.

560 Peebles was always having her nap. I would get the kitchen all cleaned and then go up to the mailbox and sit in the grass, waiting. I was perfectly happy, waiting. I forgot all about Alice Kelling and her misery and awful talk and Mrs. Peebles and her chilliness and the embarrassment of whether she told Dr. Peebles and the face of Loretta Bird, getting her fill of

565 other people's troubles. I was always smiling when the mailman got there, and continued smiling even after he gave me the mail and I saw today wasn't the day. The mailman was a Carmichael. I knew by his face because there are a lot of Carmichaels living out by us and so many of them have a sort of sticking out top lip. So I asked his name (he was a

570 young man, shy, but good-humored, anybody could ask him anything) and then I said, "I knew by your face!" He was pleased by that and always glad to see me and got a little less shy. "You've got the smile I've been waiting for all day!" he used to holler out the car window.

It never crossed my mind for a long time a letter might not come. I

575 believed in it coming just like I believed the sun would rise in the morning. I just put off my hope from day to day, and there was the goldenrod out around the mailbox and the children gone back to school, and the leaves turning, and I was wearing a sweater when I went to wait. One day walking back with the hydro bill stuck in my hand, that was all, looking across at

580 the fairgrounds with the full-blown milkweed and dark teasels, so much like fall, it just struck me: *No letter was ever going to come.* It was an impossible idea to get used to. No, not impossible. If I thought about Chris's face when he said he was going to write me, it was impossible, but if I forgot that and thought about the actual tin mailbox, empty, it was plain and true. I

585 kept on going to meet the mail, but my heart was heavy now like a lump of lead. I only smiled because I thought of the mailman counting on it, and he didn't have an easy life, with the winter driving ahead.

Till it came to me one day there were women doing this with their lives, all over. There were women just waiting and waiting by mailboxes for one

590 letter or another. I imagined me making this journey day after day and

year after year, and my hair starting to get gray, and I thought, I was never made to go on like that. So I stopped meeting the mail. If there were women all through life waiting, and women busy and not waiting, I knew which I had to be. Even though there might be things the second kind of women have to pass up and never know about, it still is better.

I was surprised when the mailman phoned the Peebleses' place in the evening and asked for me. He said he missed me. He asked if I would like to go to Goderich, where some well-known movie was on, I forget now what. So I said yes, and I went out with him for two years and he asked me to marry him, and we were engaged a year more while I got my things together, and then we did marry. He always tells the children the story of how I went after him by sitting by the mailbox every day, and naturally I laugh and let him, because I like for people to think what pleases them and makes them happy.

(1974)

# A Horse and Two Goats

R.K. Narayan (India) 1906–2001

## About the Author

*Rasipuram Krishnaswami Narayan is probably the most well-known and distinguished Indian writer who writes in English. He says he is unaware of using a foreign language when he writes in English, and his style has been widely acclaimed for its calm simplicity, natural cadences, and beautiful fluency. Born in Madras (Chennai), Narayan lived most of his life in Mysore. He transforms his childhood home into Malgudi, which is the setting of his many novels and short stories. This fictional small town, its typical inhabitants, and their daily lives allow Narayan to meditate on the universal human condition. Critics agree that all humanity dwells in Malgudi, that all life can be found there. Ever since the publication in 1935 of his first novel,* Swami and Friends: A Novel of Malgudi, *Narayan has received recognition, praise, and awards both nationally and internationally. His career was long and prolific, and his work both popular and critically acclaimed.*

*Part of his appeal is his underlying humanity, which transforms the characters of the fictional Malgudi and their realistic, mundane lives into the unexpected and yet representative. His charm is also due to the generosity and humour that underlies all his "comedies of sadness," as his works have been called. In the course of their stories, Narayan's "forgiving kindness" usually enables his characters to come to accept themselves and their lives with a certain equanimity, or allows his readers to be members of his universe. In "A Horse and Two Goats," Narayan presents a misunderstanding as the two men agree to a purchase. The reader alone appreciates the gentle irony created by their lack of a common language and the absolute contrast in cultural and economic backgrounds.*

## Terms Appearing in the Story

**drumstick tree** a deciduous tree with edible leaves and long, pod-shaped fruit, often eaten in curry

**swarga** the waiting place of souls; heaven, in Hindu beliefs

**bhang** marijuana

**Pongal** a harvest festival, named for a sweet rice dish that is offered to the gods

**Parangi** white European: a term originally applied to Portuguese missionaries, literally meaning "people who have horses and guns," and referring to low caste

**Kali Yuga** in Hinduism, the last of the four ages that make up a cycle of creation
**Yama Loka** the abode of death, in Hindu beliefs

Of the seven hundred thousand villages dotting the map of India, in which the majority of India's five hundred million live, flourish, and die, Kritam was probably the tiniest, indicated on the district survey map by a microscopic dot, the map being meant more for the revenue official

5 out to collect tax than for the guidance of the motorist, who in any case could not hope to reach it since it sprawled far from the highway at the end of a rough track furrowed up by the iron-hooped wheels of bullock carts. But its size did not prevent its giving itself the grandiose name Kritam, which meant in Tamil "coronet" or "crown" on the brow of this

10 subcontinent. The village consisted of fewer than thirty houses, only one of them built with brick and cement. Painted a brilliant yellow and blue all over with gorgeous carvings of gods and gargoyles on its balustrade, it was known as the Big House. The other houses, distributed in four streets, were generally of bamboo thatch, straw, mud, and other unspecified material.

15 Muni's was the last house in the fourth street, beyond which stretched the fields. In his prosperous days Muni had owned a flock of forty sheep and goats and sallied forth every morning driving the flock to the highway a couple of miles away. There he would sit on the pedestal of a clay statue of a horse while his cattle grazed around. He carried a crook at the end of

20 a bamboo pole and he snapped foliage from the avenue trees to feed his flock; he also gathered faggots and dry sticks, bundled them, and carried them home for fuel at sunset.

His wife lit the domestic fire at dawn, boiled water in a mud pot, threw into it a handful of millet flour, added salt, and gave him his first nour-

25 ishment for the day. When he started out, she would put in his hand a packed lunch, once again the same millet cooked into a little ball, which he could swallow with a raw onion at midday. She was old, but he was older and needed all the attention she could give him in order to be kept alive.

30 His fortunes had declined gradually, unnoticed. From a flock of forty which he drove into a pen at night, his stock had now come down to two goats, which were not worth the rent of a half rupee a month the Big House charged for the use of the pen in their backyard. And so the two goats were tethered to the trunk of a drumstick tree° which grew in front of

35 his hut and from which occasionally Muni could shake down drumsticks.

This morning he got six. He carried them in with a sense of triumph. Although no one could say precisely who owned the tree, it was his because he lived in its shadow.

She said, "If you were content with the drumstick leaves alone, I could
40 boil and salt some for you."

"Oh, I am tired of eating those leaves. I have a craving to chew the drumstick out of sauce, I tell you."

"You have only four teeth in your jaw, but your craving is for big things. All right, get the stuff for the sauce, and I will prepare it for you. After all,
45 next year you may not be alive to ask for anything. But first get me all the stuff, including a measure of rice or millet, and I will satisfy your unholy craving. Our store is empty today. Dhall, chili, curry leaves, mustard, coriander, gingelley oil, and one large potato. Go out and get all this." He repeated the list after her in order not to miss any item and walked off to
50 the shop in the third street.

He sat on an upturned packing case below the platform of the shop. The shopman paid no attention to him. Muni kept clearing his throat, coughing, and sneezing until the shopman could not stand it any more and demanded, "What ails you? You will fly off that seat into the gutter if
55 you sneeze so hard, young man." Muni laughed inordinately, in order to please the shopman, at being called "young man. The shopman softened and said, "You have enough of the imp inside to keep a second wife busy, but for the fact the old lady is still alive." Muni laughed appropriately again at this joke. It completely won the shopman over; he liked his sense
60 of humor to be appreciated. Muni engaged his attention in local gossip for a few minutes, which always ended with a reference to the postman's wife, who had eloped to the city some months before.

The shopman felt most pleased to hear the worst of the postman, who had cheated him. Being an itinerant postman, he returned home to
65 Kritam only once in ten days and every time managed to slip away again without passing the shop in the third street. By thus humoring the shopman, Muni could always ask for one or two items of food, promising repayment later. Some days the shopman was in a good mood and gave in, and sometimes he would lose his temper suddenly and bark at Muni for
70 daring to ask for credit. This was such a day, and Muni could not progress beyond two items listed as essential components. The shopman was also displaying a remarkable memory for old facts and figures and took out an oblong ledger to support his observations. Muni felt impelled to rise and flee. But his self-respect kept him in his seat and made him listen to the

75 worst things about himself. The shopman concluded, "If you could find five rupees and a quarter, you will have paid off an ancient debt and then could apply for admission to swarga.° How much have you got now?"

"I will pay you everything on the first of the next month."

"As always, and whom do you expect to rob by then?"

80 Muni felt caught and mumbled, "My daughter has sent word that she will be sending me money."

"Have you a daughter?" sneered the shopman. "And she is sending you money! For what purpose, may I know?"

"Birthday, fiftieth birthday," said Muni quietly.

85 "Birthday! How old are you?"

Muni repeated weakly, not being sure of it himself, "Fifty." He always calculated his age from the time of the great famine when he stood as high as the parapet around the village well, but who could calculate such things accurately nowadays with so many famines occurring? The

90 shopman felt encouraged when other customers stood around to watch and comment. Muni thought helplessly, My poverty is exposed to everybody. But what can I do?

"More likely you are seventy," said the shopman. "You also forget that you mentioned a birthday five weeks ago when you wanted castor oil for

95 your holy bath."

"Bath! Who can dream of a bath when you have to scratch the tank-bed for a bowl of water? We would all be parched and dead but for the Big House, where they let us take a pot of water from their well." After saying this Muni unobtrusively rose and moved off.

100 He told his wife, "That scoundrel would not give me anything. So go out and sell the drumsticks for what they are worth."

He flung himself down in a corner to recoup from the fatigue of his visit to the shop. His wife said, "You are getting no sauce today, nor anything else. I can't find anything to give you to eat. Fast till the evening, it'll do

105 you good. Take the goats and be gone now," she cried and added, "Don't come back before the sun is down." He knew that if he obeyed her she would somehow conjure up some food for him in the evening. Only he must be careful not to argue and irritate her. Her temper was undependable in the morning but improved by evening time. She was sure to go out and

110 work—grind corn in the Big House, sweep or scrub somewhere, and earn enough to buy foodstuff and keep a dinner ready for him in the evening.

Unleashing the goats from the drumstick tree, Muni started out, driving them ahead and uttering weird cries from time to time in order to urge them on. He passed through the village with his head bowed in thought.

115 He did not want to look at anyone or be accosted. A couple of cronies lounging in the temple corridor hailed him, but he ignored their call. They had known him in the days of affluence when he lorded over a flock of fleecy sheep, not the miserable gawky goats that he had today. Of course he also used to have a few goats for those who fancied them, but real

120 wealth lay in sheep; they bred fast and people came and bought the fleece in the shearing season; and then that famous butcher from the town came over on the weekly market days bringing him betel leaves, tobacco, and often enough some bhang,° which they smoked in a hut in the coconut grove, undisturbed by wives and well-wishers. After a smoke one felt light

125 and elated and inclined to forgive everyone including that brother-in-law of his who had once tried to set fire to his home. But all this seemed like the memories of a previous birth. Some pestilence afflicted his cattle (he could of course guess who had laid his animals under a curse), and even the friendly butcher would not touch one at half the price...and now here

130 he was left with the two scraggy creatures. He wished someone would rid him of their company, too. The shopman had said that he was seventy. At seventy, one only waited to be summoned by God. When he was dead what would his wife do? They had lived in each other's company since they were children. He was told on their day of wedding that he was ten years

135 old and she was eight. During the wedding ceremony they had had to recite their respective ages and names. He had thrashed her only a few times in their career, and later she had the upper hand. Progeny, none. Perhaps a large progeny would have brought him the blessing of the gods. Fertility brought merit. People with fourteen sons were always so pros-

140 perous and at peace with the world and themselves. He recollected the thrill he had felt when he mentioned a daughter to that shopman; although it was not believed, what if he did not have a daughter?—his cousin in the next village had many daughters, and any one of them was as good as his; he was fond of them all and would buy them sweets if he

145 could afford it. Still, everyone in the village whispered behind their backs that Muni and his wife were a barren couple. He avoided looking at anyone; they all professed to be so high up, and everyone else in the village had more money than he. "I am the poorest fellow in our caste and no wonder that they spurn me, but I won't look at them either," and so he

150 passed on with his eyes downcast along the edge of the street, and people left him also very much alone, commenting only to the extent, "Ah, there he goes with his two goats; if he slits their throats, he may have more peace of mind." "What has he to worry about anyway? They live on nothing and have none to worry about." Thus people commented when he

155 passed through the village. Only on the outskirts did he lift his head and look up. He urged and bullied the goats until they meandered along to the foot of the horse statue on the edge of the village. He sat on its pedestal for the rest of the day. The advantage of this was that he could watch the highway and see the lorries and buses pass through to the hills, and it gave

160 him a sense of belonging to a larger world. The pedestal of the statue was broad enough for him to move around as the sun traveled up and westward; or he could also crouch under the belly of the horse, for shade.

The horse was nearly life-size, molded out of clay, baked, burnt, and brightly colored, and reared its head proudly, prancing its forelegs in the

165 air and flourishing its tail in a loop; beside the horse stood a warrior with scythe-like mustachios, bulging eyes, and aquiline nose. The old image-makers believed in indicating a man of strength by bulging out his eyes and sharpening his mustache tips, and also decorated the man's chest with beads which looked today like blobs of mud through the ravages of

170 sun and wind and rain (when it came), but Muni would insist that he had known the beads to sparkle like the nine gems at one time in his life. The horse itself was said to have been as white as a dhobi-washed sheet, and had had on its back a cover of pure brocade of red and black lace, matching the multicolored sash around the waist of the warrior. But none

175 in the village remembered the splendor as no one noticed its existence. Even Muni, who spent all his waking hours at its foot, never bothered to look up. It was untouched even by the young vandals of the village who gashed tree trunks with knives and tried to topple off milestones and inscribed lewd designs on all walls. This statue had been closer to the pop-

180 ulation of the village at one time, when this spot bordered the village; but when the highway was laid through (or perhaps when the tank and wells dried up completely here) the village moved a couple of miles inland.

Muni sat at the foot of the statue, watching his two goats graze in the arid soil among the cactus and lantana bushes. He looked at the sun; it

185 was tilted westward no doubt, but it was not the time yet to go back home; if he went too early his wife would have no food for him. Also he must give her time to cool off her temper and feel sympathetic, and then she would scrounge and manage to get some food. He watched the mountain road for a time signal. When the green bus appeared around the bend he could

190 leave, and his wife would feel pleased that he had let the goats feed long enough.

He noticed now a new sort of vehicle coming down at full speed. It looked like both a motor car and a bus. He used to be intrigued by the novelty of such spectacles, but of late work was going on at the source of the

195 river on the mountain and an assortment of people and traffic went past
him, and he took it all casually and described to his wife, later in the day,
everything he saw. Today, while he observed the yellow vehicle coming
down, he was wondering how to describe it later to his wife, when it sputtered and stopped in front of him. A red-faced foreigner, who had been
200 driving it, got down and went round it, stooping, looking, and poking
under the vehicle; then he straightened himself up, looked at the dash-
board, stared in Muni's direction, and approached him. "Excuse me, is
there a gas station nearby, or do I have to wait until another car comes—"
He suddenly looked up at the clay horse and cried, "Marvelous," without
205 completing his sentence. Muni felt he should get up and run away, and
cursed his age. He could not readily put his limbs into action; some years
ago he could outrun a cheetah, as happened once when he went to the
forest to cut fuel and it was then that two of his sheep were mauled—a sign
that bad times were coming. Though he tried, he could not easily extricate
210 himself from his seat, and then there was also the problem of the goats. He
could not leave them behind.

The red-faced man wore khaki clothes—evidently a policeman or a soldier. Muni said to himself, He will chase or shoot if I start running. Some
dogs chase only those who run—O Siva, protect me. I don't know why this
215 man should be after me. Meanwhile the foreigner cried, "Marvelous!"
again, nodding his head. He paced around the statue with his eyes fixed
on it. Muni sat frozen for a while, and then fidgeted and tried to edge
away. Now the other man suddenly pressed his palms together in a salute,
smiled, and said, "Namaste! How do you do?"
220    At which Muni spoke the only English expressions he had learnt, "Yes,
no." Having exhausted his English vocabulary, he started in Tamil: "My
name is Muni. These two goats are mine, and no one can gainsay it—
though our village is full of slanderers these days who will not hesitate to
say that what belongs to a man doesn't belong to him." He rolled his eyes
225 and shuddered at the thought of evil-minded men and women peopling
his village.

The foreigner faithfully looked in the direction indicated by Muni's fingers,
gazed for a while at the two goats and the rocks, and with a puzzled expression took out his silver cigarette case and lit a cigarette. Suddenly remem-
230 bering the courtesies of the season, he asked, "Do you smoke?" Muni
answered "Yes, no." Whereupon the red-faced man took a cigarette and gave
it to Muni, who received it with surprise, having had no offer of a smoke from
anyone for years now. Those days when he smoked bhang were gone with
his sheep and the large-hearted butcher. Nowadays he was not able to find

235 even matches, let alone bhang. (His wife went across and borrowed a fire at dawn from a neighbor.) He had always wanted to smoke a cigarette; only once did the shopman give him one on credit, and he remembered how good it had tasted. The other flicked the lighter open and offered a light to Muni. Muni felt so confused about how to act that he blew on it and put it out. The

240 other, puzzled but undaunted, flourished his lighter, presented it again, and lit Muni's cigarette. Muni drew a deep puff and started coughing; it was racking, no doubt, but extremely pleasant. When his cough subsided he wiped his eyes and took stock of the situation, understanding that the other man was not an Inquisitor of any kind. Yet, in order to make sure, he

245 remained wary. No need to run away from a man who gave him such a potent smoke. His head was reeling from the effect of one of those strong American cigarettes made with roasted tobacco. The man said, "I come from New York," took out a wallet from his hip pocket, and presented his card.

Muni shrank away from the card. Perhaps he was trying to present a

250 warrant and arrest him. Beware of khaki, one part of his mind warned. Take all the cigarettes or bhang or whatever is offered, but don't get caught. Beware of khaki. He wished he weren't seventy as the shopman had said. At seventy one didn't run, but surrendered to whatever came. He could only ward off trouble by talk. So he went on, all in the chaste Tamil for which

255 Kritam was famous. (Even the worst detractors could not deny that the famous poetess Avaiyar was born in this area, although no one could say whether it was in Kritam or Kuppam, the adjoining village.) Out of this heritage the Tamil language gushed through Muni in an unimpeded flow. He said, "Before God, sir, Bhagwan, who sees everything, I tell you, sir, that we

260 know nothing of the case. If the murder was committed, whoever did it will not escape. Bhagwan is all-seeing. Don't ask me about it. I know nothing." A body had been found mutilated and thrown under a tamarind tree at the border between Kritam and Kuppam a few weeks before, giving rise to much gossip and speculation. Muni added an explanation, "Anything is

265 possible there. People over there will stop at nothing." The foreigner nodded his head and listened courteously though he understood nothing.

"I am sure you know when this horse was made," said the red man and smiled ingratiatingly.

Muni reacted to the relaxed atmosphere by smiling himself, and

270 pleaded, "Please go away, sir, I know nothing. I promise we will hold him for you if we see any bad character around, and we will bury him up to his neck in a coconut pit if he tries to escape; but our village has always had a clean record. Must definitely be the other village."

Now the red man implored, "Please, please, I will speak slowly, please
275 try to understand me. Can't you understand even a simple word of
English? Everyone in this country seems to know English. I have gotten
along with English everywhere in this country, but you don't speak it. Have
you any religious or spiritual scruples against English speech?"

Muni made some indistinct sounds in his throat and shook his head.
280 Encouraged, the other went on to explain at length, uttering each syllable
with care and deliberation. Presently he sidled over and took a seat beside
the old man, explaining, "You see, last August, we probably had the
hottest summer in history, and I was working in shirt-sleeves in my office
on the fortieth floor of the Empire State Building. We had a power failure
285 one day, you know, and there I was stuck for four hours, no elevator, no air
conditioning. All the way in the train I kept thinking, and the minute I
reached home in Connecticut, I told my wife, Ruth, 'We will visit India this
winter, it's time to look at other civilizations.' Next day she called the travel
agent first thing and told him to fix it, and so here I am. Ruth came with
290 me but is staying back at Srinagar, and I am the one doing the rounds and
joining her later."

Muni looked reflective at the end of this long oration and said, rather
feebly, "Yes, no," as a concession to the other's language, and went on in
Tamil, "When I was this high"—he indicated a foot high—"I had heard
295 my uncle say..."

No one can tell what he was planning to say, as the other interrupted
him at this stage to ask, "Boy, what is the secret of your teeth? How old are
you?"

The old man forgot what he had started to say and remarked,
300 "Sometimes we too lose our cattle. Jackals or cheetahs may sometimes
carry them off, but sometimes it is just theft from over in the next village,
and then we will know who has done it. Our priest at the temple can see
in the camphor flame the face of the thief, and when he is caught..." He
gestured with his hands a perfect mincing of meat.
305 The American watched his hands intently and said, "I know what you
mean. Chop something? Maybe I am holding you up and you want to
chop wood? Where is your axe? Hand it to me and show me what to chop.
I do enjoy it, you know, just a hobby. We get a lot of driftwood along the
backwater near my house, and on Sundays I do nothing but chop wood for
310 the fireplace. I really feel different when I watch the fire in the fireplace,
although it may take all the sections of the Sunday *New York Times* to get
a fire started." And he smiled at this reference.

Muni felt totally confused but decided the best thing would be to make an attempt to get away from this place. He tried to edge out, saying, "Must go home," and turned to go. The other seized his shoulder and said desperately, "Is there no one, absolutely no one here, to translate for me?" He looked up and down the road, which was deserted in this hot afternoon; a sudden gust of wind churned up the dust and dead leaves on the roadside into a ghostly column and propelled it towards the mountain road. The stranger almost pinioned Muni's back to the statue and asked, "Isn't this statue yours? Why don't you sell it to me?"

The old man now understood the reference to the horse, thought for a second, and said in his own language, "I was an urchin this high when I heard my grandfather explain this horse and warrior, and my grandfather himself was this high when he heard his grandfather, whose grandfather..."

The other man interrupted him. "I don't want to seem to have stopped here for nothing. I will offer you a good price for this," he said, indicating the horse. He had concluded without the least doubt that Muni owned this mud horse. Perhaps he guessed by the way he sat on its pedestal, like other souvenir sellers in this country presiding over their wares.

Muni followed the man's eyes and pointing fingers and dimly understood the subject matter and, feeling relieved that the theme of the mutilated body had been abandoned at least for the time being, said again, enthusiastically, "I was this high when my grandfather told me about this horse and the warrior, and my grandfather was this high when he himself..." and he was getting into a deeper bog of reminiscence each time he tried to indicate the antiquity of the statue.

The Tamil that Muni spoke was stimulating even as pure sound, and the foreigner listened with fascination. "I wish I had my tape-recorder here," he said, assuming the pleasantest expression. "Your language sounds wonderful. I get a kick out of every word you utter, here"—he indicated his ears—"but you don't have to waste your breath in sales talk. I appreciate the article. You don't have to explain its points."

"I never went to a school, in those days only Brahmin went to schools, but we had to go out and work in the fields morning till night, from sowing to harvest time...and when Pongal° came and we had to cut the harvest, my father allowed me to go out and play with others at the tank, and so I don't know the Parangi° language you speak, even little fellows in your country probably speak the Parangi language, but here only learned men and officers know it. We had a postman in our village who could speak to you boldly in your language, but his wife ran away with someone and he does not speak to anyone at all nowadays. Who would if a wife did what she did? Women must be watched; otherwise they will sell themselves and the home." And he laughed at his own quip.

355　　The foreigner laughed heartily, took out another cigarette, and offered it to Muni, who now smoked with ease, deciding to stay on if the fellow was going to be so good as to keep up his cigarette supply. The American now stood up on the pedestal in the attitude of a demonstrative lecturer and said, running his finger along some of the carved decorations around the
360　horse's neck, speaking slowly and uttering his words syllable by syllable, "I could give a sales talk for this better than anyone else....This is a marvelous combination of yellow and indigo, though faded now....How do you people of this country achieve these flaming colors?"

　　Muni, now assured that the subject was still the horse and not the dead
365　body, said, "This is our guardian, it means death to our adversaries. At the end of Kali Yuga,° this world and all other worlds will be destroyed, and the Redeemer will come in the shape of a horse called Kalki; this horse will come to life and gallop and trample down all bad men." As he spoke of bad men the figures of his shopman and his brother-in-law assumed con-
370　crete forms in his mind, and he reveled for a moment in the predicament of the fellow under the horse's hoof: served him right for trying to set fire to his home....

　　While he was brooding on this pleasant vision, the foreigner utilized the pause to say, "I assure you that this will have the best home in the U.S.A.
375　I'll push away the bookcase, you know I love books and am a member of five book clubs, and the choice and bonus volumes mount up to a pile really in our living room, as high as this horse itself. But they'll have to go. Ruth may disapprove, but I will convince her. The TV may have to be shifted, too. We can't have everything in the living room. Ruth will prob-
380　ably say what about when we have a party? I'm going to keep him right in the middle of the room. I don't see how that can interfere with the party—we'll stand around him and have our drinks."

　　Muni continued his description of the end of the world. "Our pundit discoursed at the temple once how the oceans are going to close over the
385　earth in a huge wave and swallow us—this horse will grow bigger than the biggest wave and carry on its back only the good people and kick into the floods the evil ones—plenty of them about—" he said reflectively. "Do you know when it is going to happen?" he asked.

The foreigner now understood by the tone of the other that a question
390 was being asked and said, "How am I transporting it? I can push the seat
back and make room in the rear. That van can take in an elephant"—
waving precisely at the back of the seat.

Muni was still hovering on visions of avatars and said again, "I never
missed our pundit's discourses at the temple in those days during every
395 bright half of the month, although he'd go on all night, and he told us that
Vishnu is the highest god. Whenever evil men trouble us, he comes down
to save us. He has come many times. The first time he incarnated as a
great fish, and lifted the scriptures on his back when the flood and sea
waves…"

400    "I am not a millionaire, but a modest businessman. My trade is coffee."

Amidst all this wilderness of obscure sound Muni caught the word
"coffee" and said, "If you want to drink 'kapi,' drive further up, in the next
town, they have Friday market and there they open 'kapi-otels'—so I learn
from passers-by. Don't think I wander about. I go nowhere and look for
405 nothing." His thoughts went back to the avatars. "The first avatar was in
the shape of a little fish in a bowl of water, but every hour it grew bigger
and bigger and became in the end a huge whale which the seas could not
contain, and on the back of the whale the holy books were supported,
saved, and carried." Once he had launched on the first avatar, it was
410 inevitable that he should go on to the next, a wild boar on whose tusk the
earth was lifted when a vicious conqueror of the earth carried it off and hid
it at the bottom of the sea. After describing this avatar Muni concluded,
"God will always save us whenever we are troubled by evil beings. When
we were young we staged at full moon the story of the avatars. That's how
415 I know the stories; we played them all night until the sun rose, and sometimes the European collector would come to watch, bringing his own chair.
I had a good voice and so they always taught me songs and gave me the
women's roles. I was always Goddess Lakshmi, and they dressed me in a
brocade sari, loaned from the Big House…"

420    The foreigner said, "I repeat I am not a millionaire. Ours is a modest
business; after all, we can't afford to buy more than sixty minutes of TV
time in a month, which works out to two minutes a day, that's all,
although in the course of time we'll maybe sponsor a one-hour show regularly if our sales graph continues to go up…"

425    Muni was intoxicated by the memory of his theatrical days and was
about to explain how he had painted his face and worn a wig and diamond earrings when the visitor, feeling that he had spent too much time
already, said, "Tell me, will you accept a hundred rupees or not for the

horse? I'd love to take the whiskered soldier also but no space for him this
430 year. I'll have to cancel my air ticket and take a boat home, I suppose.
Ruth can go by air if she likes, but I will go with the horse and keep him
in my cabin all the way if necessary." And he smiled at the picture of himself voyaging across the seas hugging this horse. He added, "I will have to
pad it with straw so that it doesn't break..."

435 "When we played *Ramayana,* they dressed me as Sita," added Muni. "A
teacher came and taught us the songs for the drama and we gave him fifty
rupees. He incarnated himself as Rama, and he alone could destroy
Ravana, the demon with ten heads who shook all the worlds; do you know
the story of *Ramayana?"*

440 "I have my station wagon as you see. I can push the seat back and take
the horse in if you will just lend me a hand with it."

"Do you know *Mahabharata?* Krishna was the eighth avatar of Vishnu,
incarnated to help the Five Brothers regain their kingdom. When Krishna
was a baby he danced on the thousand-hooded giant serpent and tram-
445 pled it to death; and then he suckled the breasts of the demoness and left
them flat as a disc, though when she came to him her bosoms were large,
like mounds of earth on the banks of a dug-up canal." He indicated two
mounds with his hands.

The stranger was completely mystified by the gesture. For the first time
450 he said, "I really wonder what you are saying because your answer is crucial. We have come to the point when we should be ready to talk business."

"When the tenth avatar comes, do you know where you and I will be?"
asked the old man.

"Lend me a hand and I can lift off the horse from its pedestal after
455 picking out the cement at the joints. We can do anything if we have a basis
of understanding."

At this stage the mutual mystification was complete, and there was no
need even to carry on a guessing game at the meaning of words. The old
man chattered away in a spirit of balancing off the credits and debits of
460 conversational exchange, and said in order to be on the credit side, "Oh,
honorable one, I hope God has blessed you with numerous progeny. I say
this because you seem to be a good man, willing to stay beside an old man
and talk to him, while all day I have none to talk to except when somebody stops by to ask for a piece of tobacco. But I seldom have it, tobacco is
465 not what it used to be at one time, and I have given up chewing. I cannot
afford it nowadays." Noting the other's interest in his speech, Muni felt
encouraged to ask, "How many children have you?" with appropriate gestures with his hands.

Realizing that a question was being asked, the red man replied, "I said

470 a hundred," which encouraged Muni to go into details. "How many of your children are boys and how many girls? Where are they? Is your daughter married? Is it difficult to find a son-in-law in your country also?"

In answer to these questions the red man dashed his hand into his pocket and brought forth his wallet in order to take immediate advantage

475 of the bearish trend in the market. He flourished a hundred-rupee currency note and said, "Well, this is what I meant."

The old man now realized that some financial element was entering their talk. He peered closely at the currency note, the like of which he had never seen in his life; he knew the five and ten by their colors although

480 always in other people's hands, while his own earning at any time was in coppers and nickels. What was this man flourishing the note for? Perhaps asking for change. He laughed to himself at the notion of anyone coming to him for changing a thousand- or ten-thousand-rupee note. He said with a grin, "Ask our village headman, who is also a moneylender; he can

485 change even a lakh of rupees in gold sovereigns if you prefer it that way; he thinks nobody knows, but dig the floor of his puja room and your head will reel at the sight of the hoard. The man disguises himself in rags just to mislead the public. Talk to the headman yourself because he goes mad at the sight of me. Someone took away his pumpkins with the creeper and he,

490 for some reason, thinks it was me and my goats...that's why I never let my goats be seen anywhere near the farms." His eyes traveled to his goats nosing about, attempting to wrest nutrition from minute greenery peeping out from rock and dry earth.

The foreigner followed his look and decided that it would be a sound

495 policy to show an interest in the old man's pets. He went up casually to them and stroked their backs with every show of courteous attention. Now the truth dawned on the old man. His dream of a lifetime was about to be realized. He understood that the red man was actually making an offer for the goats. He had reared them up in the hope of selling them some day

500 and, with the capital, opening a small shop on this very spot. Sitting here, watching towards the hills, he had often dreamt how he would put up a thatched roof here, spread a gunny sack out on the ground, and display on it fried nuts, colored sweets, and green coconut for the thirsty and famished wayfarers on the highway, which was sometimes very busy. The ani-

505 mals were not prize ones for a cattle show, but he had spent his occasional savings to provide them some fancy diet now and then, and they did not look too bad. While he was reflecting thus, the red man shook his hand

and left on his palm one hundred rupees in tens now, suddenly realizing that this was what the old man was asking. "It is all for you or you may share it if you have a partner."

The old man pointed at the station wagon and asked, "Are you carrying them off in that?"

"Yes, of course," said the other, understanding the transportation part of it.

The old man said, "This will be their first ride in a motor car. Carry them off after I get out of sight, otherwise they will never follow you, but only me even if I am traveling on the path to Yama Loka."° He laughed at his own joke, brought his palms together in a salute, turned around and went off, and was soon out of sight beyond a clump of thicket.

The red man looked at the goats grazing peacefully. Perched on the pedestal of the horse, as the westerly sun touched off the ancient faded colors of the statue with a fresh splendor, he ruminated, "He must be gone to fetch some help, I suppose!" and settled down to wait. When a truck came downhill, he stopped it and got the help of a couple of men to detach the horse from its pedestal and place it in his station wagon. He gave them five rupees each, and for a further payment they siphoned off gas from the truck, and helped him to start his engine.

Muni hurried homeward with the cash securely tucked away at his waist in his dhoti. He shut the street door and stole up softly to his wife as she squatted before the lit oven wondering if by a miracle food would drop from the sky. Muni displayed his fortune for the day. She snatched the notes from him, counted them by the glow of the fire, and cried, "One hundred rupees! How did you come by it? Have you been stealing?"

"I have sold our goats to a red-faced man. He was absolutely crazy to have them, gave me all this money and carried them off in his motor car!"

Hardly had these words left his lips when they heard bleating outside. She opened the door and saw the two goats at her door. "Here they are!" she said. "What's the meaning of all this?"

He muttered a great curse and seized one of the goats by its ears and shouted. "Where is that man? Don't you know you are his? Why did you come back?" The goat only wriggled in his grip. He asked the same question of the other, too. The goat shook itself off. His wife glared at him and declared, "If you have thieved, the police will come tonight and break your bones. Don't involve me. I will go away to my parents...."

(1985)

# Acute Triangle

Frederic Raphael (England) 1931–

## About the Author

*Raphael is a respected, productive, and successful writer. He is well-known as a film and TV script writer. He was nominated for an Oscar for* Two for the Road *in 1996 and won the Oscar for best screenplay for* Darling *in 1965, and most recently, with Stanley Kubrick, wrote the screenplay for* Eyes Wide Shut *(1999). Raphael has also achieved fame and success as a playwright, essayist, translator, a novelist, and short story writer. Frederic Raphael was born in Chicago, the son of a British father and American mother. The family moved to Britain when he was seven years old, and there he has continued to make his home. Moving to England just before World War II and experiencing antisemitism at school had profound effects on him. Raphael refers to himself as "a witness" who, because of his upbringing—English (but not quite) and Jewish (but not quite)—is able to see its influence on him objectively. He says, "I cannot shrug off the influences of these places, nor am I certain I would wish to do so. The conflict of values reveals itself in fiction in the conflict of characters."*

*Conflict, whether as a result of social expectations, emotional inadequacy, or moral weakness, is usually the subject of Raphael's fiction. As a "witness," a keen observer, of English society, he is able to convey his characters' pain and suffering in a detached and satirical manner. This distance can be seen in "Acute Angle," which is taken from Raphael's short story collection,* Oxbridge Blues *(1984). This partic-ular story shows Raphael's interest in the conflict in values and displays his greatest skill as a writer: the ability to capture individual speech patterns.*

He knew that she had long had a lover and she knew that it had long made him unhappy. One evening she came into the drawing room, spe-cial dress rustling, and told him that she had at last broken with her lover. She came and sat on the carpet near his chair, her bare shoulder convenient
5 to the hand which held the whisky. He did not touch her with his fingers, but slid the cold, chiming glass down the slope of her shoulder and rested it, at an angle, against the blue margin of her dress. A bead of iced moisture detached itself from the base of the glass, impersonal tear, and rolled beneath the edge of the dress and down her white breast. She turned suddenly and
10 looked up at him with promising eyes. 'It was always you really,' she said.

He raised the whisky to his lips, while she found an old ticket in the turn-up of his trousers, a sixpenny one, for God's sake, and held it up to him, smiling, like some silly proof. That night, she pressed the bell off early

in the bedroom. She bathed and prepared herself, amused in the steamy
15 mirror as she perfumed herself out of sight of herself. Her neat and fleecy
apron was prematurely grey with pretty powder. In the morning she
bathed appreciative bruises and was happy.

That evening she arranged the room for her husband's return; she composed chosen flowers and lit low lamps to give him pleasure. She looked at
20 herself in the angelic mirror and saw that she was as delectable with virtue
as she had always been with vice. Already she could imagine—and it
made her walk with a particular slow stride—the urgency with which he
might again make love to her. Would he propose again the cruel pleasures
of the previous, startling night? He did, and more: she gasped and grasped
25 at the tender violence of his renewed desire. She knew now for certain that
she had done the right thing and she rejoiced all next day that virtue had
such mounting rewards.

A few evenings later, returning after a longer day, it is his abrupt
pleasure, so it seems, to question her at some length about the breach with
30 her lover. Delicately—with some sense that his desire is piqued by judicious
revelations—she discloses some of the shortcomings of the man about
whom for so long she would suffer no ill word to be spoken. She repeats,
under repeated questioning, that her lover wept when she told him of her
decision and that he even promised to marry her if she would recant. She
35 comes and kisses her husband and reassures him by encouraging his hand
to her soft breast. She draws in her breath for him to hear at the sudden
nip of thumb and forefinger. Yet that night he is more reluctant between
the sheets which have had recently to be replaced daily. Two nights later,
he misses dinner (though her cooking has again become deliciously saucy)
40 and does not even telephone to warn her. When he comes in, whisky
makes no apology. 'What is the matter?' she asks, after his coat has come
off and his jacket almost with it. 'I saw him.' 'Him?' 'Him. In the street.
With a woman.' 'Well?' 'I saw him with the same one a couple of nights
back.' 'What about it?' 'He had his arm round her. And tonight she kissed
45 him. I saw them in a taxi.' 'Why do you still spy on him? It's over. I never
lied to you.' 'She loves him,' the husband says. 'But what has that to do
with us?' She looks at him and sees the old cataract of suspicion in those
icy eyes. 'He left you,' he says. 'No,' she says, 'no!' When she goes up to the
bedroom, he is putting things into his case.

(1984)

# The Chocho Vine

Olive Senior (Canada) 1941–

## About the Author

*Olive Senior, now a Canadian citizen, is a well-respected and significant Caribbean writer. Olive Senior was born and raised in Jamaica. She attended Carleton University in Ottawa, graduating from the Journalism program in 1967; she then returned to Jamaica where she worked at a variety of jobs in journalism, communications, and publishing before emigrating to Canada in 1991. Senior is an accomplished essayist, poet, and short story writer and has won international recognition and awards for her work, in particular,* Summer Lightning and Other Stories *(1986).*

*Senior's stories present the people of Jamaica in their own voices as they struggle to find their places in a changing world. She is concerned with women's roles, class differences, and the split between urban and rural life and values. Her background as a journalist has trained Senior's keen eye for social details while her experience as a poet has developed her sensitivity to linguistic nuance. Senior has said: "For me, writing, literature, is inextricably fused with magic. Though most of my writing is in a realistic vein, I am conscious at all times of other possibilities lurking just beyond consciousness, of the great ineffable mystery that lies at the core of each life, at the heart of every story." In "The Chocho Vine," Senior so skillfully conveys the relationship between Miss Evadney and the chocho vine that the poignancy of the conclusion leaves the reader momentarily as wordless as the protagonist.*

## Terms Appearing in the Story

**Number Eleven mango** a variety of mango
**skellion** an herb
**susumber** a type of eggplant
**higgle** haggle, bargain
**ganja** marijuana
**gungo pea** a small, grayish pea or bean, also called Congo pea or pigeon pea

The only thing that flourished in Miss Evadney's yard was her chocho vine. Her son had made her sell off all the property except for the square surrounding the house, and this piece of land, neglected like her, was nothing now but hard-packed red dirt trampled by so many feet over
5 the years, sluiced so clean by the rain and by dirty water flung from kitchen and bedroom windows, that it had acquired a shiny red patina like

the ox-blood shoes her husband used to wear. By the front step, a rusting yellow margarine tin held a sickly looking Wandering Jew, and even the Ram-goat-roses which peeked out from under the house did so nervously,
10 as if ready to jerk their heads back at the first discordant note, for though it had grown increasingly feeble in volume, Miss Evadney's temper was legendary.

The chocho vine evidently felt no fear, for in the back right-hand corner, up against the property line, it had literally captured a whole quarter of
15 the yard sweeping majestically over the arbour of split bamboo originally built and extended many times to hold it, clambering over the abandoned chicken coop, and then aiming upwards to almost completely smother the old Number Eleven mango° tree which had after a while given up the battle and simply ceased bearing. It did put forth feeble blossoms each
20 year on the few bits of branches which still retained the privilege of being exposed to the sun, but the tiny fruit which actually came seemed embarrassed to compete with the magnificent chochos and dried up from confusion when they were no bigger than plums. Meanwhile, the chocho vine from its high perch on the mango tree hurled itself into the air before
25 bending down and attaching itself to a new branch, or anything else in its path, waving as if in triumph its probing tentacles and plump greeny-white offspring that were a source of unending bounty.

Miss Evadney derived great satisfaction from her splendidly robust chocho, for she was herself subject to the longest list of ailments imagi-
30 nable, and any question to her about her health elicited a torrent of words, as if her infirmities, real and imagined, were now the only topic of conversation left to her. "Ai, my dear, the gas, the gas da kill me," she would commence, rubbing that part of her anatomy which was currently the locus of her pain, looking proud and surprised if she managed to produce
35 a large belch. That greeting over, she had no trouble jumping to her "pressure," her "arthritis," her "heart," her "head," her "foot," in an endless recital which—if one didn't take care—might even include an exhibition of some afflicted part. Not that Miss Evadney had much of an audience these days since she had outlived all her contemporaries and most of the
40 younger generation had migrated to more prosperous locations. It was really only Miss Vie and her family who paid her any mind.

Miss Vie lived up the road and had been vaguely related to Miss Evadney's husband. But that wasn't the reason why she took an interest in the old lady. The real reason was that somebody had to do it, as she often
45 told her husband, and she saw it as her Christian duty. Besides, they were all fond of Miss Evadney, who, like so many people who tyrannized their

own families and those who dared to cross them, was a perfectly benign and sociable being in her relationships with others. To them, she was almost mythical, she was so old, and could always be relied upon to give the "true version" of events whenever an argument arose or someone failed to remember things that had happened in the past. Despite her physical infirmities, Miss Evadney still had a wonderful memory.

She could remember when she had planted her first chocho vine. "It was the year I get married, Miss Vie. The said year. You see all them other girls there? All of them was busy a live common-law life. But not me, Miss Vie, not me. I had *standards,* you know." So when Mr. Shaw had the impertinence to "put question" to her, she told him she wasn't that kind of woman. "Is so I tell him," she was fond of saying, "I said, 'I am not that kind of woman. I have mother and father at my yard, so if you have anything to say, go and put question to them.'"

Mr. Shaw had just come back from the Great War, in which he had served as a volunteer. He had ten acres of land, was expecting to get his soldier's pension, and he wanted to settle down with someone. Though the white people had fixed him up in the hospital, his head still felt groggy and his chest wheezed sometimes, but he knew all this would go away once he got a good woman to look after him. He liked that Evadney Gordon, liked the cut of her jib, though he still couldn't believe this tall strapping young woman he came back to find was the skinny little pickney-gal he had left behind. That more than anything else made him conscious of how quickly time was passing, so he went to her parents and took off his hat and asked for her hand in marriage.

"Well, the other girls were so jealous afterwards!" Miss Evadney loved to say. "Here I was a married woman! And Mr. Shaw would never allow me to work again. Would never hear of his wife working. I never ever went to the ground like the other women and I never work in nobody's kitchen neither." She stayed home and looked after the house and Mr. Shaw and the three children. She kept chickens and sometimes rabbits and planted skellion° and cabbages around the yard. And she planted her chocho. Mr. Shaw himself put up the arbour when the vine started to grow. Such a strong vine it was from the start.

"You have good hand with chocho," Mr. Shaw said, and she was pleased with the compliment. It was white-skin chocho, nice and fleshy inside and not too many prickles on the skin.

In those days she never sold the chochos, she gave them away, took pleasure in the fact that her vine was so bounteous she could afford to give chocho freely to all who came and asked and still have plenty left over to feed the babies on and to put in the soup or the stew. "That's the thing with chocho," she was given to saying. "It's not one of those things like pumpkin that you could get a good meal out of now. You could eat nothing but pumpkin if that was all you had and pumpkin would may yu stomach feel full. There is nothing to beat a good pumpkin soup, but chocho by itself is nothing much. Same like squash there; it's a tasteless kind of thing, you know. But to fill out the meal now, when things short, to stretch the codfish or the meat or the soup or the susumber°—nothing to beat chocho."

The other good thing, Miss Evadney said, was that once you planted chocho, you didn't have to do anything but water it and give it something to climb on; the chocho would just carry on from there. Whenever her chocho vine started to look weak, she would set another one so that by the time the old one started to wear out, the young one would be flourishing.

Anyone who wanted chocho only had to come and ask; that was one rule she had. Nobody should just come into her yard and pick chocho as they liked. If they asked, they could have chocho by the dozen. But woe betide anyone who dared to take even one little vegetable without asking. Miss Evadney's tongue could blister.

When she was first married Miss Evadney wasn't at all quarrelsome. Mr. Shaw was at his ground all day and she sang as she went around doing her chores and she set his meal on the table the minute he came home. But then Mr. Shaw began to get sickly: it happened to a lot of people who had gone away to the war—"fighting for King and Country," he proudly used to say even on his sick-bed, though she was vexed that King and Country never knew anything about his coughing out his soul-case and having to take to his bed more and more. And that was the time the boys started to give trouble and back-answer her.

"Is three boy pickney I did have—Leroy, Everald, and Joseph—that is the one there we did call Mighty," she told anyone who asked. But it was only to Miss Vie or Miss Vie's daughter Hermione that she confided all. "Well, everybody know how boy pickney hard to raise from morning. And mine was no different. But you see me here, I wasn't going to let them get away with one single thing, they had to know who was boss. I let them know from morning I wasn't going to tolerate no force-ripe man at my yard. If their father couldn't chastise them anymore, they would still find out where water walk go a pumpkin belly, for I would take the strap to them myself. 'Spare the rod and spoil the child,' the Good Book says, but nobody could say I was guilty of that sin. I had *standards*, Miss Vie, *standards*. I wanted the world to know my children come from good home. All them other little pickney around could run wild and act like ragamuffin all they want. But not mine. They had to have standards, too."

When their father got too poorly to go to his ground any more, it was
130 they who had to go. She had to take Leroy out of school before he even reached sixth standard to send him to the ground. "Leroy bawl every day because he was bright in school and had his heart set to become a teacher. Every year, every year I promise I would send him back to school, but there was no way he could go back, you almost had to say he was man-a-yard
135 now, he had to take charge of the ground and the two younger ones hardly ever had the chance to go to school at all for they had to help their brother. But nuh so life stay?"

Miss Evadney used to be upset about this, she often told Miss Vie: upset about the fact that her children had to drop out of school. "Because, my
140 dear Miss Vie, if they didn't get an education, what was there for them but slaving on the land? The land wasn't a thing now that you could ever make money out of, you know. You can see for yourself that the land there never fat. Never fat. Pure hillside and rock-stone. No matter how hard Mr. Shaw work, it was barely enough to keep body and soul together." Mr. Shaw's pit-
145 tance from the government there, well, that was something, but it wasn't enough to send the boys to school when Mr. Shaw had to go to doctor so often and buy medicine and tonic to build up his strength. Miss Evadney remembered how she used to curse the Germans every day for what they had done to Mr. Shaw, though what it was she wasn't sure. All she knew is
150 that they had reduced her big strapping man to nothing but a skeleton, skin and bone there lying on the bed. When the boys saw their father help-less like that, no wonder they felt they could just do as they liked.

Whenever things got too much for Miss Evadney she would go into the yard and stand and gaze in admiration at her chocho vine; it made her
155 feel good just to look at it. One thing in her life was flourishing exuber-antly. She always thought that it was a pity some of those nayga round the place were so bad-minded that they had to come and steal her chocho, were too red-eye and ill-mannered to come and ask, the way people were supposed to. Like those Pettigrews and those Vernons. She had caught
160 them red-handed several times and cursed them hog-rotten, them and all their generation.

When Mr. Shaw died, the pittance from the government stopped coming, and soon all the boys were gone. It was then that Miss Evadney started to sell her chocho.

165　"Miss Vie, I regret that I never had a daughter," she would often complain, "for I sure a daughter would stay faithful to her mother, a daughter
would never, never abandon you in your old age. Daughters are always
true to their mothers." Look at Miss Vie's children now, she thought to herself but didn't say out loud. Five children she has and which is the most
170　loving to her, which one always coming to visit and bring her things? Who
but the one girl pickney?

　　Of all Miss Vie's children, Miss Evadney loved Hermione the best.
Hermione never ever came to visit her mother without bringing something
for Miss Evadney. If she didn't see the old lady at her mother's, she would
175　often walk down the road to her house, calling out loudly in jest as she
neared, "Miss Evadney, Miss Evadney. Hold dog!" for Miss Evadney had not
even a cat to guard her house. On these occasions, Miss Evadney felt sorry
that all her neighbours had died off or moved away, sorry that they
couldn't see people of quality coming to visit her at her yard.

180　　Whenever Hermione visited her parents in the country, she always left
with some of Miss Evadney's chochos. It was now a family joke: Miss
Evadney and her chochos. Hermione hated the squash-like vegetables,
regarding them as useless, tasteless things, and she always gave hers away.
But she took the gift from Miss Evadney with many thanks, because she
185　knew the old lady was proud to have something to give.

　　"Thank God for you and your mother every day, Miss H," she told her
every visit, "for I don't know what I would do without you. You wouldn't
believe is three boys I did birth? Three of them. Leroy the eldest. Everald
the middle one, and Joseph who is the one we call Mighty for him did little
190　but him lion-heart. And where the three of them now, eh? I ask you that.
Why not a one to mind me?"

　　Hermione, like her mother, had heard Miss Evadney's stories so many
times she didn't need to listen as the old woman talked.

　　"Leroy was the first one to leave home. Well I did hear some rumour
195　there about Leroy and one of the Pettigrew girls, the one that did say she
studying for nurse. But I couldn't believe it, Miss H. couldn't believe Leroy
would do his mother such a thing, take up with the daughter of my enemy,
those thieving red-eye people. And when I question that boy, he deny every
word of it. Look me straight in mi face and tell me lie, and to think how I
200　did try to beat the lying out of them. So how I could tell anybody to this
day how I did feel when my son Leroy and that girl run away together, run
off to Kingston without a word to his mother?"

Miss Evadney would stand there silent for a long, long time, contemplating her fate and the injustice of it all. "Well, maybe the girl's parents
205 did know about it, that is the hurtful part. Maybe is them fix it up to tief
away my good-good boy," she would finally say in a wondering tone, as if
thinking about this for the first time. "For next thing I hear, Miss H, them
nuh going off to Kingston to wedding?" She even heard long afterwards
that Leroy went back to school and turn teacher after all. But not a word
210 did Leroy ever send to her, leaving her with his sick father and the ground
to look after. What did she ever do to make him treat her like that?

"Miss H, I cry over Leroy, I tell you, for nothing in life never hot me so.
Not even when Mr. Shaw die and leave me." She told Hermione this
standing up in the middle of the road, with tears welling up in her eyes.

215 Mr. Shaw didn't have long to go after that disappointment and there
was barely enough to bury him. "We had was to sell the three goat, though
Mr. Shaw always said that because he was an old soldier the government
would give something toward the burial. Well, I send and ask the government
about that, and I still waiting. Thirty years now and I still waiting.
220 You think they get the letter yet?"

The case of Everald now: Everald didn't walk off and leave her like
Leroy, he just brought a woman into the house. "That didn't last long, Miss
H, for though I try, God know I try, me and the girl couldn't get on, just
couldn't agree." So she gave Everald permission to build his own house
225 next door. And Everald still continued to work his father's ground and
bring her something—he used to look after her, she always said, you have
to give Everald that.

"But is only afterward that I really get the full picture of what he was
after, you know. For Everald is the one that make me sell off the land."
230 If Mighty had been around at the time, maybe she wouldn't have done
it, Miss Evadney always said, but Mighty went away, too. "Mighty get to
go away as farm worker, was earning good-good American dollar, turn
into a fine young man, except the third time Mighty go away, he jump his
contract and never come back, never send his mother another word."

235 So it was just she and Everald left and she was grateful to him for staying,
for he looked after her and she had her grandchildren next door, in and
out of her house all day. And even Cynthia, their mother, and she started
to pull together. So everything was working well and she could afford to
just give chocho away to anybody who came and asked.

240      It was the bauxite coming in that caused it, Miss Evadney always main-
tained, that caused everything to spoil. They brought in all these machines
that were digging up the earth, pulling down the mountains even, clawing
away at the red dirt to ship it to America, though she always wondered
why they wanted to do that, if America didn't have its own dirt. But it was
245 the biggest thing that had happened since the war, not the war Mr. Shaw
was in, the other one, and all the men around were rushing there to get
work. Everald went too. He got a job working with one of these machines
that was mashing down the place, and he came home beaming all over
his face. The money was so good and they were going to train him and
250 everything; he could work his way up. Everald told her that for the first
time in his life, he could see his future straight like an asphalt road out
there in front of him. She thought of Leroy and Mighty and felt she was
going to lose Everald, too, lose him to a place where he could earn proper
money and feel like a big shot, just like the others.

255      At first it was all right, Everald came home every weekend and went over
to the ground as usual; Jackie Davison, who was his playmate from morning,
and his big boy Jason were keeping an eye on things during the week. Then
he started to talk of moving his family to the town where he would be nearer
his workplace and Cynthia could learn to drive and shop in a supermarket
260 and the children could go to proper schools. She knew what was coming next
but this time she prayed. She prayed like she never prayed for anything else
in her life, prayed that Everald wouldn't leave her, too.

     Miss Evadney always said she thought it was like the devil was dealing
that deck there, for look what Everald turned around and did. She was so
265 afraid of losing him that she gave no thought to the land, said yes when he
came and asked her if she would sell the land and lend him the money.
"Leave only the house spot, Ma," Everald told her, "for there is no point in
your keeping this land that will just go to waste when you could make something off of it now when you need it. Because I cannot keep on looking after
270 it. My life change now. And you know once my children get education they
not coming back." The way he put it, it all made sense to her, and she agreed
to sell the land and let Everald borrow the money, for he needed the down
payment for a house in the town. How could she stand in his way when he
said she should come and live with them, there would be plenty space for
275 her? She said, no, she could never take to life in town. So he said all right, if
she stayed in her house he would look after her. He would pay back the
money as soon as he could, put it into the bank to mind her in her old age.

"Where is the money now, eh?" she asked Hermione, for about the hun-
dredth time. "Once Mister Everald get his hand on it, never see hide or hair
280 of it again. That Everald with his sweet mouth! Is when last I see him? Tell
me nuh?" Once in a while Everald would come, she reported, or his grown-
up children would breeze by and leave her a little something. All driving
their flashy big cars. But if she was waiting on them to live, she would
starve to death.

285    If it wasn't for Miss Vie and Hermione, God knows what would happen
to her. She was glad she had chocho to give them, for her mother always
told her, "Hand wash hand. Never take something for nothing." In all her
born days, she had never stooped to begging. Every Thursday Miss Mae,
who higgled° in the market, would come by with her little boy and a long
290 stick and the boy would climb up and pick all the ripe chochos he could
reach, and Miss Mae would pay her for them and take them to the market
to sell. That was how she lived. Anyone who came by and wanted chocho
now had to pay, unless she knew they were poor like her; only then she
would give.

295 At first, when the people moved into Everald's old house next door she paid
them no mind, for she was at an age where she couldn't be bothered with
anything new and to her they seemed orderly and manners-able enough.
Something strange was happening in the whole country these last days
anyway, Miss Evadney thought, changes were everywhere, all was topsy-
300 turvy and confusion, it would stir up your brain to take it all in. New
people were moving into the area every day. That wasn't too surprising, for
all the young people had gone away; only the old people were left and the
grandchildren that they had to mind.

    With all the young people gone, so much of the land was idle, so many
305 houses empty, that people from town or god-knows-where were simply
coming and squatting. "Take my old land there," Miss Evadney said, "from
Everald sell it to the people, they never come back once to even look at it,
let it turn into wilderness, ruinate, let Everald good-good house fall to
pieces, you almost have to say."

310    She didn't know what business these people next door had with the land
and with Everald's old house, but she didn't pay them any mind at first.
She heard them hammering and nailing, so she figured they were decent
people who had come to fix up the house. "Is only when the renk ganja°
smell start to come from over there that I sit up straight and pay atten-
315 tion," she recounted later. "And more and more people were coming till I
wonder how many of them planning to live in the house. Then I start to

see some of those bearded fellows there, those Rastas. I never wanted any of those people living near to me. They never look good in the sight of God with their long beard and natty hair." But Miss Evadney didn't complain, for though she was too old to walk and see, people said they were clearing the whole of the land, and if they were hard-working, she said, who was she to pass judgement?

They could have got on all right, would have had no trouble at all, no trouble, Miss Evadney always said, if they hadn't started to pick her chocho. When she saw it, she couldn't believe it, for not even when her own son was living next door would he do such a thing. These people were standing in their yard and using a long stick to cross the property boundary and hook chocho off her vine. She never raised her voice, only called out to them nicely: "Young man. Young man," she said, "is my chocho that you picking, you know?" She expected that he would say, "Sorry," and she would say, "Is all right this time, I don't mind you take a few. But next time, if you want chocho, all you have to do is ask. I only sell them at twenty cents apiece." To her amazement, though, the young man laughed when she called out to him and continued pulling down chochos. "Mother, rest yuself. You have plenty chocho to spare."

She was so shocked, she was speechless for a moment. But not for long. As soon as she recovered, she let him have the full length of her tongue. Miss Evadney thought she still had the voice she had used in the past to stun her children and frighten chocho thieves. But it had got so trembling and thin, it sounded laughably frail to the young man next door. He just continued to pick chocho. "Mother," he called out, still laughing, "you nuh hear is Socialist time now? All a we must share. Nothing nuh belong to you one any more." And before she had a chance to marshal her thoughts, hurl at him the most crushing abuse, he had picked up the chochos, *her* chocho, and disappeared into the house. Every day they came to the fence and picked chocho and got so bare-faced they did it even when they could see her standing in her yard. She would hobble over to the arbour and shout and wave her arms, but they paid her not the slightest attention, the stick continuing its remorseless passage, stabbing away at chochos until the picker decided that he had reaped enough. Each scene would leave Miss Evadney with just enough strength to make it back to her doorstep where she would sit for a while and fan herself to cool down and try to recover her composure. At first, she would go from there to Miss Vie as soon as she could manage it, to complain about the latest assault, but she did this less and less because she was shocked to discover that Miss Vie was not wholeheartedly on her side.

"Miss Evadney, I know just how you feel," Miss Vie had said. "I know it's an aggravation. But it's not like first time, you know. You have to be careful how you deal with everybody these days. Those people not good people to quarrel with, from what I hear. It would be better if you just leave them to take the chocho."

Leave them to take the chocho! Miss Vie couldn't know what she saying. It was all right for her, for she had house and land and husband and pickney and car. Could afford to give away all kind of thing. But all she had was her chocho and nobody had any right to just come and take. No right at all. She told Miss Vie as much, shaking with anger and disappointment at her attitude.

"Miss Evadney, if you want me to put it straight: you know what those people planting on the land there? I hear that is pure ganja them a plant, you know. You don't want to tangle with those kind of people."

"Plant ganja! Everybody a plant ganja these days," Miss Evadney cried. "That is the only thing them young people farming. Them all a plant ganja. Mek them gwan. Them could plant the whole world in ganja for all I care. But that don't give them no right to take stick so pick my chocho. I bring up my boys to know right from wrong and to respect other people property. That is one thing I beat into them. Nobody could ever complain that any of my boys ever put hand on what don't belong to them. So why I should put up with other people tiefing from me?"

Miss Vie just sighed.

One day Miss Evadney came home and found some gungo peas° laid out on a piece of plantain leaf on her doorstep. She cooked the gungo because she thought they were left there by one of the men around who sometimes brought her things from his ground. Another time it was a piece of pumpkin. Then one day she learned the truth. She'd heard a voice calling out, "Mother? Mother?" but she didn't answer because the only people who called her that were the thieving nayga boys next door. She peeked through a crack and sure enough it was one those dirty Rastas, bending down at her doorstep. She trembled in anger. What did he want? She couldn't quite see but was satisfied that he didn't stay. She watched him leave, made sure he got off her premises without stealing anything. When she opened her door and saw a piece of yam lying there on the plantain leaf, Miss Evadney's anger knew no bounds. Did they think she was the kind of person they could just sweeten up so that she would let them take chocho as they liked? All she wanted was for them

395  to leave her chocho alone. She picked up the yam and plantain leaf and
hobbled over to the fence where, cursing, she hurled them back into the
Rastas' yard.

But Miss Evadney soon realized she would have to find other means of
keeping the chocho thieves from off her vine, to let them know once and
400  for all that she meant business. She began to keep watch on the arbour,
sitting there silently hour after hour till her body got so cramped and stiff
she could hardly move. When they came, she was ready for them. By her
was a pile of stones which she had slowly and painfully collected. As soon
as she saw the stick of the chocho thieves disturbing the foliage, she would
405  hurl as many stones as she could over the fence, her strength so weakened
that she was forced to stop and catch her breath after each throw. Though
her range was short and the hail of stones ineffectual, they did cause the
young men reaping the chocho to pause and even to jump to get out of
range of the stronger throws. At first, they were more amused than any-
410  thing and took to reasoning with her: "Lawd, Mother. Behave yuself, nuh.
Why you have to fight and quarrel so with the bredren? Nuh Jah send I-
bredren so help you reap Jah blessing?"

Miss Evadney simply continued with her stone-throwing. Though she
never managed to hit anyone, after a while the amused cajoling turned
415  to curses and then to threats. Once, one of them rushed to the fence with
a raised machete. But still she didn't give up, screaming at the men "Unno
gwine stop pick mi chocho. Even if it kill me. Not one of you ever plant
chocho over here." Now they had stopped laughing, they got in the habit
of shouting words across the fence even when they weren't picking
420  chocho. And every time Miss Evadney saw them with a stick, she hurled
stones.

One day, as she sat under the arbour with her pile of stones as usual,
she saw the young men moving around the yard, heard them talking,
heard the bad words they flung about, caught the smell of ganja on the
425  wind. But no one came near the fence. No one attempted to pick chocho.
The next day it was the same. After the third day of this she felt she had
won a victory and, confident that she had finally put the chocho thieves
in their place, she slept soundly for the first time in weeks. Next morning
she walked as fast as her legs could take her to tell Miss Vie the good news,
430  so pleased with herself she forgot the usual recital of her ailments. Miss Vie
gave her chicken soup with chocho—her favourite—to celebrate. That
night, she again slept the whole night through.

It wasn't until late the following day that she walked down to her chocho vine and immediately noticed something strange. The vine was not looking good, it seemed droopy and disheartened. She rushed to water the root, carrying the margarine tin full of water back and forth. But for all the water she poured, the chocho didn't perk up as she expected. It continued to wilt. Alarmed, she rushed over to Miss Vie and begged her to come and see what she could make of the vine, why it was drying up so.

Miss Vie came and examined the chocho carefully, looking at the arbour from various angles, disturbed at the obviously dying leaves, the colourless exposed fruit which were already shrivelling. When she could find no explanation, she went and got Miss Evadney's rickety ladder and, leaning it against the mango tree, started to climb.

"You see anything, Miss Vie?" Miss Evadney called out anxiously before she was even halfway up. With great caution, Miss Vie moved steadily up the ladder until she reached a point where she had a good view of the vine. She held on to the tree with both hands and followed the main stem with her eyes. She almost shouted out then, but caught herself just in time, for she had seen where the chocho vine had been cut, sliced right through with a sharp machete. She stood very still, gazing on the arbour, wondering how on earth she was going to find the heart to come down and tell Miss Evadney the news.

Miss Evadney, using her hand to shield her eyes against the afternoon sun so she could better see Miss Vie's every move, had spent too many years scrutinizing potential chocho thieves and wayward children to miss the quick stiffening of Miss Vie's back, the droop of her neck, her sudden stillness. In that moment of recognition, Miss Evadney audibly caught her breath and felt the stillness enter and possess her own body, emptying her of anger, of memory, or desire. Cocooned in that unaccustomed softness, she experienced only the nagging thought that, for some reason, she needed to say something to cheer up Miss Vie, to get her down safely from the ladder. "Well, the thing about chocho now," Miss Evadney heard herself saying, "the thing about chocho now," she said again and kept on saying long after Miss Vie had climbed back down the ladder to find her trembling and wordless.

(1995)

# Fate

## Shi Tiesheng (China) 1951–

*(translated from Chinese by Michael L. Duke)*

## About the Author

*Shi Tiesheng is an award-winning short story writer in contemporary China. He was born in Beijing in 1951. Like millions of young people in China, Shi's formal education was interrupted by the decade-long Cultural Revolution that started in 1966. Together with a large number of students of his generation, he was sent to the countryside in 1969 to get "re-educated" by the peasants. A tragic accident crippled him in 1973 and brought him back to Beijing. He then began to write short stories for journals. Shi's prize-winning stories include "Half an Hour at Lunchtime," "On a Wintry Evening," and "Grandmother's Stars."*

*After experiencing "the three trials that God sends to test us—loneliness, frustration and fear," Shi Tiesheng found writing attractive as it helped him "transform these trials into a source of delight." Belonging to a generation of young writers who had lost faith and hope in the Cultural Revolution, Shi writes cynically about life after the turmoil. Mo Fei, the ill-fated protagonist in "Fate," tries to find the reason for his inexplicable bad luck but cannot. "There is no why," he finally concludes. The fatalistic tone is reminiscent of the English novelist Thomas Hardy (1840–1928), but the intriguing combination of the narrator's wry sense of humour and his resentful cynicism makes the story a thought-provoking masterpiece in contemporary Chinese literature.*

## Terms Appearing in the Story

**liang, jin** measures of weight

### 1

Now to talk about myself: to talk about why, because I was one second late, or because I was unable to be one second later—you might also say because I was one second early, or could not manage to be one second

5 earlier—I became a lifetime paraplegic. According to my prognosis prior to that one second, from whatever angle I looked at it, I should have had quite a beautiful future.

Prior to that one second, about thirteen people had already offered me eighteen marriage proposals, eleven of them sending along photographs, of the young women, and all eleven of them were very pretty. This may, to some extent, explain why I have been confident in my 'beautiful future'. But I wasn't thinking about marriage at the time; my ambition was much greater. 'No,' I said, 'I'm not thinking of such things now.' My erstwhile matchmakers were not without regret. They said, 'Mo Fei (Mo Fei is my name), we want to see what kind of a goddess you marry.'

Later on that one second arrived. Later on that one second passed. My once strong and healthy legs were instantly transformed into two sticks of useless furniture; they withered day by day into two sticks of exceedingly ugly furniture. All this meant that cruelty and misfortune had taken a fancy to a man named Mo Fei and clung to him for the rest of his life. I cried like a baby for several years and then, having absolutely no alternative, was reduced to a man who writes fiction for a living.

A woman reporter once asked me how I happened 'to take the road of creativity?' I thought for some time before replying, 'Having reached an utter dead end, I sank to this level.' The woman smiled so charmingly. 'You're really modest.' She really said so.

**2**

Practical reality has nothing to do with modesty.

Who knows, maybe those half-understood, half-real, half-illusory recollections of Tenth Uncle were originally premonitions from my childhood. They say children's eyes can penetrate to the bottom of many mysterious things and events, but grown-ups lose that ability.

All that is, of course, unimportant. What is important is that my legs cannot move and have no feeling; this is not a half-understood, half-real, half-illusory recollection; it's a crystal clear, absolutely indubitable reality. And from the looks of it this reality will remain a reality as long as I go on living.

I never used to curse people. I now feel the absolute necessity of all the curses ever invented in the world. A necessity, they are, and sometimes even a necessary conclusion.

**3**

It was only an accident of one second's duration. To talk about it now is of little interest. It was a summer night, cloudy; the moon was pale, the stars few, and pedestrians were already very scarce. A night soil cart came by

45 mingling the rich perfume of night soil with the sweet scent of evening
dew—a rare odour. I was riding my bike home, so happy that I had naturally begun whistling a tune. I was whistling the famous pedlar's aria from
*The Pedlar and the Maiden.* I had just been to the opera. I really believed my
luck was pretty good. I was soon to go abroad to study; my thoughts were
50 concentrated on that, on the other side of the world; not just on that side,
of course; the world is very large. My wallet was already crammed full with
my passport, visa, plane ticket, and a wad of related documents—the fruits
of one year and eleven months of difficult struggle. This wallet was firmly
attached to my belt; unless somebody ripped off my trousers, it would be
55 quite impossible to lose it. May the designer of this wallet be richly
rewarded in this life and the next—that's what I was thinking at the time.
The temperature fell gradually and a slightly cool breeze began to blow. In
the buildings along the road someone was cursing loudly while another
one was softly playing a nocturne by Chopin. The out-of-town street ven-
60 dors were spreading their baggage out in the shadows, yawning broadly,
making a racket as loud as an ancient nightwatchman's.

An ordinary summer night. I whistled a tune. The world is very large. I
think I'll go to visit the Grand Canyon in Arizona on one of my vacations,
and Niagara Falls on another. If I earn a little extra money and live very
65 frugally most of the time, maybe I can also go to Egypt and visit the Great
Pyramid of Cheops; to Venice to see St Mark's Cathedral; to the Louvre in
Paris, the Tower of London, Mount Fuji in Japan, and the wild game
reserve in Tanzania...I will see them all; it's such a rare opportunity. I'm
full of energy and as sturdy as any camel; I could even walk across the
70 Sahara Desert and go camping at the foot of Mount Kilimanjaro. I
wouldn't shoot the lions, though, those wonderful lions.

I whistled a tune, not very well, but that tune was so moving. I don't
believe in asceticism. Mo Fei is not an ascetic; he will surely have to have
a wife. She'll be very pretty and kind-hearted, very intelligent, very
75 healthy, very romantic and generous, very gentle and tender, and she'll
love me very much; when we're alone she'll just naturally think of an infi-
nite number of amazing little loving names to call me. Compared to her
I'll regard everything else in the world as light as a feather, but in comparison to her I'll probably seem stupid and clumsy, only able to call her
80 dear, or my dearest, making her so angry she'll give me an extraordinarily
loving slap on the face. A real man should have at least one opportunity
to demonstrate his weakness. Afterwards he will not, however, feel that his
'heroic ambition' has been undermined; quite the contrary, he'll be even

more outstanding in the future and make his wife proud for the rest of her
life! A pleasantly cool summer evening arouses a person's emotions,
makes his thoughts run riot in praise of the beauty of all creation.

Prior to that one second you could rightly say that Mo Fei was not
dreaming. I rode my bike and whistled that pedlar's tune. I was figuring
how I'd return home after four years with my Ph.D. and work for our
ancestral homeland. I would never be 'so happy I forgot my home in Shu,'
as the proverb goes—Mo Fei was not that sort—Heaven and Earth are my
witnesses, you know what I was going abroad to study? Education. Our
country's education is in urgent need of reform and talented people to
bring it about. Mo Fei didn't lack the ability to study astrophysics or
genetic engineering, but Mo Fei had his heart set on his country's education—right up to that one second I had been teaching in a middle school.

I turned my bike into a rather narrow street; I had to take this road to
get home; the shadows of the trees were dancing across the road surface—
later on it will be proven that the dancing of these tree shadows may
rightly be compared to someone being cut to pieces by a thousand knife
blades.

I was still whistling. I was an innocent person. I thought when I return
in four years I can have a son (of course I have to have a wife first) or
maybe a daughter; if government policy permitted it I could have a son
and a daughter; I didn't even consider which should come first and which
second—I think men and women should be equal—and only hoped my
son would look like me and my daughter like her mother, only hoped the
reverse would certainly not be the case. Was it wrong to think that way? I
can't see what was wrong with that. I was an innocent person on that
summer night and all the time prior to that summer night. I was an innocent person. Innocent, without sin, at least that is true.

I whistled that most celebrated tune from *The Pedlar and the Maiden* and
rode my bike closer and closer to that ultimately evil second. At the same
moment a young taxi driver whom I was fated to meet was also hurrying
speedily toward that one second.

## 4

In the general scheme of things that was a totally unimpressive summer
night; or would have been if someone had not dropped an aubergine on
the street. I was whistling that pedlar's tune when my bike wheels ran over
that aubergine; afterwards I knew that the aubergine was very large, very
slippery, and very hard; this aubergine caused my wheels to swerve violently to the left, the shock threw me two or three metres ahead, propelling

me directly into what had to happen in that one second. I heard the loud
screeching of a car braking and my good luck came to an abrupt end. All
125 the wonderful things mentioned in this story so far were transmuted into
a heap of nonsense. They would remain forever a dream.

There could have been an end to it then and there—the problem is it
didn't kill me outright, but only snapped my spinal cord in two. After that
everything simply vanished into thin air, vanished into thin air like smoke
130 and clouds, and after the smoke and clouds vanished, the world turned
around and showed me its utterly inhuman backside—I mean showed it to
me, to Mo Fei.

**5**

I often recalled later a battery-powered toy hen running animatedly along
135 the ground until it ran into a pebble, turned a somersault, landed on its
feet again and kept right on running animatedly forward, only its direction was completely reversed (it probably turned one revolution forward
with a one hundred and eighty degree twist).

**6**

140 I lay in the middle of the road. When I tried to roll over and stand up I
couldn't. That young taxi driver mentioned above ran over and asked me
how I felt. I said I felt pretty strange, like I better rest a minute. Then the
driver took me to the hospital.

I asked the doctor, 'When will I be well? I'm going abroad soon and
145 don't have much time to waste.' The doctor and the nurses grew very still;
I thought they didn't understand what I meant. They stripped me and took
me to the operating room; I told them to watch out carefully for the wallet
on my belt; I even told them the date on my plane ticket. A woman nurse
said, 'Aiya, look what time it is!' I thought to myself it really isn't too early;
150 I said, 'It really isn't too early, but I'm here for an emergency treatment.'
The woman nurse stared at me without moving for half a minute. Then I
realized they could not understand me in such a short time, could not
understand my ambition of many years and the course of my laborious
struggle, could not understand the hardship I had gone through in the
155 past one year and eleven months either, and thus could not possibly
understand what that wallet meant to me. I encouraged the doctor not to
tremble but to work as boldly as possible; if I, Mo Fei, let out one peep then
it just wasn't me. The doctor gripped my hand and said, 'I hope from now
on you can always maintain your present courage.' At the time I didn't
160 understand his unspoken message.

**7**

The true situation was soon apparent: I had already been planted in a sick bed, like a 'perennial' sprig of ivy that's been planted in a flowerpot. As far as that sprig of ivy is concerned, right up until the day it dies its entire
165 world will consist only of a flowerpot, the corner of a wall, or a thin strip of sky. I'm a little better off than it is. Mo Fei's a little better off than it is. 'Mo Fei, we certainly want to see what sort of a goddess you marry'—that kind of a Mo Fei, he's better off than a perennial ivy plant. At the thought I looked up and wailed unconsolably; I sounded just as though I'd returned
170 to my childhood and I looked like nothing more than a great big fool.

I have an elder sister; she hurried to my side from far away, held me tightly in her arms and called out my childhood name just like when I was little: 'Hush now, don't worry, don't worry, don't do this, don't do this, no matter what, I'll take care of you all your life.' ('Don't cry, don't fuss, the
175 grasshopper flew away, Sis will catch you another one tomorrow.') But this wasn't my childhood; the grasshopper didn't fly away; there wasn't even any grasshopper. A perfectly good spinal cord had flown away. I pushed my sister away, extracting my hand from her icy cold grip: 'Go away! Go away! Everybody leave me alone!' Sis held me close again, her strength
180 suddenly grown extraordinarily great. I glanced up at the sun; it was still the same old sun. And the sky? It too was still up there above the earth.

Mother did not come, we didn't dare to let her know. Father was like a huge shadow lacking the power of speech; coming in without a sound, going out without a sound. He bought many good things to eat and set
185 them on the table; then he went out and came in again without a sound and bought still more good things to eat and placed them on the edge of my bed. I screamed and Father started a moment and then moved out of the way. I knocked the flowerpot into the spittoon, threw the tea cups into the chamber pot, smashed my wristwatch and tossed it into the waste
190 basket, swept everything within reach onto the floor and then I started to curse: with my hands behind my head, staring at the ceiling. I railed at the world as hard as I could, repeating every dirty word I knew several times, with tears streaming down until the day grew dark; then I was exhausted, my heart a useless shrivelled mass, pulp from a tree that had been rotting
195 for a thousand years. I jabbed stealthily at my thigh; there was absolutely no feeling. I quickly pulled my hand away, afraid I had poked someone else. How the hell is this going to end? In the long, slow stillness, pigeons

were cooing outside the window...vast, empty, with seemingly no place to rest in heaven or on earth.

200   How is this going to end? No one was willing to tell Mo Fei.

## 8

A policeman explained the accident to me. That young driver was not at fault. 'No one could have anticipated that you would swerve into the centre of the road so suddenly. The driver wasn't speeding, he wasn't
205 drunk, and he put on the brakes just in time; if he had put on the brakes one second later,' the policeman emphasized, 'forgive my bluntness, but you would be dead now.' I thanked him and he said there was no reason, it was his job to tell me what had happened. I asked him if I was in any way at fault. My sister said not to be rude. The officer said I was not at fault
210 either. 'You were riding in the bicycle lane and keeping to the right; you're a good citizen who conscientiously respects the traffic rules, but nobody riding along would necessarily be watching out for an aubergine, and, besides, that stretch of road was very dark.' I said the shadows of the trees were dancing about the road.
215   'What's that you say? Right, there were many shadows from the trees; from the looks of the accident scene, you certainly did not deliberately run over that aubergine.'

'No kidding'?' I said, and my sister said, 'Mo Fei, really!'

The officer sighed. 'But you were tossed into the road just at the wrong
220 time; if it had been one second earlier, the car would not have hit you. The doctor said the same thing: "Such an unfortunate coincidence, the spinal cord was snapped in two and nothing else was even injured."'

'The way you put it makes it sound like it was my fault.'

The officer said, 'I didn't say that. I just said the road was dark and it
225 was understandable you didn't see that aubergine.'

'Then whose fault was it?'

'Mo Fei—!' exclaimed my sister.

I said, 'Sis, can't I even ask whose fault it was?'

'Comrade Mo Fei, that's an unreasonable request, and furthermore, you
230 should watch your attitude toward an officer carrying out his duty,' said the officer.

'If that's the case,' I said, 'you have an obligation to explain to me who is ultimately at fault.'

'The aubergine,' said the officer. 'If you think it's a worthwhile question
235 to ask, well then, that aubergine. Why did you have to run over it at that
precise moment?'

## 9

The days just went on like that. All I saw every day was the morning and
evening sun outside the window. The documents in my wallet were still
240 there, silent as an ancient tomb preserving the records of innumerable
heart-rending legends.

It is humanly impossible to re-attach a severed spinal cord, and so the
days just went on like that. The medical college interns often came and
stood around me while the teaching physician told them why I was a typ-
245 ical example of paraplegia: 'You see how robust the upper body is while
the lower limbs are completely atrophied.'

The days just went on like that. My digestive system was astonishingly
healthy, unhesitatingly taking in various kinds of fragrant things, which,
when they reemerged, were all marvelously transformed into a uniformly
250 smelly mass. The days just went on like that.

The sunflowers were harvested. The seeds fell from the tuberoses and
were blown into the ground by the wind. The sky hung with kites for a few
days, just for a few days, and then one by one they disappeared. The snow
fell silently. Children ran about noisily in the snow chewing on fresh hot
255 baked yams. I sighed. 'Ai, baked yams.' What I meant was the world really
had not changed, baked yams were still the same old baked yams. My
father's tall skinny shadow followed the sound haltingly across the snow
in the direction of that yam vendor's charcoal stove...

The days just went on and on like that. Heaven above knew how unjust
260 it was that Mo Fei should exist this way. I cried a while and thought a
while, thought a while and cried a while; it seemed like that cop's final
question was the only thing that made any sense.

## 10

Gradually I remembered. About two hundred metres from the accident site I
265 had run into an acquaintance. I remembered: I was whistling that pedlar's
aria when I saw him; he was fanning himself as he walked along the side of
the road, and I shouted, 'Hey!' He looked around to see who it was and
shouted, 'Oh!' I asked, 'Where are you going?' He said it was cool enough and
he was going home to sleep. 'You coming over for a while?' He lived in a big
270 apartment building about fifty metres away. I said, 'No, see you tomorrow,
I'm going on.' We waved at each other and went our separate ways.

Although I did not get off my bike, I did squeeze the brakes while I was talking, no doubt about it, I did squeeze the brakes a little. How much time did I lose squeezing the brakes? One to five seconds. Right, if I had not wasted one to five seconds talking to him, then I would have run over that aubergine one to five seconds sooner. Of course, of course, the aubergine would no doubt have caused my bike wheels to swerve to the left and I would have sprawled out in the middle of the road as before, but everything that happened later would have been changed. When the driver of any car saw a fellow laid out in the middle of the road, no matter who he was, is it possible he would not stop? No. The car would have stopped. It would have been only one inch away from me but that would have been enough. Right now I would be at the Grand Canyon or some place else in the world and not planted in this sick bed. No. I would certainly not be planted in this sick bed. That old Mo Fei. That old Mo Fei whom everyone thought would marry a goddess.

## 11

Let me tell you another thing by the way. To this day there are still only thirteen people who have proposed marriage eighteen times to Mo Fei, and eleven of them have sent along a photograph. These three numbers will never increase, and they are a further indicator that today's Mo Fei is a totally different person from yesterday's Mo Fei. Heaven and earth have been turned upside down and the human comedy has followed suit.

I have no other reason for saying all of this except to note that Mo Fei is completely innocent and without blame.

On the other hand, the young women are also quite innocent. It is not a young woman's fault if she wants to live a free, romantic, rich, full, and in short, perfectly wholesome life. It is not the fault of any young woman's parents that they want their son-in-law to be the pride and good fortune of their later years as he stands beside other people's sons-in-law. It can be deduced from analysis that the failure of these three numbers to ever increase is not any individual's fault; it is not my friends' fault, it is not anyone's fault. As sure as heaven is high and earth is thick, without question a donkey is bigger than a dog.

## 12

Mo Fei's suffering resulted from that one to five second delay.

We have to ask and we have every reason to ask: what was it that caused Mo Fei to meet up with that acquaintance about two hundred metres from the site of the accident?

310     At this point I again remembered something: somewhere between three and five minutes before I met that acquaintance, I ate a steamed bun at a little restaurant. I was hungry, not just greedy but genuinely hungry; when someone is hungry and he passes by a little restaurant, eating is a necessary action. If God punishes me on that account, then there's nothing I can say. I
315 went into that little restaurant, got in line behind six other people, becoming the seventh person waiting in line to buy steamed buns. 'When will the steamed buns be ready?' I asked. The sixth person in the line told me, 'You came in at exactly the right time; they're about to come out of the steamer; I got here just when the last batch came out and I've been waiting half an
320 hour already.' So I waited a while; I figured if I went home this late there would not be anything left to eat, and it was nine hours since I ate lunch.

    The steamed buns were ready quite soon, and the old lady selling them counted them out onto the plates. Some of the first six people ate four *liang* and some bought five *jin*° to take out; by the time it was my turn, the old
325 lady said there was only one left. *I* looked into the basket and asked, 'Are there any more in the kitchen?' 'No,' said the old lady, 'just this one, do you want it?' I asked if she was going to steam any more, and she said tomorrow she'd steam some more, but that was it for today. I looked at the big clock on the wall: ten-thirty. So I ate that single steamed bun.

330     Now let's do a little calculating: if I had eaten five steamed buns (I originally intended to eat five) instead of just one, if it took two minutes to eat one, I would have left that little restaurant at least eight minutes later. At the time I met that acquaintance, you remember; he was on his way home and was only about fifty metres away from home; any normal person
335 would certainly not take eight minutes to walk fifty metres. And he was quite normal; I can vouch for that. All this means if I had arrived a little earlier at the little restaurant and joined the line as the fifth or sixth person, I would certainly have eaten five steamed buns and would not have met up with that acquaintance. I would not have called to him,
340 would not have said those few words to him, would not have had to squeeze the brakes a little, would not have wasted one to five seconds, and would not have had my spinal cord severed—today's Mo Fei would be on the other side of the world studying for his doctorate of education and not here, certainly not sitting in a wheelchair.

345 **13**

By now the problem is already rather clear. Please pay particular attention to the words of the sixth person in line at the little restaurant: he said he had already waited there for half an hour since the last batch of steamed

buns came out. That means if I was unable to arrive at that little restaurant half an hour earlier, then I had to be the seventh in line, had to eat
only one steamed bun, had to run into that acquaintance, had to waste
one to five seconds, and had to have my spinal cord severed—today's Mo
Fei would still be sitting in a wheelchair.

We have to believe that it was all fate. Why? Because the opera *The
Pedlar and the Maiden* was over at exactly ten o'clock. No matter how close
that little restaurant was to the theatre, and no matter how fast I rode my
bike, I could not reach that little restaurant one half hour before ten-thirty.
It's a question of simple arithmetic. This all means that at the moment I
got on my bike to go to the opera God had already arranged Mo Fei's
future for him. When you're doomed you're doomed.

## 14

Now let's see how God arranged it that Mo Fei should go to see that opera.

I said before that I had been teaching for some time at a middle school.
The day of the accident I was supposed to get off at six-fifteen; that was the
usual time, and we cannot see God's hand in that. The fourth afternoon
section was my physics class; at exactly six-fifteen I promptly called out,
'Class dismissed!' The students filed out in a bunch, and I walked out, too.
I went out into the yard to look for my bicycle; I was planning to go
straight home; I was hoping to spend a little more time with my parents
before I went abroad. Just then I heard a student ask me: 'Teacher, may I
go home now?'; I suddenly remembered that I had sent this student out of
the room as a punishment during the fourth section.

This is what happened. Half-way through the class, this student suddenly started laughing out loud. He was sitting in the back row next to the
window; he was usually an extremely well-behaved student; sometimes I
even wondered if he wasn't a little below average intelligence. I asked him
to stand up. He stood up. I asked to explain why he was laughing. He put
his head down and remained silent. 'OK,' I said, 'sit down and pay attention.' He sat down, but went on laughing. I asked him to stand up again.
He stood up again. 'What's so funny?' He didn't speak. I could see from
that he was trying very hard to restrain himself from laughing; he covered
his mouth with his hand the way girls often do; I always suspected that his
intelligence was on the low side. 'Sit down,' I said, 'and don't laugh any
more.' He sat down again but was still unable to keep himself from
laughing; the classroom order was breaking down as the more mischie-
vous students took advantage of the situation to start laughing along with
him. All I could do was ask him to leave the room. 'Please go outside and

calm down,' I said, 'the rest of us cannot hear the lesson.' He walked out obediently. By the time class let out, I had just about forgotten him; I was certain at the very least he must have some sort of personality problem. The poor kid.

'You can go home now,' I said, 'but from now on pay attention to classroom discipline.' He started laughing again, went right on laughing. By this time I was getting a little angry. 'What's so damned funny anyway?' I questioned him like that for about twenty minutes with absolutely no success; he continued to laugh but refused to answer.

Just then our most respected old lady principal called me. 'Mo Fei, there's a ticket to the opera, do you want to see it?' I asked what was playing. *The Pedlar and the Maiden,* you want to see it?'

'Why do you want to give it to me? Aren't you going?' She said she wanted very much to go, but she had just received a phone call from the Department of Education; she had to attend an emergency meeting. 'You want to see it or not?'

'OK,' I said, 'I'll go.'

I have already told you what happened after that.

## 15

After a while I was released from the hospital. The hospital is not far from our home. I sat in a wheelchair while my parents took turns pushing me along the street. The poplars were once again laden with blossoms, and far off in the clear blue sky some cuckoos were calling out 'sobitter, sobitter'— it gave me a feeling of estrangement from the world. The breeze blew and the birds' cries gradually faded into the distance. I heard someone calling me. 'Mo Fei, Mo Fei! Is that you Mo Fei?'

I said, That's right, it's me.' One of my female classmates at college was standing in front of me.

'How—, Mo Fei, what are you doing here?'

'Where do you think I should be?' I asked.

'Didn't you go overseas to study? What happened to you?'

'If you're asking me, then who should I ask?'

Her eyes opened wide as though she had just noticed my legs. 'How did it happen?'

'It's very simple; it's the easiest thing in the world.'

She blushed. I used to say that to her quite often in college when she could not figure out a math problem. My mother could not restrain her tears; she pulled my father over to stand some distance away.

'It was a question of five steamed buns,' I said, 'or one aubergine.' Then I told her the essentials of what had happened.

'Really—, really—, ai—!' she said.

'We have to recognize that it was my fate,' I said.

430 'Mo Fei, you mustn't think that; Mo Fei, you have to be strong.' Tears were streaming down her face. 'Mo Fei, you have to go on living.'

My far away sister said the same thing in her letters: 'You have to go on living.' Nobody said how long to 'go on living' meant; it must mean live until death, but who doesn't live until death? My sister said not to worry, that if

435 she had only one loaf of bread, a quarter of it would be for me (the other three-fourths would be for her, my brother-in-law, and my little nephew). But I was worried about a few things more important than bread, things that my kind and virtuous sister could never give. Thus I began to write fiction. And thus when that woman reporter interviewed me I told her I'd sunk to this

440 level because I'd reached an utter dead end. Just like becoming an outlaw.

## 16

For many years now I've been secretly wondering why that student sitting in the back row had suddenly started laughing. That was the turning point in my life and fate. That kid certainly was a little stupid, but he laughed

445 in such an unfathomably obscure manner, just like the profoundly myste-rious workings of fate. Maybe children's eyes really do have clairvoyant powers of observation? I wonder what he saw at that time? I think if I could paint an accurate portrait of his laughing expression, I could then exhibit the God of Fate's true countenance for all of you to see.

450 If it had not been for that mysterious laugh, I could not have received a ticket to *The Pedlar and the Maiden;* and today Dr Mo Fei, Ph.D., would have long since returned home in fame and glory to live with his wife and a flock of children.

## 17

455 In those difficult years I started to enjoy sleeping. I placed enormous hopes in sleep; perhaps when I woke up the situation would have changed. Covered in cold sweat, I'd look at the stillness of my bedroom by moonlight and rejoice that it was only a nightmare; with my heart pounding under the covers, I'd kick my legs and rejoice that it was only a nightmare; the

460 moon would go down, the street lights would go out, the alarm clock would go off, and I'd straighten up my luggage, walk out into the fresh air, and hurry to the airport in time to catch my plane...

People who have nightmares should be considered the luckiest people in the world—because they can wake up from them; in that way they are much more fortunate than people who never have nightmares.

Every time I woke up in those days; however, I discovered that I'd had a beautiful dream of waking up from a nightmare. Having a beautiful dream is the most deceitful thing in the world—because you have to wake up.

To wake up from a nightmare or to go on sleeping and having a beautiful dream, both of these are enjoyable. But in my case the situation was exactly the opposite.

After lying in bed for two years, I started to write fiction. This was in order to eat, to drink, to dress, to pay the rent, and also because this profession provides the same satisfaction as sleep, but it offers one advantage over sleep—freedom. If you want to wake up from a nightmare, then you wake up from a nightmare; if you want to sleep and have a beautiful dream, then you sleep and get it; you have complete freedom of control. Thus, although we once dwelled at opposite ends of the earth and were totally unacquainted, now as we wander the rivers and lakes together, fiction and I mutually sustain each other. It has nothing to do with modesty.

One day I finally met that student again; that student whom I always regarded as a little stupid. He read one of my stories in a magazine and rounded up a group of students from those days to pay me a visit. These children had all grown up, they had bristly beards, and two of them were about to be married. They were all quite happy laughing and talking and remembering things they'd done in the past. One of them said, 'Let's drink to Mr Mo's becoming a writer.' Then I remembered to ask that student, 'Why couldn't you stop laughing that day?' He still looked very sheepish and said it was nothing. I took another tack and asked him, 'What did you see then?'

'A dog,' he said.

'A dog? A dog made you laugh like that?'

He said, 'That dog...' when he got that far he started laughing again and couldn't stop, but finally he restrained himself and calmed down; he had grown up after all.

'That dog,' he continued, 'aimed right at the big slogan on the front gate of the school and farted; I heard it and I saw it; it was very loud but muffled.'

500 Nobody believed him; they said he probably heard it wrong, but then he asked me, 'Do you believe me, Mr Mo? I didn't hear it wrong, really, I didn't hear it wrong. It really was because of that dog's fart. Mr Mo, you believe me?'

After a long time I said I believed him. The expression on the boy's face
505 was that of a prophet.

## 18

No matter what I'm doing these days I always hear that muffled sound pounding in my ears. It occupies my entire space and time, prolonged and unrelenting; and it will continue to shake Mo Fei's entire life with its pro-
510 longed and unrelenting vibration.

Why why why? Why did there have to be that muffled sound?

There is no why.

God said the world must have that muffled sound and that muffled sound came to pass; and God said it was good, and things simply came to
515 pass; that was the evening and the morning; and thus were all of the days after the seventh day.

(1998)

# The Cabuliwallah

## Rabindranath Tagore (India) 1861–1941

*(translated from Bengali by the author)*

## About the Author

*In 1918, in a speech given at Shantinikitan, the university he founded, Rabindranath Tagore said, "the only thing of which I feel certain is that I am a poet (ami kavi)." However, Rabindranath Tagore was a man of prodigious talents and accomplishments, He is celebrated as a short story writer, poet, playwright, novelist, musician, composer, philosopher, theologian, actor, producer, director, statesman, educator, and political, social, and cultural activist. He was, like Gandhi, instrumental in shaping India's identity in the modern world, and a leader in India's independent, cultural renaissance. Tagore hated oppression and exploitation within his culture and by foreign imperialists. He fought against the Indian caste system, founded schools, and was a passionate supporter of the Indian National Movement. Like Gandhi, he was a staunch believer in non-violence.*

*The list of his literary works alone would require many pages, so Tagore was certainly prolific, but he was also highly respected and very influential, receiving awards and honours from India and around the world. In 1913 he was awarded the Nobel Prize in Literature for his own translation from Bengali into English of a collection of poems entitled* Gitanajali. *This was the first such recognition given to a non-western writer. Tagore excelled at the short story form, writing over two hundred stories. which have been called "Rabindranath Tagore's gift to Indian literature." All of Tagore's writing was based on his religious belief. He said, "Whatever I can offer to God I offer to man and to God I give whatever I can give to man. I make God man and man God." This fundamental love for others can be found in all he wrote, including "The Cabuliwallah."*

## Term Appearing in the Story

**Cabul** also spelled Kabul, a city in Afghanistan

Mini, my five year old daughter, cannot live without chattering, I really believe that in all her life she has not wasted one minute in silence. Her mother is often vexed at this, and would stop her prattle, but I do not. To see Mini quiet is unnatural and I cannot bear it for long.
5 Because of this, our conversations are always lively.

One morning, for instance, when I was in the midst of the seventeenth chapter of my new novel, Mini stole into the room, and putting her hand into mine, said: "Father! Ramdayal the door-keeper calls a crow a krow! He doesn't know anything, does he?"

Before I could explain the language differences in this country, she was on the trace of another subject. "What do you think, Father? Shola says there is an elephant in the clouds, blowing water out of his trunk, and that is why it rains!"

The child had seated herself at my feet near the table, and was playing softly, drumming on her knees. I was hard at work on my seventeenth chapter, where Pratap Singh, the hero, had just caught Kanchanlata, the heroine, in his arms, and was about to escape with her by the third-story window of the castle, when all of a sudden Mini left her play, and ran to the window, crying: "A Cabuliwallah! a Cabuliwallah!" Sure enough, in the street below was a Cabuliwallah passing slowly along. He wore the loose, soiled clothing of his people, and a tall turban; there was a bag on his back, and he carried boxes of grapes in his hand.

I cannot tell what my daughter's feelings were at the sight of this man, but she began to call him loudly. Ah, I thought, he will come in and my seventeenth chapter will never be finished! At this exact moment the Cabuliwallah turned and looked up at the child. When she saw this she was overcome by terror, fled to her mother's protection, and disappeared. She had a blind belief that inside the bag which the big man carried were two or three children like herself. Meanwhile, the pedlar entered my doorway and greeted me with a smiling face.

So precarious was the position of my hero and my heroine that my first impulse was to stop and buy something, especially since Mini had called to the man. I made some small purchases, and a conversation began about Abdurrahman, the Russians, the English, and the Frontier Policy.

As he was about to leave, he asked: "And where is the little girl, sir?"

I, thinking that Mini must get rid of her false fear, had her brought out. She stood by my chair, watching the Cabuliwallah and his bag. He offered her nuts and raisins but she would not be tempted, and only clung closer to me, with all her doubts increased. This was their first meeting.

One morning, however, not many days later, as I was leaving the house I was startled to find Mini seated on a bench near the door, laughing and talking with the great Cabuliwallah at her feet. In all her life, it appeared, my small daughter had never found so patient a listener, except for her father. Already the corner of her little sari was stuffed with almonds and

45  raisins, gifts from her visitor. "'Why did you give her those?" I said, and taking out an eight-anna piece, handed it to him. The man accepted the money without delay, and slipped it into his pocket.

Alas, on my return an hour later, I found the unfortunate coin had made twice its own worth of trouble! The Cabuliwallah had given it to
50  Mini, and her mother seeing the bright round object, had pounced on the child with: "Where did you get that eight-anna piece?"

"The Cabuliwallah gave it to me," said Mini cheerfully.

"The Cabuliwallah gave it to you!" cried her mother much shocked. "O Mini! how could you take it from him?"

55  Entering at this moment, I saved her from impending disaster, and proceeded to make my own inquiries. I found that it was not the first or the second time the two had met. The Cabuliwallah had overcome the child's first terror by a judicious bribery of nuts and almonds, and the two were now great friends.

60  They had many quaint jokes which afforded them a great deal of amusement. Seated in front of him, and looking with all her tiny dignity on his gigantic frame, Mini would ripple her face with laughter, and begin "O Cabuliwallah! Cabuliwallah! what have you got in your bag?"

He would reply in the nasal accents of a mountaineer: "An elephant!"
65  Not much cause for merriment, perhaps, but how they both enjoyed their joke! And for me, this child's talk with a grown-up man always had in it something strangely fascinating.

Then the Cabuliwallah, not to be caught behind, would take his turn with: "Well, little one, and when are you going to the father-in-law's
70  house?"

Now most small Bengali maidens have heard long ago about the father-in-law's house, but we, being a little modern, had kept these things from our child, and at this question Mini must have been a trifle bewildered. But she would not show it, and with instant composure replied: "Are
75  you going there?"

Among men of the Cabuliwallah's class, however, it is well known that the words "father-in-law's house" have a double meaning. It is a euphemism for jail, the place where we are well cared for at no expense. The sturdy pedlar would take my daughter's question in this sense. "Ah," he
80  would say, shaking his fist at an invisible policeman, "I will thrash my father-in-law!" Hearing this, and picturing the poor, uncomfortable relative, Mini would go into peals of laughter, joined by her formidable friend.

These were autumn mornings, the time of year when kings of old went
forth to conquest; and I, never stirring from my little corner in Calcutta,
would let my mind wander over the whole world. At the very name of
another country, my heart would go out to it, and at the sight of a foreigner in the streets, I would fall to weaving a network of dreams: the
mountains, the glens, the forests of his distant homeland with a cottage in
its setting, and the free and independent life of far-away wilds. Perhaps
these scenes of travel pass in my imagination all the more vividly because
I lead a vegetable existence such that a call to travel would fall upon me
like a thunderbolt. In the presence of this Cabuliwallah I was immediately
transported to the foot of mountains, with narrow defiles twisting in and
out amongst their towering, arid peaks. I could see the string of camels
bearing merchandise, and the company of turbaned merchants carrying
queer old firearms, and some of their spears down toward the plains. I
could see—but at this point Mini's mother would intervene, imploring me
to "beware of that man."

Unfortunately Mini's mother is a very timid lady. Whenever she hears a
noise in the street or sees people coming toward the house, she always
jumps to the conclusion that they are thieves, drunkards, snakes, tigers,
malaria, cockroaches, caterpillars, or an English sailor. Even after all these
years of experience, she is not able to overcome her terror. Thus she was
full of doubts about the Cabuliwallah, and used to beg me to keep a
watchful eye on him.

I tried to gently laugh her fear away, but then she would turn on me
seriously and ask solemn questions.

Were children never kidnapped?

Was it, then, not true that there was slavery in Cabul°?

Was it so very absurd that this big man should be able to carry off a tiny
child?

I told her that, though not impossible, it was highly improbable. But
this was not enough, and her dread persisted. As her suspicion was
unfounded, however, it did not seem right to forbid the man to come to the
house, and his familiarity went unchecked.

Once a year, in the middle of January, Rahmun the Cabuliwallah was
in the habit of returning to his country, and as the time approached he
would be very busy going from house to house collecting his debts. This
year, however, he always found time to come and see Mini. It would have
seemed to an outsider that there was some conspiracy between them, for
when he could not come in the morning, he would appear in the evening.

Even to me it was a little startling now and then, to suddenly surprise this tall, loose-garmented man of bags in the corner of a dark room; but when Mini would run in, smiling, with her "O Cabuliwallah! Cabuliwallah!" and the two friends so far apart in age would subside into their old laughter and their old jokes, I felt reassured.

One morning, a few days before he had made up his mind to go, I was correcting my proof sheets in my study. It was chilly weather. Through the window the rays of the sun touched my feet, and the slight warmth was very welcome. It was almost eight o'clock, and the early pedestrians were returning home with their heads covered. All at once I heard uproar in the street, and, looking out, saw Rahmun bound and being led away between two policemen, followed by a crowd of curious boys. There were blood-stains on the clothes of the Cabuliwallah, and one of the policemen car-ried a knife. Hurrying out, I stopped them and inquired what it all meant. Partly from one, partly from another, I gathered that a certain neighbor had owed the pedlar something for a Rampuri shawl, but had falsely denied having bought it, and that in the course of the quarrel Rahmun had struck him. Now, in the heat of his excitement, the prisoner began calling his enemy all sorts of names. Suddenly, from a verandah of my house my little Mini appeared, with her usual exclamation: "O Cabuliwallah! Cabuliwallah!" Rahmun's face lighted up as he turned to her. He had no bag under his arm today, so she could not discuss the ele-phant with him. She at once therefore proceeded to the next question: "Are you going to the father-in-law's house?" Rahmun laughed and said: "Just where I am going, little one!" Then seeing that the reply did not amuse the child, he held up his fettered hands. "Ah," he said, "I would have thrashed that old father-in-law, but my hands are bound!"

On a charge of murderous assault, Rahmun was sentenced to many years of imprisonment.

Time passed and he was forgotten. The accustomed work in the accus-tomed place was ours, and the thought of the once free mountaineer spending his years in prison seldom occurred to us. Even my light-hearted Mini, I am ashamed to say, forgot her old friend. New companions filled her life. As she grew older she spent more of her time with girls, so much in fact that she came no more to her father's room. I was scarcely on speaking terms with her.

Many years passed. It was autumn once again and we had made arrange-ments for Mini's marriage; it was to take place during the Puja holidays. With the goddess Durga returning to her seasonal home in Mount Kailas, the light of our home was also to depart, leaving our house in shadows.

The morning was bright. After the rains, there was a sense of cleanness in the air, and the rays of the sun looked like pure gold; so bright that they radiated even to the sordid brick walls of our Calcutta lanes. Since early dawn, the wedding-pipes had been sounding, and at each beat my own heart throbbed. The wailing tune, Bhairavi, seemed to intensify my pain at the approaching separation. My Mini was to be married tonight.

From early morning, noise and bustle pervaded the house. In the court-yard the canopy had to be slung on its bamboo poles; the tinkling chandeliers should be hung in each room and verandah; there was great hurry and excitement. I was sitting in my study, looking through the accounts, when some one entered, saluting respectfully, and stood before me. It was Rahmun the Cabuliwallah, and at first I did not recognize him. He had no bag, nor the long hair, nor the same vigor that he used to have. But he smiled, and I knew him again.

"When did you come, Rahmun?" I asked him.

"Last evening," he said, "I was released from jail."

The words struck harsh upon my ears. I had never talked with anyone who had wounded his fellowman, and my heart shrank when I realized this, for I felt that the day would have been better-omened if he had not turned up.

"There are ceremonies going on," I said, "and I am busy. Could you perhaps come another day?"

At once he turned to go; but as he reached the door he hesitated, and said: "May I not see the little one, sir, for a moment?" It was his belief that Mini was still the same. He had pictured her running to him as she used to do, calling "O Cabuliwallah! Cabuliwallah!" He had imagined that they would laugh and talk together, just as in the past. In fact, in memory of those former days he had brought, carefully wrapped up in paper, a few almonds and raisins and grapes, somehow obtained from a countryman— his own little fund was gone.

I said again: "There is a ceremony in the house, and you will not be able to see any one today."

The man's face fell. He looked wistfully at me for a moment, said "Good morning," and went out.

I felt a little sorry, and would have called him back, but saw that he was returning of his own accord. He came close up to me holding out his offerings, and said: "I brought these few things, sir, for the little one. Will you give them to her?"

I took them and was going to pay him, but he caught my hand and said: "You are very kind, sir! Keep me in your recollection; do not offer me money! You have a little girl; I too have one like her in my own home. I thought of my own, and brought fruits to your child, not to make a profit for myself."

205   Saying this, he put his hand inside his big loose robe and brought out a small dirty piece of paper. With great care he unfolded this, and smoothed it out with both hands on my table. It bore the impression of a little hand, not a photograph, not a drawing. The impression of an ink-smeared hand

210   laid flat on the paper. This touch of his own little daughter had been always on his heart, as he had come year after year to Calcutta to sell his wares in the streets.

Tears came to my eyes. I forgot that he was a poor Cabuli fruit-seller, while I was—but no, was I more than he? He was also a father.

215   That impression of the hand of his little Parbati in her distant mountain home reminded me of my own little Mini, and I immediately sent for her from the inner apartment. Many excuses were raised, but I would not listen. Clad in the red silk of her wedding-day, with the sandal paste on her forehead, and adorned as a young bride, Mini came and stood bashfully

220   before me.

The Cabuliwallah was staggered at the sight of her. There was no hope of reviving their old friendship. At last he smiled and said:

"Little one, are you going to your father-in-law's house?"

But Mini now understood the meaning of the word "father-in-law," and

225   she could not reply to him as in the past. She flushed at the question and stood before him with her bride's face looking down.

I remembered the day when the Cabuliwallah and my Mini first met, and I felt sad. When she had gone, Rahmun heaved a deep sigh and sat down on the floor. The idea had suddenly come to him that his daughter

230   also must have grown up during this long time, and that he would have to make friends with her all over again. Surely he would not find her as he used to know her; besides, what might have happened to her in these eight years?

The marriage-pipes sounded, and the mild autumn sun streamed

235   around us. But Rahmun sat in the little Calcutta lane, and saw before him the barren mountains of Afghanistan.

I took out a bank-note and gave it to him, saying: "Go back to your own daughter, Rahmun, in your own country, and may the happiness of your meeting bring good fortune to my child!"

240  After giving this gift, I had to eliminate some of the festivities. I could not have the electric lights, nor the military band, and the ladies of the house were saddened. But to me the wedding-feast was brighter because of the thought that in a distant land a long-lost father met again with his only child.

(1892)

# Kathleen's Field

## William Trevor (Ireland) 1928–

## About the Author

*William Trevor Cox, born in Mitchelstown, County Cork, Ireland, writes under the name William Trevor. He is not only a writer but also a sculptor and has worked as an art teacher. Trevor has received recognition and numerous awards for his art and his literature in Ireland, Britain, and around the world. He is a celebrated short story writer, novelist, and playwright, and many of his stories have been made into television dramas and movies. His novel* Felicia's Journey *(1994) was made into a movie in 1999. In 2002 he was knighted by Queen Elizabeth II for his service to literature.*

*Many of Trevor's stories focus on human suffering, on those who must struggle to deal with their lives. Trevor has said that he is interested in "the victims of circumstances....I'm very interested in the sadness of fate, the things that just happen to people." His stories are not, however, depressing. Trevor presents average people caught in a determining moment that ultimately dignifies them. Trevor's stories have been praised for their characteristic depiction of "the human comedy instead of merely manipulating comic human being." It is this "paradoxical sparkle" that lends his writing a moral vision. Like so many of his characters, Kathleen in "Kathleen's Field," is compromised by her circumstances.*

'I'm after a field of land, sir.'

Hagerty's tone was modest to the bank agent, careful and cautious. He was aware that Mr Ensor would know what was coming next. He was aware that he constituted a risk, a word Mr Ensor had used a couple of
5 times when endeavouring to discuss the overdraft Hagerty already had with the bank.

'I was wondering, sir...' His voice trailed away when Mr Ensor's head began to shake. He'd like to say yes, the bank agent assured him. He would say yes this very instant, only what use would it be when Head Office
10 wouldn't agree? 'They're bad times, Mr Hagerty.'

It was a Monday morning in 1948. Leaning on the counter, his right hand still grasping the stick he'd used to drive three bullocks the seven miles from his farm, Hagerty agreed that the times were as bad as ever he'd known them. He'd brought the bullocks in to see if he could get a price
15 for them, but he hadn't been successful. All the way on his journey he'd

been thinking about the field old Lally had spent his lifetime carting the rocks out of. The widow the old man had left behind had sold the nineteen acres on the other side of the hill, but the last of her fields was awkwardly placed for anyone except Hagerty. They both knew it would be convenient
20 for him to have it; they both knew there'd be almost as much profit in that single pasture as there was in all the land he possessed already. Gently sloping, naturally drained, it was free of weeds and thistles, and the grass it grew would do you good to look at. Old Lally had known its value from the moment he'd inherited it. He had kept it ditched, with its gates and
25 stone walls always cared for. And for miles around, no one had ever cleared away rocks like old Lally had.

'I'd help you if I could, Mr Hagerty,' the bank agent assured him. 'Only there's still a fair bit owing.'

'I know there is, sir.'

30 Every December Hagerty walked into the bank with a plucked turkey as a seasonal statement of gratitude: the overdraft had undramatically con- tinued for seventeen years. It was less than it had been, but Hagerty was no longer young and he might yet be written off as a bad debt. He hadn't had much hope when he'd raised the subject of the field he coveted.

35 'I'm sorry, Mr Hagerty,' the bank agent said, stretching his hand across the width of the counter. 'I know that field well. I know you could make something of it, but there you are.'

'Ah well, you gave it your consideration, sir.'

He said it because it was his way to make matters easier for a man who
40 had lent him money in the past: Hagerty was a humble man. He had a tired look about him, his spare figure stooped from the shoulders, a black hat always on his head. He hadn't removed it in the bank, nor did he in Shaughnessy's Provisions and Bar, where he sat in a corner by himself, with a bottle of stout to console him. He had left the bullocks in Cronin's
45 yard in order to free himself for his business in the bank, and since Cronin made a small charge for this fair-day service he'd thought he might as well take full advantage of it by delaying a little longer.

He reflected as he drank that he hardly needed the bank agent's reminder about the times being bad. Seven of his ten children had emi-
50 grated, four to Canada and America, the three others to England. Kathleen, the youngest, now sixteen, was left, with Biddy, who wasn't herself, and Con, who would inherit the farm. But without the Lallys' field it wouldn't be easy for Con to keep going. Sooner or later he would want to marry the McKrill girl, and there'd always have to be a home for Biddy on the farm,
55 and for a while at least an elderly mother and father would have to be

accommodated also. Sometimes one or other of the exiled children sent back a cheque and Hagerty never objected to accepting it. But none of them could afford the price of a field, and he wasn't going to ask them. Nor would Con accept these little presents when his time came to take over the farm entirely, for how could the oldest brother be beholden like that in the prime of his life? It wasn't the same for Hagerty himself: he'd been barefoot on the farm as a child, which was when his humility had been learned.

'Are you keeping yourself well, Mr Hagerty?' Mrs Shaughnessy inquired, crossing the small bar to where he sat. She'd been busy with customers on the grocery side since soon after he'd come in; she'd drawn the cork out of his bottle, apologizing for her busyness when she gave it to him to pour himself.

'I am,' he said. 'And are you, Mrs Shaughnessy?'

'I have the winter rheumatism again. But thank God it's not severe.'

Mrs Shaughnessy was a tall, big-shouldered woman whom he remembered as a girl before she'd married into the shop. She wore a bit of makeup, and her clothes were more colourful than his wife's, although they were hidden now by her green shop overall. She had been flighty as a girl, so he remembered hearing, but in no way could you describe her as that in her late middle age; 'well-to-do' was the description that everything about Mrs Shaughnessy insisted upon.

'I was wanting to ask you, Mr Hagerty. I'm on the look-out for a country girl to assist me in the house. If they're any good they're like gold dust these days. Would you know of a country girl out your way?'

Hagerty began to shake his head and was at once reminded of the bank agent shaking his. It was then, while he was still actually engaged in that motion, that he recalled a fact which previously had been of no interest to him: Mrs Shaughnessy's husband lent people money. Mr Shaughnessy was a considerable businessman. As well as the Provisions and Bar, he owned a barber's shop and was an agent for the Property & Life Insurance Company; he had funds to spare. Hagerty had heard of people mortgaging an area of their land with Mr Shaughnessy, or maybe the farmhouse itself, and as a consequence being able to buy machinery or stock. He'd never yet heard of any unfairness or sharp practice on the part of Mr Shaughnessy after the deal had been agreed upon and had gone into operation.

'Haven't you a daughter yourself, Mr Hagerty? Pardon me now if I'm guilty of a presumption, but I always say if you don't ask you won't know. Haven't you a daughter not long left the nuns?'

Kathleen's round, open features came into his mind, momentarily softening his own. His youngest daughter was inclined to plumpness, but her
95 wide, uncomplicated smile often radiated moments of prettiness in her
face. She had always been his favourite, although Biddy, of course, had a
special place also.

'No, she's not long left the convent.'

Her face slipped away, darkening to nothing in his imagination. He
100 thought again of the Lallys' field, the curving shape of it like a tea-cloth
thrown over a bush to dry. A stream ran among the few little ash trees at
the bottom, the morning sun lingered on the heart of it.

'I'd never have another girl unless I knew the family, Mr Hagerty. Or
unless she'd be vouched for by someone the like of yourself.'
105 'Are you thinking of Kathleen, Mrs Shaughnessy?'

'Well, I am. I'll be truthful with you, I am.'

At that moment someone rapped with a coin on the counter of the grocery and Mrs Shaughnessy hurried away. If Kathleen came to work in the
house above the Provisions and Bar, he might be able to bring up the pos-
110 sibility of a mortgage. And the grass was so rich in the field that it wouldn't
be too many years before a mortgage could be paid off. Con would be left
secure, Biddy would be provided for.

Hagerty savoured a slow mouthful of stout. He didn't want Kathleen to
go to England. *I can get her fixed up,* her sister, Mary Florence, had written
115 in a letter not long ago. 'I'd rather Kilburn than Chicago,' he'd heard
Kathleen herself saying to Con, and at the time he'd been relieved because
Kilburn was nearer. Only Biddy would always be with them, for you
couldn't count on Con not being tempted by Kilburn or Chicago the way
things were at the present time. 'Sure, what choice have we in any of it?'
120 their mother had said, but enough of them had gone, he'd thought. His
father had struggled for the farm and he'd struggled for it himself.

'God, the cheek of some people!' Mrs Shaughnessy exclaimed, re-
entering the bar. 'Tinned pears and ham, and her book unpaid since
January! Would you credit that, Mr Hagerty?'
125 He wagged his head in an appropriate manner, denoting amazement.
He'd been thinking over what she'd put to him, he said. There was no girl
out his way who might be suitable, only his own Kathleen. 'You were right
enough to mention Kathleen, Mrs Shaughnessy.' The nuns had never been
displeased with her, he said as well.

130    'Of course, she would be raw, Mr Hagerty. I'd have to train every inch of her. Well, I have experience in that, all right. You train them, Mr Hagerty, and the next thing is they go off to get married. There's no sign of that, is there?'

'Ah, no, no.

135    'You'd maybe spend a year training them and then they'd be off. Sure, where's the sense in it? I often wonder I bother.'

'Kathleen wouldn't go running off, no fear of that, Mrs Shaughnessy.'

'It's best to know the family. It's best to know a father like yourself.'

As Mrs Shaughnessy spoke, her husband appeared behind the bar. He
140 was a medium-sized man, with grey hair brushed into spikes, and a map of broken veins dictating a warm redness in his complexion. He wore a collar and tie, which Mr Hagerty did not, and the waistcoat and trousers of a dark-blue suit. He carried a number of papers in his right hand and a packet of Sweet Afton cigarettes in his left. He spread the papers out on the
145 bar and, having lit a cigarette, proceeded to scrutinize them. While he listened to Mrs Shaughnessy's further exposition of her theme, Hagerty was unable to take his eyes off him.

'You get in a country girl and you wouldn't know was she clean or maybe would she take things. We had a queer one once, she used eat a raw
150 onion. You'd go into the kitchen and she'd be at it. "What are you chewing, Kitty?" you might say to her politely. And she'd open her mouth and you'd see the onion in it.'

'Kathleen wouldn't eat onions.

'Ah, I'm not saying she would. Des, will you bring Mr Hagerty another
155 bottle of stout? He has a girl for us.'

Looking up from his papers but keeping a finger in place on them, her husband asked her what she was talking about.

'Kathleen Hagerty would come in and assist me, Des.'

Mr Shaughnessy asked who Kathleen Hagerty was, and when it was
160 revealed that her father was sitting in the bar with a bottle of stout, and in need of another one, he bundled his papers into a pocket and drew the corks from two further bottles. His wife winked at Hagerty. He liked to have a maid about the house, she said. He pretended he didn't, but he liked the style of it.

165    All the way back to the farm, driving home the bullocks, Hagerty reflected on that stroke of luck. In poor spirits he'd turned into Shaughnessy's, it being the nearest public house to the bank. If he hadn't done so, and if Mrs Shaughnessy hadn't mentioned her domestic needs, and if her husband hadn't come in when he had, there wouldn't have

170 been one bit of good news to carry back. 'I'm after a field of land,' he'd said
to Mr Shaughnessy, making no bones about it. They'd both listened to
him, Mrs Shaughnessy only going away once, to pour herself half a glass
of sherry. They'd understood immediately the thing about the field being
valuable to him because of its position. 'Doesn't it sound a grand bit of
175 land, Des?' Mrs Shaughnessy had remarked with enthusiasm. 'With a
good hot sun on it?' He'd revealed the price old Lally's widow was asking;
he'd laid every fact he knew down before them.

In the end, on top of four bottles of stout, he was poured a glass of
Paddy, and then Mrs Shaughnessy made him a spreadable-cheese sand-
180 wich. He would send Kathleen in, he promised, and after that it would be
up to Mrs Shaughnessy. 'But, sure, I think we'll do business,' she'd confidently predicted.

Biddy would see him coming, he said to himself as he urged the bullocks
on. She'd see the bullocks and she'd run back into the house to say they
185 hadn't been sold. There'd be long faces then, but he'd take it easy when he
entered the kitchen and reached out for his tea. A bad old fair it had been,
he'd report, which was nothing only the truth, and he'd go through the
offers that had been made to him. He'd go through his conversation with
Mr Ensor and then explain how he'd gone into Shaughnessy's to rest him-
190 self before the journey home.

On the road ahead he saw Biddy waving at him and then doing what
he'd known she'd do: hurrying back to precede him with the news. As he
murmured the words of a thanksgiving, his youngest daughter again filled
Hagerty's mind. The day Kathleen was born it had rained from dawn till
195 dusk. People said that was lucky for the family of an infant, and it might
be they were right.

Kathleen was led from room to room and felt alarmed. She had never
experienced a carpet beneath her feet before. There were boards or
linoleum in the farmhouse, and linoleum in the Reverend Mother's room
200 at the convent. She found the papered walls startling: flowers cascaded in
the corners, and ran in a narrow band around the room, close to the
ceiling. 'I see you admiring the frieze,' Mrs Shaughnessy said. 'I had the
house redone a year ago.' She paused and then laughed, amused by the
wonder in Kathleen's face. 'Those little borders,' she said. 'I think they call
205 them friezes these days.'

When Mrs Shaughnessy laughed her chin became long and smooth,
and the skin tightened on her forehead. Her very white false teeth—which
Kathleen was later to learn she referred to as her 'delf'—shifted slightly

behind her reddened lips. The laugh was a sedate whisper that quickly
210 exhausted itself.

'You're a good riser, are you, Kathleen?'

'I'm used to getting up, ma'am.'

Always say ma'am, the Reverend Mother had adjured, for Kathleen had
been summoned when it was known that Mrs Shaughnessy was interested
215 in training her as a maid. The Reverend Mother liked to have a word with
any girl who'd been to the convent when the question of local employment
arose, or if emigration was mooted. The Reverend Mother liked to satisfy
herself that a girl's future promised to be what she would herself have
chosen for the girl; and she liked to point out certain hazards, feeling it her
220 duty to do so. The Friday fast was not observed in Protestant households,
where there would also be an absence of sacred reminders. Conditions met
with after emigration left even more to be desired.

'Now, this would be your own room, Kathleen,' Mrs Shaughnessy said,
leading her into a small bedroom at the top of the house. There was a
225 white china wash-basin with a jug standing in it, and a bed with a mattress on it, and a cupboard. The stand the basin and the jug were on was
painted white, and so was the cupboard. A net curtain covered the bottom
half of a window and at the top there was a brown blind like the ones in
the Reverend Mother's room. There wasn't a carpet on the floor and there
230 wasn't linoleum either; but a rug stretched on the boards by the bed, and
Kathleen couldn't help imagining her bare feet stepping on to its softness
first thing every morning.

'There'll be the two uniforms the last girl had,' Mrs Shaughnessy said.
'They'd easily fit, although I'd say you were bigger on the chest. You
235 wouldn't be familiar with a uniform, Kathleen?'

'I didn't have one at the convent, ma'am.'

'You'll soon get used to the dresses.'

That was the first intimation that Mrs Shaughnessy considered her suitable for the post. The dresses were hanging in the cupboard, she said.
240 There were sheets and blankets in the hot press.

'I'd rather call you Kitty,' Mrs Shaughnessy said. 'If you wouldn't object.
The last girl was Kitty, and so was another we had.'

Kathleen said that was all right. She hadn't been called Kitty at the convent, and wasn't at home because it was the pet name of her eldest sister.
245 'Well, that's great,' Mrs Shaughnessy said, the tone of her voice
implying that the arrangement had already been made.

'I was never better pleased with you,' her father said when Kathleen returned home. 'You're a great little girl.'

When she'd packed some of her clothes into a suitcase that Mary
250 Florence had left behind after a visit one time, he said it was hardly like going away at all because she was only going seven miles. She'd return every Sunday afternoon; it wasn't like Kilburn or Chicago. She sat beside him on the cart and he explained that the Shaughnessys had been generous to a degree. The wages he had agreed with them would be held back
255 and set against the debt: it was that that made the whole thing possible, reducing monthly repayments to a figure he was confident he could manage, even with the bank overdraft. 'It isn't everyone would agree to the convenience of that, Kathleen.'

She said she understood. There was a new sprightliness about her
260 father; the fatigue in his face had given way to an excited pleasure. His gratitude to the Shaughnessys, and her mother's gratitude, had made the farmhouse a different place during the last couple of weeks. Biddy and Con had been affected by it, and so had Kathleen, even though she had no idea what life would be like in the house above the Shaughnessys' Provisions
265 and Bar. Mrs Shaughnessy had not outlined her duties beyond saying that every night when she went up to bed she should carry with her the alarm clock from the kitchen dresser, and carry it down again every morning. The most important thing of all appeared to be that she should rise promptly from her bed.
270 'You'll listen well to what Mrs Shaughnessy says,' her father begged her. 'You'll attend properly to all the work, Kathleen?'

'I will of course.'

'It'll be great seeing you on Sundays, girl.'

'It'll be great coming home.'
275 A bicycle, left behind also by Mary Florence, lay in the back of the cart. Kathleen had wanted to tie the suitcase on to the carrier and cycle in herself with it, but her father wouldn't let her. It was dangerous, he said; a suitcase attached like that could easily unbalance you.

'Kathleen's field is what we call it,' her father said on their journey
280 together, and added after a moment: 'They're decent people, Kathleen. You're going to a decent house.'

'Oh, I know, I know.'

But after only half a day there Kathleen wished she was back in the farmhouse. She knew at once how much she was going to miss the comfort

285 of the kitchen she had known all her life, and the room along the passage
she shared with Biddy, where Mary Florence had slept also, and the dogs
nosing up to her in the yard. She knew how much she would miss Con, and
her father and her mother, and how she'd miss looking after Biddy.

'Now, I'll show you how to set a table,' Mrs Shaughnessy said. 'Listen to
290 this carefully, Kitty.'

Cork mats were put down on the tablecloth so that the heat of the dishes
wouldn't penetrate to the polished surface beneath. Small plates were
placed on the left of each mat, to put the skins of potatoes on. A knife and
a fork were arranged on each side of the mats and a spoon and a fork
295 across the top. The pepper and salt were placed so that Mr Shaughnessy
could easily reach them. Serving spoons were placed by the bigger mats in
the middle. The breakfast table was set the night before, with the cups
upside down on the saucers so that they wouldn't catch the dust when the
ashes were taken from the fireplace.

300 'Can you cut kindling, Kitty? I'll show you how to do it with the little
hatchet.'

She showed her, as well, how to sweep the carpet on the stairs with a stiff
hand-brush, and how to use the dust-pan. She explained that every mantelpiece in the house had to be dusted every morning, and all the places
305 where grime would gather. She showed her where saucepans and dishes
were kept, and instructed her in how to light the range, the first task of the
day. The backyard required brushing once a week, on Saturday between
four o'clock and five. And every morning after breakfast water had to be
pumped from the tank in the yard, fifteen minutes' work with the hand
310 lever.

'That's the W. C. you'd use, Kitty,' Mrs Shaughnessy indicated, leading
her to a privy in another part of the backyard. 'The maids always use this
one.'

The dresses of the uniforms didn't fit. She looked at herself in the blue
315 one and then in the black. The mirror on the dressing-table was tarnished,
but she could tell that neither uniform enhanced her in any way whatsoever. She looked as fat as a fool, she thought, with the hems all crooked,
and the sleeves too tight on her forearms. 'Oh now, that's really very good,'
Mrs Shaughnessy said when Kathleen emerged from her bedroom in the
320 black one. She demonstrated how the bodice of the apron was kept in
place and how the afternoon cap should be worn.

'Is your father fit?' Mr Shaughnessy inquired when he came upstairs for
his six o'clock tea.

'He is, sir.' Suddenly Kathleen had to choke back tears because without
325 any warning the reference to her father had made her want to cry.

'He was shook the day I saw him,' Mr Shaughnessy said, 'on account he
couldn't sell the bullocks.'

'He's all right now, sir.'

The Shaughnessys' son reappeared then too, a narrow-faced youth who
330 hadn't addressed her when he'd arrived in the dining-room in the middle
of the day and didn't address her now. There were just the three of them,
two younger children having grown up and gone away. During the day
Mrs Shaughnessy had often referred to her other son and her daughter, the
son in business in Limerick, the daughter married to a county surveyor.
335 The narrow-faced son would inherit the businesses, she'd said, the barber's
shop and the Provisions and Bar, maybe even the insurances. With a bout
of wretchedness, Kathleen was reminded of Con inheriting the farm.
Before that he'd marry Angie McKrill, who wouldn't hesitate to accept him
now that the farm was improved.

340    Kathleen finished laying the table and went back to the kitchen, where
Mrs Shaughnessy was frying rashers and eggs and slices of soda bread.
When they were ready she scooped them on to three plates and Kathleen
carried the tray, with a teapot on it as well, into the dining-room. Her
instructions were to return to the kitchen when she'd done so and to fry her
345 own rasher and eggs, and soda bread if she wanted it. 'I don't know will
we make much of that one,' she heard Mrs Shaughnessy saying as she
closed the dining-room door.

That night she lay awake in the strange bed, not wanting to sleep
because sleep would too swiftly bring the morning, and another day like
350 the day there'd been. She couldn't stay here: she'd say that on Sunday. If
they knew what it was like they wouldn't want her to. She sobbed, thinking
again of the warm kitchen she had left behind, the sheepdogs lying by the
fire and Biddy turning the wheel of the bellows, the only household task
she could do. She thought of her mother and father sitting at the table as
355 they always did, her mother knitting, her father pondering, with his hat
still on his head. If they could see her in the dresses they'd understand. If
they could see her standing there pumping up the water they'd surely be
sorry for the way she felt. 'I haven't the time to tell you twice, Kitty,' Mrs
Shaughnessy said over and over again, her long, painted face not smiling
360 in the least way whatsoever. If anything was broken, she'd said, the cost of
it would have to be stopped out of the wages, and she'd spoken as though
the wages would actually change hands. In Kathleen's dreams Mrs

Shaughnessy kept laughing, her chin going long and smooth and her large white teeth moving in her mouth. The dresses belonged to one of the King of England's daughters, she explained, which was why they didn't fit. And then Mary Florence came into the kitchen and said she was just back from Kilburn with a pair of shoes that belonged to someone else. The price of them could be stopped out of the wages, she suggested, and Mrs Shaughnessy agreed.

When Kathleen opened her eyes, roused by the alarm clock at half past six, she didn't know where she was. Then one after another the details of the previous day impinged on her waking consciousness: the cork mats, the shed where the kindling was cut, the narrow face of the Shaughnessys' son, the greasy doorknobs in the kitchen, the impatience in Mrs Shaughnessy's voice. The reality was worse than the confusion of her dreams, and there was nothing magical about the softness of the rug beneath her bare feet: she didn't even notice it. She lifted her night-dress over her head and for a moment caught a glimpse of her nakedness in the tarnished looking-glass—plumply rounded thighs and knees, the dimple in her stomach. She drew on stockings and underclothes, feeling even more lost than she had when she'd tried not to go to sleep. She knelt by her bed, and when she'd offered her usual prayers she asked that she might be taken away from the Shaughnessys' house. She asked that her father would understand when she told him.

'The master's waiting on his breakfast, Kitty.'

'I lit the range the minute I was down, ma'am.'

'If you don't get it going by twenty to seven it won't be hot in time. I told you that yesterday. Didn't you pull the dampers out?'

'The paper wouldn't catch, ma'am.'

'If the paper wouldn't catch you'll have used a damp bit. Or maybe paper out of a magazine. You can't light a fire with paper out of a magazine, Kitty.'

'If I'd had a drop of paraffin, ma'am—'

'My God, are you mad, child?'

'At home we'd throw on a half cup of paraffin if the fire was slow, ma'am.'

'Never bring paraffin near the range. If the master heard you he'd jump out of his skin.'

'I only thought it would hurry it, ma'am.'

'Set the alarm for six if you're going to be slow with the fire. If the break-fast's not on the table by a quarter to eight he'll raise the roof. Have you the plates in the bottom oven?'

When Kathleen opened the door of the bottom oven a black kitten darted out, scratching the back of her hand in its agitation.

405 'Great God Almighty!' exclaimed Mrs Shaughnessy. 'Are you trying to roast the poor cat?'

'I didn't know it was in there, ma'am.'

'You lit the fire with the poor creature inside there! What were you thinking of to do that, Kitty?'

410 'I didn't know, ma am—'

'Always look in the two ovens before you light the range, child. Didn't you hear me telling you?'

After breakfast, when Kathleen went into the dining-room to clear the table, Mrs Shaughnessy was telling her son about the kitten in the oven.

415 'Haven't they brains like turnips?' she said, even though Kathleen was in the room. The son released a half-hearted smile, but when Kathleen asked him if he'd finished with the jam he didn't reply. 'Try and speak a bit more clearly, Kitty,' Mrs Shaughnessy said later. 'It's not everyone can understand a country accent.'

420 The day was similar to the day before except that at eleven o'clock Mrs Shaughnessy said:

'Go upstairs and take off your cap. Put on your coat and go down the street to Crawley's. A half pound of round steak, and suet. Take the book off the dresser. He'll know who you are when he sees it.'

425 So far, that was the pleasantest chore she had been asked to do. She had to wait in the shop because there were two other people before her, both of whom held the butcher in conversation. 'I know your father,' Mr Crawley said when he'd asked her name, and he held her in conversation also, wanting to know if her father was in good health and asking about her

430 brothers and sisters. He'd heard about the buying of the Lallys' field. She was the last uniformed maid in the town, he said, now that Nellie Broderick at Maclure's had had to give up because of her legs.

'Are you mad?' Mrs Shaughnessy shouted at her on her return. 'I should be down in the shop and not waiting to put that meat on. Didn't I tell you

435 yesterday not to be loitering in the mornings?'

'I'm sorry, ma am, only Mr Crawley—'

'Go down to the shop and tell the master I'm delayed over cooking the dinner and can you assist him for ten minutes.'

But when Kathleen appeared in the grocery Mr Shaughnessy asked

440 her if she'd got lost. The son was weighing sugar into grey paper bags and tying string round each of them. A murmur of voices came from the bar.

'Mrs Shaughnessy is delayed over cooking the dinner,' Kathleen said. 'She was thinking I could assist you for ten minutes.'

445 'Well, that's a good one!' Mr Shaughnessy threw back his head, exploding into laughter. A little shower of spittle damped Kathleen's face. The son gave his half-hearted smile. 'Can you make a spill, Kitty? D'you know what I mean by a spill?' Mr Shaughnessy demonstrated with a piece of brown paper on the counter. Kathleen shook her head. 'Would you

450 know what to charge for a quarter pound of tea, Kitty? Can you weigh out sugar, Kitty? Go back to the missus, will you, and tell her to have sense.'

In the kitchen Kathleen put it differently, simply saying that Mr Shaughnessy hadn't required her services. 'Bring a scuttle of coal up to the dining-room,' Mrs Shaughnessy commanded. 'And get out the mustard.

455 Can you make up mustard?'

Kathleen had never tasted mustard in her life; she had heard of it but did not precisely know what it was. She began to say she wasn't sure about making some, but even before she spoke Mrs Shaughnessy sighed and told her to wash down the front steps instead.

460 'I don't want to go back there,' Kathleen said on Sunday. 'I can't understand what she says to me. It's lonesome the entire time.'

Her mother was sympathetic, but even so she shook her head. 'There's people I used to know,' she said. 'People placed like ourselves whose farms failed on them. They're walking the roads now, no better than tinkers. I

465 have ten children, Kathleen, and seven are gone from me. There's five of them I'll maybe never see again. It's that you have to think of, pet.'

'I cried the first night. I was that lonesome when I got into bed.'

'But isn't it a clean room you're in, pet? And aren't you given food to eat that's better than you'd get here? And don't the dresses she supplies

470 save us an expense again? Wouldn't you think of all that, pet?'

A bargain had been struck, her mother also reminded her, and a bargain was a bargain. Biddy said it sounded great, going out into the town for messages. She'd give anything to see a house like that, Biddy said, with the coal fires and a stairs.

475 'I'd say they were well pleased with you,' Kathleen's father said when he came in from the yard later on. 'You'd have been back here inside a day if they weren't.'

She'd done her best, she thought as she rode away from the farmhouse on Mary Florence's bicycle; if she'd done everything badly she would have

480 obtained her release. She wept because she wouldn't see Biddy and Con

and her father and mother for another week. She dreaded the return to the desolate bedroom which her mother had reminded her was clean, and the kitchen where there was no one to keep her company in the evenings. She felt as if she could not bear it, more counting of the days until Sunday and
485 when Sunday came the few hours passing so swiftly. But she knew, by now, that she would remain in the Shaughnessys' house for as long as was necessary.

'I must have you back by half six, Kitty,' Mrs Shaughnessy said when she saw her. 'It's closer to seven now.'

490 Kathleen said she was sorry. She'd had to stop to pump the back tyre of her bicycle, she said, although in fact this was not true: what she'd stopped for was to wipe away the signs of her crying and to blow her nose. In the short time she had been part of Mrs Shaughnessy's household she had developed the habit of making excuses, and of obscuring her inadequacies
495 beneath lies that were easier than the truth.

'Fry the bread like I showed you, Kitty. Get it brown on both sides. The master likes it crisp.'

There was something Mr Shaughnessy liked also, which Kathleen discovered when seven of her free Sunday afternoons had gone by. She was
500 dusting the dining-room mantelpiece one morning when he came and stood very close to her. She thought she was in his way, and moved out of it, but a week or so later he stood close to her again, his breath warm on her cheek. When it happened the third time she felt herself blushing.

It was in this manner that Mr Shaughnessy rather than his wife came
505 to occupy, for Kathleen, the central role in the household. The narrow-faced son remained as he had been since the day of her arrival, a dour presence, contributing little in the way of conversation and never revealing the fruits of his brooding silence. Mrs Shaughnessy, having instructed, had apparently played out the part she'd set herself. She came
510 into the kitchen at midday to cook meat and potatoes and one of the milk puddings her husband was addicted to, but otherwise the kitchen was Kathleen's province now and it was she who was responsible for the frying of the food for breakfast and for the six o'clock tea. Mrs Shaughnessy preferred to be in the shop. She enjoyed the social side of that, she told
515 Kathleen; and she enjoyed the occasional half glass of sherry in the bar. 'That's me all over, Kitty. I never took to housework.' She was more amiable in her manner, and confessed that she always found training a country girl an exhausting and irksome task and might therefore have been a little impatient. 'Kitty's settled in grand,' she informed Kathleen's

520 father when he looked into the bar one fair-day to make a mortgage payment. He'd been delighted to hear that, he told Kathleen the following
Sunday.

Mr Shaughnessy never said anything when he came to stand close to her,
although on other occasions he addressed her pleasantly enough, even com-
525 plimenting her on her frying. He had an easy way with him, quite different
from his son's. He was more like his two other children, the married
daughter and the son who was in Limerick, both of whom Kathleen had met
when they had returned to the house for an uncle's funeral. He occasionally
repeated a joke he'd been told, and Mrs Shaughnessy would laugh, her chin
530 becoming lengthy and the skin tightening on her forehead. On the occasion
of the uncle's funeral his other son and his daughter laughed at the jokes
also, but the son who'd remained at home only smiled. 'Wait till I tell you
this one, Kitty,' he'd sometimes say, alone with her in the dining-room. He
would tell her something Bob Crowe, who ran the barber's shop for him, had
535 heard from a customer, making the most of the anecdote in a way that suggested he was anxious to entertain her. His manner and his tone of voice
denied that it had ever been necessary for him to stand close to her, or else
that his practice of doing so had been erased from his memory.

But the scarlet complexion of Mr Shaughnessy's face and the spiky grey
540 hair, the odour of cigarette smoke that emanated from his clothes, could
not be so easily forgotten by Kathleen. She no longer wept from loneliness
in her bedroom, yet she was aware that the behaviour of Mr Shaughnessy
lent the feeling of isolation an extra, vivid dimension, for in the farmhouse
kitchen on Sundays the behaviour could not be mentioned.

545 Every evening Kathleen sat by the range, thinking about it. The black
kitten that had darted out of the oven on her second morning had grown into
a cat and sat blinking beside her chair. The alarm clock ticked loudly on the
dresser. Was it something she should confess? Was it a sin to be as silent as
she was when he came to stand beside her? Was it a sin to be unable to find
550 the courage to tell him to leave her alone? Once, in the village where the convent was, another girl in her class had pointed out a boy who was loitering
with some other boys by the sign-post. That boy was always trying to kiss
you, the girl said; he would follow you about the place, whispering to you.
But although Kathleen often went home alone the boy never came near her.
555 He wasn't a bad-looking boy, she'd thought, she wouldn't have minded
much. She'd wondered if she'd mind the boys her sisters had complained
about, who tried to kiss you when they were dancing with you. Pests, her sisters had called them, but Kathleen thought it was nice that they wanted to.

Mr Shaughnessy was different. When he stood close to her his breathing
560 would become loud and unsteady. He always moved away quite quickly,
when she wasn't expecting him to. He walked off, never looking back,
soundlessly almost.

Then one day, when Mrs Shaughnessy was buying a new skirt and the
son was in the shop, he came into the kitchen, where she was scrubbing
565 the draining boards. He came straight to where she was, as if between
them there was some understanding that he should do so. He stood in a
slightly different position from usual, behind her rather than at her side,
and she felt for the first time his hands passing over her clothes.

'Mr Shaughnessy!' she whispered. 'Mr Shaughnessy, now.'

570 He took no notice. Some part of his face was touching her hair. The
rhythm of his breathing changed.

'Mr Shaughnessy, I don't like it.'

He seemed not to hear her; she sensed that his eyes were closed. As suddenly, and as quickly as always, he went away.

575 'Well, Bob Crowe told me a queer one this evening,' he said that same
evening, while she was placing their plates of fried food in front of them
in the dining-room. 'It seems there's a woman asleep in Clery's shop
window above in Dublin.'

His wife expressed disbelief. Bob Crowe would tell you anything, she
580 said.

'In a hypnotic trance, it seems. Advertising Odearest Mattresses.'

'Ah, go on now! He's pulling your leg, Des.'

'Not a bit of him. She'll stop there a week, it seems. The Guards have to
move the crowds on.'

585 Kathleen closed the dining-room door behind her. He had turned to look
at her when he'd said there was a woman asleep in Clery's window, in an
effort to include her in what he was retailing. His eyes had betrayed
nothing of their surreptitious relationship, but Kathleen hadn't been able
to meet them.

590 'We ploughed the field,' her father said the following Sunday. 'I've never
turned up earth as good.'

She almost told him then. She longed to so much she could hardly prevent herself. She longed to let her tears come and to hear his voice con-
soling her. When she was a child she'd loved that.

595 'You're a great girl,' he said.

Mr Shaughnessy took to attending an earlier Mass than his wife and
son, and when they were out at theirs he would come into the kitchen.

When she hid in her bedroom he followed her there. She'd have locked herself in the outside W.C. if there'd been a latch on the door.

600 'Well, Kitty and myself were quiet enough here,' he'd say in the dining-room later on, when the three of them were eating their midday dinner. She couldn't understand how he could bring himself to speak like that, or how he could so hungrily eat his food, as though nothing had occurred. She couldn't understand how he could act normally with his son or with

605 his other children when they came on a visit. It was extraordinary to hear Mrs Shaughnessy humming her songs about the house and calling him by his Christian name.

'The Kenny girl's getting married,' Mrs Shaughnessy said on one of these mealtime occasions. 'Tyson from the hardware.'

610 'I didn't know she was doing a line with him.'

'Oh, that's been going on a long time.'

'Is it the middle girl? The one with the peroxide?'

'Enid she's called.'

'I wonder Bob Crowe didn't hear that. There's not much Bob misses.'

615 'I never thought much of Tyson. But, sure, maybe they're well matched.'

'Did you hear that, Kitty? Enid Kenny's getting married. Don't go taking ideas from her.' He laughed, and Mrs Shaughnessy laughed, and the son smiled. There wasn't much chance of that, Kathleen thought. 'Are you going dancing tonight?' Mr Crawley often asked her on a Friday, and she

620 would reply that she might, but she never did because it wasn't easy to go alone. In the shops and at Mass no one displayed any interest in her what-soever, no one eyed her the way Mary Florence had been eyed, and she supposed it was because her looks weren't up to much. But they were good enough for Mr Shaughnessy, with his quivering breath and his face in her

625 hair. Bitterly, she dwelt on that; bitterly, she imagined herself turning on him in the dining-room, accusing him to his wife and son.

'Did you forget to sweep the yard this week?' Mrs Shaughnessy asked her. 'Only it's looking poor.'

She explained that the wind had blown in papers and debris from a

630 knocked-over dustbin. She'd sweep it again, she said.

'I hate a dirty backyard, Kitty.'

Was this why the other girls had left, she wondered, the girls whom Mrs Shaughnessy had trained, and who'd then gone off? Those girls, whoever they were, would see her, or would know about her. They'd imagine her in

635 one uniform or the other, obedient to him because she enjoyed his atten-tions. That was how they'd think of her.

'Leave me alone, sir,' she said when she saw him approaching her the next time, but he took no notice. She could see him guessing she wouldn't scream.

640     'Please, sir,' she said. 'Please, sir. I don't like it.'

But after a time she ceased to make any protestation and remained as silent as she had been at first. Twelve years or maybe fourteen, she said to herself, lying awake in her bedroom: as long as that, or longer. In her two different uniforms she would continue to be the outward sign of Mrs
645 Shaughnessy's well-to-do status, and her ordinary looks would continue to attract the attentions of a grey-haired man. Because of the field, the nature of the farm her father had once been barefoot on would change. 'Kathleen's field,' her father would often repeat, and her mother would say again that a bargain was a bargain.

(1992)

# Siko

Marianne Villanueva (The Philippines) 1958–

## About the Author

*Marianne Villanueva is an accomplished short story writer from the Philippines. She obtained a B.A. in Interdisciplinary Studies from Ateneo de Manila University with a focus on Philippine literature. She earned two Master's degrees at Stanford University in the United States, one in Chinese literature and one in creative writing. She taught creative writing at Ateneo de Manila University, Chabot College, and Santa Clara University. Since 1999 she has been a senior project advisor in the Masters in Writing Program at the University of San Francisco. She now lives in Redwood City, California.*

*Villanueva has written many short stories, which made her the finalist for several prestigious awards, such as the O. Henry Literature Prize in 2000, Manila Critics' Circle National Book Award in 1992, and Joseph Henry Jackson and James D. Phelan Literary Awards in 1990. Some of her stories, including "Siko," are collected in* Ginseng and Other Tales from Manila *(1991) and* Landscapes *(2003). "Siko" is a story about social injustice and corruption in contemporary Philippines. Through her skillful combination of the techniques of realism and magic realism, Villanueva portrays an unforgettable picture of* Aling Saturnina, *an abandoned wife, embittered mother, and powerless victim of her political, economic, and social environment. In this story, truth can only be told in dreamland. When what belongs to the fantasy world becomes so hauntingly credible, the reader cannot but ponder over the possible reasons for the mysterious disappearance of* Aling Saturnina *and her daughter Ana.*

## Terms Appearing in the Story

*santol* **tree** a fast-growing, straight-trunked, fruit-bearing tree
*carabao* a type of water buffalo
**taxi dancer** a woman hired to dance with patrons for a fee
*Ama namin* our father

The village of Babong Silang is an untidy assortment of half a dozen palm-thatched houses, about a hundred kilometers north of Manila. It falls under the jurisdiction of the municipality of San Pablo, a town of a few hundred people, a day's walk away. The people of Babong Silang have

5 lived for generations along a narrow strip of mud road that borders the rice paddies. They are, as a rule, thrifty and industrious folk. When not toiling in the rice fields, they tend vegetable gardens. They own a few pigs, a few chickens—nothing much else of value.

Aling Saturnina used to live in the last house on the left, the one behind
10 the *santol* tree.° But last year, she and her married daughter were taken to San Pablo in a military jeep, and since then, no one has seen or heard from them. The villagers don't like to talk about the events that led to *Aling* Saturnina's disappearance. When asked, they cross themselves and their eyes slide sideways and perhaps one or two will invoke the name of the
15 town's patron saint, as though the saying of it had the power to protect them from all harm. If the questioner becomes too persistent—as lately some of these newspapermen from San Pablo have been—they escape to the rice fields, and wait there till nightfall before returning to their homes. They are simple folk and don't bother with things they cannot understand.
20   Everyone remembers *Aling* Saturnina because of her temper. She had eight children, and was always cursing and beating one or the other with the back of her wooden slippers. She was fond of *tuba*, the potent drink made from fermented palm sap. Whether or not she had money for the children's supper, she would send one of her sons to the *tiyanggi* for a
25 bottle. The eldest son, Lando, ran away when he was fourteen. A few years later, Isagani left. Then, in quick succession, Prospero, Lina, Catherine, and Rey, too, disappeared.

Siko stayed until he was nearly full-grown. When he finally left, he took the last of his mother's savings with him—a few crumpled *pesos*, which she
30 had kept in a tin tucked away under the eaves of the house. When *Aling* Saturnina discovered the loss, her curses could be heard all over the village. Now there was no money for *tuba*, and the youngest child, Ana, was a skinny, sickly girl, not much use out in the rice fields. The villagers avoided *Aling* Saturnina then because she would pace the street restlessly
35 with feverish, yellow eyes, like a bitch in heat. They felt sorry for Ana, but what could they do? Sometimes they would press a few eggs into her hands, a few clumps of spinach. No one was surprised when, soon after Siko's departure, Ana took Poldo as a husband. There was no money for a church wedding, so Poldo simply moved in. Poldo proved to be a good son-
40 in-law, a hard worker. He and Ana lived peacefully together in *Aling* Saturnina's house for many years.

One day, *Aling* Saturnina learned that Siko had been killed. It was Ana who brought her the news, Ana who came stumbling down the narrow street, crying and blowing her nose into her skirt. At first, *Aling* Saturnina
45 was confused. Hands knotting her dress in anxiety, she ordered Ana to compose herself.

"Ah, *Ina!*" Ana cried. "Siko has been shot! He was caught breaking into a colonel's house in San Pablo."

*Aling* Saturnina sighed. She was not sad, no. She had not seen him in
50 such a long time, and sometimes it pleased her to think that she could no longer remember his face, not even when, in those moments when she was without *tuba,* she wrinkled her forehead and tried hard to concentrate. He had hurt her, how he had hurt her! The memory of that bitter day, when, with trembling fingers, she had reached up to the roof and lifted down the
55 old tin can where she had ten, perhaps fifteen *pesos* lovingly stored, and prying open the lid with her anxious fingers, had seen only emptiness staring back at her—ah! That memory rushed over her once again with overwhelming clarity. She remembered the helpless feeling—as though she had been hit in the belly—that had accompanied her discovery. She had
60 no *tuba* all that day, or the next, and her body had been wracked by chills, she had been in a fever of want. Over and over again, on those sleepless nights when she found herself pacing the village like a restless animal, she asked herself, "How could he do this to me?" She thought, for a time, that of all her children, Siko loved her the most. She had kept him warm beside
65 her on cold nights. She had taken care never to beat him—not even when he had done something that angered her—preferring instead to beat Lando, because Lando was the eldest and should have been responsible for the behaviour of his younger brothers and sisters. She had never suspected Siko of stealing, though after he had gone she began to hear stories from
70 the neighbours, stories of how he had been caught more than once filching tomatoes from their vegetable gardens, and how when baby chickens disappeared, they all thought instinctively of Siko. How was it that she had never known? A son of hers a thief! *Aling* Saturnina was ashamed. And now this horrifying deed—breaking into someone's home, and that
75 someone no less than a colonel! It was beyond *Aling* Saturnina's comprehension. She should have known, she berated herself, she should have known all along. Her heart was thudding painfully. The ingrate! She wanted to curse, to beat the air with her fists.

She looked at Ana crying helplessly in a corner.

80　　"That's enough!" she cried. "You'll make yourself sick. Your brother was a fool, may lightning strike me, but he was. I would have beaten any of you with my *tsinelas* if I had caught you stealing so much as a twig from a neighbour's garden!"

Then she went to the shelf where she kept a bottle of *tuba*, and took it
85　with her to the rice fields.

As her feet trod the worn paths threading the rice paddies, *Aling* Saturnina's spirit remained cold and unforgiving. Her mind gnawed ceaselessly at the fact of Siko's betrayal. The fact had assumed the hardness and blackness of a kernel, lodged at the front of her forehead, between her eyes.
90　On this she focused all her attention. She was oblivious to the fresh green of the rice saplings that blanketed the wet earth, the brilliant blue arch of the sky, the birds gliding soundlessly overhead. The silence wrapped itself around her like a cloak. The village dropped farther and farther behind until it was no more than an indistinct blur on the horizon.

95　　*Aling* Saturnina grew tired. She decided to sit and rest for a while in one of the bamboo thickets that sprouted up here and there, forming pockets of dry land among the paddies. As she stretched out on the hard, packed earth and looked around her, her eyes beheld the great, blue bulk of The Mountain, rising straight up out of the plain. The Mountain made her
100　think contemptuously of the legend the villagers told their young children, the legend of the enchantress, Maria Cacao, who was said to live in a palace of gold on The Mountain's highest peak. Now and then, the villagers said, she ventured down to the lowlands and lured men away from their homes and families. *Aling* Saturnina had stopped believing this story
105　a long time ago. She knew now that when sons and husbands disappeared from the village, as her own had done, they had been lured away by more dangerous enchantments, such as were to be found in the big city of Manila, not far to the south. Her husband had left her after one such trip to the city, never to return. And the rest of her sons, the ones who were still
110　living—they were probably there too, living in the shantytown of Tondo, which she had heard was twice as large as the municipality of San Pablo. Some day, *Aling* Saturnina thought, some day I'll go after those bastards.

She sat in the fields, letting the wind riffle through her long, gray hair and calm her aching nerves. Now and then she took deep, long gulps of
115　the *tuba*. She sat there a long time, until it grew dark and the rice paddies, filled with water, began to reflect the light of the moon. A cold wind rose and parted the bamboo thickets. Still she sat and stared. After a while, she

thought she could hear a great clamor of barking dogs arising from the village, and she rose, suddenly expectant. She looked toward the village, ears
120 straining. The clamor increased in ferocity. She could imagine the village dogs, twisting and straining on their hind legs, jaws agape. She had seen them bark in unison like this many other times, and always, always, the sleepy villagers, rushing to their windows in the dead of night, had seen, coming down the street, strange, pale figures—ghosts, spirits, goblins. The
125 last time, they had seen the ghost of *Aling* Corazon's daughter. She had drowned herself in the Agno River after her husband left her. Her ghost had walked slowly down the middle of the street, crying silently and wringing her hands. At intervals she would stop and look around with imploring eyes. The villagers had watched *Aling* Corazon, to see what she
130 would do, but she remained dry-eyed at her window, and, after the wraith had passed, she closed her shutters and went to bed, like all the rest.

In a little while, *Aling* Saturnina thought she could hear Siko's voice, breaking through a gust of wind. The clumps of bamboo trembled and swayed. *Aling* Saturnina wondered what form her son would take in
135 coming to her. Would he come as a huge black dog or a pig? She had heard that spirits liked to assume such disguises. Would he appear as one of those bat-like creatures that fly through the air with only the upper halves of their bodies? Several of the villagers had sworn they had seen such things hovering over the rice fields.

140 Just then something dark dropped from the sky and landed before her with a soft thud. *Aling* Saturnina saw that it was a man squatting on his haunches, head lowered, palms pressed against the earth. He raised his head, revealing a blood-spattered face. It was Siko.

Even with his face so disfigured by blood, there was no mistaking the
145 gap between this two front teeth almost exactly like the one her husband had. Siko squatted, grinning in the moonlight. He was wearing blue jeans and a white cotton T-shirt, and there were dark purplish patches of clotted blood across his chest. After she recovered from her initial surprise, *Aling* Saturnina wanted to hit him. But what was the use of hitting a ghost?
150 Instead she cried: "*Walang hiya ka!* How dare you take my money, leave me and your sister to starve to death!"

As soon as she said those words, she felt her limbs stiffen and become curiously immobile. She wanted to cry out but her tongue lay leaden in her mouth. She could not even reach for the bottle of *tuba* at her feet. Siko
155 stopped grinning. He stood up and approached her, scrutinizing her face. He came so close that she could distinctly smell the odor from his rotting gums.

"Kumusta ka, Ina?" he said in a teasing voice, a tone he might have used
if he had seen her once a week all his life. "I am very pleased to see you
160 again. It's good to see you looking so well."

He laughed soundlessly and *Aling* Saturnina shuddered. She wondered
if he had returned to do her harm. She had nothing to defend herself with,
not even one of those pictures of the Holy Family which the other old
women of the village wore on cords around their necks, not even a bit of
165 ginger pinned to her dress.

"Don't be alarmed, *Ina*," Siko continued. "I've forgiven you everything,
even for the fact that you seemed to care more about the *tuba* than any of
your children. Perhaps you couldn't help it. No one wants to be poor—mud
between your toes all your life, *nipa* hut blown down with every typhoon.
170 What a life!"

You bastard, *Aling* Saturnina thought. Who told you to go and kill that
man?

"Let me tell you about that man," Siko went on. "He was rich. You know
how it is. After years in the army you become a *padrón*. People come to you
175 for special favours, and of course, you would not be so stupid as to help
without getting anything in return. It's why everyone wants to enter the
army in the first place. Take any poor boy from the provinces, give him 20
years in the army, and at the end of that time he ought to have enough to
retire comfortably in a mansion—two, if he's any kind of operator."

180 But you did not have to kill him, *Aling* Saturnina thought.

It became quiet—so quiet that *Aling* Saturnina could hear the dogs of
the village barking again. Far off she could make out one or two lights
against the darkness of the rice paddies. There were a few people awake,
but they would not venture outside on a night like this, not with the dogs
185 warning them away.

Siko was squatting on the ground again, staring morosely at his
wounds. He seemed to be remembering something. When he spoke again
his voice was sad:

"You remember *Ate* Lina? Little, snot-nosed Lina who was always falling
190 into a pile of *carabao*° dung when she was young?"

Ah, *Aling* Saturnina thought. Lina.

"You're frowning," Siko continued. "You look uncertain. Perhaps you
can't remember? No matter. She'd changed her name so many times. At
one time she was 'Fleur-de-lis,' a waitress at the Fishnet in Manila. Later
195 when she became a taxi dancer,° she changed her name to 'Pepsi.' Pepsi
Perez. When I met her again last year, she was working the bars in
Olengapo. She had gone back to using her own name because it didn't

seem to matter to her anymore what she did. She had a regular customer, this colonel. 'In a little while,' she told me, 'this life will be over for me. I'll

200 be a straight woman.'"

No, *Aling* Saturnina thought. No, that doesn't sound like Lina.

"Let me tell you, let me tell you, *Ina*," Siko said. "The colonel was not the first man I killed. There was another one in Aliga. But he was only a minor official with the Bureau of Land Transportation. After a few days,

205 the case was closed. His wife and two children lived way out in Cagayan de Oro. What could they do? No one worth anything comes from Cagayan de Oro."

Ah, how evil! *Aling* Saturnina thought.

"I admit that I felt sorry about that man afterward," Siko went on. "He

210 was only doing his duty and not even getting rich by it. But this lousy colonel…"

Siko paused. His face became momentarily indistinct. Then he said, "I'll tell you how it was. This colonel was a dog, a real dog. I don't know what gutter he crawled out from. I could have killed him when I first saw him

215 touch my sister. But Lina begged me not to. She said she had a plan, that I should be patient. 'One day,' she said, 'we'll come into our own.'"

"So I waited. I was patient. Lina became the colonel's mistress. He took her up with him to San Pablo and I did not even try to follow. Now and then I heard things. I heard this colonel had a wife, a real shrew. She was

220 used to her husband bringing home girls and she was not fooled when the colonel introduced Lina as his masseuse. Later I heard that she had threatened to go after Lina with a knife. Things were getting bad for Lina but every time I wanted to go and get her she said, 'Wait.' Well, the day came when she said, 'Come.' And when I saw her she had a broken nose and

225 bruises all over her chest and back. The colonel had gotten tired of her and stood by while his wife did this. Lina was crying and saying, 'Let's get out of here.' I said, 'Not before getting what's our due.' So that night I went up to the colonel's house. It was a mansion right at the edge of town with tennis courts in the back and a swimming pool a mile long. You see how

230 these dogs live!

"I had just gotten over the garden wall when—bang!—I heard a shot and part of my right ear flew off. A fat woman with hair all done up in curlers was standing a little way off. I guessed she must be the colonel's wife. She was very angry. 'Get him, you fool!' she kept shouting. I turned

235 and saw the colonel behind me, preparing to shoot again. But he was having trouble—his gun had jammed. I started laughing then, because he was cowering in front of me like a frightened rat. I took his gun and

cracked his skull with it. The next thing I knew I was lying on the ground and the last thing I saw before the world went black was the ugly face of the colonel's wife, leering over me with a knife."

Siko stopped, took a deep breath, and shuddered. *Aling* Saturnina moaned and closed her eyes. She was crying. She had not cried for years— not even when her husband left her, not even when her parents died, not even when, right after Siko left, the days of going without *tuba* left her weak and silly as a child. When she opened her eyes a few moments later, she was alone. Siko had disappeared.

*Aling* Saturnina got up slowly. Her legs were stiff. Her back ached, the thought struck her that she was already very old, that she would not have long to live. She hurried back to the village. How long had the dogs been silent? It was dark and peaceful in the little hut she shared with Ana, Poldo, and their two children. In the corner of the one room, a votive candle cast its reddish light on the painting of Christ which Ana had propped up on a table. Garlands of dried flowers hung from the painting's upper corners. Carefully, so as not to wake the sleepers, *Aling* Saturnina groped her way forward. Kneeling before the makeshift altar, *Aling* Saturnina gazed long and hard at the face, so foreign in its whiteness, staring back at her. The nose was long and sharp, the lips thin and straight. The long, brown hair fell in fantastic curls past the white-robed shoulders. *Aling* Saturnina clasped her hands. She wanted to pray for Siko and Lina, and for the rest of her children, who she imagined must be suffering just as Siko and Lina suffered.

"*Ama namin,*°" she prayed, "*Ama namin* …"

But that was far as she went for she had forgotten the rest of the words to the Lord's Prayer. She gazed, helpless and mute, at the painting before her. Ah, she was unworthy, she had not been taught the proper words with which to couch her requests. For a little donation, perhaps the priest in San Pablo could be induced to say a mass for her children. How had she dared to raise her voice to God—she, who had proven to be such an unfit mother! For such impertinence she should be struck by lightning! Filled with remorse, she cowered for a few moments before the amiable gaze of the Christ in the painting.

Slowly, before she realized it, her eyelids began to droop. Then she gave a tired sigh and her shoulders sagged. *Aling* Saturnina was fast asleep.

Early the next morning, a cloud of dust could be seen rolling at high speed down the narrow road that led to the village. The cloud would stop suddenly before a particularly deep pothole, the dust would subside and the outline of an army jeep could be briefly seen before being swallowed up again in a fresh cloud of dust. Just before the village, the jeep stopped, and four men in tight-fitting military uniforms stepped out. The villagers remained in their homes, peering watchfully from the windows. The four men paused at the first house they came to, the home of *Mang* Tomas. After briefly stopping to ask for directions they continued down the street until they arrived at the house of *Aling* Saturnina. One of the men approached the ladder leading up to the house. The other three remained standing near the road. Before the man near the ladder could ascend, *Aling* Saturnina's face, stiff with suspicion, appeared at a window.

"What do you want?" she said.

"Are you the mother of Francisco Dawang?" the man by the ladder inquired.

"I have no son by that name," *Aling* Saturnina said angrily, and made to shut the window.

"Wait, *Ale*! Don't be so impatient. We know that Francisco Dawang, also known as Siko, was indeed your son. We just need you to answer a few questions."

"I have not seen Siko in over ten years," *Aling* Saturnina said. "And I curse the day I bore him."

"He was shot breaking into someone's house last night in San Pablo. We have another one of your children, Lina, in the jail. Won't you please come along quietly now?"

At the mention of Lina's name, *Aling* Saturnina seemed to waver. She disappeared from the window a moment and the men could hear her speaking to someone inside the house. Finally she reappeared at the door, tying a worn bandanna around her head.

"All right," she said. "I'll come. But I have to be back by nightfall, you hear?"

"Of course, *Ale*," one of the men said. "It's only a formality."

They tried to help her down the stairs, but she waved them away angrily. Then she walked quickly away from the house, not bothering to glance at any of the neighbours who were peering from their windows.

When they had almost reached the jeep, they heard a voice calling, "Wait! Wait!" They all turned and looked. It was Ana, running down the road with her youngest child balanced on her hip.

"I'm coming, too!" Ana cried. "I can't let my mother go alone."

"*Stupida!*" *Aling* Saturnina shouted. "Go home and wait for Poldo to get back from the fields."

Ana paused only long enough to hand her child to the astonished wife of *Mang* Tomas, who was watching from her front gate.

"*Ale*, tell Poldo I've accompanied *Ina* to town. Tell him not to worry about me. I'll be back this evening."

320     *Aling* Saturnina continued to protest. "Idiot!" she berated her daughter. "You'd leave your own children!"

"Quiet!" one of the soldiers said. "We'll bring her along, too."

*Aling* Saturnina grew dazed and silent. She and Ana got into the jeep, the engine roared to life, the soldiers leaped in, and soon they were far
325 away; there was nothing to see along the narrow road but the dust steaming up from the potholes. It was quiet in the village again. *Mang* Tomas's wife cradled Ana's baby in her arms. "Shush, shush," she whispered, for it was crying.

The next morning, when *Aling* Saturnina and Ana had not returned,
330 Poldo went into town to make inquiries. That night he returned alone, looking like a much older man than the one who had set out in the morning. He had been directed to various military offices and at each one was told that the two had been turned over to the National Bureau of Investigation "for further questioning." The time for harvesting rice came
335 and went, and still *Aling* Saturnina and her daughter did not return.

Poldo and his two children live alone now in the house behind the *santol* tree. The children, seven and four, are very thin and are always crying for their mother. Poldo continues to go into town to make inquiries, but his trips are becoming more infrequent.

340     Poldo himself is gaunt and quiet, not at all like his former self. The villagers can remember a time when he could plant more rice saplings in a day than any other man in the village. Now they look sadly at him as he toils alone in the fields and note how, when he presses against the heavy wooden plow, his ribs create ridges on his chest and back. He is too thin,
345 almost tubercular. Who will take care of his children if he goes?

In the meantime, Siko's ghost continues to roam the village. Several times the villagers have begged the parish priest from San Pablo to come and exorcise him, but each time the parish priest replies that he is too busy. The ghost can sometimes be seen dancing across the rice paddies on
350 nights when there is a full moon, or sitting on the roof of someone's house, glaring with reddish eyes. In the beginning, the villagers tried to chase him away with holy water and crucifixes. He would disappear for a few days and then return. Now they merely shrug their shoulders. He has been absorbed into the pattern of their everyday existence. He is as familiar to
355 them now as the air they breathe or the water they drink. They tell their children that he is a *tikbalang*, a creature who makes his home in the forest

and who likes to play tricks on people. They avert their eyes from the shadows when walking alone at night. They have learned to live with the ghost, as they have learned to live with everything else, as they learned to 360 smile, to shrug, when pigs or chickens disappear, saying only, "It is Siko."

(1991)

# Glossary of Literary Terms

**allegory**   a form of extended metaphor in which the characters are usually personifications of abstract qualities and the action and setting represent the relationships among these abstractions (see page 146)

**alliteration**   the repetition of identical sounds, particularly at the beginning of words close to one another (e.g., *safe and sound, fine feathered friend*)

**allusion**   a reference to something or someone in history, mythology, religion, or other literary works that brings added information or emotional meaning to the present work (e.g., cultural allusions, biblical allusions, literary allusions) (see page 141)

**ambiguity**   a use of language, whether intentional or accidental, that allows for more than one meaning

**analogy**   an extended comparison of two things, similar to one another in certain aspects, usually to explain complicated or unfamiliar concepts by comparing them to simple or familiar ones

**antagonist**   the character or force in fiction or drama that opposes the protagonist; a rival or opponent of the protagonist

**antihero**   the protagonist of a modern fiction who lacks most of the traditional attributes of the hero/heroine

**atmosphere**   the prevailing tone or mood of a literary work, especially when that mood is established by setting or landscape

**author**   a person who writes a story, novel, essay, poem, etc. It is very important to distinguish an author from a *narrator,* a persona created by the author to tell a story (see page 73).

**Biblical allusion**   a type of cultural allusion making references to events recorded in the Bible (see *allusion* and page 141)

**bildungsroman**   (from German, "formative novel,") a novel that describes the protagonist's youthful development

**caricature**   an artistic or literary portrayal that exaggerates a person's prominent features or characteristics to incite ridicule (see page 36)

**causal relationship**   one of the basic principles in plot sequence—the cause-and-effect relationship between events (see page 8)

**character**   a person or object in prose fiction or drama. Characters can be classified according to their characteristics and roles in the work as major or minor, round or flat, dynamic or static, stock or stereotypical (see page 35).

**characterization**   the techniques used to portray a character or characters in a literary work, for example, by explicit presentation of characters through direct exposition (*telling*), by implicit presentation of characters in action (*showing*) and by *in-depth presentation* from within a character (see page 37)

**chronological sequence**   the arrangement of events in a story in order of occurrence (see page 7)

**cliché**   an expression that has lost its freshness and clarity through overuse

**climax**   the critical moment or turning point in a plot when conflict or tension reaches a decisive point (see *plot structure* and page 9)

**comedy**   a lighter form of drama that aims primarily to amuse and that generally has a happy ending

**complication**   the stage that takes place near the beginning of a story or a play when conflict arises (see *plot structure* and page 9)

**conflict**   the struggle that grows out of the interaction between two characters or two opposing forces of any kind. It is conflict that provides interest and suspense in any form of fiction (see page 8).

**connotation**   the associations, suggestions, or overtones of a word or expression, in addition to its *denotation*, or dictionary meaning—The scientist normally holds words to their denotative meaning while the writer of literary works relies on connotation to carry deeper meanings.

**conventional symbol**   symbols that are products of convention or traditional associations and meanings assigned by certain cultures to particular images (see page 144)

**cosmic irony**   the type of irony that reveals cosmic or universal truth (see *irony of fate* and page 143)

**crisis**   the episode or incident in a plot of fiction that marks a high turning point in the conflict that leads to the climax. The crisis and the climax may, but do not always, coincide (see *plot structure* and page 9).

**cultural allusions**   references to well-known historical, social, cultural, or religious events (e.g., *biblical allusions*) (see page 141)

**cultural setting**   the cultural context, including traditions and conventions, in which a literary work is set (see *setting* and page 115)

**denotation**   the specific, exact dictionary meaning of a word, without any of its emotional associations (see *connotation*)

**dénouement**   the resolution or outcome (literally the *unknotting*) of a plot (see *plot structure* and page 9)

**dialogue**   conversation of two or more people as reproduced in a story or play; speech

**diction**   the choice of vocabulary and of level of language, whether formal, informal, or colloquial

**drama**   a literary genre designed for performance; along with fiction and poetry, one of the three major genres of literature. The two chief types of drama are *comedy* and *tragedy*.

**dramatic irony**   a type of irony in which the words or acts of a character in a play or story carry a meaning unperceived by the character but understood by the audience (see *irony* and pages 13 and 142)

**dramatic point of view**   (also *objective point of view*) a point of view in which the narrator presents characters and scenes as in a play or a movie without editorializing or entering into the minds of the characters (see page 79)

**dynamic character**   a character who develops or changes as a result of the actions of the plot (see *character* and page 36)

**elements of fiction**   the different aspects of a fictional work, such as plot, character, narrative voice, and theme (see page 6)

**emotional or psychological setting**   the aspects of the *setting* that define and reflect the characters' emotional and/or psychological status (see page 118)

**epigraph**   a quotation at the beginning of the work, just after the title, often giving a clue to the *theme*

**epiphany**   (a critical term made popular by James Joyce) an event in a fictional work that reveals the essential nature of something—a person, a situation, an object, etc. (see page 193)

**exposition**   usually the first step in presenting the plot, which appears at or near the beginning of a narrative and presents necessary background information about characters and situations (see *plot structure* and page 9)

**fable**   a brief tale, mostly written in prose, usually using animals or non-human characters to point a moral; one of the recognizable ancestors of the short story (see page 7)

**fairy tale**   a story that involves supernatural spirits or characters, often in interaction with humans; one of the recognizable ancestors of the short story (see page 10)

**falling action**   the second half of a plot, which usually follows the crisis and brings the plot to its climax and dénouement (see *plot structure* and page 9)

**fantasy**   any literary work that takes place in a non-existent and unreal world or concerns imagined and unreal characters, as in science fiction and magic realism

**fiction**   a major literary genre, which includes a variety of narrative writing, either in prose or in verse, drawn from the imagination of the author rather than from history or fact; along with *drama* and *poetry*, one of the three major genres of literature (see *prose fiction*)

**figures of speech**   the various uses of language that depart from customary construction, order, or significance in order to achieve special effects or meanings (see page 139)

**first-person point of view**   the telling of a story from the perspective of a character or characters in the story using first-person pronouns, such as "I" or "we" (see *narrative voice, point of view,* and page 76)

**flashback**   an interruption of the chronological sequence of events to present an event that occurred earlier (see page 7)

**flat character**   a one-dimensional character, as opposed to a *round* or multidimensional character (see page 36)

**folktale**   a story from an oral tradition, such as a legend, fable, fairy story, or ghost story (see *folklore* and page 10)

**folklore**   the general term for folk literature, which may include folksong, fairy tale, folk tale, legend, etc. Much of folklore belongs to oral tradition as it is the creation of preliterate people. Folklore is one of the recognizable ancestors of modern fiction in general and of the short story in particular (see page 10)

**foreshadowing**   a hinting at important occurrences to take place later in the story (see page 12)

**genre**   a distinct type or category into which literary works are grouped according to form, technique, or subject matter (e.g., prose fiction can be divided into three genres: novel, novella, and short story)

**hero/heroine**   the central character, male or female, in a work of fiction or drama,; this character is not necessarily heroic or admirable (also see *protagonist*)

**historical setting**   the time in which a story takes place (see page 114)

**hyperbole**   a figure of speech depending on exaggeration and overstatement, used to heighten stylistic effect or to produce comic effect

**image**   a "word picture"; a literal and concrete representation of a sensory experience or of an object that can be known by one or more of the senses (see *imagery* and page 140)

**imagery**   literally, the collection of images within a literary work or a unit of a literary work. Imagery, often contributing to the mood or atmosphere of a story and sometimes commenting on characterization, may provide keys to the deeper meaning of a literary work or pointers to the unconscious motivations of its author (see *image* and page 141).

*in medias res*   ("in the middle of things") the technique of beginning a story in the middle of action and then supplying information through *flashback* and other devices for *exposition* (see page 7)

**in-depth presentation (mind reading)**  a method of presenting a character by allowing the reader to experience the action directly through the character (see *showing and telling* and page 38)

**internal monologue**  self-communing in a character's mind, normally presented by an *omniscient narrator* in the course of telling a story (see page 78)

**irony**  a broad term referring to the contrast between reality and appearance (see *verbal irony, situational irony, dramatic irony,* and pages 13 and 142)

**irony of fate**  a type of *situational irony,* emphasizes the futility of human wishes and efforts in the face of uncontrollable forces (see page 143)

**legend**  a narrative or tradition handed down from the past, differing from a myth in containing more history and perhaps less of the supernatural. Legend is one of the recognizable ancestors of the short story (see page 3).

**leitmotif**  an intentional repetition of a word, phrase, situation, or idea in the course of a narrative to unify a work (see *motif*)

**limited omniscient point of view**  a point of view that reveals all that can be seen or experienced by a single character

**literary allusion**  a reference to a well-known literary figure or text to add texture and depth by association (see *allusion* and page 141)

**literary symbol**  the use of a symbol that has appeared in another literary work well known to the reader/listener, often to illuminate otherwise difficult concepts (see page 144)

**lyric**  a short poem, often songlike, that emphasizes emotions, moods, and thoughts rather than story

**magic realism**  a term that originally referred to the matter-of-fact combination of the fantastic and everyday in South American fiction but now describes a major trend among contemporary fiction writers to mix the magical and mundane in an overall realistic context. Magic-realist fiction seems to be open to symbolic and even allegorical readings, but frustrates any easy interpretation because the supernatural, the ordinary, and the moral tradition of fables are all mixed together (see *fantasy*).

**metaphor**  a figure of speech that imaginatively identifies one object with another and ascribes to the first qualities of the second (see page 139)

**metonymy**  a figure of speech in which a word for part of one idea or object represents or is substituted for the thing itself (e.g., "the Crown" for the monarchy or the government)

**mind reading**  *in-depth presentation* from within a character, one of the common methods of characterization (also see *showing and telling*)

**monologue**  a relatively long, uninterrupted speech by one character

**montage**  in film, quick cutting of scenes; in fiction, quick shifts of incidents

**mood**  the atmosphere, usually created by descriptions of the settings and characters

**motif**  a recurrent theme within a work, or a theme common to many works (e.g., the "searching for God motif" in many literary works) (see *leitmotif*)

**motivation**  the reason behind a character's actions

**myth**  a traditional story having its roots in folk beliefs and presenting supernatural episodes as a means of interpreting natural events in an effort to support a special perception of man or a cosmic view. Myths differ from *legends* in that they have less historical background and more of the supernatural; they differ from the *fable* in that they are less concerned with moral messages and are the product of a group instead of the creation of an individual. Myth is one of the recognizable ancestors of the short story (see page 3).

**narration**  one of the four types of composition, the purpose of which is to recount an event or a series of events (see page 73)

**narrative**  an account of a sequence of events, often synonymous with story

**narrative point of view**  the vantage point from which the author presents, through a narrator, the action of a story (see *point of view* and page 5)

**narrative tone**  the narrator's attitude towards the subject or audience as shown in the choice of language, imagery, and rhythm; may be formal, informal, intimate, solemn, sombre, playful, serious, ironic, or any of many other possible attitudes, and may shift during the narrative (see page 75)

**narrative voice**  the voice of the narrator, who may be identified or unidentified (see page 75)

**narrator**  the person who tells the story (not the author, but a creation of the author). A narrator may tell a story from the first-person point of view as a participant in the story (using "I" for self-references) or from the third-person point of view as an observer or as one of the participants (watching the action of the story as an onlooker or an outsider). The second-person narrator is rarely used (see page 73).

**natural symbol**  a symbol that derives from nature (e.g., night and autumn symbolizing death) (see *conventional symbol* and page 144)

**novel**  a long fictional prose narrative, usually with some organizing principle, such as plot or theme (see page 3)

**novella**  a relatively short, compact prose narrative sharing many features with the novel (see page 3)

**objective point of view**  a narrator who reports but does not editorialize or enter into the minds of the characters (see *dramatic point of view* and page 79)

**omniscient narrator** a narrator who tells a story from an *omniscient point of view* (see page 77)

**omniscient point of view** the point of view in a work of fiction in which the narrator is *omniscient* ("all-knowing") and thus capable of knowing, seeing, and telling any aspect of the story. The focus may shift freely from the exterior world to the inner selves of a number of characters and may move about in time and place; the author can comment on the meaning of actions and state the thematic intentions of the story.

**onomatopoeia** the use of words whose pronunciations suggest their meaning (e.g., *buzz* and *whirr*)

**open ending** an ending that does not present a definite resolution, allowing the reader to imagine the possible results

**oxymoron** a rhetorical device creating sharp emphasis by bringing together two contradictory terms (e.g., *a true lie*, *deafening silence*)

**parable** a short narrative that illustrates a moral or spiritual lesson. In Christian countries the best known parables are those told by Jesus (e.g., "The Parable of the Prodigal Son").

**paradox** a statement that seems to be contradictory or absurd but, upon deeper analysis, contains a profound truth

**persona** literally a mask; a "second self" created by the author to tell a story (see page 73)

**personification** a figure of speech that endows animals, ideas, abstractions, and inanimate objects with human form, character, or sensibilities (see page 140)

**physical setting** the immediate environment of a literary work (e.g., a garden in summer) (see *setting* and page 116)

**plot** a narrative of events with its emphasis on causality or logical structure designed by the author (see *plot structure* and page 7)

**plot structure** the arrangement of events in a drama or dramatic story. Many action-focused works move from an exposition (where the setting and major character, or protagonist, are introduced) to a complication (where conflicts present themselves) through rising action and crisis (a moment of high tension) to a climax (where the outcome of the conflict is determined) and finally through falling action (or resolution) to a dénouement, or *unravelling* where the final loose ends are tied up (see page 9).

**poetry** a major literary genre that includes a variety of forms in which human beings give rhythmic expressions to their most imaginative and intense perception of the world, themselves, and the interrelationship of the two; along with drama and fiction, one of the three major genres of literature

**point of view**   the perspective from which a story is told (e.g., a major character, a minor character, or a fly on the wall) (see page 76)

**prose fiction**   fictional work written in prose, including the novel, novella, and short story

**protagonist**   the chief character or leading figure in a play or story (see *hero/heroine*)

**psychological setting**   see *emotional or psychological setting*

**pun**   a play on words based on the similarity of sound between two words with different meanings

**realism**   the writer's efforts to portray life and characters truthfully and faithfully. A truthful and faithful picture of life, however, frequently requires the writer to present all aspects of life deeply and insightfully, the inner selves of characters confronted with complex ethical choices as well as the mundane affairs in daily life. That is why good realistic fiction is truthful both socially and psychologically.

**resolution**   a synonym for *falling action,* referring to the events that follow the climax in a plot (see *plot structure* and page 9)

**rising action**   the stage in a plot in which conflict leads the action of the story to its climax (see *plot structure* and page 9)

**round character**   a multi-dimensional character, as opposed to a one-dimensional *flat character* (see page 36)

**sarcasm**   use of sharply mocking or contemptuous language; heavy verbal irony, usually intended to be hurtful

**satire**   a literary manner that blends a critical attitude with humour and wit, frequently to point out how human institutions or humanity should be improved

**science fiction**   a form of *fantasy* in which scientific facts, assumptions, or hypotheses form the basis of adventures in the future, on other planets, in other dimensions in time, or under new variants of scientific law

**second-person point of view**   a narrative voice adopted by the author to narrate a story from the perspective of second-person "you." It was used in the 18th century in novels written in the form of letters between characters, but has rarely been used since then.

**setting**   the physical, and sometimes historical, cultural, social, and spiritual, background against which the action of a narrative takes place. The elements that form a setting include geographical location, time and period in which the action takes place, and the general environment of the characters (see page 113).

**short story** a relatively brief fictional narrative in prose, generally ranging from 500 words to 15 000 words in length; along with the novel and novella, one of the three major types of prose fiction (see page 3)

**showing** a common narrative technique; revealing characters implicitly by presenting them in action and without explanation, rather than explicitly presenting them through direct exposition (*telling*). Most fictional works require a combination of both techniques (also see *mind reading* and page 38).

**simile** a figure of speech in which two essentially unlike objects are directly compared (usually introduced by "as or like") to express a resemblance in one aspect ("as warm as toast," "a smile like a spring day") (see page 139)

**situational irony** a type of irony based on a contrast or incongruity between what is intended and what is accomplished (also see *irony of fate* and page 142)

**social setting** the social context of a literary work, including political, economic, and social structure and environment (see *setting* and page 116)

**static character** a *character* in a story or play who changes little if at all in the progress of the action (see page 36)

**stock character** a character in a story or play characterized by a single personality trait (e.g., the heartless landlord, the mad scientist) (see page 36)

**stream of consciousness** a type of narrative that presents a character's unrestricted flow of thought, often with free associations, but without apparent logic

**style** the manner of expression displayed through selection and arrangement of words and sentence structure

**subplot** a minor *complication* that runs through the plot of a fictional work (see *plot structure*)

**suspense** the tension created by the reader's or audience's eagerness to learn the outcome of the events of a story or play. Suspense is a major device for getting and maintaining interest in all forms of fiction (see page 12).

**symbol** a person, object, action, or situation that remains itself and yet suggests or means something else. A symbol is often open to different readings. A symbol usually has less specificity and more ambiguity than an *allegory*, unlike a *metaphor*, it is expanded through repetition and functions by accumulating associations. The two major types of symbols are *natural/conventional symbols* and *literary symbols* (see page 143).

**symbolism** in its broad sense, the use of one object to represent or suggest another; in literature, the use of symbols in writing, particularly the serious and extensive use of such symbols (see *symbol* and page 145)

**synecdoche** a figure of speech in which a part stands for the whole or the whole stands for the part (e.g., *motor* for *automobile*)

**tale**   a simple narrative in prose or verse without complicated plot

**telling**   revealing characters explicitly through direct exposition, in the narrator's comments and descriptions, rather than *showing* implicitly. Most narratives require a combination of both techniques (see also *mind reading* and page 37).

**theme**   the central or dominating idea in a literary work; the underlying meaning of the work

**third-person point of view**   a *narrative voice* used to tell the story from the perspective of an onlooker or observer, using third-person pronouns, such as *he, she, they, them,* to refer to those in the story (see *point of view,* and page 77)

**tone**   see *narrative tone*

**tragedy**   a serious play showing the protagonist falling from good fortune into bad fortune and ending in death or a deathlike state such as insanity or banishment

**tragic flaw**   the error or defect in the tragic hero that leads to his or her downfall

**verbal irony**   a type of *irony* that indicates a contrast or discrepancy between what is said and what is meant (see page 142)

**voice**   see *narrative voice*

# Copyright Acknowledgments

p. 268: "There Is No Exile" by Assia Djebar from *Women of Algiers in Their Apartment* translated by Marjolihn de Jager. Copyright © 1992 by the Rector and Visitors of the University of Virginia. Reprinted by permission of the University of Virginia Press.

p. 280: "The Immaculate Conception Photography Gallery" by Katherine Govier extracted from *The Immaculate Conception Photography Gallery* by Katherine Govier. Copyright © 1994 by Katherine Govier. Reprinted by permission of Random House Canada.

p. 289: "Arthur" by Bruce Hunter from *Country Music Country* (Thistledown Press, 1996). Reprinted with permission.

p. 300: "Cranes" by Sunwŏn Hwang from *Modern Korean Literature: An Anthology* edited and translated by Peter H. Lee, pages 90–95. University of Hawaii Press. Copyright © 1990.

p. 315: "Cowboys and Indians" by Basil Johnston. Copyright Basil Johnston. Reprinted with permission.

p. 323: "Immortality" from *Palm-of-Hand Stories* by Yasunari Kawabata, translated by Lane Dunlop and J. Martin Holman. Translation copyright © 1988 by Lane Dunlop and J. Martin Holman. Reprinted by permission of North Point Press, a division of Farrar, Straus and Giroux, LLC.

p. 335: "Black Walls" by Liu Xinwu, translated by Alice Childs. Reprinted with permission.

p. 343: "The New Year's Sacrifice" by Lu Xun from *Selected Works of Lu Hsun*, translated by Yang Hsien-yi and Gladys Yang. Reprinted with permission of Foreign Language Press.

p. 359: "Zaabalawi" by Naguib Mahfouz, translated by Denys Johnson-Davies. Reprinted with permission.

p. 370: All pages from "Tuesday Siesta" from *No One Writes to the Colonel and Other Stories* by Gabriel Garcia Marquez and translated by J.S. Bernstein. Copyright © 1968 in the English translation by Harper & Row, Publishers, Inc. Reprinted by permission of HarperCollins Publishers Inc.

p. 385: "A Garden of Her Own" by Shani Mootoo from *Out on Main Street and Other Stories*. Reprinted by permission of Raincoast Books.

p. 394: "How I Met My Husband" by Alice Munro. Copyright © by Alice Munro. Reprinted by permission of William Morris Agency, Inc. on behalf of the author.

p. 411: "A Horse and Two Goats" by R.K. Narayan, from *Under the Banyan Tree* by R.K. Narayan, copyright © 1985 by R.K. Narayan. Used by permission of Viking Penguin, a division of Penguin Group (USA) Inc.

p. 428: "The Chocho Vine" by Olive Senior from *Discerner of Hearts* by Olive Senior. Used by permission, McClelland & Stewart Ltd. The Canadian Publishers.

p. 441: "Fate" by Shi Tiesheng. Reprinted by permission of Foreign Languages Press and Michael S. Duke.

p. 464: "Kathleen's Field" by William Trevor. Reprinted by permission of PFD on behalf of William Trevor. Copyright © William Trevor.

p. 482: "Siko" by Marianne Villanueva from *Ginseng and Other Tales from Manila* by Marianne Villanueva, 1991. Reprinted with permission from Calyx Books.

# Author and Title Index

# Subject Index